John

Cry From A Silent Planet

Published in the United Kingdom by
Compaid Graphics
T'otherside, Drumacre Lane East,
Longton, Preston. PR4 4SD.

First published in electronic format
First edition printed 2005

ISBN 1900604191

Cover designed by M. Mansfield

*To Carole and the boys,
without whose patience and understanding
this book could never have been written.*

In writing this novel, I have endeavoured to build the fiction on a solid foundation of verifiable fact. I could not have done this without the generous help of Professor Jason Lillegraven of the University of Wyoming, and his wife Linda, John F Connolly of the Solar System Exploration Division at NASA's Johnson Space Centre, and Major General Ed Boenisch, Adjutant General, Wyoming National Guard.

Recognition and sincere thanks must also go to all of the following, who gave of their time and experience so willingly.

Dr Buzz Aldrin, NASA Astronaut (Apollo, Retd.)
Dr. Ellen Baker, NASA Astronaut
David Brin, Author
Jerry R Colson, Sheriff of Carbon County, Wyoming
Hasan Ferdous, Dept. of Public Information, United Nations, New York
Linda Fisk, Image Librarian, NASA Johnson Space Centre
Dr Michael Foale, NASA Astronaut
Jim French, Aerospace Consultant
Mike Gentry, Media Resource Centre, NASA Johnson Space Centre
Ines Guerra, UN Plaza Tower, New York
Trevor Hoskins, Firestone, Nashville
Tina Jorgensen, United Nations, London
Norman Lees M.D., F.F.A.R.C.S, Victoria Infirmary, Glasgow
Lucy Lytwynsky, Astronaut Office, NASA Johnson Space Centre
Dr Patrick Moore CBE FRAS
Richard & Sylvia Nelson
Dr Robert Maltby, School of Classics, University of Leeds
Steve Nesbitt, Media Relations, NASA Johnson Space Centre
Dr Jürgen Neuberg, Department of Earth Sciences, University of Leeds

Bob Nute, Chief of Flight Planning, NASA Johnson Space Centre
Dr Scott Parazynski, NASA Astronaut
Sgt. Russell Petcoff, F.E. Warren Air Base, Cheyenne, Wyoming
Gary Raymond, Ferris Mountain Ranch, Wyoming
Laura Rochon, Newsroom, NASA Johnson Space Centre
Gary Seloff, Manager of Imagery Management, NASA Johnson Space Centre
Tim Townsend, Terry's Towing Service, Rawlins, Wyoming
Doug Willhelmey, FBI, Cheyenne, Wyoming
John Young, NASA Astronaut (Gemini, Apollo, Shuttle)
Linda Zellmer, Geology & Map Librarian, University of Wyoming

Contents

Prologue

The Voice

US Bureau of Reclamation Seismographic Network
Jackson Lake, Wyoming.
12:38 Mountain Standard Time 27th September 2012

There was no way that the duty officer in the network control room could possibly have known that those first seemingly innocuous vibrations - barely warranting a raised eyebrow - heralded a series of events that would shake mankind to its foundations, destroy our assumption of right of tenure to this planet, and place in mortal danger the very continuance of the human race.

On the high resolution screen in front of him, the traces from thirty seismographs were displayed. Today had been perfectly normal. In this seismically active area, it was not unusual for the traces to quiver continuously, so the original event was nothing out of the ordinary. It was only after he was brought up short by the alarm klaxon did he realise anything was amiss.

He leaned forwards and studied the traces on the screen. Every trace displayed the same pattern, but offset slightly in horizontal position, reflecting the differing time lags between the receipt of the signal at different stations. The amplitudes were insignificant - maybe Richter 1 or 2 - but the shapes were unusual. He typed the command which would display the vital details of the event.

Event Id 20120927/005
Date: 2012/09/27   UTC: 19:38:24
Latitude: 41.91N Longitude: 106.89W
Magnitude: 1.6 Depth 5Km ±1 Quality A*
Location: 32Km ENE of Rawlins, WY
Comments: Unidentified cause.
Event does not match any known signature.
P-wave only.
Abrupt initiation and termination.
Duration 92 seconds
Suggestions: Possible U2 effect.

"No way!" he exclaimed, as he instructed the computer to double-check its analysis.

He knew that the U2 effect suggested by the computer, was the name given by seismologists to a set of readings once recorded during a U2 concert. The amplifiers had been so powerful that vibrations from the speakers had been detected by seismographs for miles around. But for this event to be caused by the U2 effect, the speakers would have to have a power of thousands of kilowatts, and be playing in a concert hall 3 miles deep.

When the check confirmed the original data, he picked up the phone and dialled the US Geological Survey in Denver, Colorado.

"Jackson Lake here. Got a real flaky one," he said.

"Rawlins, Wyoming?"

"That's it. You confirmin' it?"

"Guess so. Just put the phone down. Utah's picked up the same thing. Canadian network seismos in Wyoming - they got it too."

The conversation was suddenly interrupted by a second outburst from the warning klaxon.

"Hold it," he exclaimed. "There goes another one!"

He again instructed the computer to display its analysis.

Event Id 20120927/006
Date: 2012/09/27 UTC: 19:50:17
Latitude: 41.91N Longitude: 106.89W
Magnitude: 1.6 Depth 5Km ±1
Location: 32Km ENE of Rawlins, WY
Comments: Unidentified cause.
Event matches Event Id 20120927/005
with100% correlation.
P-wave only.
Abrupt initiation and termination.
Duration 92 seconds
Suggestions: None.

"Screw me! I got an exact repetition of the first one. What the hell is this!"

"I dunno. Never got nothin' like this before. Look, send me a compressed version of your first event file will you. I'd like to see what our machine makes of it."

He immediately zipped the event file and prepared to send it over the net to Denver. The ten-to-one compression would reduce the duration of the event from 92 seconds to nine seconds. An added side effect would be to increase the normally inaudible frequency range of the seismic signal to within the audible range. The technique was often used deliberately, to hear the vibrations.

He reached for the headphones, placed them over his ears, and clicked the send button. The sound that he heard in those nine seconds made his eyes widen in amazement. The sound began and ended with a perfectly pure note which lasted about one second, but it was what he heard in the intervening seven seconds which made him begin to tremble.

He heard a voice.

From 240 miles away, a depth of three miles, and with a power of millions of watts, someone was speaking.

A few minutes after he sent the second event file to Denver, they phoned back.

"I couldn't figure out what the voice was saying," came the excited voice of the Denver co-ordinator. "But one of the guys here is from a Chinese family, and he says the last two words are perfectly clear - they're in Mandarin. Play the tape again. Listen carefully. There are three sets of words separated by clicks."

The officer re-ran the tape and listened to the words. The voice was sepulchral, and of such a foreboding quality that it sent a shiver down his spine.

"Eimen. Nos exstamus. Gormun chinjoy."

"Okay, I hear them," he said, "I still can't make it out. Are you saying the last two words are in Chinese, and just the last two?"

"Yes."

"Well ... for Christ's sake, tell me! What do they say?"

"We exist."

"What!"

"The last two words. They say, We exist."

Part 1

THERE, THEN

1

Dark Star

The Planet Cryon - Day 47 Year 46,431 A.G.

The call had disturbed Vorkan at midsleep. On previous occasions, the most extreme emotion Tharus had ever displayed was mild disquiet - usually when one of the probes had decided to investigate a hazardous planetary environment. But this was different - Tharus was obviously in shock.

"It shouldn't be there!" he had kept repeating.

As his shuttle flew silently along the main westbound tunnel, Vorkan tried to imagine what 'It' was. Something dramatic had obviously occurred, but what? Where? He knew he should be concerned - the probes were after all his responsibility - but realised, somewhat guiltily, that he wasn't. At least, he thought, something's happening, and allowed himself a quiver of excitement as the shuttle decelerated towards the Centrum.

In the terminal, he declined the gently humming motopods and took the elevator up to the surface level. He was determined to grasp this rare opportunity to go outside, and prove, if only to himself, that he at least had not been driven permanently underground.

"Yes, I *do* know," he replied impatiently to the external hatchway security system. "And yes, it is on my own authority."

He emerged into the deserted square, and the hatch closed behind him. Even now - well into stardown - the air was roasting hot, and for a moment, his limbs seized, but within seconds he felt his vapducts dilating and the evaporant beginning to cool his cuticle. He gazed at the florid sky and searched for stars. Yes, there was one, and another. Only the brightest were visible, and only in the south, but that tantalising glimpse was all he needed to satisfy his yearning to see with his own eyes - without the aid of technology - something outside this hell he was forced to inhabit.

He headed towards the Interstellar Monitoring complex. As he moved, he could feel his adsorbers dampening as water condensed out of the air onto his relatively cold body surface. These few hours before star-rise were now the only time that osmosis - that process so fundamental to their survival - worked outside the clinical confines of their subterranean world.

As he threaded his way between the dust dunes snaking across the square, the only sounds were his own foot-pads crushing the dust against the granite paving. All around him, the domes of the city were bathed in the lurid light from the north.

Ahead, a hatchway opened and a shaft of light pierced the night air. Vorkan recognised the figure of Tharus silhouetted in the hatchway.

"This had better be good," said Vorkan as he stepped inside. "I know I said call me anytime, but midsleep!"

Tharus glanced up at the sky before he closed the hatch firmly behind them. His sensilla were twitching nervously.

"You'll do that once too often, Sir," he said.

"Do what?" snapped Vorkan. He knew perfectly well what Tharus was talking about.

"Come over by the outside route. You know it's dangerous, not to mention against official policy."

"Rubbish!" retorted Vorkan. "And I don't need you quoting policy at me, Tharus. How I get here is my concern. I'm damned if I'm going to spend every minute of my life sub-surface. I have to feel real air round me every now and again."

He bent down and knocked the dust off his legs in irritation. Tharus backed away, as if the dust was going to make him unclean.

"Now," said Vorkan, "Let's have it. What's the problem?"

"One of the probes has crashed."

Vorkan regarded him, disdainfully.

"Impossible!" he retorted, turning and leading the way up to the control chamber. "Our probes have never failed. There must be something you haven't checked."

"It's not that, Sir," said Tharus, trotting alongside Vorkan and gesticulating emphatically. "I didn't say it had failed. That's the point. The one that crashed didn't fail. It was working perfectly when it happened. It was one of this year's fleet!"

"But they were only launched twenty days ago. The damned things can only have got to eighteen light-days away."

"Actually, we're now getting signals back that were transmitted when they were only nine light-days away," said Tharus. "The one that crashed had only got that far!"

"Are you trying to tell me that we've been launching hundreds of probes a year for over four hundred years; they've all got through to their destinations or are on their way; but now, one of the stupid things has managed to hit something on our own doorstep?"

Tharus started twitching again, and raised himself to his full stature in indignation.

"They're not stupid. You know that, Sir. The Cephtors are as intelligent as you or I, react thousands of times faster, and leave us standing on broad-band data analysis."

"I'm sorry, Tharus," said Vorkan, realising that Tharus treated each probe as a much loved protégé. "But the thing can't have crashed into something so close to our system. There's nothing out there to crash into!"

"Isn't there?," rasped Tharus, looking up at Vorkan with fear in his eyes. "Isn't there!"

"I have to see the data. This is ridiculous," said Vorkan, quickening his pace. Tharus had to run to keep up with him.

In the control chamber, one hundred and twenty eight holocubes, each one tuned by the controller to the probe of his choice, glowed and flickered silently in the subdued light. The image in each cube was coming in live, as its probe sailed between the stars, orbited a distant planet, or swept down to the surface and performed its survey, responding intelligently to its own discoveries.

Vorkan recalled the first occasion he ever came to this chamber, and how, from the very first moment, he was totally captivated by the sights and sounds it revealed. To see natural wonders, strange creatures, emerging civilisations, and events as they happened on worlds light years away, fired his imagination and fuelled his desire to leave his crippled planet. He deplored the notion - supported by some of the older Councillors - that they should delay the migration until their star grew so large that they were forced to leave. Life on Cryon was already intolerable; venturing outside was only possible at night; the entire population spent their whole lives underground. Cryon and its sun were dying. The future was out there, in space.

Vorkan wanted to go now.

He walked round, stroking the invisible faces of the cubes. Somehow, touching their surfaces made him feel closer to where the probes actually were - to where the action was.

Tharus sat at the main control panel, above which was a much larger holocube.

"Look, Sir," he said, as he re-ran the last few minutes of the crashed probe's transmission.

Vorkan forced himself to stop peering into one of the cubes, in which a group of worm-like creatures with long tentacles were slithering across a mud flat towards the probe which had landed on their planet.

"Now look there," he said. "It's doing its astrometry - checking star positions for navigation."

Vorkan could see selected stars ahead of the probe being identified in rapid succession, and the vehicle's course being slightly corrected each time.

"But now!" Tharus's voice fluttered with emotion as he froze the frame in question. "It's lost the star dead ahead."

Vorkan peered at the screen in astonishment. There, in the centre, where the target star had been, was nothing.

"Give me maximum magnification," he said.

The image, now magnified some six thousand times, showed the target star's corona just visible round the outside of a circular jet black object.

"Now watch the last few seconds," said Tharus. He had to grip the bench to stop himself shaking uncontrollably.

The display showed the probe rapidly re-checking its databanks, confirming that the star should have been there, and deciding it had been eclipsed by a hitherto unknown object. The size, range and closing speed of the object are determined in the final second. The command to fire the lateral thrusters at full power is given. The screen shows the stars ahead rapidly blacked out by an unseen object that seems to lunge from the centre of the display. It veers slightly to one side but not far enough. The probe slams into it at ninety percent the speed of light. The screen goes blank.

Vorkan winced at the thought of all that technology - the end result of forty six thousand years of progress - vaporising in a trillionth of a second.

"How the hell could it miss spotting something like that," he exclaimed. "It's enormous!"

"The probe wasn't expecting anything that size so near to home," said Tharus. "It was in tele-navigation mode, through what it thought was clear local space. That thing shouldn't be there."

"Well it obviously is," said Vorkan ruefully. "We've got to get an independent observation. Have you got access to the VLAT from here?"

"Not without authority," said Tharus. Then, seeing the lie of Vorkan's sensilla, "We've got authority. Right?"

"Right," said Vorkan. "There are one or two benefits that come with a High Councillor job!"

Vorkan took Tharus's place at the console and entered the access code for the Very Large Array Telescope in orbit some eighty thousand miles above Cryon. On his authority, the twelve great interferometric dishes broke off their current observation and locked onto the co-ordinates provided by the probe.

"It's found it - just," said Vorkan. "A tenth of an arc second across, and only twenty four degrees above absolute zero. No wonder we never saw it before."

As the results came back, Vorkan merged them with the data from the probe. The two Cryons stared in disbelief as the full extent of the discovery became clear.

"It's a dead star, and coming straight at us!" cried Tharus.

He gazed at Vorkan as if expecting him to make it go away with a sweep of his hand. But Vorkan could barely conceal his delight.

He instructed the system to extrapolate the black star's trajectory forward in time, and display it on the large holoview screen, together with a dynamic data table.

"A hundred and forty billion miles, thirty miles per second," said Vorkan, reading aloud. "Don't worry, Tharus. We've got a few years yet!"

Tharus was not impressed. He just crouched in silence, obviously terrified by the scenario unfolding before him.

But Vorkan was gripped. *Please, Oh Great One, let it be going to hit us*, he prayed.

As the years ticked by on the prediction display, the black star moved closer, its speed slowly increasing as the gravitational attraction between it and their star tightened its grip on the two bodies. At a hundred and thirty eight years into the future, the simulation homed in on local space, and showed the planets circling normally round Agorra, their parent star. Slowly at first then increasing in speed, the black star entered their system. Meeras, the outer planet, was the first to be perturbed. Caught by overpowering gravitational forces as the black star passed nearby, it was suddenly projected like a sling-shot up from its normal orbital plane and out, out from the system until it disappeared off the display.

"The Meerians!" Tharus cried out in dismay.

Vorkan said nothing, but sat rigid as he watched the black star, now well within the system and travelling at astonishing speed, graze Agorra and fling the two inner planets, Pyrexus and Velocaur, into crazy orbits. One planet remained - Cryon. At first, it looked as if it might not be affected, but as the black star moved away, Cryon followed it. The end of the sequence showed the black star receding into interstellar space, but now, with their planet encircling it in a highly elliptical orbit.

In one hundred and thirty nine years time, Cryon would be captured, and doomed to a silent death by refrigeration.

Vorkan's mind was racing. His hearts started pounding, and a cool invigorating feeling spread over the surface of his body. Here at last was an opportunity for him to shine in his father's eyes. It was a daunting challenge, but it matched his knowledge and desires perfectly. He *must* grasp it.

There could be no more procrastination; the Council would have to act immediately; the very survival of the race depended upon it. With his expertise, they would turn to him for suggestions for planets to escape to. That would be his opportunity. He would mastermind the salvation of his entire nation, and lead their migration to a new world.

Out there, in the vastness of space, orbiting a younger friendlier star, there had to be a planet suited to them.

There had to be ... Somewhere.

It was star-rise by the time Vorkan and Tharus completed their report for the Council. Vorkan sent it - by cable only - to The Master and other Councillors. He knew that within minutes, an extra-Cryonic communications blackout would be imposed - the first in his lifetime. The citizens would not like it, but until their destination planet was decided, it would be folly to allow planets on nearby systems to get wind of Cryon's plight.

He left the control chamber and headed down the ramp towards the tunnels below. Its windows afforded a dramatic view of the domes, looking like gigantic bubble polythene, with all the bubbles sprayed silver.

As he walked, shafts of bright orange light began streaming across the ramp. The mists which had been obscuring the slowly rising star were beginning to clear. The heat shields silently cut in, and the patches of light on the ramp-way walls faded, to be replaced with the cooler more soothing light from the plasma illumination panels.

As Agorra climbed slowly over the horizon, its heat began to fry every surface exposed to it. Vorkan watched uneasily as the vortices of mini tornadoes swept up columns of dust and sand rising hundreds of feet into the air, creating a macabre forest of writhing spires against the purple dawn. The angry light from the star played across the city and flashed off the dome surfaces in an ever-changing dance.

He could still see Agorra through the shields. This red giant, in the final stage of its stellar evolution, was so large that even from Cryon's distance of three hundred and sixty million miles, it covered a tenth of the sky. The centre of the massive disc - bright in the middle and fading towards its edge - was just now clearing the distant horizon. Its presence was evil and menacing behind the dark silhouette of the city skyline.

He stood for a while and gazed pensively out of the windows before finally going down to the shuttle platforms. As he watched this incandescent ball from which they had protected themselves for millennia, he pondered the strange irony that now, the death of their planet was to be brought about by cooling to absolute zero.

Noviksar was about one hundred and forty degrees round the planet, and at the same high latitude as the Centrum. In ancient times, it would have been on a different time zone, but now everyone had to remain sub-surface when Agorra was up, the whole planet was on Centrum Time. The eighteen hundred mile underground shuttle trip took only fifty minutes, so by the time Vorkan emerged from the elevator into his home entrecept, the others had been up for only two hours but it was mid-afternoon. The moist air, heady with the scent of damp soil and Safrani flowers, comforted him as he opened the hatch to his family residence.

Charis and Nitra, his neutant siblings, were the first to greet him. They were very attached and totally loyal to their brother, and hated it when he went anywhere without them.

"Faro!" cried Charis, looking up at him. "What's this we've been hearing about a collision? Is that why you went out at midsleep?"

"Yes, please tell us," said Nitra, as he ordered a block of crushed weaver worms - Vorkan's favourite snack - from the dispenser unit set into the wall.

"And why are all the v-comms dead?" said Charis indignantly. "With only the fibro working, I can't call Tsavo on Meeras. I was going to send him a terrasond today."

Vorkan did not answer. He could not face telling Charis what fate awaited his friend's planet. He just bowed his head in gratitude as he accepted the weaver worms from Nitra. He crunched them slowly, letting the flavour linger on his staphyla before sucking them down.

"All in good time," he said gently.

Vorkan's mother Meena appeared, came over and looped a long arm round him.

"Are you all right, Faro?" she asked anxiously. "Have you been working since midsleep? You must be tired. You were going to Jasoma's today weren't you. Are you going to rest before you go?"

"Mother, Mother!" said Vorkan kindly. "I'm fine. Don't fuss. But I can't see Jasoma today - there's too much to do. I've got something very important to tell you all. Where's father?"

Vorkan began to feel his breathing tubes drying up - a sure sign he was under stress. He knew that any talk of migration was an anathema to his father, and that his first hurdle was to convince him, once and for all, that the moment had now come to bring the subject out into the open.

"I'm here, Faro," came a deep voice from behind him. "We will assemble in the balcony chamber."

Even though Vorkan was a High Councillor - one of the most powerful Cryons on the planet - here in the family home, his father Patara reigned supreme. The four of them followed him obediently, as he climbed the ramp-way.

"Hasten slowly," whispered his mother. "He'll come round eventually."

"All I ask is that he gives me some credit for my ideas and opinions," replied Vorkan. "I couldn't have tried harder."

The mis-named balcony chamber - for its balcony had been ripped off years ago during a particularly violent storm - was a circular structure at the crown of the vivarium. Its sloping windows faced only north, away from Agorra. In its centre was an eleplatform, giving access to a hatch in the ceiling. The hatch was firmly shut. Vorkan recalled how when he was young, he and his elder brother Maazak would open up the hatch at night, gaze at the night sky, and wonder.

Outside, and inaudible through the triple-insulation, the inevitable day-long storm was firing the dust, as if from the nozzle of a giant sandblaster, at every exposed surface above ground level. The five Cryons took no notice of this lethal hurricane only a few feet away from them, as they crouched in a circle.

"Proceed, Faro," said his father.

Vorkan's mind was in turmoil. He wanted to share his mission for the future - his desire for adventures beyond their wildest dreams - with his family. But at the same time he craved the support of his father, the last person in the world to be interested in adventure. He decided to start with the facts.

"There's no easy way to put this," he began, "But far from having three thousand years before Agorra's increasing heat renders life impossible, we have less than one hundred and forty years before we must leave Cryon."

"A hundred and forty years - three thousand years. What difference does it make," said his father, wearily.

"A great deal of difference, Father," said Vorkan. "You may be prepared to accept your fate. I am not!"

Meena looked pleadingly at her son.

"No, Mother," said Vorkan emphatically. "It's time we had this out."

He turned to his father.

"This planet is going to be captured by a dead star, and swept out to space within the lifetime of any children Jasoma and I have. *That's* what's going to happen," he said, standing up. "Anyone who remains will freeze to death. I am not prepared to stand by and let that happen to them. If Maazak had still been alive and this was going to happen to him, you would change your tune."

A deathly silence hung over the chamber as Patara rose. The others looked on terrified as father and son stood not five feet apart, sensilla bristling, eyes glaring at each other. Vorkan could see the upper surfaces of his father's legs and arms glistening with coolant. Even after hundreds of millennia of instinct suppression, anger still triggered the same autonomic reaction.

"How *dare* you bring Maazak into this!" he boomed. "It's got nothing to do with Maazak."

"It's got everything to do with Maazak, Father" said Vorkan, looking him straight in the eyes. "Ever since he was killed, you've done nothing but peddle this ridiculous notion that we should just give up. Cosmic destiny indeed! You have no right - no right at all - to make me feel guilty about supporting a migration. And you certainly have no right to condemn my children - your grandchildren - to death. What about them?"

His father's stony stare seemed to turn inwards on himself. Slowly, his anger melted away, to be replaced with an expression of deep sadness.

"You know less than you think, Faro, about my ability to have grandchildren," he said, turning away and gazing with lifeless eyes out of the window.

"What do you mean, Father?" said Vorkan. "Tell me! What do you mean?"

"Patara! No more!" interjected his mother, fixing his father with a commanding stare.

His father paused. His distant gaze refocussed.

"The forces of nature should not be tampered with, Faro," he said. "Maazak's death was his destiny. Our planet's death is its destiny. We should accept them both."

"How can you say that!" exclaimed Vorkan. "You have never accepted Maazak's death. You have never faced up to the real facts. You blame anybody and anything except Maazak. You even blame destiny. Maazak's death was just an accident. That's all it was. I was there. I know. I saw what happened. It's not destiny! Maazak made a mistake! The sooner you accept that Maazak was not infallible, the better it will be for all of us."

His father made as if to say something in reply, but his mother stood up and stopped him with her hand.

"Patara! Faro!" she said. "Enough!"

She led her husband towards the ramp-way. He stopped at the top and turned to Vorkan.

"Do what you like, Faro," he said dispassionately. He started down, suddenly looking very tired and very old. "I wash my hands of you. Do what you like."

Meena followed him. Vorkan walked over to the window and stared out dispiritedly at the raging storm. The only hope of gaining his father's respect was to prove to him that the whole Cryon nation supported his migration plan. He would surely come round then. He had to.

From the floor below, came the muffled sounds of his mother and father in animated conversation, then silence. Shortly afterwards, his mother reappeared, and walked purposefully across to a cabinet in which she kept some of her personal possessions. She unlocked it and took from it a small amulet. It matched the one that she had worn ever since he could remember. She came to Vorkan and gently clasped it round his lower left arm. Embedded in the amulet was an exquisite solaramine block with a diamond-shaped crystal at its centre. Something about it was familiar and comforting, as it laid over his sensilla.

"Don't condemn him, Faro," she said quietly. "Nothing can change the past. But one day, you will come to understand. Take this, my son. Keep it with you always. It is from your father and me, who love you more than life itself."

She held his head in her hands and gazed deep into his eyes. "Follow your destiny, Faro," she said. "Whatever it may seem to you, your father and I will be with you, always." She embraced him, then left once more to join her husband.

Charis and Nitra moved near, and eyed him silently.

Vorkan was crying inside. He wanted to reach out to his father and touch him, but the moment had gone.

2
MIND

After the feverish activity in the public chambers of the administration centre, Vorkan was grateful for the serenity of his private quarters. Down there, surrounded by his collection of ancient records, works of art from Cryon and other planets, and pictograms of fantastic scenes from the universe at large, he could relax. He settled himself onto the master rester in front of the communications station and stared into the ghostly outline of the holocube.

To achieve his objective, he had to try to forget the scene with his father and concentrate on the task ahead. Tomorrow, not only would he be expected to vote on the migration issue, but he would have the opportunity to propose a destination planet. He had to come up with something radical - something no-one else had dreamt of - something amazing.

As he flipped the arms of the cerebra-sensor to each side of his skull, a feeling of utter peace swept over him. The communication station provided an interface to the most powerful computer system known. In all the civilisations the Cryons had visited, there was nothing that approached the power or authority of this machine, if indeed 'machine' was the correct word. It was actually a hybrid of genetically engineered brain material and electro-nucleic processors. It was capable of regeneration, self-analysis, repair, and continuous expansion. It was MIND.

A voice, which seemed to come from within his brain, welcomed him.

"Hello, Faro," it said.

The voice was neither male nor female, or young or old, but neither was it neutral or metallic. It had a unique liquid velvet quality of calm authority, with a tone that changed naturally to match the mood. Vorkan always had the feeling that he was talking to a favourite uncle or guardian. And this feeling was constantly reinforced by the form of address that MIND used when conversing with him. It used 'Faro', his familiar name. When it used this for the first time, he was indignant at its lack of respect, but now, the thought that such a close friend as MIND could use any other form of address was out of the question.

Vorkan felt that the rapport he and MIND had established was unique, and in some ways superior to his relationships with fellow Cryons.

"Hello MIND," he replied.

"You are ill at ease, Faro.".

Vorkan accepted that MIND had access to every stored item of information on the planet, and monitored every communication, but its ability to read his thoughts and understand his feelings never failed to amaze him.

"You're right," said Vorkan out loud. "I've had an argument with my father." He still found it difficult to communicate in silence, though he knew it was possible.

"That is sad. Would you like to talk about it?" said MIND. "I know why you're here, and we won't achieve much until you can put the incident behind you."

"My father has lost the will to continue. I've tried so hard to gain his respect for my views, but it's hopeless."

"Your father - everybody - needs something to live for. The death of a son is always a crippling blow. He will never completely get over it."

"But what about me? He still has me. Why can he not live for me and what I stand for? And what about Mother?"

"I cannot speak of his relationship with your mother, but is it possible that you are trying too hard to replace your dead brother? Might your father see you doing this, knowing you can never replace Maazak? Perhaps he resents your trying."

Vorkan reflected on what MIND had just said.

"Perhaps," continued MIND, "You should concentrate on just being yourself. Stop trying to live up to how you imagine Maazak might have been. Perhaps if you do this, your father will ultimately recognise the strength and wisdom of your actions. I do."

"*You do!*"

"Oh yes, Faro," said MIND warmly. "There is no doubt that your intellect is of the highest order, and the motives governing its direction - though a touch misguided sometimes -

are most sincere. Succeed for *yourself,* Faro. Succeed for yourself."

Vorkan felt as if a great weight had been lifted from his shoulders. MIND was right - he often fell into the trap of striving for recognition rather than for the true objective of his activities. He recognised once more, how this close relationship with MIND was of immense importance to him. He longed to reach out and touch MIND, but of course, it was just a machine.

"Thank you," he said with feeling. It didn't seem enough though.

"All part of the service," said MIND.

"Right, let's get on with it," said Vorkan, revitalised.

"Before we start," said MIND, "May I ask where you got the amulet?"

"Oh. Mother," said Vorkan, surprised. "She gave it to me this foreday, after the argument with my father."

"It is very beautiful," said MIND. "Strange, it reminds me of something, but I don't know what."

Vorkan was speechless. Never before had MIND ever admitted to not knowing something. He would have to explore this unique event later.

"The planet search results please," he said.

"Certainly. The Master has instructed me to draw your attention to a shortlist of planets I prepared using his search criteria. Do you want to see the list now?"

"I suppose so," said Vorkan. But he was not happy with the implication that their destination planet had to be selected from this list.

"I will convert that answer into an official 'Yes'," said MIND wryly.

The list - of eight planets - appeared instantly in the holocube, scrolling automatically as MIND sensed his reading speed. The critical data for each planet was shown, including the biolevel - a measure of the level of advancement of any animal life. Vorkan did not like what he saw. A major tenet of Cryon philosophy was that the natural forces of evolution must not be disturbed, on their planet or anywhere else. This was one of the reasons why, thousands of years ago, they had abandoned their expansionist activities and recalled their people from the colonial planets. They had realised that growth and colonisation served no long-term purpose, and inappropriately manipulated development of the civilisations they were colonising. If the planet was inhabited by animals and creatures below a certain evolutionary level, there was a slender thread of justification for colonisation, but to interfere with a race of intellectually advanced beings was not an option. This is why it had always been unthinkable to consider escaping by migrating to Meeras, the outer - and only other inhabited planet - in their system.

"Two of these planets have intolerable conditions, and the rest have technologically advanced life forms," he said indignantly. "Is the Master condoning an invasion? Because eighty million of us are hardly going to be welcomed with open arms!"

"You know I cannot comment on the motives of others, and particularly the Master's," said MIND. "I simply present you with the list, as instructed."

"Well, we have both done as instructed," said Vorkan. "Now, I want to go through this in my own way."

Vorkan decided to start from scratch. They must find a planet round a normal star - not one whose light and other properties were as extreme as their own. His nation needed to escape from the confines of their specially-constructed artificial environment and emerge, free to lead normal lives on the surface. This meant searching for what Vorkan knew to be a main sequence star. He also recognised that the reason for Agorra's rapid evolution into a red giant was its unusually high mass. A smaller star would not only age more slowly, but emit light compatible with their red-sensitive eyes.

He settled more firmly onto his rester. "Please summarise the data from all the probes," he said.

"The data set involves information on over 60,000 stars and 150,000 planets within a 200 light-year radius," said MIND.

"How many planets are there round main sequence F6 to G9 stars?" he asked.

"28,954" came the immediate reply.

"And how many of those have a mean surface temperature within three degrees of forty eight centigrade?"

"1,934"

"How many of those have water, and a mean relative humidity of 90% or more?"

"187"

"How many of those have an atmospheric composition which would support life as we know it?"

"There is a correlation between atmospheric composition and pressure toleration," replied MIND. "When we consider these two together, we drop to 19.

"What extremes of surface gravity could we accommodate?"

"From 10% to 200% of the surface gravity of Cryon could be accommodated by all but the most frail and elderly of our citizens and animals."

"So how many planets are left after the gravity filter?"

"Twelve," replied MIND.

"How many of those planets have rotation periods between two thirds and one-and-a-half times that of our own?"

"Six," came the reply.

Not looking good, thought Vorkan. Already down to two fewer than the Master's list.

The next filter would identify only those planets on which intellectual development had not surpassed a primitive level. He already suspected what the result would be.

"How many of those six planets have life developed only to bio-level 4 or below?"

"None," came the reply. "The six planets we arrived at before the bio filter were the six condition-tolerable ones on the Master's original list."

Vorkan felt weary. He had hoped that somehow, his analysis would throw up an original destination. But five of the six planets had bio-level 8 civilisations - only one less than their own.

The sixth planet was Atalan-3, otherwise known as Saarus. The Atalan system was only 24 light years away, and Saarus was one of the first planets to be visited by the Cryons during the colonisation era. After some 2,000 years of occupation, there came the great Saarian uprising, their complaint being that whilst they may be benefiting from Cryon technology and improvements and advancing to bio-level 6, the place was no longer theirs. They just wanted to be left alone. The Cryons recognised the error of their ways and withdrew their people. A treaty was signed, promising mutual non-interference, which to this day had been honoured by both sides.

This is leading nowhere, thought Vorkan despairingly. There are 150,000 known planets out there, and not one of them is currently suitable. I have to think of something.

He sat in silence, cleared his mind, and expunged all his pre-conceptions. The key question was, 'What do you do when you have no remaining options?'

Then he remembered his mother, and what she did when she wanted to grow Safrani flowers in their home. She chose a little-used chamber in which she artificially maintained the extreme conditions they needed. She chose the most suitable place, and *modified it*. That was the answer! It was so blindingly obvious.

"MIND," he said eagerly, "I would like to investigate the possibility of finding a planet whose conditions might respond to imposed adjustment."

There was an unusually long silence before MIND responded.

"A fascinating and possibly fruitful suggestion, Faro. However, it is my duty to remind you that to impose any adjustment on the evolution of a planet is contrary to Fundamental Law."

"Thank you MIND," retorted Vorkan, unable to hide his irritation, "But leave the Law to me and the Council. When it comes to survival of our civilisation, I don't think it will take much persuasion to get the Law changed. Six of the planets on the Master's list would have required an invasion anyway. My plan involves modifying a planet with only primitive life forms. This must be a preferable option."

"I'm sorry," said MIND. "I was merely wishing to protect you from possible charges of Incitement to Planetary

Interference. Your argument that an adjustment is preferable to an invasion seems sound."

"So, can we get on with it?" said Vorkan restlessly.

"Certainly," said MIND. "What do you want to know?"

"Firstly, do you agree that of the filter factors we have considered, some are totally beyond our control but some of them may respond to adjustment?"

"Yes," said MIND, taking care to simply answer Vorkan's question without comment, bearing in mind his mood.

"And do you agree that the only factors we can change are surface temperature, availability of water, relative humidity, and minor adjustments to atmospheric composition?"

"Yes."

"Then how many planets are there which satisfy the factors we cannot change, but which might respond to adjustment of the factors we can change?"

"Five," replied MIND.

"That's more like it!" said Vorkan, elatedly. "Now, please give me your initial assessment on the possibilities for climate and condition adjustment on each of these planets."

"That is easy. Only one planet of the five has the potential to be adjusted. The rest are too different to be considered. Further, until I do a complete analysis of this planet's data, there is no guarantee that even this one could be changed."

Vorkan cursed quietly to himself. He had visions of his master plan failing before it began. He asked MIND to explain why each of the four planets was out of the running.

"One has all its water locked up in vast ice sheets. No amount of adjustment is going to warm it to anywhere near 48°C. Another, whilst its temperature is reasonable, is too dry, and offers no geological compounds from which sufficient water could be created. The third planet is too hot. Even if we could induce total cloud cover to reflect the heat from its star, we would be defeated by heat coming up from its contracting core. The fourth planet is ripe for adjustment, but suffers a periodic bombardment by asteroids once every 12,700 years, which wipes out all but the most primitive uni-cellular organisms."

"Thank you," said Vorkan. "So, one planet left. Where is it? What is it called?"

"It is the third planet in a nine planet system round the star Pronigon," said MIND. "Pronigon is a type G2 star, fifty four light years away. As yet, Pronigon-3 has not been named."

A nine planet system, thought Vorkan. Sounds interesting.

"What are conditions like on Pronigon-3?" he said.

"Mean surface temperature 15°C; mean Relative Humidity 55%. This is far too cold and dry for us, the survival time in such conditions being a little less than six hours."

"So, what are the factors, which influence Pronigon-3's temperature and humidity?"

MIND displayed the answer to this question as well as answering it verbally.

1. Total quantity of water vapour
2. Proportion of Carbon Dioxide
3. Extent of forestation and other plants
4. Micro-organism biomass
5. Actions of and numbers of other animals
6. Amount of atmospheric dust
7. Extent of any ice caps
8. Amount of volcanism
9. Land distribution with respect to the poles
10. Land surface area
11. Eccentricity of planet's orbit
12. Inclination of planet's axis of rotation
13. Precession of planet's equinoxes
14. Parent star's heat output cycle
15. Galactic flux variations
16. Clarity of the interstellar medium.

Those are the main ones," said MIND.

"Well, I did ask!" said Vorkan as he studied the list. "Which of those factors could we change?"

"The first seven, and temporarily, the eighth. However, all the factors interrelate in a very complex way, including the ones beyond our control. And the last six - the cosmological ones - exhibit a cyclical variation from a few hundred years to tens of millions of years. This means that even if we change the ones over which we have control, such changes may be counteracted in time by the factors which are beyond our control. If we could, it would be better to wait until the cosmological factors combined together in our favour, then simultaneously hit the planet with our imposed changes."

"Well we can't wait can we," said Vorkan irritably. "Just tell me what we could do now."

"There is much water in the form of vast oceans, and the geological data indicates a large quantity of carbon dioxide dissolved in subterranean magma. If these two compounds could be transferred to the atmosphere in suitable quantities, this would have an immediate effect on it, and the target conditions of 48°C and 94% humidity could be approached, but not sustained. I repeat, we need the cosmological factors to be favourable as well. Then, the target conditions can not only be achieved, but sustained indefinitely."

"How would they be sustained?" said Vorkan.

"Pronigon-3 can exist in a number of stable states, one of which is eminently suitable for us," replied MIND. "Once any state is achieved, the planet will resist quite powerful de-stabilising factors, but to achieve the state in the first place - to flip the planet into a new state - *all* the factors have to be right, including the cosmological ones."

We have three choices, thought Vorkan. Remain on Cryon and die, invade Saarus, or migrate to Pronigon-3 and somehow flip its state.

There was no excuse for an invasion of Saarus. But Pronigon-3, with only its primitive life forms, and situated in a rich planetary environment - was a definite possibility. It was the *only* possibility. The state transition had to be made to work.

"How could we transfer the water and carbon dioxide into the planet's atmosphere?" said Vorkan.

There was a long pause. Vorkan knew that MIND would be modelling all the transition mechanisms available to them.

“The most effective method would be to detonate two powerful thermatrons in a limestone area - for the carbon dioxide; another two under the oceans - for the water vapour; and drive in a magma plume accelerator- to trigger volcanic activity and provide an on-going source of heat and out-gassing in the critical period following the explosions.”

“And the power of the explosions and volcanism?”

“Twenty million megatons per device,” said MIND.

“Great heavens!” said Vorkan. “One hundred million megatons! There won’t be anything of the planet left after that, surely!”

“The explosions would certainly devastate much of the surface, and disrupt marine life too,” said MIND

“And what will happen to the lifeforms?”

“Many lifeforms will perish as a direct result of the explosions. Following that, the planet will be shrouded in a thick dust cloud which will prevent sunlight reaching the surface for many months. More will perish as the planet experiences a temporary ‘winter’, either because of the low temperatures, or because photosynthesis will be prevented and their plant food stocks will run out. Finally, as the artificial winter ends, the vastly increased levels of carbon dioxide and water vapour will raise the planet’s temperature and humidity towards the levels we seek, and many of the creatures who survived the explosions and the winter will then perish under the new conditions. In total, roughly seventy five percent of all living things would be destroyed.”

The extent of the death and destruction shocked and saddened Vorkan. He began to wonder how the Council would react to being asked to accept responsibility for such an Armageddon.

“I understand your concern, Faro,” said MIND without prompting. “However, you should realise that even if the transition could be achieved using thermon vaporisers - no explosions - only some twenty five percent of the lifeforms could survive under the new conditions anyway. The remaining seventy five percent would perish, but more slowly. There is a strong case for .... how can I put it, ‘a clean kill’. This way, the total amount of suffering will be minimised.”

Vorkan was still unhappy.

"But such a catastrophe," he said sadly.

"Faro," began MIND. "Catastrophes are a normal part of planetary evolution. They prevent life on the planet from evolving along pre-ordained pathways. They result in the purging of many species whose evolutionary potential has ground to a halt. They provide the opportunity for new species to develop and occupy niches previously occupied by non-evolving species. They give light, air, and space to new evolutionary flexibility and adaptability. They are by no means a bad thing."

"But you are referring to *natural* catastrophes, such as an asteroid impact," said Vorkan. "Ours would be imposed, and far from natural."

"What's one more catastrophe in the entire history of a planet? Pronigon-3 has experienced many such events - all from impacting asteroids - over its history. One more won't make much difference."

Vorkan was appalled. He had never heard MIND speak like this before.

"How can you be so callous?" he said. "You're talking about killing millions of creatures."

"Objectivity is part of my primary function, Faro. I am responding to your request for adjustment mechanisms. Do you want to save the Cryon nation or don't you?"

MIND was right of course. It always was. But all its calculations were based on theory. What if it was wrong? Vorkan needed a fail-safe plan to put before the Council.

"What if the transition mechanism doesn't work?" he said. "What if we go there, wreak all that devastation, then find the plan has failed? It would be a sin against Fundamental Law - against the Great One. We would be branded as murderers; we would have achieved nothing but destruction, and we would still not have found a solution to our problem."

MIND was silent once more. Vorkan wondered whether it was capable of feeling indignation that the validity of its calculations had been questioned.

"A valid point," it said. "Would you like me to outline a fail-safe plan?"

"Yes, of course."

"Send an advance party to the planet. Conduct a thorough survey of conditions, including a study of the lifeforms. Save large numbers of the full range of life found and store them safely in cryostatic encapsulation far below the surface. I will predict the combined effects of a test explosion and magma plume accelerator. You then detonate those devices and measure the results. If my predictions match, my predictive ability can be relied upon."

"And if they don't?"

"The planet will revert to its original state. At which time, we can reinstate the lifeforms saved. They will soon re-establish."

"That's more like it. But what would we do if the test devices fail?"

"As Pronigon is so near, the advance party could be there sixty years from now," said MIND. "Allow two years for the survey and specimen collection before the test detonations - I recommend an Iridium thermatron for the surface device, by the way - and a further two years to fully assess the results. Whether or not we succeed, the advance party transmits the result back to Cryon. The signal will take a further 54 years to get here. The total time is 118 years. That leaves 30 years before the black star arrives. If the devices don't work, Pronigon-3 is reinstated, and the advance party leave for Saarus, which by the time they arrive, will have been taken. If however my predictions prove accurate and the devices work, the main migration party leaves Cryon for Pronigon-3."

"Brilliant!" said Vorkan.

"Thank you. But I must reiterate, even if the tests are successful, we still have the problem that to sustain any transition long-term, the cosmological factors must be favourable too."

"Right now, I'm more concerned with ensuring that we have a plan which will give us some breathing space and that we can action now. I'm confident we'll find a solution to the cosmological problem in due course. At least, I have something I can present to the Council tomorrow."

"There's something else," said MIND. "There is a secondary advantage of the test explosion strategy. Currently, there are large numbers of creatures on the planet. Many of these are extremely aggressive, and some show the potential to evolve to a highly technical level. Such creatures can develop into the most dangerous and destructive agents know, and present a real threat to the peace and safety of surrounding civilisations. Such creatures could certainly not co-exist with us. My suggestion is that the surface explosion be of sufficient magnitude to wipe them out. The threat, present or future, will then be eliminated."

Aggressive or not, thought Vorkan, they still deserved compassion, especially if the Pronigon-3 plan was abandoned.

"But they could be re-instated out of cryostatic encapsulation if necessary," said Vorkan.

"Oh certainly. As you know, cryostatic encapsulation allows objects - even complex life forms - to be stored indefinitely. Two years, two million years, it makes no difference."

Only one niggling detail remained. MIND had recommended an Iridium thermatron rather than the more conventional Hafnium device.

"Why Iridium?" he asked.

"I was hoping you were not going to ask that," said MIND, in an almost embarrassed tone. "It would be, how can I put it, fortuitous, if, after an unsuccessful surface explosion, any investigation - perhaps millions of years in the future - discovered an Iridium anomaly in the geological record. As Iridium is commonly found in asteroids, the event will be indistinguishable from and thus attributed to, a major meteorite strike and not to ... well ... us."

"That's deception!" said Vorkan, amazed at MIND's cunning.

"Not at all, Faro," said MIND innocently. "It won't be our fault if invalid conclusions are drawn - now will it?."

Vorkan realised he had not been aware of this facet of MIND's personality. The level of wiliness it had displayed was akin to that of some of his nonconformist friends. Secretly, Vorkan found it very appealing and would have liked to explore further, but now they had come up with a feasible plan, he was keen to know more about Pronigon-3, potentially, their new home.

"Please show me the film from the probe, taken as Pronigon-3 was first encountered," he said.

"Certainly," said MIND. "Pronigon-3 has a single moon. I will start the film as this is approached."

MIND started the film. It was in full colour 3D, and displayed with maximum size in the holocube. It started as the probe drew near to the planet-moon system. A barren, lifeless moon was approached and orbited. A low pass gave him thrilling views of dramatic, high-contrast mountain ranges, valleys, rilles, and flat-floored craters. He felt that he was actually there, gliding across this awe-inspiring terrain. He imagined he could almost reach out and touch the mountain tops.

Then, the probe turned its attention to the main planet and started towards it. There it hung in the vastness of space, like a precious stone on a cloth of black velvet. It was exceptionally beautiful, with greens and yellows and browns, and vast blue oceans. Intricate swirls of cloud, brilliantly white in the blue-rich sunshine, encircled the equator. Vorkan found himself gazing in wonderment at this spectacular object, now filling the entire display.

"Great heavens," he said. "I've never seen such an exquisite planet."

Its beauty, and particularly the delicate tracery of its clouds against the blue water, reminded him of his solaramine amulet. Solaramine was a precious mineral found in just one equatorial region of their planet. Since the last polar migration and the final abandonment of the equatorial latitudes, solaramine was almost impossible to obtain, and had come to represent rarity, purity, and perfection.

"Does anyone claim to have discovered this planet?" he asked MIND.

"No," came the reply. "As you are Director of the Interstellar Monitoring Foundation, and you have highlighted the potential of this planet, you can claim that privilege yourself."

"I wish to name it," said Vorkan. "I wish to name it Solara, the blue jewel."

"That is indeed a worthy name for such a rare find," said MIND. "Solara it is then. The name is duly registered."

Vorkan sat and gazed in awe at the planet in front of him. The more he gazed, the more convinced he became that this planet was their destiny. He absolutely had to persuade the Council to adopt his plan. They might, if the plan was accepted, even put him in charge of the migration.

He became captivated with the thought that one day, he might walk upon its surface. If he could lead the advance party, then he himself would be able to claim the planet as the new home of the Cryons. He would be acclaimed, and go down in the annals of history as the saviour of their race. He would be supreme. He would become the nearest living thing to a deity.

He would be Vorkan, Master of Solara.

Part 2

HERE, NOW

3

Excursion

15 miles NE of Rawlins, Wyoming
27th September 2012

The melodic voice of Garth Brooks' *If Tomorrow Never Comes* filled the passenger compartment as Phil Newheart swung the powerful motorhome round the switchback curves of the Seminoe Road. Country radio would not have been his choice, but it matched the setting, and the kids liked it.

He glanced across at his daughter Tess. Despite the scenery - a budding geologist's paradise - she was hardly taking any notice. Instead, after every bend, her eyes followed the road to its most distant point. She turned momentarily and smiled at him. She had her mother's smile - intense, mysterious, and with a hint of sadness - and at sixteen, was fully aware of the importance of the imminent rendezvous. The smile said, 'Don't worry, Dad,' but he couldn't help it. He looked at his watch for the umpteenth time.

"Read out Mum's directions again please, Nick," he said.

His son's bright-eyed face appeared alongside him, beaming as usual. Unlike Tess, he had inherited his mother's confidence and vitality but not her wilfulness. Nick could lighten a room by just walking into it.

He crouched down between the two front seats and unfolded the piece of paper he had been entrusted with.

"Interstate 80 west to Sinclair," he said, cheerfully. "North up the Seminoe Road towards Alcova. Road follows river."

"Okay. That'll be the North Platte we're following right now. What's the next bit?"

"At straight section after river, look out for Tess's sign. Pull over and switch on headlights but don't turn off road. I will find you. Oh, and there's the time of course - 4pm."

Phil looked at his watch again - three twenty five. He found himself taking deeper breaths than usual.

The road was following a canyon, obviously cut by the river through the barren sandstone rock. The only green vegetation was down by the water, on the inside of the bends.

After a while, the canyon ended and they found themselves driving across a level brush-covered plain. There was absolutely no sign of life - man nor beast - for as far as the eye could see. Distant mountains ringed the skyline. The road stretched straight ahead of them miles into the distance until it disappeared into a lake-like mirage. Phil turned on the headlights.

"Now Tess, what will your sign say exactly?" He succeeded in concealing his irritation that Tess's Internet pen-pal at the University in Laramie - someone she had only met in person yesterday - had not been more specific.

"He said if I really knew anything about geology, I'd recognise the sign when I saw it," she replied, coolly.

"I'll help," said Nick, digging into his rucksack and pulling out a pair of binoculars.

At that moment, over the noise of the engine, came the insistent warble of Phil's mobile phone.

"It's Mum!" cried Nick, expectantly.

Phil pulled up at the side of the road. He could feel his hands shaking slightly as he managed a grin, for the children.

"Hello," he said, warily.

"It's me. I'm at Alcova." He could only just hear Jo's voice over the background din from her vehicle. "Won't make it by four I'm afraid. Won't be long though. Sorry Phil. Kids okay?"

Phil closed his eyes and suppressed his irritation. He and the children had not seen Jo-Ann for three months; they had flown thousands of miles from England; they'd left Laramie in plenty of time earlier that day. Jo had a two-hour drive from Riverton. But this was not the moment to start arguing about punctuality.

"That's okay, Jo," he said, calmly. "Everybody's fine."

He just made out, "You got your headlights on? Oh damn! Low battery! See you soon." before the call cut off.

"She's going to be a bit late," he said, maintaining his blasé pose.

Nick and Tess exchanged glances but did not react.

It wasn't that Jo-Ann was irresponsible or heartless, though she was definitely much firmer with the children than he. It was that she habitually filled her day with activities which demanded of others an energy which matched her own. The result was her continual frustration.

"We'll wait for her by the sign, when we find it," said Phil as he pulled back onto the road.

"There's a sign ahead!" exclaimed Nick proudly, struggling to steady his binoculars.

When they got near, Phil eased off the gas, but he could see it wasn't what they were looking for.

"Bar Q Ranch," announced Nick.

Phil accelerated, and returned his gaze to the road's vanishing point far ahead. The barren landscape shimmered in the afternoon heat as the vehicle purred along. He started re-living the last transatlantic telephone conversation with Jo - the one that had resulted in this trip - when she said she didn't know whether she would be returning to England. His stomach started to churn as he imagined the battles to come.

"Look out, Dad!" yelled Tess just in time. An antelope was running diagonally from their right and heading for the road, trying to beat the vehicle.

Phil braked and swerved to the left as the frightened creature crossed in front of them. The camper lurched precariously as smoke poured from its nearside wheels.

"Damn it!" he exclaimed, regaining control and bringing the vehicle to rest. He was annoyed he hadn't seen it. "If they just stayed where they were, they'd be fine."

"It's stopped over there," said Tess. "Oh let's go and see it."

"Okay, but just a few minutes. We still haven't found the sign, and we don't want to be later than your mother."

The children got out. Phil turned the radio off, sat back in his seat and closed his eyes. A gentle breeze rustling the sage brush and the click-click-click of the cooling engine were the only sounds. The smell of hot rubber drifted in through the windows. Suddenly he was seven and sitting at the kitchen table back in Iowa, and his father was returning from work at the Firestone factory. Although his mother hated the smell on his clothes, she always kissed him on the cheek and gave him a mug of tea - she insisted this was better for him than coffee. Once, he winked at Phil and whispered, "A small price to pay for marrying a beautiful English rose." It was in that same kitchen that the two police officers told him and his mother about the plane crash, and the death of his father.

He suddenly became aware of the sound of another vehicle. It was on the limit of audibility, and more like a faint vibration than an audible sound. He sat up and peered along the road, checked his mirrors and scanned the surrounding plain, but there was nothing in sight. Must be a distant truck, he thought to himself.

The children were walking back across the road. Tess' height, long straight hair, secretary-like spectacles and severe expression accentuated the two years difference between them. But Nick was growing fast, and what he lacked in stature he made up for in sheer energy.

"No sign of Mum yet then?" said Tess, quietly.

Phil reached over and squeezed her hand. "Soon," he said, encouragingly.

They set off again. Phil was concentrating on the far distance.

"That's it!" yelled Tess. "We've just passed it!"

"What did it say?" said Phil, bringing the vehicle to a halt once more.

"K-T Road. That's got to be it."

"Sounds like another ranch to me," said Nick.

"You don't know anything about it," retorted Tess superciliously. "K-T stands for Cretaceous - Tertiary. It's the boundary between the end of the Mesozoic and the start of the Cainozoic era in the Earth's geological past. It was the K-T event that wiped out the dinosaurs."

"Okay smarty-pants," said Nick, "So what've the Meso and Cano what's it, got to do with K and T?"

"Because the Cretaceous was the final period in the Mesozoic, and the Tertiary was the first period in the Cainozoic, bone brain!"

Phil found himself wondering about the 'K' and the spelling of Cretaceous, but kept quiet.

The sign had been shot at by gun-toting vehicle passengers, but at the bottom were the four letters 'UWDG'.

"There! I told you," exclaimed Tess triumphantly. "University of Wyoming Department of Geology. This is definitely it, Dad."

"Okay. Well spotted, Tess," said Phil. He kept the engine idling and checked the headlights were on high beam. He looked at his watch. Five to four - perfect timing.

"How about some tea?" said Tess, getting up and filling the kettle.

"I'm going to make Mum her favourite sandwich," said Nick, as he proudly produced a jar of Marmite he had brought all the way from England for her.

Phil turned the radio back on softly, and as the children busied themselves, tried to collect his thoughts. Like it or not, the marriage had reached a crisis point. Was it really his fault, as Jo claimed? It flew in the face of reason for her to hold him to that promise - made in England before they were married. Yes, he *had* said they would settle in Wyoming within five years, but things had changed. Who in their right mind would have wanted to bring up children in a place where alcoholism is rampant, jobs are few, and there is nothing else to do other than sit around listening to the wind blow. For sure as dammit, Jo-Ann wouldn't have been satisfied with Cheyenne or Laramie - she would have wanted to go all the way, and live within the reservation.

But in any case, that promise was made before he started the business. There was no way that he could just uproot and move it to the States now. Why should he? The USA - his own country - had done nothing but obstruct his attempts to export his vehicles. It had taken years to gather his R&D team; sales were gradually improving; their compact battery breakthrough was surely just around the corner. In another few years - that's all he needed - it would be the USA who would be begging him to sell them his design. That would be a sweet moment, when he could avenge the death of his father.

"I can see a light!" yelled Nick suddenly. He grabbed his binoculars. "It's Mum!"

Phil felt a shudder of pleasure ripple through his body. But at the same time, his stomach felt cold. He gazed at the light. It was at the point where the road disappeared over the furthest ridge, maybe three or four miles away. The light was like a brilliant star rising out of a tranquil sea, weaving and shimmering in the late afternoon's heat.

At first, it was a single point, but as it grew nearer, it resolved into two. Then they were obviously headlights. Now, he could see the vehicle itself. The lights flashed on and off. Nick squealed with delight and almost fell out of the camper door, then ran, arms waving frantically, down the road towards the approaching vehicle. Tess followed, walking, but waving too.

What the hell am I going to say to her? thought Phil as he stepped down and began walking towards what he could now see was a dishevelled and very dusty Ford pick-up.

He needn't have worried. Jo turned the rattling truck across the road, pulled up in a swirl of dust, opened the door and stepped out. Nick and Tess flung themselves at her. Crying with joy, she cradled them in her arms, and hugged and kissed them. Then, quite naturally, Nick and Tess led their mother by the hand towards him.

"God, I've missed you," he said, reaching out and folding her in his arms.

Her body pressed up against his, felt warm and comforting. He took a handful of her long raven hair and covered his face with it as he kissed her neck and breathed in the scent of her.

"I need you, Phil," she whispered hoarsely into his ear.

But after a few moments, and with the children still hugging them both, it was as if common sense intervened to break the spell. Simultaneously, they unwrapped themselves from each other and took a couple of paces backwards.

"You look well," Phil found himself saying, mechanically.

In fact, she looked incredible. Although she was only half Indian, he saw more clearly now, the almond eyes and olive skin of her Shoshone father. Her tan had deepened, and her big brown eyes seemed to mirror the wide-open landscape around her. Her hair, flowing like shot silk, looked as if it had been created to give the wind something to caress. The close-fitting jeans emphasised her figure, and her breasts - she was clearly not wearing a bra - were as proud as the day he had first seen her - and them - seventeen years ago. If there was a single word that described Jo-Ann as she stood before him, it was a word she had used increasingly in the months before her final departure.

That word, was *freedom*.

"She's not coming back is she, Dad?" said Tess sadly, as Phil eased the camper off the highway and down onto the track leading to the east. The heavy vehicle pitched and rolled as tarmac gave way to gravel, and clouds of dust billowed from the wheels. In his mirror, he could see Nick waving from Jo-Ann's car, as she turned to follow them.

"I don't know, Tess," he replied, giving her a knowing look. He was very close to his daughter, and it wasn't worth pretending anymore. He felt he would like to have talked about it, but now, he had to concentrate.

"How far is it down here?" he said.

"Randy said the track went all the way across to the river, and there's only one difficult bit, across a gulch. Once we get to where we can see the river, that's where the K-T boundary is. That's where the fossils are."

Phil grimaced, and gripped the steering wheel a little tighter as he fought with the concept that reliable directions could ever be given by a callow youth with a name like 'Randy'. He probably had loins to match.

After about four miles, Phil eased the lurching camper over the three steel tubes at the bottom of the dip. He wondered what the RV rental company would say if they knew where he was taking their precious camper, and began to question the wisdom of this excursion, bearing in mind the isolation of the place. He turned the radio down to help him concentrate. He was beginning to feel nervous, but there was no way he was going to admit this to Tess.

At last, as they reached the top of a ridge, they saw the North Platte widened into the Seminoe Reservoir - a stretch of tranquil blue giving relief and contrast to the barren surroundings. Phil followed the track towards it, then pulled off onto an area of gently sloping ground. As he did this however, the engine began to labour. He floored the gas pedal and tried to turn back towards the track, but it was too late. The heavy motorhome dug deeper into the sandy ground and came to a shuddering halt.

"That's all we need," he muttered, jumping down. "Mum'll never let me live this one down!"

They were twenty yards from the track. Jo's pick-up was still on it. She and Nick were walking down towards them.

"You're not in Richmond Park now, Phil!" she said, accusingly. "You never drive off the road 'less you test it first."

"Oh wow!" said Nick, dropping to his knees by the camper.

"Looked like a good place to stop," said Phil sheepishly. The motorhome was up to its axles in the sand. He cursed himself for being so stupid. "Can you tow us out, Jo?"

"No way. Haven't got a rope in the back anyway. We'll have to phone the boys."

Phil felt ashamed he had never met any of Jo's extended family. In fact this was the first time he had returned to America since his childhood. He knew it was unreasonable, but his instinct to distance himself from the country of his birth was insuppressible. Jo had been the exception. He had only forced himself over here to persuade her to return. Dragging her Indian relatives from Wind River was hardly going to make him Mr Popularity or help maintain his detachment

"They're a two hour drive away!" he said. Then wincing at his own insincerity, "It wouldn't be right to bother them."

He and Nick began clearing the sand from the wheels. Jo just looked at him knowingly, then muttering to herself, followed suit.

"Okay gang," panted Phil.. "Let's give it a try."

The others put their backs to the rear bumper, dug their heels into the ground and heaved with all their might as Phil took up the strain. The RV moved forwards about a foot, then, the rear wheels spinning like circular saws, settled irrevocably down on its rear axle.

"Shit!" mouthed Phil, as he realised they were never going to get out without help. He rummaged in the glove box, for the hire company folder.

Jo-Ann climbed in and sat down next to him. Her expression of hopelessness was tinged with regret. She reached for his phone and started punching in a number.

"I'm goin' to phone the boys," she said. "This is ridiculous."

"No!" he said, grabbing the phone from her.

"God, you're a stubborn bugger," she said, glaring at him.

"Best way," he said, looking for the Emergency Assistance page.

But he knew she was right. His stubbornness was his immovable object. Her wilfulness was her irresistible force.

"Please yourself," she said impatiently, jumping to her feet and heading for the door. "It's Triple A you need."

"Triple A. That's not a *Federal* organisation is it?" he said.

"Jesus Phil! Don't you *ever* give up! I don't give a shit what sort of organisation it is. It'll get us out of the mess you've got us into!"

The door slammed behind her.

"Sorry," said Phil to himself. "Can't help it."

Triple A patched him through to a local garage. The phone call eased the tension. Calmed, he climbed out of the van.

"Somebody called Duke's coming in the morning," he announced. "Said he'd come now if we insisted. Bit late though. We were going to stay here anyway weren't we."

He walked over to Jo, and laid his hands gently on her shoulders.

"Sorry," he whispered.

They stood and gazed at the panorama before them. To the east was the reservoir, its banks forming gently-sloping beaches of rock-peppered sand. A high sandstone outcrop to their left formed a promontory into the softly lapping waters. A gentle breeze - unusually kind for Wyoming - brought the unmistakable scent of sage to their nostrils. As Phil stood drinking in the scene and watching the far bank turning orange in the glow of the rapidly setting sun, he realised he hadn't stopped rushing since they left England. Now, suddenly, there was peace. It felt good.

"This really is an exceptionally beautiful place," he said.

"Bit late to realise that, Phil," she lamented, pulling away from him and killing the moment. She walked over to the van and started organising the children to help her prepare a meal.

Phil strolled to the water's edge and stared into the distance. A terrible emptiness took hold of him as he sank down onto the sand, dropped his head into his hands, and cried like a baby.

***

How am I going to tell him? thought Jo-Ann as she made the after-dinner coffee. Leaving Tess tut-tutting at a programme on acid rain in Canada, she went outside with two mugs and sat down at the camp table. Phil had bought Nick a telescope in Denver. They had unpacked it earlier and set it up on some flat rocks nearby. Now, they were taking it in turns to look at the Moon.

Phil was superb with the children. As she watched him encouraging Nick and saying all the right things, she yet again agonised over her feelings and what had brought them to this point.

Phil's mother had been against the marriage from the start. After the crash, she had bankrupted herself trying to expose alleged corruption in the Federal Aviation Administration and Trans-America, the airline. 'Your country,' she would say, 'is sick from the top down. Do you wonder why I brought him to England?' And at the wedding in London, she had whispered, 'You'll never get him to go back. Never.'

Jo had believed that once they were married, she could rebuild Phil's love for his country so cruelly demolished by fifteen years of his mother's bitterness. But now, finally, she was staring defeat in the face, and yet again, without trying, Phil was making her feel guilty.

Damn him! *He* was the one who had let *her* down. Every time she reminded him of his promise, he had used that infuriatingly logical mind of his to press arguments which persuaded her to wait just a bit longer.

So why was she doing this?

Phil had left Nick at the telescope, and was walking towards her. There was still that spring in his step which more than compensated for his medium height, and at forty, his figure could have been that of a man half his age. And yes - his natural ice-melting smile was working again. Swine!

"Thanks luv," he said. His soft blue eyes sparkled as he cupped his hands round the steaming mug. Those hands, which had explored and caressed every inch of her body and fine-tuned her response to them - those hands might never touch her again once she told him.

They sat together silently in the gathering darkness. Occasionally they heard a fish break the surface of the now tranquil waters, and once - just once - the howl of a distant coyote drifted across the evening air. The golden glow of a glorious sunset had given way to the splendour of the mountain night. The milky way arched from south west to north east. Cygnus hung high overhead and the gibbous Moon shone low in the south. In the east, the Great Square of Pegasus hung majestically over the Shirley Mountains. Last month, just two weeks after her father was taken ill, that same constellation had been in the west, setting behind the Wind River Mountains in the pre-dawn sky.

That dawn had been very special. As if she was there, she could see the outline of the Sun Lodge - a circle of cottonwood boughs with the leaves still on, forming a great cone - from which before sunrise, the dancers emerge. Even with their full regalia, she can recognise most of the men - indeed some are her relatives. In the distance, is the low thump-thump-thump of oil pumping rigs, but the sound of the great drum and the men wailing an ancient song soon drown that out. The sky grows bright, and all eyes turn to the eastern horizon. They wait, then suddenly the first brilliant sliver of sun appears, and a shrill, unearthly shriek fills the air. She whirls round to see the dancers in a line, blowing on eagle-bone whistles to greet the sun. The people around her are holding out their hands to catch its first rays, and stroking them over their heads and bodies. She looks around, at the grey-green plateau, the mountains, and the blue sky - of a colour never seen in England - and she knows that no place will ever be home to her in the same sense as this place is.

That's why she was doing this. That's why.

***

"Dad!"

Nick's voice was anxious, urgent. Phil opened his eyes and looked around him. Jo-Ann was back in the RV.

"What's up?"

"There's something wrong with the telescope drive," he said sadly.

"Really! You sure you've got the polar axis lined up okay? If that isn't spot on, it won't track properly?"

"No. The tracking's fine. But I get this vibration every now and again. It's really annoying."

Phil knew that telescope drive motors could suffer a form of cyclical error if there was inaccuracy in the gear train. It was almost certain to be that. He got up and walked over to the telescope

"How often does it happen?" he said.

"Well, it's happened at least five times since we set it up. Maybe once every ten minutes. Lasts at least a minute or so. Next one's due soon. You look. Bet you."

Phil peered through the eyepiece. The image of the Moon was steady as a rock.

"When it starts again, we'll turn off the drive," he said. "That should tell us."

He stood waiting, with the drive control in his hand. Then, as Nick had predicted, the image began to vibrate. He had never seen this sort of vibration in a telescope before. He expected a slow, rhythmical and gentle meander, but this was a definite vibration - the sort you would expect if there was a machine at work nearby.

"That's odd," he said, and switched off the drive. To his surprise, the vibrations continued.

"I don't believe it!" Phil exclaimed. "It can't be the scope."

"Maybe it's coming through the ground from the RV," said Nick.

"Of course! Good thinking, Nick."

Phil recalled that professional astronomers spend a fortune isolating big telescopes from local ground vibrations. It was a real problem.

"Take over, Nick," he said, ran over to the RV, and threw the primary isolator switch. Total silence and darkness descended upon them.

"Dad!" wailed Tess from inside. "I was watching that!"

"What's up, Honey?" said Jo.

"Vibrations. Explain in a minute. Keep still everyone. Well, Nick?"

"Still vibrating."

"We heard some faint vibrations when the TV was off," said Jo, calmly. "It's probably a mine."

A mine! Of course! Phil could have kissed her and strangled her at the same time. She had this infuriating ability to arrive at the solution to a problem after an irresponsibly short time. He would carefully weigh up all the factors, make lists even, and arrive at a well-reasoned conclusion. Jo would just go with her feelings - it could only be that - but she got it right!

"Stopped again," called Nick.

Cursing to himself, he switched everything back on, then went out to join Nick.

"I ... your mother thinks it might be a mine."

"I haven't seen or heard anything."

"The mine head could be miles away," said Phil, "But the shafts and seams could be below us right now. That'll be it. It'll be the machine cutting at the coal face. We could probably hear it if we put our ears to the ground."

They waited until the image in the telescope started dancing once more, then lay down and pressed their ears against the cold bedrock. There was no question. At the limit of audibility, Phil could hear a deep resonant rumble - like distant thunder - interspersed with short periods of silence.

"Well I'm damned," he said. "It is a mine. Strange sound."

They were getting up off the ground and were starting to peer into the distance for signs of life, when a movement not twenty yards away caught their attention. Nick grabbed Phil's arm.

"There's something there," he whispered hoarsely.

"Torch. Quick!" said Phil.

As he turned it on, its beam caught a huge non-human face coming slowly towards them. Phil caught his breath, and Nick stepped backwards and nearly knocked his telescope over. They started edging slowly towards the camper. Phil had visions of having to fight off some wild mountain beast, and wondered whether he'd come out of it alive.

But, with Nick peering from behind him, he kept the torch firmly on the animal, only to realise with considerable relief, that it was a horse and rider.

"Howdy folks," came a gruff but gentle voice out of the darkness. "Saw yur lights just now. Mind if I join you for a moment?"

"Who are you? What do you want," said Phil, trying to sound as deep and husky as possible.

"Powd's ma name, Sir. Done roundin' the strays from the Bar Q. On my way to Coal Creek. Thought I'd come back 'long the water seein' there's a good moon n'all."

He dismounted and walked slowly towards them, removing the glove from his right hand and extending it towards Phil. Phil grasped it. It was warm and leathery, the grip firm and controlled. He felt relieved - he had half expected a bone crusher. He introduced himself and Nick to the stranger, then led him to the camper, calling Jo-Ann to warn her.

"Jo-Ann. Perhaps er, Powd, would like a cup of coffee," said Phil after the introductions.

He felt he had little choice other than to be friendly. The man was obviously a local, had transport, probably had a gun, and might even own the land they were on.

"That's right hospitable of you Sir, Ma'am," he said. Phil offered him a place at the picnic table. Jo-Ann studied him intently for a moment, then, apparently satisfied, went in to the RV. The children stood looking at the horse.

"He's an Appaloosa isn't he," said Tess. "What's his name?"

"Well that's right, young lady!" said Powd, his eyes brightening. "That's Slick. Just walk up to him real gentle, and he'll be fine. He'll take a cookie if you got one."

Nick went to get some biscuits, and he and Tess stood stroking Slick, standing statuesquely in the moonlight.

In the light from the RV, Phil could see that Powd was well past sixty. Under the brown leather-banded Stetson was a kindly face which had obviously withstood years of buffeting in the unrelenting Wyoming winds. He sported a full black and grey beard, which fell untidily over his thick leather jacket.

"Is this your land?" said Phil, tentatively.

"I sure don't own it, if that's what you mean," replied Powd, smiling. "But this is my land all right. I work the ranches from here 'cross to the Granite Mountains. Done so all my life."

Jo-Ann emerged with the coffee, and sat next to Phil.

"Thank you kindly Ma'am," said Powd, cradling the mug in his hands.

"It must be a lonely life, working out here," said Phil, looking into Powd's clear brown eyes.

"Lonely ya say!" said Powd, settling back in his chair. "Alone maybe, but never lonely. Sure, I don't get to meet many people. Fact is, you're the first folks I've seen today. But I got the antelopes, I got the coyotes, I got the eagles, I got the fish, I got all sorts of little critters y'd never see 'till you get down there. And I got the stars and the Moon and the planets. I got my readin' and my thoughts, and then there's always old Slick there."

He turned, and gazed warmly at his partner.

"No Sir. I got plenty."

"You read?" said Phil, but cursed himself as he said it, with its thinly-veiled implication. He recovered with, "Where do you get the books from?"

"The ranchers. They get the books for me, then I pick 'em up next time round. I got books in all the ranches round here. Real nice folks. They read 'em too. I kinda circulate them."

Phil smarted at how Powd's simple method was breathtakingly obvious once it was explained.

"You'll be from a big city then," said Powd, glancing at the RV.

"Er ... London actually," said Phil, after an awkward pause.

"London eh. D'you like it?"

There was an even longer pause.

"It's okay. We get by." He deliberately avoided Jo-Ann's eyes.

"Once the business grows, we'll get by even better," he said, grasping the opportunity to score a point..

"Got to grow it huh?" said Powd thoughtfully.

"Of course!" said Phil indignantly. "You've got to grow. You can't not try to grow a business!"

"Is that a fact?" said Powd gently.

Phil felt a touch uneasy. It was as if he had to justify this most basic principle.

"You've got to hold your market share," he said, "And better still, increase it. Mind you, it's an uphill struggle, what with the big boys and their petrol engines."

"How's that?"

"I'm sorry. I design electric vehicles. My company sells them."

"'Lectric eh," said Powd, looking interested. "But those guys from Detroit. I bet they're as mean as a bag of Rattlers."

This was an ideal opportunity to re-emphasise to Jo that *this* was the reason why they couldn't move to America. But even as he was forming the words, he knew that using Detroit as a scapegoat was deceiving himself as much as Jo-Ann.

"Mean! They certainly are," he said. "They don't give us a look in. Not just that. They're underhand. They use their power to corrupt. It's they who've stopped us getting import licences to the US. I can't bear corruption. It stinks. I despise it."

The last bits were genuine. Phil could feel his lower lip quivering.

"You really hate 'em, don't you," said Powd, eyeing him closely.

"Too right I do," said Phil.

"Best not grow too big then young fella," said Powd wryly. "You don't want to get so's you hate yourself!"

Phil looked at Powd in astonishment. He sat silently, weighing up the implications of that razor-sharp comment.

"Too many big cities if you ask me," said Powd, stretching his legs out in front of him as if to emphasise his unity with the land. "Too many folks by half. This ol' Earth never meant to have cities. Time I was in Denver, all the folks rushin' about. Didn't seem to be doin' them any kinda good - all miserable 'n all. And the noise and smoke! Give me the open spaces any time."

Phil thought Powd would approve of the *Electra*, but was wary of bringing up the subject again. He did not interrupt.

"Now take a place like this," Powd continued. "Folks livin' in harmony with the land. Not too many of nothin'. All creatures need so much space, see. There's a kinda balance here you don't find in y'r big cities."

Jo sat nodding. Her eyes seemed to looking at something far away. Phil reflected on Powd's remark. The peace which radiated from the old man was a perfect complement to the setting. He thought back to their home in London. Such tranquillity was unheard of there.

"We haven't seen that many animals," said Nick, walking over and sitting at Powd's feet.

"You go up to the Ferris Mountains top end of Gerry Clayton's place 'n you'll see plenty," said Powd. "It ain't far from here. You tell old Gerry you're a friend of mine. Did you see a line of grey outcrops like a row of teeth over to the north-west as you drove over?"

"I did," said Tess.

"Well them's called the Flat-Irons. Ferris Mountain Road runs right to them. Gerry's place is at the end of that road. Go there. You can't move for wildlife. Mind you, some uv the critters been behaving real crazy since midday."

"What do you mean?" said Jo-Ann curiously.

"Well. Runnin' around like they got ants in their pants. Real strange." He looked at Jo-Ann. "Say, you're not from London are you Ma'am?"

"Fort Washakie actually. My father is Shoshone," said Jo-Ann proudly. "I met Phil when I was over studying history at London University."

Powd straightened up. He seemed suddenly relieved, as if a weight had been lifted from his shoulders.

"Shoshone! History!" he said. "I knew it! I was beginning to think I was goin' crazy, seein' stuff. You're here for the doorway ain't ya. *That's* what you're doing' here."

"Doorway?" said Phil. "What doorway?"

"You mean you ain't heard of it? You ain't come to see it?"

"No. What doorway? Where?"

"Why, up against the hill not a quarter mile from here," said Powd. He pointed along the shore to their left. "Other side of that spur. Helluva big door. Got to be an old Aztec thing or something like that. Mind you. Didn't know they'd got this far north. Has to be old though. Rains last week must've loosened the rock. Wasn't there last time I was here. Strange though, hows it's been covered all this time. Never seen nothin' like it before. It really is the darndest thing. You gotta see it before you go, specially you Ma'am, you bein' a historian . . . and your ancestors and all."

Jo-Ann and Tess looked at each other, as if each expected the other to offer an explanation.

"Don't ask me!" Tess blurted out. "Randy didn't say anything about any archaeological stuff being here."

Jo-Ann got up and started collecting the coffee mugs. As she passed behind the old man, Phil saw her mouthing, "No way," and shaking her head sadly.

Phil felt let down. He had found himself sympathising with Powd's natural philosophy, but now, his faith in him was undermined. It was getting cold. He stood up, pulled his jacket collar closer round his neck, and somewhat deliberately began folding the chairs.

"Thanks Powd," he said. "We'll be sure to take a walk over there in the morning. It's been a pleasure talking with you, Sir. But now, if you'll excuse us, we'll bid you good night and let you get on your way. Suppose you'll be making camp soon yourself?"

"Sure," said Powd, getting up and stretching. "I gotta git anyways. Might see you folks around. Been right nice talkin' to ya. And thanks for the coffee."

With that, he mounted his horse and started slowly down towards the river.

"Oh, one thing," called Phil after him. "What's the name of this place?"

"Turtle Forest. G'night now."

And with that, he disappeared into the darkness to the sound of squeaking leather and the soft footfalls of his faithful companion.

It had been three months since Phil had shared a bed with Jo, and even longer since they had made love. Now, lying together in the darkness in the RV, on the cramped and rather public double mattress, Jo was distant, choosing not to respond to his tentative attempts at the sort of intimacies they could get away with without disturbing the children. He lay in the silence, the events of that extraordinary day turning over in his mind. There was Jo, the rift between them, the involvement of the children, getting stuck, and Powd. The problem between him and Jo was by far the most important issue, but at least that was explicable. What didn't make sense was the old man, and the strange things he had said just before he left. He had felt so sure of Powd's rationality, but his talk of an Aztec doorway, and the name, 'Turtle Forest'. He couldn't imagine anything more unlike turtles and forests than this place. Yet somehow he was convinced that he was quite genuine. Then there were the vibrations. He should have asked Powd about the mine.

And to cap it all, as he finally drifted off to sleep, he kept on imagining he could still hear them.

4
The Door

The freshness of a bright new day raised Phil's spirits as he emerged into the early morning sunshine. Soon, the smell and sound of sizzling ham and eggs drifted across the cool morning air. The unresolved events of the previous day still prayed on his mind, but there was no reason why Tess shouldn't do her fossil hunting. As for himself, he was determined to check out Powd's Aztec door story.

"I don't suppose the breakdown truck will arrive just yet," he said, washing down his last bite of toast with a gulp of tea. "How about you and Mum looking for fossils Tess, while Nick and I see if we can find this door thing? Okay with you, darling?"

Jo-Ann gave him a disapproving look. They needed to talk, and it would have been more sensible for the children to go off together. But really, he couldn't face that - not yet.

"Okay, but don't be long," she grunted.

Phil glanced at Nick and winked. Nick scuttled into the RV and emerged with his camera. It was a 2¼ square that Phil used in the lab before everything went digital.

"You never know," he said, patting it lovingly.

"If the guy does arrive, ask him to drive over there and pick us up," said Phil. "Looks as if you could get round the point in a four wheel drive."

As Phil and Nick walked shorewards, the strengthening breeze was singing in the undergrowth, and small waves were running onto the beach. The sky was completely clear, and of the deepest blue, and the morning sunlight danced and tripped across the water ahead of them.

"Should be just round the point, if the old man got it right," said Phil.

On the far side was a small bay between two sandstone outcrops. As they stopped and looked landwards, the sight which greeted them took their breath away. Hard up against a steep cliff and some hundred yards back from the shore was an enormous doorway. It was in the form of a Roman portico, and Phil guessed it was at least forty feet high and sixty feet wide. It looked like a cross between the gable end of a temple and the proscenium arch of some massive outdoor theatre. Two beautifully engineered columns supported a massive pitched superstructure. The material was like black granite - smooth, with a hint of pearlescence about it. What would have been the way through - or the theatre curtains - consisted of a single slab of the same black material. At each side above the columns, and looking distinctly out of place, were hemispherical protrusions. On the gentle slope at the foot of this structure were the fragmented remains of the face of the cliff, which had apparently fallen away, revealing the door.

"Oh wow!" said Nick.

"Good God!" said Phil. "The old man wasn't kidding was he? It's magnificent, and perfectly preserved."

They set off at a quick pace towards it.

"But the style," he continued as they got nearer. "That's never Aztec. It's Greek, or maybe Roman. But it can't be. Must be a replica. The Romans didn't get to the Americas."

"Maybe it's a film set," said Nick excitedly.

"Could be," said Phil. "But where's the crew? Did they do their shooting and just leave it d'you reckon?"

He looked around. There were no vehicle tracks - no vestiges of the paraphernalia associated with film-making - nothing but the desiccated brush. They were now some fifty yards from the door, and found themselves instinctively walking more slowly - more cautiously - up the slope towards it. As they approached, it towered menacingly above them. The only sound was the wind, singing in the ornately decorated frieze.

"There's some writing on it!" exclaimed Nick.

In a line across the top of the central slab, were a series of petroglyphs the like of which Phil had never seen. Below these and in three separate vertical sections like pages, were inscriptions. The left hand section looked like Greek, and the right hand section Chinese or Japanese. The central section was however, unmistakable.

"That's Latin!" he said, staring in astonishment. "Now what on Earth's this all about."

They both walked gingerly up to the door and studied it. Below the inscriptions, was a short horizontal line, and below that, what looked like a river valley. About four feet above the ground and below the valley, were five small circles in a horizontal row. The central circle was split by a short vertical line. To the right and left of the row of circles were indentations in the shape of right and left human hands. Phil got the definite impression that the circles - which were like push-buttons - and the hand imprints were in some way connected.

"Stand in front of it, Dad," said Nick. "Let's get a picture."

Phil obliged, standing to one side, so his body did not obscure the valley drawing and other features.

As Nick set up the shot, Phil, who was now almost touching the door, began to study its surface. Something about the way the material reflected light made it look like granite, but there were no crystalline facets. It was strange.

"Face this way, Dad!" called Nick, his finger on the take button. "Smile please."

The picture taken, they studied the door carefully. The smoothness of the finish, the quality of the flutes of the columns, everything about the construction was quite remarkable. Then Phil noticed that the whole thing was spotlessly clean. There wasn't a speck of dust anywhere, not even the faintest covering - extraordinary for something so exposed to the elements. He placed his fingertips on the surface of the door. It felt as smooth as silk. In fact, he got the impression that he wasn't actually touching it at all. He carefully examined the drawing of the valley. It looked like a slender tadpole, or a snake. The head, he thought, might be a lake, and the body ran from this in a sinuous curve, getting narrower towards the end. But it clearly was a valley, because he could see its steeply-walled sides. The carving was extraordinarily detailed, so much so that he felt a magnifying glass was needed to see everything. About a third of the way along the valley, a tiny dot of translucent light could be seen embedded in the carving. There was something strange yet familiar about the valley. He felt sure he had seen it before somewhere, but couldn't put his finger on why it looked so unusual.

"This is quite amazing. I've never seen such high quality workmanship, even on a tombstone."

"What does the writing say, Dad? Can you translate it?"

Phil stepped back and studied the Latin section.

ANIMUM ATTENDITEADITUS AD HUNC LOCUM CIRCUMSCRIPTUS EST.
INUTILE ET MAXIME PERICULOSUM EST ADITUM SINE CLAVE TEMPTARE.
EI QUI CLAUSTRUM PATEFACIT CLAVEM RECUPERARE ET UTI LICET.
CLAVIS REPERIETUR IN VALLE INFRA DESCRIPTA.
SIGNUM MITTITE UNDAE LONGITUDINE LINEAE INFRA SCRIPTAE ET CLAVIS RESPONDEBIT.
PORTA UTILIS MANEBIT TRES MAXIME MENSES LUNARES EX QUO TEMPORE CLAUSTRUM PATEFIT.

For the first time in his life, he regretted he had dropped Latin after the first term.

"Oh my goodness! Well. Let's see."

"Attend? Listen maybe."

"Circumscriptus. Restrict? Be cautious perhaps."

"Maxime periculosum - Maximum danger. Clave means key."

"The key again. Licet - licence maybe."

"The fifth line says something about the key and a valley. Infra descripta? Beyond description? Beyond described? No, below described. The key something the valley described below. That's it!"

"That'll be the valley drawn on the door Dad. Maybe there's a key hidden in a valley somewhere! Go on!" said Nick confidently. Phil continued.

"The sixth's a bit tough. Sign? Longitude? Below, key again. Respond?"

"Respond to what?" said Nick in frustration.

"And the last sentence, I can just about sort out. It says, Door, utilisable, three maximum months lunar, time, something or other. Your mother could do it. She's studied Latin."

"Did you say door, Dad? So it *is* a door, and there's a key hidden somewhere in a valley, and the door will respond. Maybe it means open. Do you think we could find the key and open it?"

Phil didn't reply, but found himself drawn towards the buttons and hand marks. Maybe 'key' meant the key *to* getting in rather than the key *for* getting in.

"These remind me of those conundrums you see in puzzle books," he said. "What d'you think?"

"Maybe it's another way to open the door," said Nick. "You know, a sort of interlocking mechanism. It's like in those old Indiana Jones films where he finds his way into ancient tombs. You don't think there could be treasure inside do you Dad?"

"Could be," said Phil, placing his hands into the two palm places.

But as he did this, the indentations changed shape slightly. They felt like supple leather gloves. The stone of the door surface seemed to mould itself round his hands. The feeling was not unpleasant, but its unexpectedness made him pull back instinctively.

"Wow!" he found himself saying. "It's soft there!"

"Soft! Let me feel," said Nick eagerly, moving towards the palm prints.

A gut feeling - something he rarely allowed to influence him - told him to stop Nick going anywhere near the thing. An ever-growing doubt about the nature of this apparition was beginning to enter his mind. He kept telling himself not to be ridiculous, but there was something wrong, something unreal here. He wanted to run, but an irresistible curiosity held him fast.

"No. Wait," he said firmly, taking Nick by the hand. "Hasten slowly."

They took a few steps backwards and studied the door again. Nothing made sense. Phil was proud of his analytical skills, but on this one, he drew a blank on every approach. He needed more information. The buttons and hand-marks cried out to be investigated. He had to give it a try.

He studied them. The line through the central button suggested a split. Perhaps if the central one was pressed first, then the others in an expanding fashion, then you pressed on the palm prints, this would signify that the door was to open, inwards maybe. He couldn't think of anything else.

"I'm going to try suggesting a separating motion, then push on the palm places," he said to a very sceptical-looking Nick.

He touched the central circle with his right forefinger, then the two adjacent buttons simultaneously with both forefingers, then the outer buttons in the same manner. Then he placed his hands in the indentations and pushed.

"This is probably a complete waste of time."

The door didn't give. Nothing happened, so he removed his hands.

"Why did you pause, Dad?" Nick was regarding him strangely.

"What?"

"You said 'prob', then waited, then 'ably'."

"No I didn't."

"Yes you did. Honest. It was really weird."

"I don't know what you're talking about, Nick."

They were both so busy arguing that Phil hadn't noticed what had happened to the door until he saw Nick's eyes widen. He was staring at it, open-mouthed, pointing. Phil swung round.

"Bloody hell, Dad! It's changed!"

The five buttons and palm indentations had disappeared. In their place, in the centre of the door, was now a hexagonal opening about six inches across.

Instinctively, they both turned and ran, scrambling over the sandy hillocks as fast as they could, down the slope and away from the door. Only when they rounded the headland did they stop, gasping for breath, then crouch down and peer back at it from behind a rock. Phil had visions of the hole getting bigger, or some mechanism causing the door to swing open, or even something coming out.

But nothing else happened. Total silence. No further change or movement. They looked at each other, then back to the door. After a few minutes, Phil stood up.

"Stay there, Nick," he said, as he walked hesitantly back to the face of the door.

He approached it cautiously, stopping every now and again to look and listen for any further change. Eventually, now next to the door again, he peered into the hexagonal hole. He could see that it did not go right through, but was more like a socket, angled slightly downwards and about ten inches to a foot deep. Clearly, the door was either very thick or not a door at all. The sides and base of the socket were completely smooth. He resisted the temptation to put his hand inside.

He was in despair. He found himself clawing at the recesses of his mind in search of anything - any tid-bit of information - which could explain this almost magical behaviour of what seemed to be solid material. Whatever explained the door's properties was certainly completely beyond his experience. As a trained engineer with a broad knowledge of materials, he found it inexplicable. The scene was dream-like. Here he was, standing in the middle of the Wyoming plains, facing a Roman portal of black granite, and witnessing transmogrification of its material. For the first time in his adult life, he was totally perplexed.

He walked back towards Nick, glancing over his shoulder every so often. He half expected to see an audience laughing at him as he was fooled by some sort of practical joke. But there was nothing - nobody around - only the ubiquitous sage brush waving in the wind, and his son, waiting for an explanation.

"What's going on, Dad?" he said nervously, walking up to meet him. "How did that happen?"

"I don't know, Nick I just don't know."

At that moment, they heard the sound of a vehicle approaching, and turned to see a large flamboyant breakdown truck, its lights flashing, round the headland and rumble across the dusty ground towards them. It stopped some thirty yards back from the door. Phil could see 'Tony's Towing', and a large Tasmanian Devil motif painted on its side panel. Tess was sitting in the passenger seat, grinning.

"This is Duke, Dad," she said, jumping out and gazing admiringly at the rugged young man now walking towards them as if he had just stepped out of a Marlboro advert. "He runs the line dancing at the Golden Spike in Rawlins."

"Howdy folks," he said, in a low-pitched Wyoming drawl. Then, as he looked in astonishment at the door, "What in tarnation is *that*!"

"You don't know anything about it?" said Phil.

"No Sir. Lived around here all my life. Wasn't here last week when I came fishin'. I'll be damned!"

He walked up to the door, and gave it a kick with his cowboy-booted foot. To everybody's surprise, not the least Duke's, his foot rebounded off the door, catching him off balance and throwing him to the ground. Tess's hand went up to her mouth as she stifled a giggle.

"Son of a bitch!" he exclaimed, his Marlboro image somewhat tarnished. He jumped to his feet, but now, only one of his cowboy boot toes was pointed.

"What the hell's this thing made of?" he growled, limping towards his truck. Phil found himself smiling, as he imagined how this might somewhat take the edge off Duke's line dancing prowess.

"I wouldn't try anything," warned Phil. "One of the words means Dangerous."

"Bullshit!" exclaimed Duke, and to Phil's horror, reached into the back of the truck for a large sledge hammer.

"He's going to hit it!" whispered Tess. "Stop him, Dad!"

But Phil could see that Duke was determined to retaliate and recover a little pride after being so ignominiously floored. He was obviously in no mood to take advice from a limey, and anyway, he was big!

"If you must do that, at least wait until the children are out the way," called Phil reproachfully. He ushered Nick and Tess to what he guessed was a safe distance.

"Okay," said Duke confidently as he stood sideways to the door, the hammer handle held firmly in his huge sunburnt hands. He raised it like a pro-golfer at the 18th, and swung it down at the base of the door with all his strength. As it made contact, Phil expected to hear a bang, a thud - something. But the strike was completely silent. The hammer ricocheted back from the door, out of Duke's grasp, and flew in a low curving arc, coming to rest embedded in the Tasmanian Devil.

"Holy shit!" exclaimed Duke, staring in horror at what had been his immaculate truck. Exhausted of further expletives and looking decidedly sheepish, he lolloped back to it and extricated the hammer. The others looked on, no-one believing what they had seen - and not heard.

"What is it Dad?" said Tess. "I don't understand. What's happening?"

"I'm gonna radio Gary Collins down in Rawlins," said Duke. "No goddamned stupid door gonna beat up my rig like that."

Phil resisted the temptation to engage Duke in a philosophical discussion on the cause of the damage to his truck, preferring to start analysing all that had happened. He and the children sat on the ground, stared at the door, and listened to Duke's garbled efforts at describing the events to the sheriff. As they sat, Phil had the strangest impression that somehow, behind the door, someone was watching them, as stage staff observe an audience silently and secretly before the curtain rises.

There has to be a logical explanation, thought Phil. This is some sort of hush-hush government establishment. But if it's so secret, why announce it with a damned great door which is bound to attract attention? Then he thought about the material of the door. Hard as rock, smooth as silk, spotlessly clean, *active*, and able to soundlessly resist impact like the highest quality rubber. The stuff could be worth a fortune if he could get hold of some of it.

"We have to find out what the inscription says," he said.

Phil copied the Latin text onto one of Duke's call-out sheets, taking meticulous care to get every word exactly right. It was while he was sketching the river valley that Tess suddenly realised why it looked so strange.

"It's got near-vertical sides and a flat floor," she exclaimed. "It's not a river. It's a a *canyon*!"

"That's it, Tess. I knew it didn't look right. Now where on earth have I seen that?"

"You've got to go back for Mum. She might recognise it. And wasn't she doing European history when you met? She'll know about the Latin and stuff."

"One minute Tess, then I'll get her."

He continued sketching, and did not allow himself to be distracted as another vehicle drove up and parked nearby. When he had finished, he looked up, to see a Dodge all-terrain-vehicle with 'Wyoming State Geological Survey' emblazoned on its side. A middle-aged man with a bright metallic hard hat and a leather belt bristling with an assortment of tools was talking to Duke. Two younger men began digging a hole and setting up some apparatus.

"Vibrations?" said Duke.

"Yes," said the man, staring incredulously at the door. "We've been out here since first light. They're coming from right under here."

Phil saw Nick's eyes widen.

"They're not for a minute or so every ten are they?" said Phil.

"They are, Sir." The man's eyebrows raised. "You're not from the Survey are you? How did you know about them?"

Phil introduced himself and explained about the telescope. The man was extremely interested. He extended his hand. "Bjorn Jorgensen, Head of the State Geological Survey in Laramie."

"So the vibrations aren't from mining?" said Phil. "What's causing them then?"

Jorgensen looked uncomfortable.

"I'm sorry, I can't tell you," he said mysteriously. "USGS in Denver have asked us to do a local survey."

Phil persuaded Jorgensen to run him and the children back to collect Jo.

"You're from Laramie, Doctor Jorgensen?" said Tess as they set off. She was looking back at his two young assistants.

"We've come from there this morning to pin-point the epicentre."

"Epicentre?" said Phil. "Sounds like you're talking about an earthquake!"

"I'm using the term loosely. But these vibrations, they're from about three miles down. They sound artificial but they've gotten all the qualities of minor tremors. And it's BJ by the way."

"My wife thought there were mines around here."

"There're some strip mines, but forget them. This source is deeper than the world's deepest mine. No Sir. This is something quite different; something we've never had before; something from way down."

"What sort of rock is it?" said Phil, wondering whether his shaky notion about a government establishment could be true.

"Well," said BJ. "All around here and for miles down, is sediment and ash which has come via ancient rivers or volcanic eruptions from the mountains to the west there. Hundred million years ago this whole area was covered by a vast, shallow sea which ran right through from the Gulf Of Mexico to the Arctic ocean. Gradually, the sea retreated, leaving wide stretches of sand and silt behind it. That was added to by meandering rivers bringing further deposits off the mountains to the north and west. There used to be an extensive, dinosaur-rich, crocodile-rich, turtle-rich, life-rich tropical rain forest here."

"Did you say turtles, and a forest?"

"Oh sure. We call this Turtle Forest actually."

Phil felt sick as he recalled the way he had unceremoniously ended the conversation with Powd.

"Anyway, to answer your question," continued BJ, "The rocks are sedimentary, and fairly soft."

"Easy to drill through?"

"Oh yes - definitely. You heard of the GEGA project?"

"The millennium geothermal energy experiment. Yes, I remember. Ran out of funds or something. That was here?"

"Sure was. Well, nine miles north west of here actually. GEGA stood for Geothermal Energy and Geological Anomaly. We'd known for years that deep below this basin, was some sort of anomalous structure."

"Structure?" said Phil, intrigued.

"The signals weren't right. There's a seismologically opaque mass down there. Anyway, the Greens were pushing for some positive action on geothermal energy sources - extracting free heat from the ground. So a project was set up to drive a shaft down towards this anomaly."

"Killing two birds with one bore, as it were."

"Exactly. Discover the cause of the anomaly, and get free heat at the same time."

"So what happened?"

"The machine got three miles down, then broke. Probably came up against what it was trying to investigate."

"No way to get down there and fix it?"

"You're joking! Nobody could go that deep and survive. Too hot, too dangerous, too many unknowns. No. They re-named it the Hell-Hole actually. The project was abandoned."

"Pity," said Phil. "The shaft still there?"

"Oh sure. The shaft's fine - just useless. They capped it off years back."

"So apart from the Hell-Hole, and that's nine miles away, there's nothing down there?"

"Nothing."

At the RV, Phil put Jo-Ann in the picture, then thrust the piece of paper into her hand. She studied it intently, then stared at Phil as if he was mad.

"You gotta be kidding."

"No, he's not, Mrs Newman," said BJ. "Can you translate it?"

Jo-Ann did not answer, but climbed into the Dodge and continued pouring over the Latin.

"Show me," she said.

When they got back to the door, the astounded Jo-Ann observed it with profound interest.

"If this wasn't Wyoming, and the material wasn't black, I'd say we were looking at a genuine Roman or Greek structure," she said.

She pointed out various parts of the door to her now captivated audience.

"Those are engaged Corinthian columns. See the twelve semi-circular flutes and the Acanthus capitals. And that structure across the top - that's a classic example of a denticulated entablature topped with a pitched pediment. It's amazingly authentic."

"The language on the left, it is Greek isn't it luv?" said Phil.

"Sure is," she said authoritatively.

"What about the Latin?", said Tess. "What does it say, Mum?"

"Greek, Latin, Chinese?" queried Phil. "There doesn't seem to be much of a connection between those."

"Hang on," said Jo-Ann pensively. "If this was written in the past, or written with only a knowledge of some period in the past ..."

"Of course!" said Phil. "It would be written in the most widely used languages of the day."

"Maybe," said Jo-Ann. She started walking to and fro, muttering to herself. "Egyptian civilisation over, Persian and

Phoenician fallen into disuse, Byzantine and Japanese not started. Greek, Latin and Chinese together."

"Well?" said Phil. "Come on. When?"

"Difficult to pin down, but I'd say some time between 300 B.C. and 400 A.D. I'll go for the first century A.D. plus or minus 300 years or so."

"Wow!" said Nick. "Like the Rosetta Stone? We did it at school last term. Maybe it says the same in all three languages."

Phil realised they were forgetting the main point.

"This is ridiculous," he said. "We're not in the ancient world. We're in Wyoming, in the twenty first century. This thing can't be two thousand years old. It doesn't make any sense."

One of the seismologists - a good looking fresh-faced man of about twenty - walked up to BJ.

"The vibrations have stopped, Doctor," he said in a soft cultured voice. "Least ways, the seismograph isn't picking them up."

"Damn!" said BJ. "Okay. Go take a look at the door material Michael. I'll be over in a minute."

He turned back and looked earnestly at Phil and Jo-Ann.

"If that doorway was built and then covered by the material which now appears to have revealed it," he whispered, "We're not talking thousands of years - we're talking millions! We're talking scores of millions. The K-T boundary is just the other side of that hill. These rocks right here were laid down about sixty four million years ago. No. That door has appeared. It can't have been here then."

He walked slowly over to the others, now gathered by the door.

"Watch your step," called Duke. "That thing bites!"

The wail of a single siren heralded the arrival of the police. Phil saw one of their white and green-striped four-wheel-drives appear at the top of the hill above the door. Another came along the shore and stopped nearby. The driver's door opened and a man with short-cropped brown hair and a strong, square set jaw got out. He was immaculately dressed, with a crisp fawn shirt, beautifully pressed brown trousers, and highly polished matching shoes. He walked purposefully towards them, his gait clearly revealing a military background.

"Mornin' folks. Gary Collins - Sheriff of Carbon County," he announced, then, walking up to Duke and his truck, "Well Duke. This the hole in the truck then?"

After he had established who everybody was, he turned and studied the doorway. The two deputies from the other vehicle were standing high on the hill above it. Another deputy had got out of the Sheriff's car, and was standing open-mouthed.

"Wondered what Duke was on when he called me up! Guess it's really true. How'd the hell that thing git here?"

He walked up to the door and examined it.

"Duke - move your truck out the way then bring that sledge over here. Larry - get the video camera and shoot this. I gotta try it for myself."

Duke obliged, and, after checking that nobody was going to get hurt, the Sheriff repeated what Duke had done. As before, the hammer bounced silently off the door, but this time flew swiftly and harmlessly, landing some thirty yards away. He stood by the door, touching its surface, and thinking. He then walked back from it and to the side, picked up a pebble, and idly lobbed it at the door. To his immense surprise - for he had to duck to avoid it - the pebble bounced back off the door in such a way as to precisely reverse its original trajectory.

"That defies the laws of physics," exclaimed Phil.

"Sure doesn't like being hit does it," said the Sheriff ruefully. He called out to all his deputies, "For God's sake don't nobody take a shot at it. Like as not you'll end up shootin' yourself!"

The sheriff questioned Nick and Phil at length about their experience with the door. He also questioned Jo-Ann about the historical information, and carefully wrote everything down in a small notepad. Phil could tell that despite his calm and matter-of-fact approach, Collins was completely mystified, and obviously scared.

"I'll need the film you took, son," he said, smiling at Nick.

"Will I get it back?" said Nick anxiously as he rewound the film.

"I hope so," said the sheriff kindly. "We just wanna make sure we got all the evidence."

He stood awkwardly, as if he needed space to breathe. Phil guessed he was ex-army. He had to be used to danger. But this silent sinister presence which had appeared in his County was something no-one could be trained for.

"And now, you'll be wanting to get on your way, folks," he said suddenly to Phil and the family. Phil and Jo-Ann exchanged glances - they hadn't actually decided what they were going to do once they met up - and Phil felt Nick tugging at his arm. He turned, to see him shaking his head.

"Well actually Sheriff," said Phil, "We'd rather like to stick around and see what happens. And my daughter - she'd like to search for fossils."

"I'm sorry Sir. That won't be possible," said Collins "I'm gonna have this whole area sealed off. You're goin' to have to leave now I'm afraid."

With that, he called over to Duke, "Get these folks' RV back onto the road Duke, then get yourself back here. Go. Do it."

Phil felt a surge of indignation and opened his mouth to remonstrate with the sheriff, but Jo-Ann, who had been unusually quiet, dug him in the ribs and put her finger up to her mouth.

"Why?" mouthed Philip silently to her, puzzled.

"The Latin," she whispered. "I've been translating it. He'll change his tune soon enough. We need to talk."

They clambered into Duke's truck. Phil noticed that Tess didn't go out of her way to sit next to Duke, preferring to gaze out of the window at one of BJ's handsome young assistants.

"Case we need to contact you, where ya headed for tonight?" said Collins as he closed the truck door.

Phil and Jo-Ann looked at each other, embarrassed to admit they had no idea. Then Phil remembered old Powd's advice.

"We'll be over by the Ferris Mountains tonight and tomorrow. Gerry Clayton's place," he replied.

With that, Duke powered up the Ford and headed back to the RV. A ground anchor and two powerful winches on Duke's truck made short work of hauling the motorhome back onto the track. Once Duke had gone, Nick joined Phil, Tess rode with her mother, and the two vehicles negotiated the bumpy track back to the Seminoe Road. Jo-Ann led the way as they turned right and headed towards Alcova.

For the next twenty miles, the uncanny dream-like silence in the RV was broken only occasionally by Nick or Phil suddenly offering an explanation of what had happened, only to retract when a fatal flaw was pointed out. Then Jo-Ann suddenly pulled over. Phil stopped behind her. She and Tess ran back and joined them in the RV.

"I've got to phone Oxford. Giles - I knew him at UC - teaches classics. He'll know." She unfolded the piece of paper with the Latin on it and sat at the table, phone in hand.

After what seemed an eternity, they located him. She spelled out a number of the Latin words. There were long pauses, then gasps.

"Lock! So *that's* what it is!"

"Reveals! And retrieves. Yes, of course."

"Length of wave. Wavelength! No! In Latin!"

Eventually, Jo-Ann ended the call. She had scribbled furiously each time Giles unlocked another piece of the puzzle. Now, with a triumphal flourish, she laid the sheet on the table. The translation was finished.

<u>Pay attention.</u>

Access to this place is restricted.

It is useless and extremely dangerous to attempt an entry without the key.

Whosoever revealed the lock may retrieve and use the key.

The key will be found in the valley illustrated below.

Send a signal of the length of wave (wavelength) of the line drawn below and the key will respond.

The portal will remain usable for a maximum of three lunar months from the moment the lock was revealed.

The whole family sat silently reading the text, then sat some more, then read it again. Phil found himself staring out of the window, back towards the place they had come from - Turtle Forest. He realised that he had participated in something that could not be accounted for by any known earthly explanation. Unbelievable though it was, the door and events surrounding it were supernatural. They were unearthly.

They were *alien.*

He had never felt like this before. Always in the past - apart from his childhood trauma - he had been able to deal with problems and challenges using cold clinical logic. But this was different. Emotion was taking over, and he didn't like it. He felt his throat drying up, and he started to shiver as he broke into a clammy sweat. He thought of Nick, and how close both of them had been to the door, and how he himself had actually touched it.

Jo-Ann got up, walked round the table, and hugged him.

"It's okay, honey. I'm here," she said. It was the first real tenderness she had shown him since he arrived in America. Tears came to his eyes as he held her tightly.

"Whatever this thing is," she said, "We'll face it together."

All four of them sat for a while, hands clasped. Nick was the first to break the silence.

"You don't think that this thing could really be, well, aliens do you?"

"Of course not, Nick!" said Jo-Ann protectively, feigning laughter.

"Don't, Jo-Ann," said Phil seriously. "It's no good pretending. We're all thinking the same thing."

"But Aliens!" said Tess incredulously.

Phil didn't respond. He couldn't. He just sat motionless, eyes closed.

"One thing's for sure, oh brave husband!" said Jo-Ann encouragingly, rocking him to and fro in her arms, "If what you did was reveal the lock, then *you* are 'Whosoever'! *You* may retrieve and use the key, wherever it is."

Phil was not at all sure that he felt the least bit brave, or wanted to be 'Whosoever', and even less sure about the prospect of retrieving and using the key - whatever it was. He had after all only come over here to retrieve his wife!

He managed a grim smile as he resigned himself to accepting that this trip was going to be a tad trickier than he had envisaged.

5

In an Ocean of Storms

Major General Ted Beemish, Adjutant General of the Wyoming National Guard, walked into his office, hung his flight cap on the hat stand in the corner, and sank down thankfully into his familiar high-backed leather chair. He could see at a glance that nothing had changed in the two weeks he had been away. The old F-86 fighter still stood silently on the lawn outside, and the American and Wyoming flags still fluttered in the wind. Inside the room, the flags and battle streamers proclaiming the proud history of the Air and Army National Guard hung silently on their row of poles. Under the window, the polished burlwood coffee table, cut by his own hand from the bowl of a fallen tree, cast its intricate pattern on the pale grey carpet. On his desk, the bronze musket-carrying 'Citizen Soldier' he had made six years earlier stood guard over models of a C130 transporter and a Black Hawk helicopter. He reached forward and started sifting through the pile of papers that had accumulated in his absence.

No, nothing had changed. The same old letters and requisitions to sign, a monthly report to the Governor to complete, a training program to prepare. At fifty, he could feel his appetite for action being eroded by a disconcerting need for the comfort of routine.

His executive officer came in with coffee and biscuits and laid them quietly down on the desk.

"How were the conferences, Sir?" he asked, encouragingly.

"No better or worse than any others," he said wryly. "Most of the issues - urban violence, drugs, illegal immigration - doesn't apply in Wyoming. We know in advance when the Guard is needed round here don't we, Sam."

"Right, Sir. Same every year, and no floods, tornadoes or blizzards to report since you've been away! All quiet on the home front as they say."

"Talking of which, Sergeant Mecham's wife had the baby yet?"

"She has. A boy. Mum and junior both fine."

"Wonderful! Think I'll call by there tonight." He took a sip of the coffee. "And how's the porch coming along? Linda keeping you hard at it?"

"I'm glazing it this weekend," he replied proudly, smiling appreciatively. He checked himself as he was about to leave. "Talking of home Sir, how is Mrs Beemish?"

The General knew that Sam was only being polite, but one of the advantages of these trips to Washington, was being able - just for a few days - to forget about the accident; to be able to relax in the evening without feeling guilty; to drift off to sleep without the lingering smell of incontinence in the nostrils. His nightly domestic routine was far from comforting. Paraplegia in a loved one was a living hell.

"Oh she's comfortable thank you Sam," he said.

It was midday when Sheriff Collins radioed in and described the door. Beemish had heard his old Marine Sergeant in just about every mental state, but never helplessness.

"You gotta get over here," said Collins.

"Okay Gary. I will, straight away. Do you need troops?"

"No. The fewer you bring the better. Just get here Ted. Now - please."

"I'll be less than an hour."

Beemish felt the exhilaration of an adrenaline rush. He had almost forgotten what it was like, but the old responses kicked in like afterburners on a jet. He yelled to his Executive Officer.

"Who's on stand by? I want a Black Hawk fired up right away. Destination, Seminoe Reservoir. Move, move, move!"

He grabbed his battle dress uniform out of the cupboard behind his desk and walked quickly down the corridor to change.

"Battle dress, Sir! What's up?" said the Exec. as he dialled the flight crew room.

"Don't know, Sam. You stay here. If anyone wants me, just say I'm out. Don't tell them where I've gone."

"And the Governor, Sir?"

"*Especially* the Governor!" came the reply echoing from the changing room.

It had just turned one o'clock as the Black Hawk skimmed over the reservoir and powered gently down towards the large white 'H' pegged out on the far shoreline. In the adjoining bay to the north, the structure Collins had described stood out against the sandy landscape like a large black beetle on a bed sheet.

"You gotta see it to believe it, Ted," said Collins, shaking his hand warmly and leading him away from the others. "I need you to see it and try the tests we've been doing. Then I want you to tell me this ain't a dream."

They walked round the point, examined the door, and Collins guided Beemish through the impact and other tests. The door responded exactly as before. Duly unnerved, Beemish sat on a rock, lit up a large White Owl cigar, and listened intently while Collins relayed Jo-Ann's thoughts about the history. He took some good long puffs of the cigar while he collected his thoughts.

"How are the translations going?" he said.

"University's workin' on them. No problem with the Latin, but they gotta see the Greek and Chinese. We're sending them pictures over the net."

"And the petroglyphs along the top?"

"They're on the film too, but nobody's recognised them from our descriptions. Indian maybe. We'll see."

"And what's this guy's name - Newheart? What about his film?"

"It's celluloid. We're having to scan that, then it'll go over the net as well. They'll compare his shots with the door as it is now, seein' as he reckoned it had changed and stuff."

Beemish walked up to the door and peered cautiously into the hexagonal hole.

"He said this wasn't here at the start?"

"So he claims."

"And the geologist can't identify the material?"

"Nope. Says it doesn't exist!"

"And he can't identify the valley?"

"No. But he thinks it's an old collapsed lava tube, like in Hawaii."

"You know, Gary, I'm sure I've seen that valley before," said Beemish, studying the bright point part way along it.

"We've examined that with Jorgensen's magnifying glass. Right along the carving, the detail's finer than we can make out," said Collins. "And the point of light, even if we cover it with a box or something, damn thing keeps on shinin'. Real spooky. What the hell we got here, Ted?"

At that moment, the Sheriff's radio burst into life.

"Think you'd better get back here, Sheriff, away from that door," said the voice. "We got word from Laramie - the translations 'n all, and Newheart's film."

"And the valley, Russ? We got an ID on that?"

"Yes we have, Sir," came the cautious voice. "As I said, best you get back here."

***

Alcova turned out to be an isolated petrol station and general store, run by a sweet couple with a son in his sixties. As if in a dream, Phil gassed up the vehicles whilst Jo-Ann bought some food. Then they headed towards Muddy Gap. The road followed the route of the old Oregon trail, along which thousands of hopeful souls had trekked in the nineteenth century on their way west. Phil recognised some of the names - Independence Rock, Devils Gate - that Jo-Ann had mentioned in the past. These were the lands of her Shoshone forefathers and their enemy the Arapaho. Jo-Ann, he knew, would have liked to have been with him on this leg of the journey, but it was her choice. She was the one who insisted on keeping her own vehicle - her independence.

South of Muddy Gap, they turned onto the Ferris Mountain Ranch road, and followed it along a desolate windswept valley until, as the track crossed an almost dried-up stream, they arrived at an isolated ranch house. Phil felt drained of physical and mental energy. He just rolled the window down an sat waiting. From a nearby barn, a middle-aged man appeared, and walked up to the RV.

"You must be the folks from London," he said in a friendly voice, extending his hand up to the window. "Gerry Clayton. Powd phoned me from Coal Creek. You're real welcome to stay a while."

They thanked Mr Clayton and followed his directions to a meadow, parking below a large haystack. A bright orange sun was just dipping behind the hill to their west, and the Flat-Irons against the green-carpeted mountain beyond them looked like a yellow sea snake arching out of a primeval swamp.

Phil knew that they were all in shock. It took a superhuman effort to rally Nick and Tess together to help Jo-Ann prepare the meal. They ate early, inside the van, and in silence.

As the food began to warm them, their spirits lifted slightly. Tess turned on the radio and sat watching the western sky. Jo-Ann got up and started making some coffee. Phil, who had been idly fiddling with an old penknife, went outside, and in the failing light carved his name and the date - Phil Newheart 28/9/2012 - on one of the old wooden feed troughs. Somehow, doing this, made him feel more real - more alive.

"What you doing, Dad?" came Nick's voice from behind him. "You'd tell me off for doing that back home."

"Today's different," said Phil, handing him the penknife. "Here. Help yourself."

Nick just added the simple word Nick and a big plus sign, above his father's name.

"Now we both know we've been here," said Nick wistfully.

The Moon had risen over the hills to their east, and the wind had dropped to a soft zephyr. Apart from the faint sound of country music from the van, the stillness was absolute.

"Coffee's getting cold," called Jo-Ann from the camper.

Phil felt weary. The events of the day kept turning over in his mind. He could hardly find the energy to rise to his feet..

"I'm going to set up my telescope," said Nick suddenly and determinedly, "And I'm going to see if the vibrations are still there."

Phil marvelled at the energy of youth. It never ceased to amaze him how youngsters seemed to have the capacity to ride over troubles. So long as they had security and support, they were irrepressible.

"Great idea!" he found himself saying, somehow feeding on Nick's energy. They walked together to the van. Phil climbed in and handed the telescope case down to Nick, then sat with Jo-Ann drinking his coffee.

"We have to sort out this door thing, Phil," said Jo-Ann after a few moment's silence. "We have to accept it and deal with it. Something world-shattering happened out there today, and you are probably intimately involved, whether you like it or not."

"I know," said Phil. "It's just that it's taking me a while to really believe it - and I'm frightened. We're so used to seeing science fiction films and reading stories, we've become conditioned to just enjoying the fun and false-fear of them. Nobody really thinks any of that stuff can actually happen. I don't. Well - I didn't!"

"It is scary, Honey, but if you think about it, the door didn't actually hurt anybody. It only responded to being hit. Nothing horrible came out. It's just that it's there. It has a presence. It seems to be alive."

"It *changed*," said Phil, remembering the unnerving feeling he had when he pressed the palm-prints. "And *I* changed it. I could have been killed!"

"Yes, you could've been, Honey, but you weren't. I think, if the door was in the business of killing people, it would have done so by now."

She sat forward, and fiddled with her empty coffee mug.

"No Phil. That door is doing its best to announce itself. The vibrations came from below it, and I think the stuff with the buttons was a sort of test, and I think you passed!"

Phil was already feeling better, now the thing was being openly accepted and discussed. Jo-Ann continued.

"Those fourth and last sentences are definitely in the past tense. Whosoever *revealed* - not reveals. The moment the lock *was* revealed - not 'is revealed'. I think that hexagonal hole is the lock, and I think *you* have to find that key!"

Suddenly, from the darkness outside the camper, Phil heard Nick shrieking. It wasn't in pain or terror, but in intense excitement.

"Dad! Mum! Everybody! Come quick! Look!"

Phil jumped up and leapt towards the door. Jo-Ann instinctively called out her son's name, and Tess screamed. All three of them scrambled over one another to get out of the camper, and started running towards Nick's voice in the darkness.

"I've found it! I've found it!"

"Found what?", yelled Phil, panting as he ran.

Phil could now see that Nick was peering through the telescope, his eye glued to the eyepiece, his arms waving about almost uncontrollably.

"Look!" he said triumphantly.

Phil bent down. Light from the Moon shone through the tiny eye lens of the high power eyepiece. He steadied himself and peered through it. The terminator had moved westwards across the Moon's surface since last night. As he adjusted the focus and let the instrument settle, there, shimmering and rippling slightly, as does the reflection off near-still water, was a valley. It was unmistakable. It was winding its way across the lunar surface.

It was the valley illustrated on the door.

***

Sheriff Collins and General Beemish climbed into the sheriff's car to take the call from the university in Laramie. Collins switched on the loudspeaker and held the microphone in his hand.

"Sheriff Collins here. Go ahead please."

A cultured voice came clearly across.

"First the translations, Sheriff. Nobody can decipher the petroglyphs, but we've done okay on the Greek, Latin and Chinese. The message is exactly the same in all three languages, and there's a difference between the film from, er, Mr Newheart, and from your deputy." There was a pause.

"Well go on! What does it say?" said Collins, raising his eyes to the sky.

"Do you mind my asking where this text - this structure - is?" said the voice.

"Yes I do!" replied Collins irritably. "If you wouldn't mind Sir, just tell me."

"Okay. This is the text from Mr Newheart's film. *Attention. Access to this place is restricted. It is useless and extremely dangerous to attempt to gain entry without the key. Whosoever reveals the lock is allowed to retrieve and use the key. The key will be found in the valley illustrated below. Send a signal with a wavelength equal to the length of the line below, and the key will respond. This portal will be available for a maximum of three lunar months from the date the lock is revealed.*"

Collins and Beemish stared at each other in amazement. Beemish asked that the text be repeated slowly. He made some notes in a small notepad.

"And the text from my deputy's film?"

"The only differences are in two sentences. Your deputy's film shows the words, 'He who *revealed* the lock', not *'reveals'*. And, 'from the date the lock *was* revealed', not '*is* revealed'."

Beemish indicated to Collins to ensure the mike was turned off.

"Hang on please," said Collins.

"Newheart must have revealed the lock," said Beemish straight away.

"What lock?"

"Must be the hexagonal hole."

"This is crazy!" said Collins, staring out across the reservoir.

"Let's get the facts. Then we'll decide whether it's crazy or not, Gary. Ask him about the valley."

Collins switched on the mike again.

"Sorry about that. So where's the valley?"

"Are you sitting down, Sheriff?" came the controlled reply.

"Sure I am!" exclaimed Collins, glancing at his friend. "Just tell us where the goddamn thing is!"

"It's on the Moon."

"Holy crow!" Collins' eyes closed in disbelief. "You gotta be kidding!"

A long-forgotten memory suddenly sprang back into Beemish' mind. He cursed himself that he hadn't recalled it when he first saw the valley drawing on the door. He placed a restraining hand on the sheriff's arm.

"He's right, Gary. Now I remember where I've seen it. It's in a book I bought my nephew way back, *The Apollo Story*. It's a valley on the Moon."

Collins had been so taken aback, he hadn't let go of the talk button on his microphone.

"Whoever that is with you Sheriff, they're right," said the voice. "It's called Schröter's Valley. It's a one hundred mile long rille in the Oceanus Procellarum - the Ocean of Storms, near the crater Aristarchus. One of our undergrads happened to recognise it. He's a keen amateur astronomer. Apparently, the head of the valley is called the Cobra Head. We've checked it in the lunar atlas in the library. There's no doubt. Fact is, the carving on the door seems to be more detailed than the entry in the atlas!"

Beemish held his hand out towards Collins for the microphone.

"Major General Beemish here Sir, Wyoming National Guard. Tell me. Does your atlas show anything special at the place in the valley corresponding to the bright pinpoint on the door?"

"Not really, General. The valley is featureless around that area. There's certainly nothing obvious"

"Then can you tell me the lunar latitude and longitude of that point please?"

"Certainly. It's 25°.

Beemish noted these co-ordinates, but then Collins took back the microphone. It was obvious he wasn't going to let his old Marine Captain take the reins - at least, not in his own car.

"What about the door material?" he said. "Any news on that?"

"No Sir. The results - well, the lack of them - from the limited tests Dr Jorgensen has fed back to us suggest its not metal or stone of any sort, or ceramic, or plastic. Our Materials Department knows no material which exhibits those properties. Mind you, we'll have to come out there with a truck full of gear to check that out, seeing as you can't even get a small chip of it to us here. Shall we do that? Where are you?"

Collins was too cute to fall for that one, and anyway, Beemish was shaking his head vigorously.

"No. Thanks a lot for your work." said Collins. "We'll get back to you soon as we can. Thanks. Bye now."

The two men sat in silence, absorbing the implications of all they had heard. As for providing him with a diversion from routine, this event, thought Beemish, was the ultimate. It could change his life. The prospect of making contact with visitors from another planet gripped his imagination. He also realised, that if he reported it immediately to the Governor, he would lose control at a stage which would prevent him regaining it. He felt torn between loyalty to his position, and self-interest. But he had always acted honourably, jumped when his political masters said jump, put on a show, cleaned up after their failed schemes, and kept his mouth shut. This time - just for once - he was going to do what *he* wanted to do. The first stage, was handling Gary.

"If this gets out, we're going to be swarming with folks from miles around, and all the weirdoes from flying saucer freaks to day of judgement evangelists," he said. "What have you done about securing the site?"

"I got a couple of guys down on the Seminoe Road. They'll stop anybody comin' down the K-T track."

"K-T track?"

"Sure. The folks from the university call it that leastways. There's some important geological boundary round here. Ask Jorgensen."

Beemish sat and reflected for a few moments, then continued.

"You're going to need more than couple of deputies aren't you Gary."

"Oh yeah. I'm gonna contact County Road and Bridge and get them to put a chain link round the whole place. Game and Fish can secure the reservoir."

"I think you need to cover it as well," said Beemish. "And if the press get hold of this, you'll be overrun. I also think the fewer non-military personnel we use the better."

"Now you're not goin' to give me any of the Governor's restriction of information crap are you Ted?" said Collins, beginning to flush round his collar. "I've had Jim Cranford's, *Let's keep this under our hats shall we Gary*, 'till I'm sick up to here. The only way that guy got elected was to suppress evidence against his brother. People round here got the right to know what's goin' on in their own back yard."

"Take it easy Gary. All I'm saying is, it needs careful handling. If this turns out to be what I think it is, you're going to have the world coming down on top of you - never mind a few rubber-necks. I think you're going to need my help."

"Okay," said Collins moving uncomfortably in his seat, "But this is my County and my jurisdiction. Your help - *my* terms."

"Whilst it's within my power, I promise, Gary."

"So let's get it all sorted *before* you report upstairs. Okay?"

"Okay," said Beemish, content that Collins was asking him to do precisely what he was going to do anyway. He started writing an action list in his notebook.

"Now, why don't you and your men secure the road and the immediate area round the door, and I'll get my guys to do the fence and the cover. I can get a couple of patrol boats for the reservoir, and I'll get the FAA to impose a five mile radius air exclusion zone round the site. Once I've put that into motion, *then* I'll call the Governor. I can't say fairer than that."

He deliberately didn't mention the Newheart family. *He* wanted them. He did not want to deceive his old friend, but he knew there was no way that Gary would hold them against their will. But they had to be found, and found quickly. If the furore over a few bacteria brought back from Europa by the New Millennium III mission was anything to go by, this alien visitation - for alien it undoubtedly was - would rock the world to its foundations. It looked like the aliens had visited Earth at a time in its history when the three languages on the door were in common use. Now they had returned, and were using those languages in an attempt to communicate. If there was a chance of contact, he *had* to be there. This could be the most important moment in his life, and in the history of the world. He had to retain control. He had to get to Newheart. Once anybody else cottoned on to the fact that Newheart might be the only person who could get that door to open, he would lose him. Not only that, but the family would be in shock, in demand, and more than anything, in danger.

By this time, Collins had got out of the car and walked over to his group of deputies. He was giving them instructions about the arrangements for protecting the site. Beemish glanced down, to see Collins' note book lying by the gear shift lever. He pretended to be fiddling with the cigar lighter, but flicked rapidly through the last few pages of the book. There it was: details of the whole family, their vehicle, and the entry, Gerry Clayton, Ferris Mtn Ranch Fri/Sat nights.

As he got out of Collins' car and walked across to his helicopter, he was weighing priorities. Getting a response from the Moon would be the clincher. If the key was there on the Moon's surface, and responded to a transmission, that would settle it. But once that had been done, things would happen very quickly. He needed everything set up in anticipation of a positive lunar response. He would issue the orders for the fence, cover and boats, organise the air exclusion zone, get a secure place organised for the Newhearts, then check out the signal. If the key location was confirmed, he could then tell Governor Cranford everything, but get to the Newhearts before Cranford's men did. He glanced at his watch - half past three. It was an open secret amongst those close to Cranford that one of his peccadilloes involved a barmaid from the Silver Spur, and that every Thursday afternoon, during his weekly 'Policy Meetings', he could never be disturbed. If he waited until after four, it would be safe. The time the message was received would be logged by Cranford's secretary, but the Governor would only receive it after six o'clock. Plenty of time to set unstoppable wheels into motion.

"Chance to take a stroll, Frank," he said to his pilot, as he climbed aboard the helicopter. "I've got to make some calls. I'll be a while."

Once he was alone, he radioed his Executive Officer and got the Guard to start on the fence and door cover. Then he got the boats and the air exclusion zone organised. Those were the easy bits. Now for the Newhearts. He had come to the conclusion that the only completely secure place to house them was the F.E.Warren Air Force Base. The base was just down the road from his own headquarters, so he could ensure that arrangements were under his direct and personal control. Colonel Winters, the base commander, would doubtless peddle the lie that he never had any empty houses, but Beemish knew he had. He always had at least two, which he would lend on a short term basis to visiting high ranking officers he wanted to ingratiate himself with. He contacted the base on the military link, and was put straight through to Winters. The conversation proceeded as expected.

"Civilians! Round the clock guard by your people! And you can't tell me who they are and why they're so important? Bit unconventional isn't it, General?"

"I know. Very hush-hush apparently. But I was just saying to the Governor, if anybody's got the guts, sensitivity and diplomacy to handle this situation, you have. But I told him, you can't be expected to work miracles. If you haven't got a house, you haven't got a house. We might have to ask Fort Carson"

There was a long pause at the other end of the line.

"Well, I do have one house. It was earmarked for a junior officer from Maryland. I think I can put him off."

"I don't think Governor Cranford will fail to recognise your contribution when he goes up to Washington, Colonel. Can I tell him it's settled then?"

"Yes General. You do that."

Beemish smiled as he put down the phone. He looked at his watch. It was safe to phone the Governor. He left the message, "Am assisting Sheriff Collins in investigation of strange discovery near Seminoe Reservoir. Limited National Guard involvement. Will clarify when more information available. Beemish." Enough, he thought, to prevent his being accused of not keeping the Governor informed, yet not enough to cause Cranford's secretary to disturb his 'Policy Meeting'.

Now for the signal to the Moon. As he was working out how this could be done, he realised he had not measured the length of the line inscribed on the door. He needed the wavelength.

He reaching into the flight folder and found the pilot's navigation ruler, then jumped down and headed for the door.

This was the first time he had been alone next to it. He could feel the hairs on the back of his neck rising as he placed the ruler up against it. But there was no friction between the ruler and the door surface. When he held the ruler up against one end of the line, it moved before he could read off its length.

"Need a hand?" came a friendly voice from behind him. It was BJ.

"Oh thanks. If we could do this together perhaps."

With both of them steadying the ruler, one could hold the zero end of the scale up against the line, whilst the other read off the line's length. After repeating a few times and swapping ends, they agreed that the line was 314 mm long, plus or minus no more than one millimetre. Beemish wrote this down in his notebook, thanked BJ, and returned to the helicopter.

He could remember from way back, that frequency equals velocity divided by wavelength. The pilot's navigational calculator had the speed of light as a built-in constant. The division gave him a radio frequency of 954.75 Megahertz plus or minus 3 Megahertz.

"Get me NASA's Jet Propulsion Laboratory in Pasadena," he barked to his now totally perplexed Executive Officer back in Cheyenne.

Beemish knew that JPL managed the world's most sophisticated deep space communication network, and had a seventy metre dish, at Goldstone, out in California's Mojave desert. If that couldn't transmit the signal and listen for a response, nothing could. He eventually got through to the duty officer.

"Control room."

Beemish introduced himself. Now for the tough bit. He knew it was pointless trying to fool Goldstone, so he was as straightforward as he dare be.

"Please don't ask me why I need this information, " he said, "But how soon tonight could your seventy metre dish see the Moon?"

There was a pause at the other end.

"Moonrise here is at 17:33 our time General - that's 18:33 your time. Then we'd need to wait until the Moon was at least six degrees in elevation - the dish won't go lower than that. So that would take us to 18:05 our time, 19:05 yours. Why?"

"Please. Who has the telescope booked from that time onwards tonight?" said Beemish without answering the question.

"The seventy metre is being used continuously by JPL for essential comms passes to the Orion missions, except for one half-hour slot at 20:00," came the reply. "UCLA have been waiting for this slot for two months now. Some people wait years for time on this telescope."

Beemish thought quickly. The only way UCLA would give up their slot is if they could be given even more time, albeit at a later date. And the only way somebody would swap a long slot for a short one is if they could be convinced that the short one was going to be more productive. The one organisation who could be guaranteed success - if the door thing was true - was SETI, the Search for Extra-Terrestrial Intelligence. It was common knowledge that SETI's continued funding was in jeopardy, as despite years of searching, they had not found a single extra-terrestrial signal. If they could be persuaded that tonight's half hour slot would yield a world-shattering discovery, they would certainly agree to a swap.

"Have SETI got any time booked with you in the near future?"

"Hold on. Yes. They have two one-hour slots next month. One in the evening and one during the day."

Beemish got Goldstone to give him the contact numbers of UCLA and SETI, then spent the next hour persuading the two organisations to swap slots. Only after faxes had been exchanged between all four parties, was the deal finally struck. SETI had tonight's slot, and would be credited with any discoveries. Goldstone now needed the transmission frequency. Beemish consulted his notebook.

"951.75 to 957.75 Megahertz," he said.

"That's very imprecise," came the supercilious reply. "What band width are we talking about?"

Beemish had no idea what they were talking about, but it apparently was something to do with how accurate the frequency needed to be. He had of course, no idea.

"That's a six megahertz range," said the controller. "We'll start at 951.750 and ramp it by 1 Kilohertz every 100 milliseconds. There'll be six thousand transmissions to do at ten per second. That'll take ten minutes. We'll do interlaced send-receives and allow for the three second delay from transmission to reception. If we get a response, we'll know that was in response to the signal we sent out three seconds earlier. How's that?"

"That'll be fine," said Beemish, trying to sound as knowledgeable as possible. "I'd like to be on the phone to you during the transmission."

Arrangements were agreed. He would phone them at 8pm their time - 9pm in Wyoming. He had three hours to finalise the collection and transportation of the Newhearts to the F.E.Warren.

***

By nine o'clock, Beemish was at his desk in Cheyenne, and a small team of hand-picked officers was waiting in two helicopters outside. He had been standing at the window watching the Moon - now almost full - for the last ten minutes. His palms began to sweat as he slowly walked to his desk, sat down, and dialled Goldstone. Tonight, he thought, the world may change.

"Goldstone control," said a calm voice.

"Beemish."

"Oh yes, General. We have the Moon now. Shall we begin the send-receive cycles?"

Beemish felt his throat drying up, and took a quick gulp from a stone-cold cup of coffee.

"Yes please. Begin."

"We'll convert the response to audio," said the controller. "You'll hear a note, or whatever the transponder sends us as it happens."

Beemish pressed the handset to his ear. He could hear someone in the background reading off the transmission frequencies every ten seconds.

"951.8 ..... 951.9 ..... 952.0 ..... 952.1 ..... "

The minutes ticked by. Beemish looked at his watch. Nearly half way there. He felt like a criminal in the dock, awaiting the verdict of the jury. He strained to hear something - anything, over and above the relentless count.

Nothing. Only a faint hiss.

"955.1 ..... 955.2 ..... 955.3 ....."

At 956.9, he began to feel physically sick. This was turning into the longest ten minutes of his life. He saw his credibility about to be demolished. Then suddenly, just after the 957.1 mark, the telephone burst into life with an ear-splitting high-pitched whistle which sounded like a FAX machine in overdrive.

"Jesus!" came the amazed voice of the controller shouting over the din. "What in hell's name have you got up there? That's no transponder! That's a god-damned radio station!"

Then as suddenly as it had started, the noise ceased.

"Stop the transmission! What you got, Steve?"

"957.092"

"That's it! Set it to that. Try again."

Beemish listened in amazement as the voices of excited engineers lulled to a hush.

"Go!"

After three seconds, the shrieking FAX-like machine started up again, but this time, continuously. The controller turned down the volume and spoke to Beemish.

"We've got it, General! 957.092 MHz. And how! Whatever's up there, it sure is telling us."

Beemish felt wild with excitement. He knew he was listening to a response from an alien civilisation. It took all his willpower to stop himself screaming with delight.

"Can you pinpoint the source of the transmission?" he said.

"Sure. At this frequency, we can locate it to about one three thousandths of a degree.,"

"What's that on the Moon's surface?"

"Just over a mile, but we'll have to do a raster scan," replied the controller. "We'll have that information in about fifteen minutes."

"Is it roughly where I said?"

"Sure is. Near lunar 26 North, 50 West."

"Phone the exact location through to my Exec," said Beemish, "And thank you."

He flung the phone down, jumped up, and made for the door.

"Phone the Governor, Sam. Tell him what you like. No. Tell him everything. This is history."

Beemish ran out into the darkness to the waiting helicopters, gesticulating wildly with his right arm that they should power up. He clambered into his seat, hyperventilating.

"The Ferris Mountain Ranch!" he said jubilantly. "Let's go get em!"

***

Jo-Ann led her dumb-struck husband away from the telescope and back to the camper. They sat together on the edge of the bed and hugged each other. She could tell Phil was trying to be strong, but this discovery - this revelation, coming as it did after all the other events of the day - was obviously the last straw.

"It *can't* be real, Jo," he said, trembling. "Tell me this is all a dream. The Moon!"

Jo-Ann had never seen Phil so unnerved. He was usually so confident, so much in control. Bewilderment did not sit well on his shoulders; he was clearly unprepared for its debilitating effects; he needed her help. He needed a boost.

"What are we going to do?" he said, lifting his head towards her. She could see that the brightness had gone from his eyes. They were grey and listless, as if drained of their spirit.

"We're going to get to the bottom of it," she said, stroking his face. "If anybody can, you can, Honey."

He sat and thought for a while.

"But do you realise what you're saying?" he said. "If this thing's real and that key's on the Moon ...."

He went to the table and picked up the translation, and for the umpteenth time, read it again.

"Are you absolutely certain this is right?" he said.

"Yes, Phil. Giles is the best."

Jo-Ann's mind was in turmoil. At long last, Phil had taken her pleas about moving to the States seriously. Maybe, given a few more days, she could have persuaded him. As a last resort she could have presented her ultimatum. But this alien doorway changed everything. It could drive him away completely ... or it might cause him to stay. It might be dangerous. Oh God, he could be killed! What would happen to the children? She and Phil hadn't found out yet which country they would choose. What if he jumped right in and got involved completely? Should she support him? Could she support him? They surely wouldn't want him to go to the Moon. Phil - an astronaut! He's daft enough to go. This might just be the one thing that could prise him away from his precious battery research for long enough for her to win him over. At least, he was here. Whilst he was, she would support him. What else could she do?

Her thoughts were interrupted by the sounds of helicopters approaching. They peered out, to see searchlights beaming down at them from the sky. She and Phil ran outside and grabbed the children. The lights played on the crest of the ridge a hundred yards away. A loudspeaker barked from somewhere above them.

"This is the Wyoming National Guard. Please stay where you are. You are in no danger, but there will be flying debris. Shield your eyes."

The two helicopters landed, creating a blizzard of sand and sage brush twigs. Out of the swirling dust, men with dazzling torches made there way across to them, and stood silently, their helmets and flying suits silhouetted dramatically against the lights from the helicopters. One of the men stepped forward.

"Mr and Mrs Newheart?"

The voice was cultured, calm and reassuring. The man removed his helmet and walked into the light from the camper's windows. He was tall, with close-cropped greying hair, and looked about fifty. His face was finely chiselled, his nose hawk-like, and a pair of kind blue-grey eyes regarded her intently as he extended his hand.

"I am Major General Ted Beemish. I'm sorry to drop in on you like this," he said with a generous smile, "But I've come about the door. Can we talk?"

They ushered him in to the camper, then sat round the table. The children stood looking on. Jo-Ann realised that this was it. It was really happening.

"You're obviously aware, Mr Newheart, that the events back at the Seminoe this morning could be of great significance. Have you had any thoughts about what it is that we've got there?"

"I'll put you out of you misery straight away," said Phil. "We know what the message on the door says, and we've seen the valley. It's on the Moon isn't it?"

Beemish was thunderstruck.

"That's extraordinarily enterprising of you, Sir," he said, with more than a little respect in his eyes. Then turning to her, "You have an amazing husband here, Mrs Newheart."

Jo-Ann immediately recognised his response was an attempt to disarm by flattery, and whilst she realised it was a deliberate ploy, it seemed to be genuinely well-meant.

"Actually," admitted Phil calmly, "My part in all this is purely accidental. If it hadn't been for Tess's interest in dinosaurs, we wouldn't have been there in the first place; it was Jo-Ann who translated the Latin; and it was Nick here who spotted the valley. We've just been looking at it through his telescope."

"You can see it! Now?" exclaimed Beemish, his eyes glowing with excitement. "May I ......"

They led Beemish out into the darkness, and Nick showed him the valley through the telescope.

"My God, that's incredible!" he said. He turned to Nick and smiled. "If you were my son, I'd be very proud of you, young fella. Well spotted."

Nick beamed, and looked up at his dad.

"We must talk, Sir. There isn't much time, " said Beemish, his voice assuming a serious tone.

They returned to the camper, and Beemish outlined everything he had discovered, including the Latin text before Phil had changed the door, and the confirmatory radio pinpointing of the alien transponder.

"It would appear, Mr Newheart," he concluded, "That the world needs you."

He looked at Phil for a reaction. Jo-Ann could see the torment in Phil's eyes. It was obvious that he did and didn't want to get involved, and was fearful but curious, all at the same time. He began studying Beemish, trying to weigh him up. Beemish did the same to him.

"Nobody knows how to play this, Sir," he said. "But one thing's for sure. Whether you like it or not, you're going to be the centre of attention for quite a while. You need an ally. You and your family need a safe place to stay, away from the press, away from the general public. We have to work this out away from the glare of publicity. You really can't stay here or move on alone. It'd be too risky."

Phil began to look uncomfortable. He hated being boxed in.

"I really don't know ...." was all he could muster.

Beemish leant across the table and fixed him with an iron stare.

"Sir. As we speak, the Governor is headed this way with his pals. He can be very persuasive, not to mention manipulative. What plans he has for you, I dread to think, but between you and me, those plans will be in the best interests of one person and one person only - him. And I should know. He's my boss."

At the mention of the Governor, Jo-Ann knew exactly what line she should take. Phil did not know this, but she had met Governor Cranford twice - in her recently assumed capacity of spokesperson for the Shoshoni tribe - and rarely had she felt so uncomfortable in a man's presence.

Beemish's stare mellowed as he addressed the whole family. "Believe me. Trust me. Its the devil you know - well, have met - or the devil you don't. I've reserved a wonderful house, all ready and waiting for you. I can fly you all there in no time. My men will bring your vehicles. What do you say?"

He inclined his head slightly to one side as he spoke. His eyes had a roguish twinkle about them, but at the same time, a hint of mystery. Jo-Ann could imagine this charmer breaking a few hearts when he was younger. He had to be a better bet than Cranford.

"I think we should go along with General Beemish, Honey," she said with all the authority at her command.

Phil turned to her, agony in his eyes. She had long recognised that the prospect of co-operation with any U.S. organisation - political or military - was an anathema to him.

"I'm not trying to force you to do anything you don't wish to do," continued Beemish. "But if I read you right, Sir, you seem the sort of man who would be fascinated to get to the bottom of this business. I know I am."

"I must admit," said Phil cautiously, "I'm certainly intrigued. The prospect of contact ......"

Jo-Ann could see that despite himself, Phil was becoming ensnared by his own curiosity. He needed a face saver, and a little push. Instinct told her that Beemish was sincere.

"In the interests of science, I think you both need each other," she said diplomatically.

Phil thought for a moment.

"Okay," he said, nodding. "I'm with you, but for *science*."

Jo-Ann glanced at Beemish, and a flicker of understanding passed between them.

6
Warren

Phil could not tell whether the sound was still in his dream or whether it was real. It was the unmistakable 'Phut-phut-phut' of helicopter blades. He lay motionless for a moment, his eyes still closed. He could feel the crisp starchiness of a freshly-laundered sheet. He opened his eyes. In the dim light, he made out the outline of a Victorian ceiling lamp hanging menacingly above him. To his left -still sleeping - lay Jo-Ann in the adjoining twin bed. Across the room, curtains blocked most of the light from the window. The sound was coming from that direction. It was definitely a helicopter, and sounded as if it was landing nearby. Then, the events of the previous evening came flooding back. They seemed like a dream, but he knew they weren't.

He recalled the dizzying night flight to Cheyenne. The midnight arrival, a short car journey, a house with a pillared porch, a night-cap with Beemish and a lady officer, climbing creaking stairs with an ornate banister, calling 'Good Night' to the children, a bed, a feeling of overwhelming tiredness, then oblivion.

He put one leg out of bed, made contact with the floor, and with his head still reeling, sat upright. He could feel the slightly uneven floorboards beneath the rug. His mouth was dry and there was a faint ringing in his ears. He rose unsteadily to his feet. His outstretched hand made contact with a solid piece of furniture which he used to help him towards the window. The curtains were heavy, and felt like velvet. He moved one aside, and cursed as the brilliant daylight hit his eyes. He shielded them, dropped down onto a padded bow-back chair nearby, and peered through the full-length lace curtain covering the window. Beemish had said the house would be on an air base, so he expected to see barracks, offices, perhaps even part of a runway, but the sight which met his eyes was as if he had been transported to New England in the fall at the end of the nineteenth century. The house was one of a circle of houses arranged round a neat tree-studded green. All the houses were of brick, and with white-painted wood, but each was distinctive. All had wooden porches and flagpoles bearing the Stars and Stripes; some had in addition, different state flags. Beyond the houses, Phil could see open green areas, more trees, and to his considerable relief, some buildings of a more utilitarian design. Below the window, in the front driveway, he could see Jo-Ann's pickup and the end of the motorhome, which had obviously been driven here during the night. A neat path led from the house to the road running round the green, and at the end of this path, complete with machine guns, stood two National Guardsmen. He found himself wondering whether their function was to keep others out, or them in. He looked at his watch - five past eleven. He drew back the curtains. One of the guards noticed this and waved, then turned and began speaking into a personal radio. Phil discovered two neatly-folded towelling robes, put one on, then sat on the edge of the bed and with some difficulty, woke Jo-Ann.

"My God! I feel like I've been asleep for days," she said, rubbing her face with her hands. She gazed around, then suddenly sat up and grabbed Phil's arm. "Are the children all right?"

Phil remembered that Nick and Tess were in bedrooms nearby. He stood up and opened the oak panelled door to the landing. Similar doors led to three other bedrooms, two of which, to his considerable relief, held their slumbering children.

"They're okay, Jo. Just where we left them." Jo-Ann had already donned her bathrobe and was close on his heels.

They woke the children, and began drawing back the curtains and exploring the house. The top floor comprised a huge Victorian-style bathroom and the bedrooms, two of which had their own en-suite facilities. A wide hardwood staircase led gracefully down to a large hallway in which was a mahogany table. On the table was a bowl of fresh flowers, and laid out - military fashion - four sets of house keys. Off the hall were a number of elegantly furnished rooms. All the rooms were oak floored and had ornate moulded ceilings. Some had real fireplaces. Four suitcases were neatly arranged in the hallway.

"I don't remember us bringing these in," said Jo-Ann, unzipping one of them. "They've been beautifully packed."

"Must have been General Beemish's people," said Phil, wondering what else might have been done on their behalf without their knowledge.

"I'm going to try the shower in our room," said Jo-Ann, rubbing Phil's chin as she climbed the stairs. "And I suggest you have a shave, Honey. That designer stubble went out of fashion years ago!"

At that moment, a figure appeared beyond the patterned glass of the front door and rang the bell. Phil opened the door to a clean cut Air Force officer. Alongside the guards, and waiting 'at ease' at the end of the pathway were two young men in plain white uniforms.

"Good morning Mr Newheart. Captain Sam Palmer," he said with a broad smile, extending his hand. "I'm General Beemish's executive officer. I trust you all slept well."

"Better and longer than I could ever have imagined," replied Phil.

"I have your cook and your houseman here," said Palmer, indicating towards the two men, who immediately came to attention. "They will prepare and serve brunch, if that is convenient."

Phil swallowed hard, and suppressed a smile. He had always fancied the idea of servants. And here, in this elegant house, he found himself thinking that one could simply not do without them.

"Certainly," he said, grandly. "Have them come in."

The two men, whose names turned out to be Chuck and Charlie, made straight for the kitchen, which appeared to have been well stocked with all the necessities. Phil invited Palmer into the lounge.

"This is one hell of a house, Captain Palmer," he said, fingering the tassels on the settee cushions. "And I see the others nearby are similar. All your air bases aren't like this, surely?"

"Regrettably not Sir," said Palmer smiling. "The Francis E. Warren Air Force Base began its life as Fort Russell in 1867. These officers' houses - the 'bricks' as we call them - were built between 1885 and 1933 for the cavalry and infantry regiments that were here then. We've got over a hundred and fifty of them; they're all on the national historic preservation list; this base is unique."

"Where's the runway?" said Phil, getting up and peering out of the side window. "I haven't heard any planes, only the helicopter which woke me up."

"Er, that's another reason why Warren's unique. It hasn't got a runway. It's the only air force base in the States that hasn't got a runway."

Phil began to feel unreal again.

"So what's here then?"

"Missiles," said Palmer seriously. "This base is the Headquarters for the 90th Space Wing. They control hundreds of ICBMs from right here."

Phil had a vision of the ground opening up in the field he could see beyond the houses, and a salvo of rockets screaming skywards, bearing their lethal nuclear warheads.

"You mean there are underground silos, here? Where are they?"

"No. There are no silos anywhere on the base. They're scattered over Wyoming, Nebraska and Colorado, but the officers who man the silos - the missileers - they're based here."

Phil could see that Palmer was beginning to feel ill at ease, and had obviously just been making polite conversation as a lead-up to the real reason he was here. He decided to help him out.

"So what's the plan, Captain? I'm sure there's lots to be done." Palmer looked relieved.

"Well Sir, there's a meeting this afternoon. General Beemish has been up half the night organising things, and right now he's back at the door showing people what's what. He has asked me to let you know, and well, make sure you find your way there."

"You mean it's your job to make sure we attend," said Phil, giving Palmer a knowing smile.

"I suppose so, Sir. You are after all, a key player as it were." Palmer looked uncomfortable again. "But there's no need for Mrs Newheart and the children to come."

Phil was by nature a respecter of law, order and authority, including military authority. But he was in a country he didn't really want to be in, and facing a situation that could engulf him if he wasn't careful. There was no way he was going to allow himself to relinquish control. This business would affect the whole family. They had to be seen to stick together.

"Yes there is," he retorted, surprising even himself. "My wife and children come with me. It's as simple as that."

"But ... it's in the *briefing* room," blustered Palmer. "It was difficult enough getting General Miller's permission for *you* to go in there, let alone Mrs Newheart and the children."

"Then that's General Miller's problem, whoever he is," said Phil calmly. "I'm sure Major General Beemish will persuade him."

Palmer looked disquieted as he turned to go.

"We'll send a car for you at two twenty, Sir. The meeting's at two thirty."

"Make it a big one," called Phil firmly as Palmer walked down the path. "There'll be the four of us!"

He closed the door, then lay back against it and took a deep breath. He was not used to being so assertive.

The smell of cooking set his mouth watering as he headed for the stairs. As he passed the dining room door, Charlie was laying places for four on the large mahogany table.

But a well-known phrase kept repeating itself in his mind.

And the condemned man ate a hearty breakfast.

***

By two fifteen, the family had eaten, unpacked, and were beginning to take stock of their situation. Jo-Ann had insisted that the children make their own beds and put away their clothes, despite several assurances from Charlie that it was not necessary.

"We mustn't spoil them," she said, taking him to one side. "They've never expected things to be done for them in the past, and I don't intend to let them think that this is to be the norm from now on."

Phil and Jo-Ann didn't speak much while they were waiting for the car. For one thing, neither was used to there being 'servants' in the house. But more than anything, Phil was considering their position, and speculating on what might emerge from the meeting. He still found it difficult to shake off the feeling that this whole thing was some sort of fantastic and elaborate dream, and what was going on around him, unreal. He resolved even more firmly to remain in control of the situation. He knew he would be up against forces he had never encountered before, and that the family could be disadvantaged unless he was strong.

His thoughts were interrupted by the shrill ringing of the front door bell. As he opened the door, Jo-Ann and the children behind him, it was General Beemish who greeted them.

"Mr Newheart, Mrs Newheart, Tess, Nick," he said warmly. "I see you're all ready. House okay I hope. Chuck and Charlie looking after you? You will let me know if there's anything you need won't you."

Phil found himself marvelling at Beemish's energy. He stood to one side as they filed out.

"My, it's good to see you folks in the daylight," he joked, as Jo-Ann passed him. "This is a bit better than crashing in on you in the middle of the night isn't it. I am so sorry about that."

There was no mention of the briefing room problem. In fact, Beemish gave them each a security badge with their name on it.

"We'll do the photos later," he said casually, as he led the way to the waiting military minibus. Phil wondered about locking the front door, but realised it was pointless. 'They' obviously had duplicate keys if they had wanted to get in, and nobody else was going to try running the gauntlet of the two armed guards, still standing menacingly outside.

A short drive through avenues lined with cottonwood trees flashing yellow in their autumn foliage brought them to a main thoroughfare. Beemish explained that the base was like a small town, with banks, shops, a library, two chapels, an activities centre and sports and fitness halls. Nick was interested. Tess wasn't so sure. Phil could tell that Jo-Ann was reserving judgement. For his own part, he was speculating on what on Earth was going to happen next, how Jo-Ann and he would be at the end of it, and how long his business could manage without him.

They drew up outside a gaunt single-storey concrete building. It had no windows, and the only opening that Phil could make out in the slightly sloping walls was the steel front door. Two heavily-armed security police officers moved aside as they walked up the steps.

"I'm sorry about this," said Beemish as they paused in an ante-room inside. "But the scan is necessary. You understand."

Two more security guards then scanned each of them with hand-held sensors, and ushered them through a final doorway which reminded Phil of the security doors at airports. Beemish led the way down a wide plain corridor with a rubberised floor and softly hissing ceiling vents until they came to door bearing the sign, "Briefing Room 1".

"Ready?" he said, turning and smiling.

Phil and the others just nodded.

Beemish pressed a small button beside the door, and looked towards an overhead camera. A loudspeaker crackled.

"General Beemish and the Newhearts," he announced.

A lock disengaged, and the door was opened by a guard inside. Beemish led the way into a windowless room. It smelt of warm plastic and stale after-shave, and contained a large, well-lit central table round which a number of men of varying ages were seated. Some were in uniform; some were in suits. Phil recognised Sheriff Collins, and was comforted to see BJ nearby, but did not recognise anyone else. A hush fell upon the room as the family walked in. Phil could see from their eyes that many were far more interested in Jo-Ann and her Pocahontas looks, than they were curious about him.

Each place at the table had been provided with a notepad, soft drinks, iced water and a tumbler. Clustered about the centre of the table was an array of projectors and other audio-visual devices. Many of the men had small telephones in front of them, with wires leading to a central unit. The proceedings were obviously being recorded by two fixed video cameras in opposite corners of the room. At one end of the room, a special wall surface served as a projection screen. Above the screen was a row of clocks, their second hands sweeping in precise unison, showing the times across the USA and in various cities of the world.

"Please, sit down," said Beemish, indicating two empty chairs at the table itself and two immediately behind them. Phil felt very uncomfortable, but turned to wink encouragingly at the children. Beemish indicated to the guard on the door that he should leave, then took his seat on the right of an elderly portly man in an expensive suit who was obviously chairing the meeting. The portly man was staring at Jo-Ann, a look of disbelief on his face.

"Now we are all here," he began rather shakily, "I think introductions are in order. I am James Cranford, Governor of the State of Wyoming."

He leaned forward and studied Jo-Ann even more carefully.

"But you already know that, do you not, Ms White Eagle."

Everyone looked at Jo-Ann. So did Phil.

"What the hell ...?" he whispered.

"If you'd taken more interest in what I was doing, I'd have told you about Cranford weeks ago," she hissed under her breath.

At this point, Phil had a strange and unpleasant feeling that he had heard the name Cranford before. But Beemish had simply referred to him as the Governor. Jo definitely had not mentioned him. No, he was sure he had not heard the name at any time recently, but he had definitely heard it before. Why was it so familiar? He looked closely at Cranford. He did not recognise the face; he certainly had never met the man. So what was it?

"I should explain, gentlemen," Cranford continued, "That I have encountered Mrs Newheart - Jo-Ann White Eagle - in her capacity as leader of the Wyoming branch of the recently-formed Indigenous American Peoples' Action Committee, or *IMPACT* as it calls itself."

Leader! Action Committee! Phil had suspected for some time that Jo-Ann's increasingly lengthy stays in America had been driven by something more than a simple longing to return home. But Governor Cranford's use of the word 'encountered' and his barely disguised sneer left Phil in no doubt that the organisation Jo-Ann was now mixed up in was no Mothers' Union.

Cranford recovered from his surprise and continued.

"On my left is Colonel Winters, F.E.Warren's Base Commander, then Major General Nathan Miller, Commander 90th Space Wing based here, then Major General Doug Norman, Commander 5th Mech. from our nearest army base, Fort Carson in Colorado. On his left is Sheriff Gary Collins from Carbon County, in whose patch this er, apparition, has appeared; and lastly, fresh in from NASA's Johnson Space Centre in Houston, is Rob Klute."

Cranford broke off to consult his notes.

"Your official title, Mr Klute ... ?"

"Chief, Flight Planning. I sign off the flight plans for every mission," explained Klute in a beautiful Texan drawl. "I'm responsible for who and what goes up there, what they do when they get there, and how we get 'em back again."

"Thank you Mr Klute. Now for this side of the table. On my immediate right is my Adjutant General, Major General Ted Beemish. General Beemish is in overall charge of all military action, reporting directly to me - unless this thing goes Federal that is. General Beemish has as you know been a very active player in convening this meeting and arranging accommodation for the Newheart family."

Phil detected a slight emphasis on the words 'very active', and what seemed to be a forced smile on Cranford's lips, which did not match the displeasure in his eyes. Beemish just sat, a look of boyish innocence on his face.

"Along the table here we have Philip and Jo-Ann Newheart and their children Tess and Nick. Then we have Doctor Bjorn Jorgensen, Head of the Wyoming State Geological Survey in Laramie, who prefers we call him ......" Cranford looked towards BJ for prompting.

"BJ," he smiled, then leaning towards Jo-Ann and Phil, whispered "Welcome to the bear pit!"

"And finally, on Doctor Jorgensen's right," continued Cranford, "Is Professor Don Pulanski, head of SETI, the Search for Extra-Terrestrial Intelligence. Professor Pulanski has come to us today from Harvard, so we made sure we knocked the horse shit off our boots before we came in. Wouldn't want our old West ways to get up his nose would we!"

There was an awkward silence before a ripple of forced laughter. Phil could see that it was probably impossible to find two people more opposite in everything about them - appearance, background, education - than Cranford and Pulanski. Cranford looked like a cross between a successful used car salesman and an overweight cattle rancher, and Pulanski would not have been out of place amongst the first violins of the Vienna Symphony. He studied the other faces round the table. There were few men at ease. Perhaps those with the power were unused to it being weakened by their enforced drafting into this unlikely team. Or perhaps the problem itself - of such mysterious portent - was bound to create insecurity. But Phil got the impression that behind the mask of courtesy, each man was concealing a hidden agenda, a need, a fear perhaps.

It was as he was looking round, that Jo-Ann nudged him in the ribs.

"Who's that?" she whispered, pointing with her eyes at a man sitting in the corner behind General Miller. Phil hadn't even seen him. It was as if he was trying to be as inconspicuous as possible, back from the table, in the shadows. Phil noticed that like many of the others, he also had a small phone. He was talking quietly into it even now. Ted Beemish saw Phil and Jo-Ann looking across, and leaned towards Phil.

"Mr Smith - from Washington," he whispered, eyebrows raised.

"Right gentlemen, and I'm sorry, ladies," announced Cranford, "There will be three phases to this meeting: The facts - or what we think are facts, discussion and interpretation of those facts, and finally a plan of action. I will ask General Beemish to run through all we know about this, development."

Beemish, with the help of slides, video recordings, computer print-outs, and even a tape recording of the lunar signal response, then described, in chronological order and considerable detail, the subterranean voice and all that had happened by the door and thereafter. By the time he sat down, the expressions round the table ranged from total scepticism to avid excitement.

"Gentlemen?" said Cranford, casting round for contributions.

General Norman, an ageing and ruddy-faced bull of a man, leaned forward impatiently.

"What attempts have been made to get through or round this door from the top or side, Governor?"

"We've removed a lot of the rock from each side of the doorway," said Sheriff Collins, "But this structure seems to be at the end of a very large tube which slopes downwards into the ground. The tube material is the same as the door - quite impenetrable."

Norman grimaced, and muttered something to Miller on his right. Miller's mouth curled into the semblance of a smile, but his eyes remained as hard as steel.

"We've tried diamond-tipped drills, oxyacetylene, and saws of every description," said Beemish. "The material resists all means at our disposal. We are not going to get in there by force, that's for sure."

"Nor should we try," came a censorious voice from Phil's right. It was Professor Pulanski. He leaned forward slightly, and it was only then that Phil realised he was in a wheelchair. "In my opinion, this door is presenting us with a challenge."

Some of the audience looked interested. Cranford was clearly irritated. Phil got the impression that he would like to have made a sensible contribution to the debate himself, but didn't have the wherewithal. Pulanski continued.

"There is no doubt that its origin - or should I say the manner of its manufacture - is alien to us, and therefore extra-terrestrial. We surely have here gentlemen, the most amazing and portentous event in the history of mankind. We at SETI have been searching the sky for signs of intelligent life for decades, and now, we find it right here, under our feet as it were. The three languages used on the door and in the underground message, and the whole design of the door, strongly suggest we have been visited before, possibly on numerous occasions, but without doubt the last time was roughly two thousand years ago. Whoever it was has returned, and is offering to communicate with us."

"If that's true," said General Miller dismissively, "What's the point of this ridiculous charade about the key being on the Moon? Whatever's in there is playing games with us. If they want to talk, let them come out and talk. Otherwise, let them get the hell back where they came from. I don't see why they don't just show themselves?"

Phil studied Miller. His face was gaunt and colourless, and his close-cropped hair was a dusty grey. He had a thin, cruel mouth, and his deep-set pale blue eyes had a coldness about them which sent a chill down his spine. Miller's uncompromising attitude did not sit comfortably with a man who had the world's most powerful nuclear missile fleet at his fingertips.

"Perhaps they're worried they might meet someone like you, General," said Pulanski frostily. "Maybe they view us as we might consider a budgie in a pet store. If it doesn't talk enough, we don't buy it; if we don't talk sense, they move on and leave us to ourselves and our bigotry."

Beemish, obviously saddened by this exchange, interjected.

"I agree with Professor Pulanski," he said. "I think we have to prove we're bright enough. We have to go to the Moon and find that key."

Cranford addressed NASA's Rob Klute.

"Tell us, Mr Klute, can we get to the Moon and find the key?"

"Within three lunar months," Beemish added.

Before Klute could reply, Pulanski raised his hand.

"It's not whether *we* can get to the Moon gentlemen, it's whether we can get *Mr Newheart* to the Moon. That is the question."

All eyes turned towards Phil. Although he had anticipated that the inscription's 'Whosoever' might be expected to place the key in the door's lock, he had dismissed the notion that that same person would have to personally retrieve it. He swallowed hard and tried to remain detached.

"Dad," Nick whispered excitedly from behind him. "You're going to be an astronaut!"

"Now you really are in fantasy land, Pulanski," said Miller, contemptuously. He shook his head, and uttered a guttural sound that Phil took to be a laugh.

"General Miller," said Pulanski, "I think you have failed to grasp the significance of the inscription. It was Mr Newheart who revealed the lock. We must take the inscription seriously. No-one but he should attempt to collect the key. It may ruin everything if we send someone else, or a robot."

"Is that true, Professor?" said the Governor. "The inscription doesn't say that the only person who can go get the key is the guy who revealed the lock."

"No it doesn't. But it does say whosoever reveals it *can* retrieve it. That sentence tells us unambiguously that Mr Newheart *would be allowed* to retrieve and use the key. We simply cannot afford to take the chance of sending someone else. Mr Newheart - and only Mr Newheart - should physically retrieve the key from the Moon's surface and bring it back here."

Miller took on the demeanour of a Rottweiler. It was as if he was gripping some unseen victim's leg between his teeth, which did not move as he spoke.

"And how the hell is anybody to know who it is who collects the key?" he said. "The man who does it will be in a space suit. We've all seen what they look like. You can't tell who's inside."

"That's a good point," said Cranford. "A regular astronaut could pick up the key, bring it back here, and give it to Mr Newheart to try in the lock. Who's to know?"

Miller sat back looking smug.

Phil felt a movement behind him, and was astonished to see Nick coming to his feet.

"Excuse me," he said, "But I saw something that nobody else saw."

Jo-Ann made as if to reach out and get Nick to sit down, then checked herself. She knew her son. If it hadn't been important, he wouldn't have got up. It must have taken guts.

Governor Cranford turned his head towards Nick, disdain in his eyes.

"Yes?" he said.

"Well," began Nick hesitantly, "As Dad put his hands on the palm hole things, he was speaking, but halfway through a word, he, well … stopped."

"So?" said Cranford, impatiently.

"Well, it's that everything seemed to stop. He was wearing his old leather jacket. It was like, flapping in the breeze, you know. That's what was so weird. I remember now. It stopped flapping as he stopped speaking - like when you press the pause button on a video."

"Do you mean Nick, that *time* seemed to stop?" said Pulanski, wide -eyed.

"Yes, exactly. That's just what it was like."

"For how long?"

"Oh just a second or so. It was so quick, but he did stop. Dad and I were arguing about it straight afterwards. Then we saw the door had changed."

"Mr Newheart," said Pulanski excitedly, "I presume you have a radio-sonde watch?"

"Naturally," said Phil, glancing at his watch.

Pulanski swung his wheelchair round and rolled quickly to where Phil was sitting.

"May I see it please?" he said reaching out.

Phil removed the watch and handed it over. Pulanski grabbed it eagerly and held it up towards the clocks on the wall. His eyes flitted from the watch to the clocks and back again. Then he turned it over and examined the small print etched on its rear surface.

"It's a seven-day update type," he announced triumphantly. "This type of watch is updated once a week, at 2a.m. UT each Sunday morning. It hasn't been re-set since last Sunday, before Mr Newheart encountered the door."

He handed it back to Phil. He was almost beside himself with excitement.

"And it's two seconds slow!"

Phil looked at his watch, and repeated the checks against the clocks. Sure enough, to his astonishment, his sweep second hand lagged by two seconds.

"May I see that?" said Beemish. "I assume you were wearing it yesterday, and that it couldn't have lost the two seconds anyway, in the six days since last Sunday?"

"Yes I was, and no it couldn't," said Phil. "This watch keeps excellent time. It's guaranteed to one second a month even if it's taken to a part of the world outside the radio update area."

Phil's watch was passed round the table, and treated with a reverence normally reserved for delicate icons.

"Something happened to Mr Newheart in those two seconds," said Pulanski, gliding back to his place.

"And why do you think this has got to do with someone else collecting the key?" said Cranford to Nick, who was still standing.

"Well it's obvious Sir," said Nick confidently. "He was being scanned. Whoever goes to the Moon will be scanned too. They'll compare the scans. If it's not Dad ......"

He sat down, trembling slightly. Phil could see that every person in the room had been disarmed by Nick's unshakeable belief in his own theory. He began to think that there may perhaps be something to be said for Nick reading so many science fiction novels. Then he realised - Nick's interjection had sealed his fate!

"That's a great boy you got there, Newheart," said Klute, winking roguishly at Nick.

"That settles it," said Pulanski earnestly. "It *has* to be Mr Newheart. So, can NASA get him to the Moon, Mr Klute?"

The realisation began to dawn on Phil that these men - this committee - were actually talking seriously about sending him to the Moon, and discussing it as if he wasn't there!

"That rather depends I would say, on whether Mr Newheart is willing to go," said Klute, staring straight at Phil and smiling broadly.

At last! Thank you! thought Phil.

"Are you willing to go to the Moon, Mr Newheart?" said Governor Cranford.

The question was overwhelming. Phil looked round at Jo-Ann and the children. Jo's expression was enigmatic - she had been uncharacteristically silent for the whole session. Tess looked seriously worried. Nick looked as if he was going to explode.

He tried to order his thoughts. Apart from the small matter of running the business in his absence, he and Jo had made zero progress towards resolving their differences, he couldn't imagine where the children would live or go to school, and he was being manoeuvred into a partnership with the American authorities. America, the very place he had succeeded in avoiding all these years, was now set to trap him. Not only that, this trip - this whole thing - could be dangerous. Bloody dangerous!

"I don't know ... I'm really not happy about this," he said, ineffectively.

He felt his mind going into overload. He hated having to make snap decisions, especially on something so important. He needed time to think, and more information.

"What would be involved?" he said, turning to Rob Klute. "What would I have to do?"

Klute rested his elbows on the table, leaned forward and locked his hands together. His silvery hair contrasted strikingly with his Gulf tan and boyish face.

"Those of you who keep up to date on space activities will know that in 2010, we established Phoebe, a permanently manned space station in polar orbit round the Moon. What you may not be aware of is that now, we have one return flight per month from the ISS to this orbiting station."

"The ISS?" interrupted Cranford.

"Sorry. The International Space Station. That's the one we've had up and running in orbit round the Earth for ten years now, Governor."

"Of course," said Cranford quickly. "I just wanted to check that everybody knew what you were talking about, Mr Klute."

"Cranford is something else," whispered Jo-Ann.

"What vehicle do you use for the return trips to Phoebe?" said Beemish.

"We call it Artemis, or the LTV - Lunar Transfer Vehicle. It's a relatively small vehicle, like a mini shuttle. We run one main shuttle a month from the Kennedy Space Centre in Florida up to the ISS. A few days after it gets there, Artemis leaves for the Moon and the shuttle returns to Earth. Twenty days after that, Artemis gets back to the ISS and connects with the next shuttle from Kennedy."

"And getting to the lunar surface from Phoebe?" said Phil, beginning to enter into the spirit of things.

"We've got a couple of descent vehicles which spend part of their time docked with Phoebe, and part of their time on the surface. Actually, they're prototype Mars landers. We're using the Moon to test them out."

"Tests going okay?" said Phil wryly.

Sympathetic laughter ran round the table.

"Don't worry, Mr Newheart. They'll get you there."

"Not so fast," came a low voice out of the darkness. It was the man from Washington. He leaned forward slightly and fixed Phil with a penetrating stare. "Are you an American citizen, Mr Newheart?"

"I have dual nationality, a British and an American passport."

"May I enquire how this came about?"

"I was born in Des Moines, to an American father and an English mother," said Phil guardedly. "Is that a problem?"

"You now reside in the UK, do you not? When and why did you move there and where is your father?" said Smith, disregarding Phil's question.

Phil had always been able to change the subject whenever anyone had asked him about his parents. It was his only way to avoid the pain. But being given the third degree - and in public - was something he had not been ready for. The old feelings, coupled with the resentment passed on to him by his mother, came flooding back.

"My father is dead," he said coldly. "Killed, together with my brother, in an air crash, in an American aircraft, on American soil, in 1979. My mother took me to England. Hardly surprising wouldn't you say."

Phil could feel his eyes beginning to water.

"I'm very sorry, Mr Newheart," said Smith. "I just wanted to establish your citizenship - technical reasons."

Phil looked up, to see Cranford, visibly shaken, staring at him.

"Did you say 1979? Where was the crash?"

"Omaha," said Phil, regarding him curiously. "What does it matter?"

The colour drained from Cranford's face. He took the handkerchief from his top pocket and started wiping his hands.

"It ... it doesn't," he blustered. "I was just wondering whether it was local. It was insensitive of me to ask. Forget it. I'm sorry."

He turned to Smith once more, but he was engaged in yet another inaudible conversation on his telephone. Phil was relieved that the subject had been dropped, but Cranford's reaction puzzled him.

There was an awkward pause. General Beemish picked up where the Governor had left off.

"Perhaps Mr Klute could tell us more. For instance, how long will it take to get Mr Newheart trained up? How long is this whole thing going to take?"

"I didn't actually say we could get him there, General," said Klute. "It's not like we're booking him a weekender to Orlando! Our medical people got to check him first, then he's gotta be the right sort of guy. Zero 'g' - now that's talkin' big. He's gotta be aware of all sorts of stuff. And he's gotta be okay in one sixth 'g' too. That ain't easy. Twenty five percent of our guys can't take that environment. We won't have the chance to try him out first. It's up there, zero-g for eight days, down to the Moon, an EVA - well more on that one later - back to orbit, then more than another two weeks in zero-g before the poor sucker gets back down again. No Sir. This ain't no pleasure cruise."

That's over three weeks in space! Phil was beginning to realise that this whole thing would be no joke. Beemish looked sympathetic.

"Does it have to take that long, Mr Klute," he said.

"Look," said Klute. "Everybody gotta realise. Even if we could re-arrange flight schedules, or even do a special launch just for this mission, we're still up against the laws of physics. The lunar orbiter's in a polar orbit. We can only hook into it when its orbital plane lines up with the Earth. Then we gotta wait for the Moon to rotate under the orbit until the landing site's below it, then we come back to the orbit and wait until it lines up with the Earth again. All this takes time. I tell you, we're lucky it's even possible, but it is - just. And before that, we gotta train you Mr Newheart. Nobody's ever been up there with so little time to train. You've got to understand Sir, we're going to have to start with you right away, like tomorrow. And looks like you'll just get back here before the Christmas deadline."

"I thought we'd got until the twenty eighth," blurted Colonel Winters, the Base Commander. It was first contribution he had made to the proceedings.

"Lunar months, Colonel! Three *lunar* months, not calendar months," moaned General Norman, then under his breath to General Miller, "Jesus, what a bone-head!"

"That's right," said Beemish. "Mr Newheart revealed the lock yesterday. It's full moon tomorrow. So he revealed it two days before full moon. We've got until two days before December's full moon, which is on December 27th. So as it happens, we've got until Christmas Day."

"Well I just hope this Christmas present - from God knows where - is something you can handle once you unwrap it, General," hissed Miller under his breath."

Cranford leaned back in his chair and motioned to Smith. He walked over, and the two men muttered to each other, occasionally casting glances towards Phil and the family. Eventually, Smith returned to his seat in the corner and proceeded yet again to whisper into his telephone. With a self-satisfied expression, Cranford turned to Phil.

"Mr Newheart. Seems like it's got to be you, and seems like NASA could do it. Now, what can we do that'll persuade you to go?"

Jo-Ann leaned over and whispered into Phil's ear. "Ask for an adjournment. We need to talk."

***

If it hadn't been for the door, it would have been quite straightforward. Jo-Ann had silently rehearsed her words so many times over the last few days. The official separation starts today, Phil. Join me over here within two years or I file for divorce. It's as simple as that.

But that's not the sort of thing you say to your husband the day he offers to put his life on the line.

Over coffee, Phil had been collared by Beemish and Klute. They were in animated discussion about the mission, insurance, Phil's business, and accommodation arrangements for herself and the children. BJ had joined them, occasionally drawing the youngsters into the conversation. Tess and Nick's delighted expressions spoke volumes. There was obviously no doubt that they had unfaltering confidence in their father, and in NASA's ability to bring him back to them safely.

Maybe this is the miracle I've been praying for, she said to herself. If this extraordinary business doesn't end up killing him, it might be the very thing which kick-starts Phil's move to the States. Maybe ... maybe I won't need to tell him. Maybe ...

She found herself switching into 'negotiation mode'. If Phil was going to go - and knowing him, his curiosity and scientific background would demand that he went - they might as well extract a concession or two from the authorities. Her thoughts turned immediately to the Water Rights for the reservation. Governor Cranford had been their main adversary. He had blocked every move her father had made, and now, he was doing the same to her. But here was a unique opportunity. At last, she might be able to make a breakthrough.

But, if she could get Phil and the children to come over for good, she would be able to fight with them behind her. He needed something to entice him.

She eyed Cranford warily from across the room. He wasn't the sort of guy who gave concessions easily, and she got the impression he didn't really care too much whether Phil went or not. He would probably give on one, but not two. The decision was not easy. If she went for the Water Rights, she might be throwing away the final opportunity to get Phil to move. If she went for him and it failed, she would have let her tribe down, and lost her family as well.

Then, she remembered what Phil had said to Powd about the vehicle import licenses. If she could swing that .....

As Phil listened to General Beemish, he became increasingly convinced of the man's integrity. He displayed a level of concern and thoughtfulness that Phil had rarely encountered, often raising issues and work-arounds that had not even occurred to Phil. Jo-Ann and the children would be accommodated - at the Air Force's expense - on the air base. Nick would attend the local school. Tess would be ferried to and from Laramie, stay with BJ and his wife during the week, attend freshman courses at the University in the morning, and work in BJ's department in the afternoon. The State would pay the salary of a temporary manager - chosen by Phil - to fill in at Newheart Electric Vehicles whilst he was away. It was during the negotiations on the level of life insurance cover that Jo-Ann drew Phil to one side.

"Play hard to get," she whispered mysteriously. Her eyes flitted towards the Governor, who was on his way towards them.

But that was another thing Jo never quite grasped. He simply didn't have it in him to be devious. (He would make a lousy salesman.) Jo was the schemer of the family. Apart from his side-stepping when it came to moving permanently to the States, he couldn't help being perfectly open about everything. He hated deception, and despised corruption.

"Mrs Newheart tells me you're in the electric car business," said Cranford nonchalantly to Phil, leading him gently but firmly away from the others. "There's quite a strong environmental lobby here that would support your efforts."

"Oh yes. Could have fooled me."

"I must say, I haven't heard of your Company. Do you sell over here?"

Jo-Ann was hovering behind Cranford's back, signalling Phil with her eyes.

"Chance would be a fine thing Governor. Your import restrictions ..."

Cranford regarded him intently and spoke very quietly.

"I might be able to do something about that. At least, in Wyoming."

Phil's eyes widened. Sales to the US would dramatically boost company turnover and profits. He could increase the R&D budget. At that moment, it did not occur to him that this might tie him closer to America. He simply saw it as a means to increase sales.

"How?" he said.

"There are ways," said Cranford, tapping his nose with the tip of his forefinger. "I have a great deal of influence around here. I could get you an import licence. Mind you, the Feds mightn't be too happy if they found out we hadn't gone through the proper procedures. We might have to, how shall I put it, offer one or two incentives."

He looked at Phil shrewdly. "Do you understand?" he said.

Phil felt a surge of indignation. The very idea of using the same underhand tactics that he so despised in others sickened him. Cranford was obviously completely unprincipled. And to use the word, 'we', as if he had already assumed collusion between them. What a bloody nerve! He responded without thinking.

"Absolutely not, Governor! I do *not* need this sort of incentive. If I go, it'll be because *I choose to*."

Behind Cranford, Phil saw Jo-Ann's eyes widen. A look of absolute horror was followed by intense frustration then unbridled fury. Like a spring uncoiling, she whipped round and made for the door.

"That's *it*!"

The sound she had emitted was more like an explosion than speech. She fumbled aggressively with the door lock, then flung open the door, strode out, and slammed it behind her with a force that shook the entire room.

Phil looked around him. Many of the faces wore shocked expressions. However, Miller seemed to be smiling. Beemish and the children looked very anxious.

"I ... Excuse me ... I think I'd better ..." stuttered Phil as he turned to follow her.

In the corridor, the horrified guard just pointed towards the washroom at the end. Phil walked in without knocking. Jo-Ann was shaking, and gripping the sink with one hand whilst splashing water onto her face with the other. She did not turn to look at him.

"You never had any intention, did you Phil ..." she said, staring steadfastly at the blank wall in front of her.

"What?" he said, desperately.

"Of coming *here*!" she shouted at the top of her voice.

She let go of the sink, swung round, and smashed the flat of her hand full force onto his left cheek. The intense stinging pain was nothing compared to the shock and horror.

"Bastard!" she cried.

She grabbed the door handle and marched purposefully towards the briefing room.

"I want a divorce!" echoed back towards him.

Back in the Briefing Room, an embarrassing silence hung over the table. Most of the men had resumed their seats. Jo-Ann sat stony faced with the children. Cranford, Beemish and Smith were in a huddle in the corner, and occasionally cast glances towards Phil. Smith as usual, remained in contact with his unseen companion in the Pentagon. Eventually they all nodded and returned to their seats, but Cranford remained standing.

"Would you stand please, Mr Newheart," he said, in a manner reminiscent of a monarch about to bestow a peerage.

It sounded as if the words were waking Phil from a dream. Like a zombie, he pushed his chair back and rose to his feet.

"Mr Newheart. We recognise that what we are asking you to do for our country goes well beyond what would be expected of even a full-time resident and citizen. We also recognise the worry and sacrifice - of your time that is - that this mission will mean to you and your family. We have already agreed insurance, and arrangements for your family's accommodation and your business interests. In addition, Washington have granted a substantial ex-gratia payment to be credited to your account immediately. And finally, by the power vested in me by the people, the Constitution, and the President of the United States of America, I hereby grant you, Mr Newheart, an honorary commission as a Major in the Wyoming Air National Guard. During this temporary posting, you will, Major, report directly to Major General Beemish. This position carries with it the salary and all the benefits of the rank, will allow you and your family to remain officially in the house you are in now, and will I think, help at the NASA end. Welcome to the Department of Defense, Major."

At that, Cranford initiated a round of applause, walked round the table and shook Phil firmly by the hand.

But Phil felt numb. His comfortable and well-ordered world had been turned upside down. He was looking towards Cranford, but in his mind he saw Jo-Ann's radiant and carefree face, a two-year old Tess next to her, and Nick as a tiny baby in her arms.

But that was a world away. Another time, another place, another life. That was before their innocent dream became the nightmare of reality.

And that was before, The Door.

As the applause died down, and handshakes were exchanged all round, General Miller and General Norman stood impassively, talking quietly into each other's ears.

"This whole crack-pot scheme's a non-starter Nathan. If there are any alien sons-of-bitches behind that door, we gotta get 'em before they get us."

"Or we just make sure Newheart never gets to them, Doug."

"Got any ideas, Nathan?"

"Yep."

7
Letters from the Gulf

NASA Johnson Space Center
Houston, Texas
20th October 2012

Dear Jo,

Received the legal documents yesterday. So, a no-fault divorce with an 18 months timestamp. I can't believe this is happening, but at least, I've got 18 months to win you back.

I've been very stupid, Jo, and I'm sorry. Over the years, I got so caught up with everything, I let you slip away. Now I need to win you back. Right now, I have no choice but to focus on the lunar mission training, but once I come back, all I ask is that you let me try.

It's really strange having to write to you. Are you sure you don't want me to phone?

Have you made any progress on the Reservation Water Rights? It must be useful being in Cheyenne, where all the people are who you need to lobby.

Please write or e-mail (phil.newheart@jsc.nasa.gov). If we don't communicate, it's going to be much more difficult later.

I've enclosed a letter to Tess and Nick, and some photos.

I love you Jo. Believe me.
Phil

Dear Tess & Nick,

It was great getting your letters the other day. I'm so pleased both of you are settling in. I don't know whether you realised this Nick, but General Beemish is on your School Board, and he tells me you've made quite an impression. (Good, that is!) And Tess, BJ says you can stay as long as you like, so long as you keep doing the washing up for Linda, and tone down your environmental lectures when he tweaks the thermostat instead of putting on a sweater!

I know it's difficult for you, keeping quiet about The Door, but don't relax your guard. Stick to the agreed line. It's only because I've convinced the authorities that you can be trusted, that you haven't been confined to the base. One day, you'll be able to let it all out.

Well, I've been here three weeks now. I daren't tell you what the medical was like! I'm normal apparently, so there! I've been on land and sea survival exercises, parachute jumping, scuba diving, and been fitted for a space suit (Yes, that's me behind the visor). Last week, I was up in a KC-135 for zero-g training. That's a 20 second drop from 35,000 to 24,000 feet. Unbelievable! It was great the first time, but after the 20th go - yes 20th - I began to feel green. But no, I didn't throw up. I've been in mock-ups of the Shuttle, ISS and Phoebe. During the day we practise emergency procedures, and each evening, I'm expected to read the manuals. One thing's for sure, if anything does go wrong up there, these guys have got some way to fix it. Safety is paramount. So don't worry. I don't.

You'd love it here Tess. One of the buildings has got this fantastic store of moonrock, plus minerals brought back from the three Mars Sample Return missions. There's also a cold store with asteroid and comet material from the Muses-C and Stardust missions. And best of all, there are ice cores from Europa. Fascinating!

Got to go. They're calling me for an LTV re-entry simulation.

The business with Mum and me. This isn't a easy time, but please don't worry. All marriages go through bad patches. We'll ride the storm, and with a bit of luck be all the closer afterwards.

Look after her for me. She's very precious.

With lots of love as always,
Dad

From: phil.newheart@jsc.nasa.gov
To: newheartj@wyarng.army.mil
Sent: 07 November 2012 15:43

Dear Jo,

I'm sorry not to have heard from you. But there's no way I'm going to give up.

Ted (Beemish) videphoned me this morning to tell me something's afoot. There's word in intelligence that someone high up - maybe in the military or a politician - is trying to sabotage the mission. I don't know how he knows or what form this action may take. But knowing some of the feelings flying around, I wouldn't be surprised at anything happening. So a word of warning - watch your back.

I go in three weeks. Any chance of a word before then?

Love and miss you, more than I ever knew I could.

Phil

P.S. More info for the kids attached. You might be interested too.

Dear Tess & Nick,

Your letters were wonderful. It's a real treat getting non-NASA mail. Thanks so much.

Nick, the activities centre sounds great, but once you finish the radio-controlled plane, don't fly it in the wrong place on the base - you don't want it shot down!!

Tess, Michael sounds nice. I bet he's the one who was with BJ at the door. Is he? Don't let him forget what a lucky chap he is will you.

I met the crew of EMT18 (my Earth-Moon transfer flight on Artemis) last week. Mission Commander is Don Ricard. You remember in the press last year - he's the one who heated the first percolator of coffee on the Moon using water extracted from the regolith at the lunar south pole and oxygen produced by the Alphonsus Base Lunox plant. But the guy who's most important to me is Dave "Rocky" Gentry. (He's one of NASA's tallest astronauts, and lives and breathes geology.) He's the Lunar Excursion Vehicle pilot, and will be my buddy when we go down to the surface. He's a man of few words, but boy, does he know his stuff!

Here's my flight plan (AST=Advanced Shuttle Transport, EMT=Earth-Moon Transfer, ISS=International Space Station, Phoebe - lunar orbiter, LEV=Lunar Excursion Vehicle)

Nov 28
AST49 from Cape Canaveral to ISS. 3 crew + we three + one or two payload specialists. 5 days there.

Dec 4
Don, Dave & I leave for Moon on Artemis (EMT18)

Dec 7
LEV-1 ascends from Alphonsus Base to Phoebe with no-one on board.
Artemis docks with Phoebe, which will have LEV-2 already docked with it, all powered up and ready to go.
Don takes LEV-2 straight down to Alphonsus base.

Dec 7-10
On Phoebe. Dave & I check out LEV-1 for descent.
During this time, the Moon is rotating under Phoebe's polar orbit. We have to wait until the landing point is within reach (not too far off Phoebe's ground track

Dec11
Descend, find "The Item", ascend within 6 hours (8 in an emergency). If we miss that window, we're stuck there for 2 weeks, don't get back in time, and totally fail! No way!

Dec12-20
On Phoebe. That's going to be 8 very long days.

Dec 21
Don ascends from Alphonsus Base to Phoebe in LEV-2.
We leave Phoebe and come back to the ISS on Artemis.

Dec24
Artemis docks with ISS. We transfer to AST50 and return to Earth immediately.

Very tight schedule. No room for hiccups. But be back to you guys for Xmas!

More later. Love you.
Dad

P.S. I have a nickname. It's "Spock". I can't imagine why!

From: phil.newheart@jsc.nasa.gov
To: newheartj@wyarng.army.mil
Sent: 21 November 2012 22:17

Dear Jo,
This is the last e-mail I'll be able to send before I leave for the Cape, and I won't have the chance to go on-line down there. I'm terribly sad you haven't replied at all. Guess I really screwed up didn't I. Will you ever forgive me?
Give the kids a hug for me, Jo.
Ted's got all the paperwork if ... you know.

Love you for ever.
Your husband,
Phil

Dear Tess & Nick,
We go in seven days. I can't believe it.
Dave and I went over to photo archives just after I wrote to you last. We were shown a superb photo (better than all the Lunar Prospector images) taken by Apollo 15 of the exact spot we're going to land. I've attached a copy. It's Photo-Id AS15-0334 in case any of your friends would like a copy. The valley is 2,900 ft deep and a mile across - very dramatic. If you look carefully, you'll see where a huge boulder has tumbled end-over-end from the terraces at the top down to the bottom, leaving a row of gouges where it bounced. The boulder's shaped like a peanut and it's extremely near to our destination, so we've named it "Peanut Rock". That's what we'll be looking out for (at least initially!) when we get down there.
Oh, get this - we're going to have to land on the Moon during the lunar night!
See you both at Christmas. I'll be thinking of you.

Your ever-loving,
Dad

8

Beyond the Blue

The imposing outlines of the two sleek space vehicles cast long glancing shadows across the runway as Phil stepped off the bus that had brought them the two miles from the quarantine quarters of the Kennedy Space Centre. He paused for a moment to look eastwards, the direction in which they would be climbing after take-off. In the middle distance, a squall line of low grey clouds was rolling in off the Atlantic. Above and beyond that, and slightly pink in the light of the setting sun behind him, rose a bank of towering cumulo-nimbus. Yet further off and much higher, possibly over a hundred miles away, and maintaining a tenuous hold on the upper limits of the atmosphere, was a pearlescent veil of cirrus. Above the cirrus, it was perfectly clear, and of the deepest blue. To Phil, these clouds, leading inexorably onwards and upwards, were like a stairway to the sky, and in the far distance, beyond that life-supporting canopy - beyond the blue - was the awesome majesty of space.

He turned and followed the four other astronauts - all of them clad in their orange launch-and-entry suits - up the steps and onto the mid-deck of the primary launch vehicle.

The Advanced Shuttle Transport system consisted of two complementary vehicles. The primary launch vehicle had evolved from the original shuttle design but was much larger, and its ultra high pressure main engines were twice as efficient as the original. It was a hybrid spaceplane which combined the propulsion system of a rocket with the airfoil characteristics and jet engines of the latest supersonic aircraft. It could, given an only partly-filled oxidiser tank, take off like a plane, and lift a payload of 25 tonnes to a height of 90,000 ft. and 700 mph. At that height, it could do a gravity drop to pick up speed, then switch to its rocket engines, but needed to fill up with propellants - oxidiser and fuel - before doing so. The secondary, or support vehicle, also took off like a plane, and achieved the same height and speed, but its payload consisted entirely of propellants for use by the primary. At 90,000 ft - on the verge of space - the propellants were transferred from the support to the primary craft. The support vehicle would then return to base empty, and the fully charged primary would ignite its main engines and blast off into orbit. To descend from orbit, it would use the standard hypergolic-driven retro-burn followed by aero-braking, and finally, return to base using powered flight with the small reserve of jet fuel remaining. This AST system, developed by a consortium of aerospace corporations, overcame in one stroke virtually all the limitations associated with the original shuttle design:- launch and landing safety, system complexity, slow component recycle time, and overall cost. It allowed more launches per year; the requirements for travelling on it were far less stringent; in short, space became accessible.

The three-man crew of AST49's primary vehicle - mission commander, pilot, and systems controller - had been aboard for the last two hours running through the pre-launch checks, and were already seated on the flight deck. As Phil strapped on his escape gear and took his assigned seat, the friendly face of the pilot appeared in the hatch above him.

"Welcome aboard folks," he said. "This is flight AST49 non-stop to heaven. Have your halos ready please!"

Along with Phil, Don and Dave were Loc, a Chinese payload specialist accompanying his company's satellite, and a French materials physicist called Jules who was going to the ISS to conduct microgravity dendrite research. Phil had to explain to Loc what a halo was, and explain that the pilot was only joking.

As the mid-deck hatch was closed by the ground crew, Phil could hear the mission commander talking on the radio to the support craft standing a hundred yards ahead of them down the runway.

"Fifteen minutes to launch. I have go on all systems. Do you copy?"

Phil and the others put on their helmets, checked each other's comms and safety equipment, and strapped in. He had run through this routine dozens of times during simulation training, and now found it came as second nature. But today - at last - it was for real. He considered the date, 28th November. It had been an incredibly short two months and one day since the

RV ran off the road in Wyoming, yet he felt that was a lifetime away. If anybody had told him then, that in two months he would be strapped into a space craft and be projected into orbit at 17,000 mph, he would have said they were completely mad.

"Three minutes," came the pilot's voice over his headset, just before the jet engines began winding up. The noise and vibrations were exactly the same as the simulations. Phil remembered his training and tried to control his breathing. He was listening intently to both sides of the conversation between the pilot and launch control.

"RP-1 tank pressure?"

"Go!"

"LH2 final?"

"Go!"

"LOX final?"

"Go!"

"RP-1 pump pressure?

Then, when there shouldn't have been, there was silence from ground control. The anxious voice of the pilot repeated the last check request.

"Control. Do you have RP-1 pump pressure?"

Further silence. Then suddenly, an alarm started sounding. Phil recognised it instantly from his abort training. The urgent voice of the ground controller came over his headset.

"Abort! Abort! Abort! Mode 1! Mode 1 abort!"

Then the voice of the mission commander, "But we have all green lights here!"

"Power down! Get out of there! There's a bomb on board!"

A bomb! This was a contingency that had not been covered before. Phil felt his heart pounding, and an adrenaline rush unparalleled in his training. In a matter of seconds, he had unbuckled, unplugged his comms, and was heading for the hatch. Don had got there before him and fired the explosive bolts which projected the hatch outwards onto the runway. Immediately, a bright yellow escape chute deployed and came to rest on the tarmac below. Don jumped out, slid down, and began running towards the emergency vehicles lined up ready for such an eventuality, but Phil noticed that Dave held back and ensured that everyone got out before he jumped clear. As Phil slid downwards, the three AST flight crew were already on the tarmac. Down the runway, the crew of the support craft were clambering into their armour-plated ground escape vehicle. Phil was sweating profusely as he and the others from the primary ship tumbled into their seats and the vehicle accelerated towards Launch Control Centre.

"If there's a bomb on the support vehicle and it blows," shouted Dave, "It'll take us all out. For God's sake, step on it!"

Phil knew they would have to be at least a mile away to be safe. 350,000 lbs of propellant going up would break windows in Titusville.

It was only when they got to the safety of the launch control building and looked back, that Phil felt the anti-climax, then the all-consuming horror that after all this - after everything he had gone through - the mission would be cancelled.

He strained his eyes to see the two ships, sitting like large tired birds. But neither ship blew up. They just sat there.

***

Dick Clancy, facilities director of Kennedy Space Center, and Pete Slyger from the FBI, walked into the press briefing room to a salvo of flashbulbs. They sat down behind an array of microphones, and Clancy held his arms high in the air as representatives of the world media bombarded them with questions. The interview was going out live to virtually every country in the world, and anyone watching this embattled southerner could tell at a glance that he was furious.

"Ladies and gentlemen," he said, his gravelly voice wrought with tension, "I will now issue a short statement regarding AST49, following which there will be three minutes for questions. Then you must allow us to get on with our jobs."

This was met with a chorus of disapproval from the assembled company, which Clancy countered by rising to his feet and turning towards the door.

"It's that or nothing," he said. "Do you want the statement or don't you? I've no time to screw around."

Silence descended. Clancy sat down once more and read from a prepared text.

"At 1825 yesterday evening, five minutes before launch, Kennedy Launch control received a phone call, patched through from the FBI in Washington, from a man who claimed that an explosive device had been planted somewhere on one of the two vehicles participating in the launch of AST49, and it was due to detonate at some time in the next six hours. The caller quoted two code words which are only known to the FBI and certain terrorist organisations, and which are used to facilitate discrimination between hoax and genuine calls. The caller described certain details of the craft, that would only be known by someone with intimate knowledge of them. We had no choice but to take the threat seriously, so the launch of both vehicles was aborted. Since that time, no explosions have occurred. Volunteer engineers, assisted by bomb disposal teams, have since off-loaded the propellants from the vehicles to minimise the effects of an explosion should one occur. A thorough search of both craft is now taking place, but as of this time, no device has been found on either vehicle. There will be no further announcements until six hours from now - at 1800 hours this evening. Questions?"

A tall brunette from NBC, with an authoritative voice, was the first to catch Clancy's eye.

"You say the caller would have to have an intimate knowledge of the vehicles themselves to be able to describe certain details about them. Is it possible that any person with a reasonable understanding of rocket or jet propulsion systems could have described those vehicles without gaining access to them? What I mean to say is, could it be a hoax, perpetrated by someone with the relevant knowledge?"

Clancy looked uncomfortable.

"Well I guess so, but this person, whoever he is, would have to be a rocket expert."

Pete Craven from CNN stood up.

"Do you have any information on the source of the phone call, and presumably you have a tape of it?"

"The call was made from a public phone booth in Cheyenne, Wyoming," replied Slyger. "The caller had disguised his voice by making a modulated tape recording and playing the tape into the mouthpiece of the instrument. Our current information is that no surveillance cameras cover this particular booth, so we have no record of who used it around that time or who could have made the call."

An elderly correspondent from CBS rose to his feet.

"Mr Slyger, is it not somewhere near to Cheyenne that an air exclusion zone has been declared, and about which there has been a news blackout for the last two months? And do you consider that these two events may in some way be related?"

"I am not aware of this, and I see no reason why the two events should be related," said Slyger mechanically.

"Then can you tell us, Mr Clancy, why Kurt Froebels was dropped from the crew of EMT18, and replaced by this ....." He consulted his note pad. "Major Newheart, about whom we know absolutely nothing?"

"No comment," said Clancy awkwardly.

The CBS correspondent remained standing.

"Come come Dick. You can do better than that. My information is that Major Newheart's wife and family are currently being accommodated at the Government's expense at the Warren Air Base in Cheyenne. Are you telling me that this is a coincidence?"

It was clear from the gasps of surprise, that most of the correspondents in the room were unaware of the Cheyenne connection. Many rose to their feet to claim Clancy's attention. But before he had an opportunity to answer, which it was clear he had no intention of doing, Martin Soames from the BBC held the floor.

"Then can you tell us, Mr Clancy, what was Major Newheart's role to be in AST49 and flight EMT18 to the Moon, and who could possibly gain from sabotaging this mission?"

Clancy, clearly wrong-footed by the last two questions, and aware that unless he was more forthcoming would have a riot on his hands, raised his hand once more and leant forward to speak.

"The fact is, Mr Soames, that Major Newheart is an expert on TLPs - Transient Lunar Phenomena. I can imagine no party who could possibly gain by preventing him pursuing his research in this field. However, if there was such a party, which I very much doubt, and they think they have succeeded in grounding Major Newheart, they are sadly mistaken. We are at this moment, preparing two reserve craft which will leave in time to connect with EMT18. AST49 will be launched, albeit a few days late."

"Are you saying Mr Clancy," called a voice with a Californian accent, "That there has been a TLP on the Moon? A TLP so important that you have replaced one of the crew of EMT18 virtually at the last moment? And if so, what is the nature of this phenomenon?"

"We have no further comment at this time," replied Clancy. "I'm sorry, but you must now let us get on with re-organising the launch. That is all. Thank you."

And with that, and to a cacophony of indignant appeals and further questions, Clancy and Slyger rose from their seats and swept from the room.

***

For the second time in four days, Phil again sat strapped inside the primary launch vehicle. Unlike the previous occasion, his fellow passengers did not include Loc, the satellite specialist. The authorities at the Cape, realising that the bomb - if bomb there was - could be hidden anywhere on either vehicle including the primary payload, had decided the only way to guarantee the launch safety was to exclude the payload. It had been impossible to thoroughly check the complex innards of the Chinese satellite in time, and indeed most of the payload of the original AST49 had been left aboard the threatened craft.

Now, four days late, they were ready to go again. The delayed launch meant that the three of them would only spend two days on the ISS instead of six, but that there would still be just enough time to refuel and check out EMT18 prior to its journey.

As he sat there, the last few minutes ticking away, he reflected once more on who might have been responsible for the bomb hoax. As the call came from Cheyenne, it was almost certainly connected with him. Apart from a small group of support staff at Kennedy and Houston, none of whom could gain a great deal, the only people who knew the real purpose of his mission were those who had been at the meeting in Cheyenne. One or more of those men had to be responsible. But who? Why? Was it that someone knew more about the door than they were admitting, or was it exactly the opposite - fear of the unknown? Phil couldn't help wondering whether the saboteur would try again, and if so, how far he would go.

The whine and vibrations of the engines brought him back to the present. They were moving - accelerating down the runway. Very quickly, he felt the craft pitch up, the wheels lost contact with the ground, and they climbed steadily and peacefully into the sky. The mid-deck windows all had their shades in place, so he could not see out, but the continuous chatter between the two craft and Ground Control kept him in touch with their progress. Soon, the motion changed to a smoother, more silent riding sensation, and he knew that the refuelling was imminent. Then, the satisfying clang of the fuel take-on pipe engaging in the delivery cup of the support craft reverberated through the ship. The fuel and oxidiser loading was one of the more dangerous and delicate operations for both pilots. A mistake now could mean an aborted mission, or at worst, the destruction of both craft. Phil sat and gripped his arm-rests, and listened to the volatile liquids - first the fuel then the oxidiser - filling the tanks, and converting their craft from a plane into a fully charged rocket.

"Tanking complete" came the pilot's voice. "Decouple."

Phil knew that at this stage, the support craft would be veering away. After the final checks, their jet engine would be cut, the craft would free fall, then the main engines would fire.

"Make ready for switchover!" announced the pilot.

Phil's mouth was dry. He double-checked his strap buckles, rested his helmeted head firmly on his head-rest, and waited.

"Switchover!"

The pitch of the jet engines dropped suddenly, then were silent. All he could hear was the whoosh of the tenuously thin atmosphere rushing along the fuselage. As he felt the craft falling, he heard the main engine turbopumps start up, then with an ear-splitting roar, the engines burst into life. There was an initial jolt, then his moulded seat began pressing into him. It did not feel that he was being carried by the craft, but rather being pushed by it. The feeling of genuine acceleration was overwhelming and gradually increasing. The initial 2g, whilst the spaceplane was heavy with fuel, would increase ultimately to 4g. Phil found himself tapping out the seconds with his middle finger, each second representing an increase in speed of up to 80 mph. He knew the burn was only going to last four minutes or so - he had practised in the centrifuge at Houston - but as the time dragged on, the feeling of an ever-increasing weight on his chest, and the difficulty he was having breathing put pay to his initial exhilaration. At last the pilot's voice cut through the roar.

"MECO 5"

Phil knew this meant five seconds to main engine cut off.

Then it happened. One moment it was all noise and thrust and weight, and the next, pure peace, and weightlessness.

Phil had been advised not to unbuckle immediately, and to move his head only very slowly at first, until his balance organs got used to the continuous weightless environment. But the sight of big Dave, slowly rising from his seat and floating off to the side, made him instinctively turn his head. As he did so, a wave of nausea swept over him. It was as if he were wearing a new pair of glasses which made everything move strangely, but a hundred times worse. He made sure the tag of his sick bag was just peeking out of his suit pocket, just in case.

Don and Dave started removing the window shades.

"Reckon you should see this, Phil," said Dave, calmly. "Better move it though."

Phil unbuckled, and making sure he never let go or floated freely, moved carefully over to the port window and peered out. The sight that greeted him was unexpectedly and unbelievably beautiful. From their 200 mile altitude, he could see the English Channel and the entire British Isles. Away to the north, and distinctly curved, was the horizon, a thin sliver of dark blue light caressing the surface of the Earth. Above that, and unfathomably dark, was space. It was the contrast between the brilliant blue-white life-rich planet and the pitiless black majesty of the cosmos which struck him the most. For the first time, he saw the Earth from beyond it, hanging in an infinite void. Mankind's spaceship. The temptation to accept that somehow, the hand of a designer had been at work, was overwhelming.

As he watched and marvelled, he became aware of his headlong speed. In less than a minute, he was passing Belgium and Holland, and in another, the snow-covered Austrian Alps. Three minutes after that, he could make out Istanbul and the deep blue waters of the Black Sea.

"ISS in sight," came the pilot's voice. "Hold fast for orbital trims."

By squinting through the window, Phil could just see what literally looked like a pointed star floating in the blackness ahead of them. As the spaceplane drew to within five hundred yards of it, Phil was able to see what an amazingly complex structure it was. It looked like a haphazard collection of tin cans fixed together at various angles, and surrounded by a flimsy arrangement of rectangular sails like a child's wind-vane toy. Phil knew that the tin cans were in fact the various nations' habitation and laboratory modules, and the vanes, massive solar arrays to collect sunlight and provide power. At one hundred yards however, in the dazzlingly strong sunlight, it was clear that this was no toy. Its sheer size - over 100 yards long and 120 yards wide - dwarfed the spaceplane, and the intricate detail of each component demonstrated that here was a marvel of technological achievement unsurpassed in the history of mankind.

As they approached, Phil recognised the familiar shapes of the two lunar transfer vehicles docked to the Russian modules at the far end. One of these craft was always at hand at the ISS, and could be used to return to Earth in an emergency. The other would be for them - Artemis, their ferry to the Moon.

The spaceplane inched towards the US docking module, and, after some delicate positional adjustments, latched on to it with a satisfactory clunk.

"Capture. All change please!" said the pilot.

A green light came on. Phil and the others removed their helmets and prepared to disembark.

After two months of arduous and intensive training, it had taken just eight minutes to get into space.

***

Phil spent the next two days acclimatising to zero g and life aboard the labyrinthine tunnels of the space station. The station was manned by an international crew of six, mainly mission specialists and scientists. In addition, there were three passengers and crew who had brought Artemis back from the Moon as EMT17, the three crew of AST49, Jules - who was replacing one of the six, himself, Don and Dave. As there were only six sleep stations aboard the ISS, the spaceplane and the EMTs were also used as accommodation units. Convention dictated that each person slept in the vehicle he or she was about to use, so Phil, Don and Dave used Artemis - now designated EMT18 - as their home. Because of his as yet unknown reaction to zero g, Phil had been assigned only one primary duty. He was to ensure that the two hand-held transceivers he and Dave were to use on the Moon to locate the key, were in working order and stowed correctly in their lockers aboard Artemis. His secondary responsibilities were to ensure he did not get in the way, did not touch anything he hadn't been trained on, and did not throw up.

He learnt to cook, eat, drink, use the toilet, wash, shave, shower, change and sleep in zero g - all activities fraught with difficulty when gravity was totally absent. Without its restraining force and the friction with the floor produced by it, every movement - every attempt at changing position in any way - had to be thought through and pre-planned. He also learned that everybody spent a large proportion of their time making sure they did not lose things. It was amazing just how many objects one used in the normal course of living on Earth, and how one was used to those objects staying where you put them. But in space, you cannot put something 'down' or leave it unstowed. If you do, within a few minutes, it has floated away. It was in the ISS that Phil learned the power and versatility of Velcro. Everywhere he explored, there were Velcro strips and patches glued to the cabin walls, and almost every object he encountered, regardless of its mass, also had Velcro glued to it.

His sleep station consisted of something about the size of a phone booth, containing a felt cotton-lined zip-up bag, a Velcro strap to prevent his head lolling about, a light, and a small locker for personal possessions. He could never quite get used to the idea of sleeping 'standing up', but of course in space, it didn't matter.

His favourite place on the station was the cupola. This was a half-dodecahedral structure about seven feet across, jutting out from the US accommodation module. All its faces were windows, providing an Olympian platform from which at least two people could observe the spectacle below. He spent hours on the second day, just floating in the cupola and watching the planet glide by beneath him. Every ninety minutes, he could see the sun rise, gaze in awe at the ever-changing panorama, watch a sunset, and then, in the darkness below, glimpse the ghostly flickering of lightning, like night sprites dancing across a mist-covered pool. Once, he saw a meteor blaze a fiery trail into the atmosphere far below him. When he saw that, he knew he was in space.

Suddenly, Phil was aware that Dave was next to him. He hung there, gazing pensively out of the window, and sucking on an orange juice flexipack.

"What I can't get used to, Dave, is that you can't see any frontiers between the countries. It's just one unbelievably beautiful and precious whole. From here, the thought of carving it up and saying, 'This bit's mine, and that bit's yours' is completely ridiculous. It belongs to all of us. We each have a personal responsibility not only to share it, but to protect it too. I never thought of it like that before. And another thing I've realised: it's the only planet we've got!"

Dave said nothing. He just smiled serenely. Words were inadequate. Phil felt that somehow, they were witnessing a miracle.

***

Phil looked back at the Earth with some trepidation. It had been three days since they had left the ISS on Artemis, and they were about to do the burn which would slow them down to match the orbital velocity of Phoebe, the lunar polar-orbiting space station. This manoeuvre was done as Artemis passed behind the Moon. For the first time in his life, Phil would be somewhere from which the Earth could not be seen. Over the last three days he had watched it receding into the distance, and now, if he wanted to, he could hide it with his thumb at arm's length. But he could always take his thumb away, and the Earth would be there.

As they coasted silently towards the south pole of the Moon, Phil gazed in awe at its dry and lifeless surface. A scene of fearsome desolation was spread out before him. He looked back once more at the dazzling blue and white orb of the Earth, hanging like a Christmas tree decoration and just glowing with life, then shivered as the surface of the Moon - like the encrusted shell of some monstrous turtle - rose up and occulted it.

They executed the lunar orbit insertion burn, and - though Phil could not hear the replies - Don established radio contact with the Russian Commander on Phoebe. Phil knew that Phoebe was manned by a lone cosmonaut, but the other astronauts had been strangely evasive when asked any questions. In fact, they would simply smile shiftily and fob him off with something like, "Oh you'll see."

The automatic docking system had locked on, and they expected visual contact at any minute.

"There she is!" announced Don, as the space station came into view. Dave, who had been his usual taciturn self all the way from the ISS, was craning his neck to catch sight of Phoebe. For a moment, he reminded Phil of a child on a coach trip, pressing his face against the window as they arrive at the seaside.

"How many times have you been to Phoebe before, Dave?" asked Phil.

"Twice," said Dave, without taking his eyes off it.

Phil could now see that both lunar excursion vehicles were docked with Phoebe. LEV-1, the craft he and Dave would use to descend to the lunar surface, had just come up empty from Alphonsus Base on autoguide. LEV-2 was there waiting, all powered up, for Don to use to get down to Alphonsus. Don had already put on his Lunar Habitation Suit in readiness.

As they approached, Phil could see that Phoebe's central module was of a similar design to the ISS, and also had a cupola. He thought he saw a movement - a figure perhaps - in the cupola, but it disappeared before he could make it out.

As their vehicle finally docked, and the hatch began to open, Don whispered into Phil's ear.

"And now for your surprise, Major," then turning to the hatch and speaking normally, "Colonel Askinov, we bring salutations from mother Earth, and seek your permission to come aboard."

As the hatch was removed, Phil stared, wide-eyed. There, floating as might an angel, was the most beautiful woman he had ever seen. She was about thirty, had long auburn hair held in a loose side pony tail, big brown eyes, and a gentle face. A white T-shirt covered what must have been the most perfectly formed breasts imaginable, and a brief pair of shorts served to highlight to perfection, her smooth, white, slender legs. Her arms reached out towards the three men, her eyes lit up, and an inviting smile came to her lips.

"Dobro pozhalovat," she said, huskily.

"May I present Major Philip Newheart of the US Air National Guard," said Don, grinning at Phil, whose mouth was silently opening and closing like a goldfish.

She reached through the hatch and took Phil by the hand. As she did so, he felt a sudden and overwhelming sensation the like of which he had never experienced before. It was as if his whole body had started to hum, like a powerful transformer that had been plugged in to the mains. The shock of it took his breath away, so much so that he could not speak. Neither could he, for a brief and unforgettable moment, contemplate letting go of her hand.

It was obvious that she had felt it too. As their bodies glided past one another, her eyes - now even more welcoming than before - followed his for a few seconds longer than the occasion demanded, and her expression changed briefly from one of genuine pleasure to disquiet.

"It's ... Svetlana, Major," she said, after an involuntary intake of breath. "Come inside. Make yourself at home."

Phil glanced back at Don, who just winked roguishly as he came through. Dave remained hovering in the hatchway, regarding Svetlana coyly. It was as if he was too embarrassed to move.

"Golubchik," she said lovingly. "Still the deep silent one are we, Dave? Come on. You can't stay there all day!"

She pulled him through, looped an arm round him, kissed him on the cheek, and whispered something into his ear which made him blush. Don drew Phil to one side.

"We never tell rookies about Svetlana unless we have to. Spoils the fun." He was grinning from ear to ear. "You should see your face!"

Phil kept facing Don, but his eyes followed Svetlana's every movement.

"My God, who *is* she?" he gasped.

"Daughter of two Russian cosmonauts. Apparently, she was conceived in space..."

"Conceived! You don't mean..... They... On a spacecraft!"

Don gave him a knowing look.

"Oh yes. It *can* be done apparently! Some of the guys claim they've made it with her." He cast Svetlana a lecherous look. "Mind you, that's probably wishful thinking. Now Dave over there. He's different. He's never claimed nothin'. Far as I know, he's never tried nothin' either."

"Really? But he is single isn't he? He's not gay?"

"No, no. He's straight. Had a fiancée back in NC a few years back. Dunno what happened. He's kinda old fashioned too. Bible belt family values - that sort of stuff."

And so saying, Don started busying himself ready to take LEV-2 down to Alphonsus.

Svetlana appeared alongside Phil once more.

"Do come through, Major," she said, with the air of a dinner hostess, and led the way from the service module through a side hatch. "This is my little nest."

Phil could not take his eyes off Svetlana as she glided through into the module and floated in front of him. Eventually, he forced himself to look around the room. It took him a moment to orient himself and get used to the more subdued lighting, but once he did, he could scarcely believe his eyes. Although it was the same basic shell as that on the ISS, the module was completely different inside. The walls, instead of having drab, utilitarian, wipe-down surface, had soft fabric coverings, and some had paintings fixed to them. Some storage racking components had been improvised to form two simple seats - like dentists' chairs but without arm rests. They were each covered with foam padding and fitted with lap straps, and were bolted down near to the cupola. The metal hand-holds round the cupola had been replaced with fabric straps. In place of the harsh fluorescent lights was an assortment of table lamps, again, bolted down. Strategically placed all over the module were capacious pockets - some made of soft material - all with Velcro fastenings. A perspex-fronted bookcase screwed to one surface looked uncanny, as its contents drifted about within it. There were many potted plants, their pots obviously fixed to what might be loosely described as walls and the ceiling. At first glance, they resembled ivy, but Phil recognised a prayer plant, an African Violet and at least one vine. He wondered why they looked so strange, until he realised that they were not growing 'upwards'. As there was no 'up', they could not. Rather, their exceptionally spindly stems and side branches were heading off in all directions at once as if their main concern was light and space rather than strength and stability. The scene was completed by the strains of Beethoven's Pastoral from a multi-channel compact stereo system.

"It's... It's beautiful," stammered Phil. "Where did you get all this stuff from?"

"My boys," she said, looking back towards the hatch, where Dave was hovering, wondering whether to follow them inside. "Once they've been here, when they come back they bring me presents."

On cue, Dave glided in with a small parcel tied up with an elastic band and sent it floating slowly towards her. She grabbed it eagerly and unwrapped it.

"I got the CDs you wanted," he said, awkwardly. "Schubert's *Rosamunde* and Ravel's *Daphnis and Chloé*. Oh, and I got you an original Russian version of the Cherry Orchard. I don't think you've got that have you?"

Svetlana squealed with delight and made as if to kiss Dave again, but he turned nervously away and made for the hatch.

"Better help Don," he said.

Svetlana smiled at Phil, then, moving with the speed and dexterity of a water-seal, stowed the gifts and vanished through into the service module.

Phil took a deep breath and moved to the cupola. The Earth was just reappearing as Phoebe passed over the Moon's north pole. The craters below him were thrown into sharp and jagged relief by the low angle of the sun. At the same time, the final movement of the Pastoral drifted across the room, serving as a poignant reminder of the green and pleasant land he had not seen since September. A wave of home-sickness washed over him as he thought of Jo-Ann and the children, and how life had been when all seemed so secure, so uncomplicated. He looked around him again, and tried to come to terms with his dream-like situation. He was now not only disconcertingly involved with America; his links with his own company and his future home were at best uncertain; his wife had asked for a divorce and had not communicated with him for two months; and he was flying around over a desolate and terrifying landscape, hunting alien artefacts. And now, to add torment to his overwhelming loneliness and emptiness, he was feeling guilt - guilt and disgust that the most important thing in his life at this moment was a base and all-consuming urge to screw the pants off the Russian.

At that point, Don called from the service module, that he was about to board LEV-2 for his descent to the surface. Phil moved through and joined the others. Handshakes were exchanged. Don pulled himself through the docking hatch, and Svetlana closed the two airlock doors. She then moved to the command station and spoke to Don over the radio.

"Clear to undock, Don. Five minutes to retro-burn."

"Sealing LEV airlock doors," came Don's voice in reply. Then, after a minute's pause, "Undocking."

Phil heard the undock latches spring open, and saw on the monitor, Don's craft moving slowly and gracefully away from Phoebe. At one hundred metres, its attitude thrusters rotated it so its main engines were facing the direction of travel, ready for the retro-burn. Exactly as the LEV's auto-descent countdown clock - relayed to Phoebe - changed from minus one second to zero, its main engines fired. With amazing rapidity, it accelerated backwards and began slowly falling towards the lunar surface.

"My love to boys down there," called Svetlana huskily, "And don't forget to bring us some Lunox when you come back up!"

"I won't," replied Don cheerily. "Good luck on Tuesday. See you all in two weeks. Bye now."

The lunar base in the crater Alphonsus used the latest In-Situ Resource Utilisation techniques to manufacture oxygen from lunar minerals. It was this important development which had made possible the construction and maintenance of the base and Phoebe. As a high proportion of the propellant mass used by all spacecraft was oxygen, to have an unending supply of Lunox just where it was needed the most, made lunar exploration and development commercially viable. All that needed to be brought from Earth were supplies and a small amount of fuel. The payload capacity that this system provided opened the door to an ever-expanding exploitation of the Moon.

Phil made his way back to the cupola, and watched the LEV slowly falling away. It sailed along beneath him, its motion against the lunar surface emphasising dramatically the speed of both craft. Eventually it receded into the distance and disappeared from view.

It was Friday 7th December. It was sobering to realise that on Tuesday - a mere four days away - that would be him.

***

Phil spent the next three days practising his lunar landing procedures on the LEV's simulation computer and adjusting to the pattern of life aboard Phoebe. Dave was always the first up. He would, like a couchette attendant, gently wake Phil then

Svetlana, and prepare breakfast for them all. At 0840, they would communicate with Mission Control in Houston and agree the activities for the day. This usually involved Dave splitting, examining and analysing the station's seemingly inexhaustible supply of moonrock, and Svetlana - she was an accomplished botanist - continuing her experiments on plant growth in micro-gravity. On the second day, Svetlana invited Phil into her plant laboratory. This was a large module with banks of propagators, each one testing the effect of heat, light, soil (including lunar regolith), moisture and other factors on plant growth and crop yield. Phil tried to listen as she outlined her experiments, but was distracted by a series of fantasies sparked off by what Don had said. It was also clear that Svetlana was not at ease. She kept looking disconcerted, fiddled nervously with her hair, and seemed unable to maintain eye-to-eye contact with him during their conversations.

Dave and Svetlana worked together in perfect harmony. For most of the time, they would remain in their separate modules, but often Dave would sail excitedly into the plant lab with some crushed rock and a print-out of his analysis, and he and Svetlana would engage in animated discussion on the pros and cons of this as a growing medium. It was strange to hear Dave talking so much, and so naturally, and it was clear to Phil that these two could do far worse than expand their relationship from the purely professional.

At about 1800, formal work would stop, Dave and Phil would exercise and shower, and Svetlana would prepare the evening meal. At 1900 they would eat together in the galley, standing - or rather floating - round the small breakfast bar table, their feet in the foot-restrainers provided. This was an occasion when, at least on the ISS, the conversation turned from work towards more informal topics. But on Phoebe, the situation was different. Mealtimes were somewhat strained. Whenever Svetlana attempted to guide the conversation away from work, Dave would clam up and retreat into a private world of his own. It wasn't that he was hostile - far from it. In fact at all times, Dave was friendly, thoughtful, and even protective towards Svetlana. For her part, she was attentive - almost motherly - towards Dave, and continually presented him with opportunities to get closer to her. But these attempts were frustrated by his apparent reticence to become involved, and more importantly, by the distraction to her efforts occasioned by Phil. He did not knowingly do anything, but the ever-increasing charge that was building up between him and Svetlana was undeniable. He would quietly watch and listen to her attempts to draw Dave closer, but all too often, even as she did this she would look - with an expression of helplessness - past Dave at Phil. Even when he deliberately looked away, he could feel her eyes, her presence, her very being, there, tantalisingly near. He knew, that despite their finer feelings, the chemistry between them was palpable and undeniable.

It was a well-established practise that between 20:00 and 21:00, male astronauts did not enter the shower and habitation module. Since the accident on the ISS in 2008, all modules were fitted with hatch doors that closed if there was a pressure loss, or could be controlled from strategically placed push buttons inside the modules. The normally-closed habitation module hatch door allowed Svetlana - and any other women on the space station - to have at least a short period of privacy. So after the meal, Dave and Phil would clear up the galley then retire to the cupola room to relax. Once Svetlana joined them, Phil would stay chatting for a while, but would then take his leave. This was partly because he believed the relationship between Dave and Svetlana needed an opportunity to blossom, but mainly because the near-animal desires that consumed him whenever she was around were more than he could bear. When he left them, he would usually drift into the galley, fix a drink, then retire to his sleep station to read. But on the three nights he had done this, he heard Dave follow him within a very short time.

On Monday, the day before the descent, Phil spent most of his time floating silently in the cupola. Three days before, as Phoebe's two hour orbit brought it over the Moon's north pole, the Earth had been dead ahead. Now, the Earth was 36° to the left, the Moon had turned that amount below their orbit, and Phoebe's ground track - the line on the Moon's surface directly below it - was only 14° away from 50 West, the longitude of

Schröter's Valley. Every orbit brought them 28 Kilometres nearer to it, nearer to the alien key, and nearer to his lunar EVA.

At unpredictable moments during that long day, panic and nausea had gripped him, and he found himself clutching at the straps round the cupola window to steady his movements - and his nerves. On one occasion, he realised that Svetlana had come in. Smiling, she gently pressed a dampened and slightly scented cloth onto his forehead.

"Be calm, Major Phil," she said soothingly, holding him firmly by the forearm. She looked straight into his eyes. "Dave is the best pilot I know, and all you have to do is repeat what you did in vacuum chamber. Rob tells me you were one of best trainees he's had. You can do it. Now, relax."

Her eyes were wider than ever, and her body, floating next to him like a mermaid, was distraction enough. But her touch! The transformer-like hum started up again, but now, there was a tingle as well, like champagne in the veins.

They hung there in the cupola, gazing at each other. Phil's bout of nerves had left him. Now, there was something else.

The sound of Dave operating one of the galley drink dispensers brought a fleeting look of horror to Svetlana's face. She let go of Phil's arm and pushed herself across the room towards the hatch.

"Get me a pineapple juice please, Dave," she called nonchalantly. But as she floated through the hatchway, she turned towards Phil, a look of desperation on her face.

The tension between Phil and Svetlana during that evening meal was undeniable and debilitating. So much so, that Phil decided that once Svetlana returned after her shower, he would leave the cupola room immediately.

Once the meal was over and Svetlana had moved through into the habitation module, Phil went into the cupola room and selected a CD to listen to whilst they cleared up the galley. The Ravel - the one Svetlana had asked Dave to bring her - was the first to hand. He opened the player drawer, placed the CD inside, and pressed the play button. The drawer slid smoothly and effortlessly - almost sensually Phil thought - into its berth in the machine.

God help me. Even her CD player makes me feel sexy!

The unearthly sounds of the first movement of Daphnis et Chloé echoed through the space station as Phil went back to join Dave. Once they had finished clearing up, they drifted into the cupola room. Phil strapped himself onto one of the two seats, stretched out, listened to the music, and tried to relax.

"She needs to return to Earth," said Dave suddenly with feeling.

"Svetlana?"

"Of course. Who else. This is no life for a woman like her. Not to mention the bone mass loss ..."

"Because of the zero-g?"

"Absolutely, and she needs a proper home - not this." Dave looked glumly about him. "Not this lonely artificial world."

This was the first time Dave had ever touched even remotely on a subject which might be linked to emotion. Phil looked across at him, wide eyed.

"I'd like ... I ..." Dave started, but Svetlana came in at that moment.

As she drifted between them en-route to her favourite place - the cupola itself - the sight of her took Phil's breath away. As usual, and very obviously, she was bra-less, but she had changed into a black, body-hugging lycra one-piece number he had not seen before. It was armless, low backed, had legs like hot pants, and a very long front zip. The zipper was a short way down from the top. She looked absolutely ravishing.

Phil swallowed hard. She had obviously pulled out all the stops - but for whom?

It took a superhuman effort of will, but Phil decided to stick to his plan to leave the cupola room once Svetlana arrived. He forced a picture of Jo-Ann and the children into his mind, convinced himself to remain cool and unemotional, and drew his breath to speak. But as he did so, Dave, who was looking distinctly uncomfortable - almost as if he were trapped - began moving towards the hatch.

"Big day tomorrow. Going to turn in early. Good night folks."

Dave, what are you doing! screamed Phil to himself as Dave disappeared. Svetlana gazed despairingly after him and made as if to follow, but didn't. She stopped. She was between the two seats, alongside Phil.

There was an agonising pause, then the sound of the habitation hatch door closing. Svetlana's mouth opened slightly, and her tongue moved briefly over her lips. There was a look of hypnotic resignation on her face as she reached up, pressed the button which closed the cupola room hatch, then glided over to the cupola once more.

She was silhouetted against the starry background, and moving slowly up and down like a ship riding at anchor in a gentle swell. Outside, the unlit surface of the Moon, glowing mysteriously in the Earthlight, glided slowly past the window.

"This music," she said huskily. "Why did you choose it?"

Phil listened. The music had an atmospheric quality about it - almost mystical. He even though he heard what sounded like wind moaning through trees. Before he was able to form an answer, she moved a little closer.

"This is the most sensual ballet that Ravel ever wrote," she said. Her voice was trembling. "A hundred years ago, Diaghilev produced this in Paris, with Nijinski and Karsavina in the title roles. Can't you just imagine them?"

She closed her eyes, and began swaying her head slightly from side to side.

"Do you know anything about ballet, Major?"

"Not this one, I'm afraid." His body had started to hum again, but now, deep in his abdomen was a terrible yearning. He stared at Svetlana. She was drawing nearer and nearer.

"What is so beautiful about this - the Dawn Passage - is that at the end, Daphnis and Chloé make love," she said longingly. The fingers of her right hand began caressing her neck, and moving downwards.

Now, her body was very close, at the side of his chair as if she were kneeling by a bed. The smell of her filled his nostrils. She was taking long, deep breaths, which made her breasts rise and fall tantalisingly. The zipper of her body suit was, of its own accord, inching lower and lower. But then, still with her eyes closed, she raised her head slightly, took the zipper in her own hand, and slowly drew it all the way down.

Any lingering doubts Phil may have had regarding the morality of continuing left him completely. In response to this sublime enticement, he gave himself utterly to the insatiable demands of his body. Still loosely strapped to his seat, he reached out, and with both hands, pulled Svetlana's body suit down off her shoulders and arms. Her mouth flew open, she threw her head back and let out a long lustful sigh of delight and relief as - holding her by the waist to prevent her gliding away from him - he covered her breasts with kisses. She pulled herself towards him, and her eyes wild with passion, began tugging at his tracksuit and T-shirt to remove them. He in turn started to peel her body suit down over her hips. In the ensuing mêlée, he realised she had released the seat lap strap. Now, they were floating free, and gently tumbling towards the cupola. He still had his boxer shorts on, but other items of clothing were drifting away from him in all directions. At the window, Svetlana grabbed one of the loop straps and steadied their movements.

"Wait," she said, between breaths. She looked at him hungrily. "I know what we can do."

She bent down and slipped her bare left foot into one of the six loop straps round the cupola, then her right foot into the next one. With her feet well tethered, she reached up and gabbed the two opposite straps with her outstretched arms.

Phil was open mouthed as she presented herself to him. She was spread-eagled across the cupola, her firm proud breasts glistening slightly in the subdued light and her only garment now a diaphanous pair of panties which seemed to be joined at the hip with thin Velcro strips. He reached out to touch her, but found he was pushing himself away from her.

"Go behind. Lock your legs round mine," she said.

Phil obliged, and ended up clamped to her as if he were riding piggy-back. Her skin was soft and warm, and seemed to be aching to be stroked.

"Loosen my hair," she demanded as he began to kiss her neck. "I must be free. We must both be completely free."

Phil removed the band round her pony tail, and her hair fanned out like a halo, its softness on his cheeks and shoulders adding to the pleasure. He began to caress and run his fingers up and down her body with the virtuosity of a harpist during a solo performance.

"Completely free," Svetlana repeated, her eyes closing in anticipation. Phil reached down, unpeeled the two Velcro strips on her panties, and sent them floating across the room. Never before had the sound of Velcro evoked such exquisite anticipation, and never again, he thought, would he ever hear that sound without thinking of this moment. He unwrapped his legs and began to cover her with kisses. Svetlana moaned with pleasure as Phil, now with total abandon, moved around her like a dolphin, fondling, kissing and nuzzling her. He quivered as his fingertips explored her contours, and his tongue, fluttering over the gossamer hairs on her skin, tasted the nectarous sheen now covering her body. Never had he felt such exquisite pleasure during foreplay, as, unconstrained by gravity and unimpeded by contact with anything other than Svetlana's body, he discovered a freedom and potential for innovation unsurpassed in his experience.

"Yob menya. Yob menya," she implored hoarsely, as she gave herself completely to his voracious desires.

Phil, his loins near to bursting, and with an alacrity that surprised even himself, threw off his boxer shorts and pinioned himself to Svetlana. She gasped, her head jerking wildly and her hips thrusting forwards as he drove into her. She flailed furiously in her tethers and clamped herself round him like a limpet.

"Bozhe Moi! Bozhe Moi!" she howled, squirming and writhing like a snake. The room filled with the urgent and rhythmical chants of the ballet chorus as Phil pressed harder and harder. Then, as the music reached its climax, and with Svetlana screaming and shaking convulsively, he came to an explosive consummation as wave after wave of relief rippled through his body.

As their panting subsided, Svetlana removed her feet from the straps and wrapped her legs around him, then let go with her hands and closed him in her arms in a passionate embrace. They hung there, their bodies fused like Siamese twins, cocooned by the womb-like protection of the space station.

Phil woke to find Svetlana reaching behind him and undoing the knot in his tracksuit leggings that she had used to hold them together as they floated gently round the cabin. The front of their bodies remained in intimate contact as she slowly slid towards his legs. He opened his eyes momentarily. The silent Earth had moved about half its diameter leftwards since he had drifted into a blissful sleep. Near the lunar horizon, he could now make out the rim of the bright crater Aristarchus - next to which was Schröter's Valley, his destination.

Svetlana reached down and placed first his left, then his right foot through the cupola loop straps. Then, her hands sliding slowly up his legs, she moved until her head was next to his. Her tongue flitted briefly round his left ear before her lips came lightly to rest.

"My turn," she whispered, her right hand leaving him in no doubt as to her intentions.

Trance-like, Phil reached up, grasped the straps above his head, then closed his eyes.

From the sunless floor of Schroter's valley, Phoebe was well above the eastern horizon as it passed silently from north to south - a silvery dew-drop of life in the pitiless void of space.

9

A Walk in the Valley of Shadows

The tapping had a persistent urgency to it.

Phil turned towards the cupola windows. Outside, floating below the surface of an unfathomably deep ocean were Jo-Ann and the children. Nick and Tess were in their night clothes, but Jo-Ann was completely naked, her hair flowing listlessly around her face and stroking the outside of the window pane. She was desperately beating on the window and mouthing his name

Horrified, and consumed by guilt and remorse, he tried to move towards her, but his feet were trapped by invisible bonds. His left arm felt numb, but he could feel Svetlana's hands pulling him backwards by his right forearm.

"Come, Major Phil," she was saying. "Come with me. Come now!"

He opened his eyes, to find Svetlana had switched on the light in his sleep station. He was in his zip-up bag but his right arm was free. She was tapping on the concertina door and gently tugging on his arm to wake him up.

"Come quickly, Major," she said, smiling. "Your wife ... Video link from Houston. Not long before radio blackout. Come to comms room."

Clawing himself back to reality, he struggled to unzip the bag, drag on his tracksuit, and follow Svetlana through to the Command module. As he passed the galley, Dave's friendly face peered out.

"Morning, sleepy head! Svetlana said you'd stayed up a long time, so I thought I'd leave you as late as possible. Don't worry. Plenty of time."

Phil suppressed a nervous cough, blinked, rubbed his eyes, and tried to tidy his hair with his hand. He looked closely at Dave, who just smiled innocently back at him. *He has no idea!* he thought.

"Thanks Dave," he said, as guilt and apprehension at the prospect of facing his wife began to build.

In the seventeen years of their marriage, he had never been unfaithful. Sure, there had been moments of temptation -

especially during Jo-Ann's trips to America - but he never let it go further than the occasional fantasy. So what had happened last night? He needed time - time to come to terms with what he had done - time to construct a justification. But time was the very thing he did not have. He took a deep breath, tidied his collar, and pulled himself into the comms room.

Jo-Ann's anxious face filled the screen. Phil moved to a position in front of the tiny screen-top camera. After the three second delay for the signal's 480,000 mile round trip, her expression changed to one of relief.

"Oh hi, honey. I wanted to wish you good luck today." She leaned forwards slightly, and zoomed the picture out to show Nick and Tess next to her. "We're all rooting for you darling, aren't we, gang."

"Yeah!" cried Nick and Tess, their faces full of pride and joy.

"Good luck, Dad. I know you can do it," said Nick.

"We love you, Dad. Get back soon," said Tess, a tear coming to her eye.

They moved to one side, and Ted Beemish's face appeared.

"Good morning, Phil. We're in my office in Cheyenne by the way. NASA fixed us up with this patch through. Everything's fine here. Rob Klute says you've been brilliant. We have every confidence in you, but if you do hit any problems, do not, repeat do not, take any risks. Just follow the drill, and get back safe and sound."

He turned sideways and indicated to Jo-Ann to come back on camera.

"You have a wonderful wife and family here, Major. I am so sorry that I'm the one organising your separation from them. Believe me, we'll make it up to you when you get back."

He saluted, moved aside, and Jo-Ann reappeared.

"Are the others there?" she said. "I'd like to see them. We didn't speak for long but I really like Svetlana - so confident. Can I talk to Dave?"

Phil's feeling of dread vanished as he turned round. Dave and Svetlana were a short distance behind him. Svetlana, astutely, was holding Dave by the arm. She smiled broadly and moved him towards the camera.

“Hi there. Nice to meet you, Mrs Newheart,” said Dave. “Don’t worry. We won’t let you down. He’s in good hands.”

Svetlana gazed admiringly at Dave, smiled sweetly and nodded. True to form, Dave even blushed a little. Phil swallowed hard as a memory of the night’s activities came and went. Svetlana was unbelievably cool - so much so, he began to wonder whether he had dreamed the whole thing.

The others floated from the room, leaving him alone with Jo. It was the first time they had spoken to each other since September. As he gazed at her face, he knew exactly what his priorities were. Jo-Ann meant the world to him. Nothing, absolutely nothing was more important. Somehow, he would have to work something out. He was overcome with such a longing to be back with her, that he started to ache, and a lump came to his throat. He began to speak, but she had already started.

“Will you ever forgive me for the last two months, Phil? I’ve been a crazy idiot. I don’t want to lose you. I want you to know that. Oh God ...”

Her eyes were full of remorse. She reached forward. It looked as if she might be touching the screen with her hand.

“I can’t tell you how much I love you, Jo,” he said, choking back the tears. “When I get back, let me prove it.”

“I will, darling. I will,” she said.

She kissed her fingertips, held them up to the camera, then the screen went blank.

***

“Clear to undock, Dave. Five minutes to de-orbit,” came Svetlana’s clear and calm voice over Phil’s in-suit comms system.

Unlike Don’s LEV-2 descent to Alphonsus Base four days previously, Phil and Dave had spent the last three hours getting into and checking their lunar EVA suits, and preparing *Argus* - their Lunar Excursion Vehicle - for an immediate moonwalk once they landed. This would save precious time on the surface, and give them the maximum duration down there, before they had to return. *Argus’s* cockpit had already been evacuated of air, and they had connected their suits to the in-cabin oxygen supply. Once they landed, they could disconnect from the cabin supply, switch over to their portable units, open the air-lock doors, and exit without delay.

Since the video call, Phil's mind had been completely focused on the task ahead. He had run through the procedures so many times during simulator and SESL training, that now, they were second nature to him. His confidence in NASA, its people, and the equipment was absolute, and he was actually looking forward to his history-making excursion.

"Sealing LEV airlock doors," said Dave.

After a moment, two confirmatory green lights showed on the panel in front of them.

"Undocking."

There was a slight acceleration backwards, then completely silently, *Argus* floated away from Phoebe. After a few minutes, Dave adjusted the craft's attitude in preparation for the retro burn.

The Lunar Excursion Vehicles looked, in essence, like four-legged coffee tables. Instead of the table top, there were fuel tanks and two sets of main engines - one forward and one aft. From a large rectangular central section of this platform could be slung any one of a variety of modules, depending upon the task, and the craft could ferry these modules to and from the surface. Today, *Argus* was fitted with a personnel module, designed, if the need arose, to support a four man crew on the surface for over two weeks. The cockpit was a windowed compartment from which the pilot had a clear view of all four of the craft's spindly legs. In the cockpit's rear bulkhead, an air-tight hatch led to the living area. On the floor of the cockpit was another air-tight hatch leading to the airlock, a horizontal tube some six feet in diameter and length and with an air-tight external hatch four feet in diameter at its forward end. This airlock was used to enter and leave the craft when it was docked to Phoebe, and, by using a short ramp stowed outside it, as the ground exit and entrance when the LEV was parked on the lunar surface.

"De-orbit burn in five seconds," said Dave.

The main engines burst into life, and for the first time for four days, Phil was no longer weightless. It was only a 1g burn, but it felt much more. He had got used to zero-g.

When the engines stopped, whilst the weightlessness felt the same as before, Phil knew that this time, the 'free-fall' really did mean they were falling. They were plummeting towards the lunar surface at an ever-increasing speed, and although he knew that this was the most efficient method - in terms of fuel use - to achieve the descent, he could not shake off the disturbing feeling that they were in a lift whose rope had broken.

Dave had elected to use a 'head-up' approach. This meant that as they sat one behind the other in their forward-facing seats and approached the lunar surface, they were flying feet-first with the Moon below their backs. In that attitude, Dave, but not Phil, could just see the lunar horizon low down ahead of him. However, near the end of the descent burn, the craft would slowly pitch forwards, providing an ever-improving view of the terrain below. The final phase - hovering and selecting a landing site - was done with the craft in horizontal, touch-down mode.

"Good luck boys," called Svetlana over the radio. "And don't forget my postcard, Dave! Switching you to Mission Control now."

On cue, the familiar and almost disconcertingly calm voice of Keith Smith - their CapCom for the lunar sortie - crackled into their headsets.

"Looks like a nice night for a stroll," he said. "Argus, we have you on the nose and looking good. As for your illumination, you've probably noticed, there's not much cloud over the Pacific today. We have an albedo of 0.31 for you. Not ideal, but not bad."

As they were landing in the lunar night, their only light source - Earthlight - was important. CapCom was letting them know how bright it was going to be.

"Any last minute update on the landing zone rock distribution?" said Dave.

"Sorry Dave," came the reply three seconds later. "You'll have to rely on the Mark 1 eyeball. The photos you've been working with are still the best we've got."

"Ready for the burn?" said Dave, twisting round and glancing reassuringly at Phil. "Don't forget, as we approach touchdown, keep your chest strap tight and your helmet resting on the back of the seat. Don't move. I've got to see what I'm doing."

"Don't worry. I'll probably have my eyes closed!" said Phil.

Once the descent burn started, and Phil began to see the lunar surface, things happened very quickly. They seemed to be travelling at breakneck speed, and very low. In the far distance was the relatively featureless expanse of the Ocean of Storms, and just rising into view on its near edge, the spectacular terraced walls of the Aristarchus crater. It looked as if a gigantic yellow snowball had been flung down onto a slab of plasticized pumice. The clarity, contrast, detail, and range of colours visible from this height were even more impressive than from orbit. The immediate foreground - the mountainous area north of Herodotus, and their destination, Schröter's Valley - was below Phil's line of vision. But it was obvious that Dave could see them.

"Oh boy! That valley is something else," he exclaimed. "Look at those terraces in Aristarchus. Yankee Stadium - eat your heart out!"

Mission Design at Houston had pre-set the descent control computer to bring the craft to rest - hovering within the valley - 1500 feet below the level of the plain across which the valley was gouged. Even that far down into it, there would still be a further 1400 feet to descend before they reached the valley floor. Half a mile above the north rim of the valley, and with a descent rate of 250 mph, they reached pitchover point. This was when the LEV, having killed almost all its orbital velocity, pitched forwards. As it did so, Phil saw the horizon rise rapidly up the windows, and suddenly he had a panoramic view of the surrounding terrain. At the same time, the LEV, still travelling downwards at over 180 mph, dropped below the level of the surrounding plain, and into the valley proper. Although he had seen this in the simulations, the real thing was absolutely terrifying. The valley seemed to close around them like a shroud, and the precipitous cliffs looked like the inexorably-closing jaws of some gigantic car crusher. Ten seconds after that, the LEV came automatically to rest, holding steady at 1400 feet.

"I got the peanut!" exclaimed Dave. "Clear as a bell. Straight down the line."

Phil peered briefly past Dave. Sure enough, near the bottom of the south wall of the valley was the unmistakable shape of Peanut Rock, christened when they first spotted it on the photo in Houston.

"You're Go at six minutes," came CapCom's calm voice from Houston.

"Okay Phil. Give me the readings," said Dave.

Whilst Dave had a head-up display of their altitude and rate of descent, this was the moment when Phil had to continuously feed him with three sets of data. Argus was fitted with a standard transceiving radio direction-finder, and this had been tuned to the response frequency of the key - 957.092 MHz. This had been switched on before the burn, and was already providing Phil with a display of the key's direction with respect to the front of the LEV, and its range in feet. The third item Dave wanted was the percentage remaining of the fuel allocated to hovering and landing.

"Nine right. 2500. 98 percent," called Phil.

"Argus. You're go for landing," crackled CapCom.

Phil felt the craft turning, and moving downwards and forwards.

"On the nose. 2300. 94 percent."

As the craft descended, Phil was able to snatch a brief glimpse out of the window. The terrain ahead of them, at the foot of the daunting south wall of the canyon was far more rock-strewn than he had imagined.

"Two left. 2000. 89 percent."

"Don't like the look of those boulders," said Dave warily.

As he brought the LEV lower and lower, he was also moving it sideways, to gain a different perspective of the ground ahead.

"Five right. 1500. 75 percent."

"We have you at 500 feet," said CapCom.

At that moment, to Phil's dismay, the response from the transceiver flickered, then showed an error condition. He knew it would do this if it received conflicting signals.

"I've lost the signal!" he cried. "Null. Null. 70 percent!"

"It's those goddamn rocks!" called Dave.

The LEV rose and tracked to the left. The signal returned.

"Ten right. 1400. 60 percent."

"We have you at 600 feet," said CapCom, the merest hint of surprise in his voice. "Do you have a problem, Argus?"

"There are hells great rocks all over the place!" said Dave, his voice rising slightly. "We'll be lucky to find a clear spot."

"Fifteen right. 1350. 50 percent." said Phil, trying to stay calm.

"I think we have a place over to the right," said Dave. The LEV moved rightwards and down.

"Thirty left. 1300. 40 percent."

"Forget the direction readings Phil," said Dave. "It's there or nowhere. But keep going on the fuel."

"We have you at 100 feet," said CapCom.

Phil continued watching his display. The direction increased dramatically to the left and continued blinking on and off as Dave headed the craft westwards along the valley. The key was obviously appearing and disappearing behind the forest of boulders littering the valley floor.

"Twenty percent, Dave!" called Phil.

Ahead of them and to the left, Phil saw a relatively clear area. As Dave turned the LEV to make his final approach, Phil's display gave a range of 1200 feet. The fuel was now critical.

"Ten percent fuel!"

"Altitude 50 feet," came CapCom.

"Some dust," said Dave.

He was now turning his head frantically, checking that all four legs of the LEV were going to avoid the boulders, and that no large obstruction was in danger of fouling the pilot cabin and exit hatch. He had to rotate the craft about a vertical axis to achieve this, descending as he did so. Dust began spraying in all directions from the down draft of the powerful engines.

"Five percent fuel."

Another minor rotation. Still hovering.

"Three percent!"

The LEV shuddered slightly as, in almost perfect unison, all four legs touched down. Simultaneously, four green lights flashed on the panel in front of Dave.

"Touchdown!" he said, thankfully.

The LEV settled gracefully and firmly onto the lunar surface. Then there was silence.

"Okay Houston, Argus has landed!" said Dave. The relief in his voice was all too obvious.

Phil checked the fuel gauge readout. They had made it with two percent spare.

***

Phil, his pulse thumping in his ears, stepped off the end of the ramp leading down from the LEV, and onto the Moon.

In front of him towered the 2900 foot ramparts of the south wall of Schröter's Valley. To his left and right, and uncannily clear in the airless void, the valley curved quickly over the unfamiliarly near horizon. High above him, near the top of the wall, there were rough areas in the rock face, confirming the source of the hundreds of rocks and boulders now strewn across the gradually rising ground at the foot of the wall. In an unfathomably black sky above the wall to his left hung the Earth, a nearly-full disc of blue and white, contrasting starkly with the magnificent desolation all around him. The boulders in that direction were dark and menacing, and cast long black shadows towards him across the ghostly-grey surface. They looked like tombstones in a moonlit graveyard.

Dave's voice came over his headset. "You okay, Phil?" he said.

"Yes. I'm okay," he replied. "Just can't quite take it in. It has a terrifying grandeur. So pure, yet so lifeless."

"We oughta move," said Dave. "I can see Peanut Rock way over to the left there - and look, there're the marks down the wall where it fell."

Phil gazed up at the wall in awe, and recalled when he first saw those marks, and how he felt at the time. Now, it was for real.

"We got a four hundred yard walk," Dave continued. "Shouldn't be too bad. You lead the way, Phil. I'll be with you, on your right and ten paces behind you."

This was the configuration they had pre-planned. Phil would set off, using his hand-held transceiver to guide his direction, and Dave would follow in such a position that he could see where Phil was about to walk, and double-check he wasn't heading into anything untoward. Dave's transceiver was to be used only as a back-up, or as a cross-reference to Phil's.

Phil unhooked the device from his waist belt, turned it on and held it out in front of him, turning slowly as he did so, but the reflections from the rocks caused the heading reading to keep changing.

"Don't have a clear heading," he said, "But the best signal is in this direction."

"We know it's near Peanut Rock," said Dave. "Let's just walk in that direction and try later."

They set off together, taking long bounding strides, like adjacent horses on a carousel. As they got nearer to their destination - and nearer to the foot of the wall - the number and size of the rocks increased. Now, they were wending their way through a veritable forest of boulders, some well over ten feet high, and the way ahead was by no means obvious. They lost sight of Peanut Rock, but kept going towards the foot of the line of gouge marks. Every fifty yards or so, they stopped and checked out the signal. It was getting stronger, nearer.

As they walked, they hardly spoke. Neither he nor Dave had any idea of exactly where the key would be, or what else they might find when they got to it. Phil found himself checking the shadows in response to the uncanny feeling that from behind this rock or that, something was watching him. Occasionally he could not prevent himself instinctively stopping, looking, and even listening, even though he knew perfectly well that there was no such thing as sound in the vacuum that surrounded them.

Eventually, with the transceiver registering a distance of 200 feet, they emerged into a relatively clear area. Straight ahead of them was Peanut rock, and about sixty feet to its right, a structure. Both men stopped dead in their tracks.

"My God! It really is here," said Dave.

CapCom's voice came over the headsets. "Have you located the item?" There was a firm emphasis on the word 'item'.

"Affirmative," said Dave, in disbelief.

In front of them were three slender poles standing some 15 feet high and about thirty feet apart, arranged in a triangular formation. At the top of each pole was a jet black sphere about two feet in diameter. The spheres were so black, that the only way Phil could see them at all was because they eclipsed the stars behind them. At the centre of the triangle was a raised circular platform less than a foot high, on which stood a four foot high fluted pillar. And sitting on the top of this pillar, was the key.

Both men stood in silence, awed.

Phil had often imagined how he would feel when this moment came, and reverence had not occurred to him. But knowing he was looking at something that had been constructed by an alien civilisation - undoubtedly far in advance of humanity - brought home to him that he was probably in the presence of an entity, a 'Knowledge Force', beyond his comprehension.

"Moving in," he said, as almost trance-like, he walked slowly forwards. He stopped in the shadow thrown by the nearest pole and looked up at it. The Earth was behind the sphere at its top, and he found himself wondering whether the ease with which this alien device could blot out his entire planet was an omen.

Dave was standing some twenty yards behind him, and filming. Phil could also hear him attempting to describe the scene to Mission Control. The voice communications between Houston and themselves were scrambled, but he still had to be careful what was said.

"I don't think you should come any closer," said Phil. "If those spheres do what I think they do, they'll scan anybody who walks between them, and it has to be me."

"Don't you worry," said Dave. "I ain't going anywhere near the things!"

"About to retrieve the item," said Phil. He could not bare the suspense any longer. "Starting the count transmission."

He pressed a button on his transceiver, then hooked it back onto his belt. The button switched it over from its 957.092 transceive mode, to a pulsed transmit on another frequency. This would be received by Dave's instrument, and checked for any transmission freezes.

He slowly walked into the triangle formed by the poles, but felt nothing. He was now standing next to the raised platform. The drama and majesty of the setting, the dais, and the overwhelming feeling of humility he was experiencing, made him feel as if he was approaching a throne or an altar. Gently, he stepped onto the platform and walked to the pillar. The key was as expected, a hexagonal object about as long as the hole in the door. On one end, was a handle. He had no idea how heavy it was going to be, or whether something would stop him lifting it off its pillar. His mouth was dry, and he could feel his hands shaking. He raised his right arm, extended his gloved hand towards the key, and touched it lightly. There was the merest hint of a tingle in his fingers - not unlike the feeling when he put his hands into the palm places on the door, but nothing like as strong. He looked up at the Earth, and wondered whether this view would be his last, then, instinctively holding his breath, grasped the handle and lifted.

To his surprise, the key was remarkably light. He was easily able to hold it out in front of him with one hand. He turned round without lowering it, stepped off the dais and walked out of the triangle.

"Let's keep going!" he said, relieved.

The two men stopped at the edge of the rock clearing. Dave regarded the key with fascination and suspicion, then gingerly took it from Phil and placed it in the special bio-barrier container fixed to the top of Phil's back-pack, and sealed it closed.

"Item successfully retrieved," reported Dave to Houston. "No apparent problems."

"Congratulations Argus," replied CapCom. Phil could hear cheers and clapping in the background from Mission Control.

"Were the pulsed transmissions continuous?" said Phil to Dave.

"No, they weren't. Fact is, as you walked between the poles, you and the signals stopped dead for two seconds then continued. Wouldn't have believed it if I hadn't seen it with my own eyes. Never seen nothin' like it in my life before. Weirdest thing."

"Same as by the door then. Seems as if they checked me, just like Nick said they would," said Phil. An image of Jo-Ann and the children came into his mind, emphasising the awful loneliness he was now feeling.

They headed back to the LEV, following their tracks in the lifeless dust.

Back at the spacecraft, they transferred the key container to its assigned locker, and stowed the transceivers. The whole operation had been completed in only just over one hour. This was too long to give them time to lift off and dock with Phoebe on the orbit following the one from which they had descended, but they would be able to see it fly over, some 28 Kilometres to their east in about twenty minutes. Dave prepared *Argus* for launch, setting the ascent computer into auto-ascent mode, and keying in the orbit number of the orbit with which they were to rendezvous. This would be the overpass orbit - the one where Phoebe passed directly overhead - and would therefore be the one which used the least fuel for the ascent. The computer displayed the time to launch - 1 hr 55 minutes.

"We've got time for another sortie," said Dave. "Might as well utilise the time. We should take a few more shots of those pole things, and collect some rock samples and stuff from around the area. Never know what we might find. That okay with you Phil?"

Whilst Phil did not relish the prospect of remaining on this lifeless world for one moment longer than necessary, it was pointless wasting time just sitting doing nothing for nearly two hours. And now the goal of the mission was accomplished, perhaps he might enjoy a stroll.

"Okay," he said, "But let's make sure we do get back in plenty of time. I don't fancy yet another two hours stuck here."

"We need to be back here in one and a half hours. That's plenty of time," said Dave. "I gotta see those things again, and anyway, saw some good stuff near the base of some of the boulders at the edge of the clearing."

Dave checked with Mission Control, picked up some sample containers and an arm-extender, and led the way outside once more.

"Phoebe should be passing over any minute," he said excitedly. "Let's see if we can see her."

They scanned the sky to the north-east. Right on schedule, a faint star rose and tracked silently across it, just visible in the comparatively faint Earthlight.

"We can see you!" called Dave over the ground-to-station radio link.

"Come home soon," replied Svetlana. "It's lonely up here."

"Be with you in two hours," said Dave. "Have that coffee brewing!"

They stood staring at the receding point of light until it disappeared behind the south wall of the canyon. Once its signal cut off, Dave turned his helmeted head towards Phil.

"What a woman. When this thing's over, I'm going to ask Svetlana to marry me," he said.

The unexpectedness of this announcement rendered Phil speechless.

"Do you think she'll have me?" Dave continued.

"Good God, man! Are you blind? She couldn't have made it any plainer. Why the hell haven't you asked her before?" Phil's irritation was unsuppressible. If it had been him ...

Dave gazed up at the Earth.

"Had a girl back in Shelby. Beautiful thing. Came on strong, just like Svetlana. Even got me to the altar. Trouble is, she didn't get herself there. Didn't want that to happen again. Couldn't bear it."

Phil closed his eyes. He felt sick inside.

"I'm so sorry, Dave."

"Got to stay in control this time. *I* ask *her*, when I'm ready. What d'you reckon?"

Phil clenched his fist and prodded Dave on his bulky forearm.

"Just go for it, Rocky, and good luck to you - and the sooner the better. I would." The advice was not altogether altruistic. Phil could not bear the thought of another ten days with Svetlana unreined.

"I will," said Dave, assertively. "I will."

They set off once more, two tiny capsules of life in a bone-chilling airless desert. Phil followed Dave this time. On each step forwards, a spray of fine dust flew backwards from Dave's boots.

At the edge of the rock clearing, they stopped, then walked all the way round it, taking photos and searching for footprints or other evidence of the aliens. They found nothing, nor did they find any clue as to how the structure got there. After a while, Dave's interest reverted to his speciality. He had brought a flashlight, and seemed to be particularly fascinated by the ground round the bases of the boulders. His arm extender was a three foot long device which allowed him to pick up small rocks up to about eight inches across without the inconvenience of bending down. It was a bit like the sort of thing litter collectors use in parks. Dave started using it to collect samples from round the base of the boulders.

"These areas are special," he explained. "They're protected from sunlight and micro-meteorites, and haven't been covered by dust like in the open places. See how much deeper and darker the colours are down in there."

Phil looked, and mumbled courteous responses, but was more concerned with their proximity to the alien poles, standing there like sentinels in the ghostly light.

Dave moved nimbly from place to place, shining his flashlight and inserting his arm-extender into otherwise inaccessible places, and wowing every now and again as he did so. Phil gave up following him like a shadow, and took the opportunity of collecting three small rocks for Jo-Ann and the children, then stood at the edge of the clearing watching Dave moving from boulder to boulder. It was when he was under an overhanging portion of a rather tall one that he found a prize specimen.

"Oh boy! Get that!" he cried. "Orange rocks!"

From his vantage point some fifty feet away, Phil saw Dave grab hold of one of the rocks using the arm-extender, but the rock was caught between the boulder and the ground below it. He held on, moved to one side, and twisted and jerked the rock out from its hiding place. As he removed it from the steel jaws of the arm-extender and began studying it closely, another movement caught Phil's eye. A delicate stream of dust had begun to trickle from the top of the boulder. The boulder itself was beginning to topple. Even in one sixth g, it probably weighed several tons.

"Dave! Dave!" he cried, "The boulder's moving. Get out of there!"

Dave was standing right under the thing. He looked up at it and began to turn to move away, but slipped and fell onto his back. In agonising slow-motion, the massive boulder began to fall.

"Get up Dave! For God's sake!" shouted Phil into his microphone as he started running towards him. "Roll away. Roll away to your right!"

But Dave was like an upturned beetle. He could certainly get up from such a position, but not in the time available. He put his left hand out to push himself rightwards, but as he did so, the boulder landed on his left leg and arm. Phil heard an agonising scream come over his headset, then saw the boulder roll back slightly and come to rest. He got to Dave a second or so afterwards, and dropped down onto his knees next to him. His left leg was free, but the lower part of it was pointing at a crazy angle out to the side. His left hand was still trapped by the boulder. Dave continued to scream in agony.

"Oh God! Oh God! My leg. Oh God help me! Is the suit okay?" he gasped frantically.

Phil grabbed the flashlight and closely examined the suit. It was still inflated, indicating the pressure was being maintained. He checked the pressure gauge just above Dave's right wrist. It was reading normal.

"The suit's okay Dave," he said, trying not to convey the feeling of panic and utter hopelessness which was beginning to seize him. He looked around instinctively, as if to shout to someone to call an ambulance, but of course, there was nobody there.

"What's happening, Argus?" came CapCom.

"An accident!" panted Phil. "Boulder rolled onto Dave. Wait."

Dave's left elbow started to move, and at the same time he let out a series of agonised coughing gasps.

"My left hand!" he said. "I can't move it."

Phil shone the flashlight into the crevice formed by the boulder and the ground. The boulder had split the sealing ring between the lower end of the arm and the glove. The Mark IV suits were fitted with a 'Wrist Dam' which prevented the air from the suit escaping if you lost a glove. That way, you only lost your hand - not your life. Phil could see Dave's wrist exposed in the gap. The now distorted glove ring was trapped under the boulder but the rest of the glove looked as if it could be free. As he examined it, he could see Dave's wrist beginning to swell, as the pressure of blood inside it attempted to break out into the surrounding vacuum. He reached into the crevice and tried to pull the glove out, but it was stuck solid. Dave's wrist was turning a deep shade of red and swelling more and more. Phil took hold of Dave's elbow and moved it, and as he did so, his hand began to move out of the trapped glove. Phil had to act quickly. If he left the hand in the glove, it would offer some protection from the intense cold, but the hand would continue to swell, possibly so much as to prevent its removal from the glove. If that happened, Dave would be trapped indefinitely by his hand.

It's your hand or your life, thought Phil, as he gently coaxed Dave's hand out of the glove and into the pitiless freezing vacuum.

Phil shone the flashlight through Dave's visor. His eyes were wide with horror and his face was contorted with agony.

"You're going to be okay, Dave, but don't move your left hand or fingers," said Phil, as he slipped a polythene collection bag over the now hideously distended hand. He repeated the procedure with two more bags, sealing them with rubber bands. He then knelt next to Dave, and shone the flashlight into his own face so Dave would see him.

"I'm going to have a word with Houston," he said. "I'm switching off your comms so you're not bothered by all the detailed stuff."

He didn't give Dave a chance to reply; he just flipped the switches on Dave's comms module. Phil could feel himself starting to shake with fear. He was breathing fast and a yawning pit was opening up in his stomach.

"Don't worry Phil," said the ever calm voice of CapCom. "We'll get you out of there. Now, what exactly is your status?"

Phil explained about Dave's broken leg and lost left glove.

"O2?" said CapCom.

The gauges on both suits read 5.4 hours. Phil gave this and other information requested by Houston. After what seemed an eternity, CapCom's confident voice came over his headset.

"Okay Phil," he said. "This is what we're going to do. The arm extender still there?"

Phil looked around. It was there, lying near to Dave and slightly bent.

"Got it."

"You're going to have to improvise, and use that as a splint," said CapCom. "You know from training, that there's no way you're going to be able to carry him, but so long as he stays conscious and has a good leg, he should make it with your help. But it's no good trying to move him without immobilising the fracture. He wouldn't make it ten yards. You're going to have to fetch the duck tape from the LEV, fix the splint, then help Dave back. Now, time you do all that, you're going to miss the deadline for the overpass orbit rendezvous, but don't worry. You got another orbit spare."

"But we landed two orbits ahead of the overpass orbit," said Phil. "I thought we could go for two orbits after it in an emergency - not just one."

"Well, theoretically," replied CapCom, "But to achieve that would use up every drop of fuel you've got left. There'd be no leeway. We can't afford to take that chance. No. You have to go for overpass plus one. You've got well over two hours, and plenty of oxygen. Now, reckon you can do all that, Phil?"

"Sure. The sooner the better."

"Good man. Now for Phoebe. We'll liaise with Svetlana. We'll go through all the reception procedures with her, so when you arrive she'll be all geared up. And finally, all communications will be through myself unless direct comms to her would help. Okay?"

"Okay. I'm going to switch Dave on again. You keep talking to him won't you, once I go."

He switched Dave's comms back on, quickly explained the plan to him, patted him on the right arm, and set off towards the LEV. As he threaded his way along the now familiar route, he found his fear beginning to be replaced with a determination to get himself, and Dave, back up to *Argus* safely.

After all, if he didn't do it, nobody else was going to do it for him.

As he made his way back across the lifeless moonscape towards Dave, he looked up at the Earth. The Americas were slipping round the right hand limb, and the vast blue Pacific glistened in the sunlight. Australia's east coast was just emerging from the darkness. In Cairns, he thought, people will be taking their morning swims in the warm wet softness of the ocean.

He had been talking to Dave over the radio the whole time, keeping him in touch with what was going on. Dave hardly replied, but Phil knew he was okay because Mission Control were monitoring both men's condition on the bio-telemetry channel.

When he got to him, he knelt down and peered into his helmet. Dave's eyes looked back at him, appealing. He was utterly helpless, like a wounded animal caught in a trap.

"Going to tape up your leg now Dave," he said.

The job wasn't easy. For a start, the tape would not stick to the outside of Dave's suit - it was too dusty. He had to wrap the tape round and round the leg and improvised splint, making sure he did not raise more dust. Every movement brought gasps and winces from his patient. He also managed to tape Dave's left wrist to a fixing loop on his waist belt. As he did that, he noticed that the polythene bags he had put over Dave's hand were white and frosted inside, as if they had just come out of a freezer. Phil checked the countdown timer display on his chest-mounted service pack. One hour twenty eight minutes before launch. Four hundred yards to walk. He got down on his knees to Dave's right.

"Okay big fella," he said. "Time to get going."

To the most tortured cries of agony Phil had ever heard, he got Dave to a standing position, his right arm looped over Phil's shoulder, and Phil's left hand grasping - as well as the bulky suit would allow - Dave's right upper arm.

"Can't move," cried Dave.

"You've got to move," said Phil. "Think of Svetlana. She's up there waiting for you. Now ready. Move!"

Dave leaned forward and into Phil, and managed a one-foot hop, then screamed in agony as the vibration shuddered through his smashed leg.

"BP 100 over 60. Pulse 150 and rising," said CapCom quietly to Phil. "If the fracture is compound, he may be losing blood from it into the leg of his suit. Keep him going."

"Painkillers in the LEV, Dave," said Phil. "Not too far to get there, then you'll be fine. Come on. Another step."

Dave managed another hop, then another.

"That's great, Dave," said Phil. "You've got a good rhythm going. Now keep at it."

With agonising slowness, they continued forwards. Three yards, four, five, ten. Phil could hear Dave's laboured breathing between the cries. At each step, Dave wanted to stop, but Phil forced him onwards.

Silently, Phoebe sailed above them on its overpass orbit. Svetlana's soothing voice came over their headsets.

"I'm all ready for you up here, Dave," she said. "We'll have you fixed up in no time.

"Her voice was calm and authoritative. There was not the merest hint of the helplessness she must have been feeling.

"What is your estimate of the distance covered?" asked CapCom, about twenty minutes after they started walking.

Phil looked around. The fallen boulder was less than fifty yards behind him - the LEV, at least 300 yards ahead. He checked his timer - exactly one hour to launch. He knew what Houston was thinking.

"I'm not answering that," he said. "We're going to make it. We *have* to make it."

"BP 80 over 45. Pulse 180 and rising," said CapCom.

Phil unhooked his flashlight and shone it into at Dave's face. It had turned a ghastly pallid white colour, and his eyelids were nearly closed. *Oh God, don't pass out on me*, he said to himself as he gave another great heave upwards on Dave's arm.

"You're going to make it, Dave," he urged, and started humming 'Ho, heave, ho' from the Volga Boat Song - he couldn't think of anything more appropriate. "Come on Dave. Hum along! Hum, damn you!"

Dave's feeble voice came over Phil's headset. He was panting, and his teeth were chattering.

"Tell her, Phil. Tell Svetlana I love her."

It was shortly after that, that Dave went limp and his right leg gave way under him. Phil held firm and shouted into his mouthpiece, but when he looked at Dave's face, his eyes were closed and his head was slumped forward, resting on the inner visor.

"He's passed out!" gasped Phil to Mission Control. "He's not going to die is he? Oh God, don't let him die!"

"BP steady at 80 over 40. Pulse 200. Breathing rapid and shallow," said CapCom as calmly as he could. "No he isn't gonna die, Phil. He's just unconscious."

Phil tried desperately to keep Dave on his feet. He had the idea that despite what they had told him back in Houston, he could carry or even drag him back to the LEV. After all, on the Moon, he only weighed 60lbs. He wouldn't be able to carry him in his arms - he knew that - but what about across his shoulders? He tried bending down and pulling the now totally limp body up over his back pack, but the bulkiness and awkwardness of both suits prevented it.

"What are you doing?" asked Houston. "Your pulse and breathing are way over the top. Phil, whatever it is, the suit won't take it."

Phil was too breathless to reply. After one final superhuman effort, he had to lower Dave to the ground. He dropped to his knees, gasping for breath, and cradled Dave's helmeted head in his arms. With his mind in an agony of despair, he gazed up at the Earth, hanging there so sweet and beautiful, then looked round at the hostile world about him. It was as if ghostly fingers were reaching out of the shadows, and wrapping themselves around him, pulling, pulling him down and chaining him to the barren dead ground. He staggered to his feet, grabbed hold of Dave's right arm and tried to drag him, but it was impossible. The bulky back-pack just dug into the all-enveloping lunar dust.

Phil raised his head to the pitiless sky, and let out a scream as the awful truth about his situation overwhelmed him.

There was no way his pilot was going to make it back to the LEV.

10

The Breath of Life

Stan Silverman, NASA's Administrator, drummed his fingers nervously on his desk and waited. He hated being put on hold, but for this call to the Pentagon, he had no choice.

"The Secretary of Defense is at the White House, Mr Silverman," came the authoritative voice of Rod Straker's personal assistant. "I don't think I can disturb him."

"He needs to hear this immediately," said Silverman firmly. "Tell him I have grave concerns about a particular item."

"An item, Sir?"

"An item."

There was a long pause, then Straker's gritty voice came over the phone.

"Stan. Rod Straker. What you got?".

"Secretary Straker, we have the item on board the Lunar Excursion Vehicle but they haven't been able to lift off. There's a problem." There was a hint of an echo on the line, as if the phone was on speaker at the other end.

"Oh yeah? What's up? Newheart better be okay."

"Yes he's fine, Sir. But Dave Gentry, the LEV pilot has broken his leg."

"What!"

"And we think he's probably going to lose a hand."

"Shit! How the hell did that happen, or can't you tell me?"

"Nothing sinister - just an unfortunate accident. Trouble is, Gentry's passed out."

"Jesus, Stan! How're they goin' to get back? Can Newheart fly the thing?"

"Argus can fly itself, Sir. No, problem is that right now, they're over three hundred yards from the spacecraft. Newheart's trying to get Gentry back there."

"What are the deadlines? Is this putting Newheart's own return at risk?"

“If he doesn’t get Gentry back to the LEV within about six hours, Gentry will die through lack of oxygen. But whatever happens to him, if they don’t get back within three hours, the LEV will miss its last chance to rendezvous with Phoebe. They’ll have to stay on the surface for the next two weeks.”

There was a pause. Silverman heard Straker close his hand over the mouthpiece, then a muffled conversation. Straker came back on.

“What are Gentry’s chances of surviving his injuries if he’s stuck in the LEV for two weeks? I mean, doesn’t he need to be up on Phoebe?”

“Difficult to say. Not good.”

“So if Newheart doesn’t get him to the LEV in time for lift-off, he’s probably going to die anyway.”

“I didn’t say that, Sir.”

“I know you didn’t. I’m saying it. Newheart has *got* to make that rendezvous, with or without Gentry. Do you understand what I’m saying?”

“Are you trying to tell me that this ... item is more important than the life of one of my astronauts?”

“I am saying, Stan, that this decision is not up to you. It’s a matter of national security, and that’s my business ... and of course, the President.”

Silverman pulled out the handkerchief from his breast pocket and began to wipe his brow. A different and familiar voice came on the phone.

“Mr Silverman, oblige us. Get Newheart back NOW.” It was the President.

***

“Phil.” CapCom’s voice crackled once more into his headset. “You’re going to be okay. We’re going to get you back home.”

There was something missing. Something sinister in CapCom’s matter-of-fact tone. Something unsaid.

“But what about Dave!” said Phil, bending down to the helpless figure of his friend lying at his feet. “How am I going to get him to the LEV? Who’s going to fly it?”

"You are, Phil," said CapCom. "The LEV's all fired up and ready to go. All you've got to do is confirm a couple of commands on the console, and flip a few switches. Argus will get itself back to Phoebe."

"And Dave?" said Phil once more, the terrible truth beginning to dawn.

"Phil," said CapCom, "You only got fifty yards in half an hour when Dave was conscious. You've got another three hundred to go at least. You can't do it. Even if you could drag him, which we know you can't, you aren't going to get him there in time."

Phil was frantic. They hadn't said it yet, but Houston was telling him to leave Dave behind.

"I *can't* Keith," said Phil. "What about Don? What about LEV-2?"

"Do you think we haven't explored every possibility. Don could get over to you, but not before you had to lift off, and then he'd be stuck too - not enough fuel. He'd have to be there now. There simply isn't time. You're going to have to go."

CapCom sounded near to breaking point. "Phil. You're going to have to leave Dave."

Phil closed his eyes. Tears were beginning to form and run down his cheeks. He could taste the salt as he licked them from the corners of his mouth, but he couldn't wipe them away.

The torment between the instinctive need to save his own life, and the overpowering desire to help Dave began tearing him apart. He thought back to the crash in which his father had died, and how he, but not his brother Nick, had escaped death. This was surely the day of judgement, the day that he would pay for not being on that aircraft. Even if he died in the attempt, he had to try to get Dave back to safety. At least this way, he could expunge the guilt he had carried for so many years. Somehow, some way, he had got to do it.

"I won't" he said, his voice charged with determination. "I will not leave Dave. There's still one more orbit."

"Phil," said CapCom. "Listen to me. Overpass plus two is a negative. Repeat, negative. We have to balance the priorities against the risks."

"Bollocks!" replied Phil. "*I'm* the one who's down here, and I'm telling you that I will not leave Dave. I know I can make it."

There was an unusually long silence from Houston, then CapCom came back to him.

"I have the Secretary of Defense on a direct link from Washington. He wants to talk to you."

There were some clicks, then a strong cultured voice came over.

"Major Newheart. Phil." The tone was ingratiating and supplicatory. "Secretary of Defense Straker here. I want to thank you for what you have done for America, for the world. But your primary responsibility now is to ensure that you, and the item, get back to Earth safely. Nothing is more important. The life of one man, however much we honour and respect him, is of minimal importance compared with your mission. I know you feel loyal towards him. I know you see yourself as his only hope for survival. But the future of the entire world may also be in your hands. You must think of the greater issue. Return to the LEV now."

Whilst being perfectly logical, Straker's appeal was not having the desired effect on Phil - in fact quite the opposite. After years of devotion to logic and a respect for authority, Phil realised that right now, he wanted - no *needed* - to defy both. Strangely, instead of feeling guilty about doing so, he was actually getting a thrill from it. As Straker was speaking, Phil could feel himself being galvanised into action. Until all hope was gone, all options exhausted, he was going to try to save Dave.

"With respect, Secretary Straker," he replied, "The item is not posing a threat to humanity, but leaving Dave Gentry behind when there is still a chance to save him is inhuman, and something I cannot comply with."

"Major!" demanded Straker, "May I remind you that you come under my direct command. I now order you to return to the LEV."

"And may I remind you, Mr Straker, that the Moon is non-terrestrial territory, and does not come under the jurisdiction of the USA. Your authority does not extend to here, and it certainly does not permit you to play God. I shall continue to try to save Dave Gentry until the last possible moment. Now please, clear this channel and leave me to get on with it."

He was breathing hard, but the buzz he was getting from the encounter was strangely exhilarating.

There were some further clicks, then CapCom's familiar voice came back.

"I hope you know what you're doing, Phil," he said.

"The LEV won't take off until I command it to will it?"

"Impossible. Whatever it's set to now or at any time in the future by ourselves, it cannot fire unless someone down there physically enters the confirmatory commands."

"Right. Now just leave me alone. You may not hear anything from me for some time."

And before CapCom had a chance to reply, Phil switched off both the send and receive switches on his comms. He checked his timer again. He had one hour before lift off to rendezvous with orbit overpass plus one. That meant he had three hours before the absolute last chance - overpass plus two.

He set off back towards the LEV. When he got there, he climbed the ramp, opened the inner airlock door, and started searching. There had to be something - some item of equipment - that he could use to help drag Dave back there. He sat down, tried to calm himself, and apply his mind to the problem. What *was* the problem? Weight, awkwardness, friction. He couldn't drag Dave by his arm or shoulders because he was too heavy, and his backpack or suit just gouged itself into the soft lunar surface. What if he could drag him by his legs? He could tape his legs together. Less weight to lift. But now most of the weight would be dragging along the ground. Reduce the friction. How?

He cast around frantically for ideas. As he stared at the floor panels, a memory came back to him of what he and his brother used to do in Des Moines in the winter. They didn't have sleds, but his mum lent them tin trays. They used to slide downhill on the trays. Just frost on the grass was enough. You didn't even need snow.

The inner floor panels were sturdy aluminium sheets about three feet wide and four feet long. Rear of the airlock hatch, the sheets met at the centre of the floor, and curled up where they met the walls. The shape was perfect. All he had to do was remove one. They were screwed onto the floor with twelve inset hexagonal bolts. He turned round and pulled open a locker labelled 'Tools - Mechanical'. He had never used it before, but the ratchet socket set was ready to hand. He frantically tried a number of sockets until he found the one that fitted the bolts, the job being made even more difficult by the clumsiness and relative lack of feeling in the gloves. It seemed to take for ever undoing the bolts, and one - the last of course - was tighter than the rest. Eventually, the panel was free. He lifted it out. The edges and corners were sharp, and he had to be careful handling it - after all, he was still working in a vacuum. But it was amazingly light in the low gravity, and he soon manhandled it out though the airlock, and threw it down onto the lunar surface.

The only other thing needed was some sort of rope or strap. He opened the 'Fasteners' locker and pulled out a webbing strap about four feet long. It had hooks at each end, and was used for securing bulky equipment in the cargo bay. As he paused for a moment, checking through the plan in his mind, he noticed the LEV control panel. A number of lights were flashing red, and the launch countdown timer was just passing the five minute mark. On the display screen, messages in large print were flashing amber, informing him what he had not done to confirm that he was ready for lift-off. This was the launch Houston had wanted him to engage. He had two hours left.

He left the craft - leaving the airlock door open - gathered his makeshift equipment, and made his way - for the third time - towards Peanut Rock. This time, there was no feeling of trepidation or fear. The only thing he felt was a dogged determination to make his plan work. It had to.

When he got to Dave, he hadn't moved, but his O_2 gauge had fallen to 2.5 hours. He was still breathing. He checked his own gauge - 1.5 hours. Less than he had thought. He must have used up more than normal trying to move Dave.

He taped Dave's legs together, then taped his right arm to his chest. He rolled him to one side, placed the floor panel alongside him, then rolled him back onto it so the lower end of Dave's back-pack sat snugly against the upturned leading edge of the improvised sled. He hooked the strap through the tape round Dave's legs, grabbed the other end, then leaning backwards, took up the strain. To his relief, Dave began to move. He was able to pull him five yards before a build-up of dust stopped the sled going further. He cleared the dust with the back of his gloved hands and tried again, this time with a shorter length of strap. He soon learnt that the angle and speed of the pull were critical in achieving any sort of distance. What was not good, was the fact that his own suit was beginning to overheat with his continued exertions, and that he was obviously using more oxygen than he should.

After pulling for some twenty minutes, he had to rest. His muscles were aching, the heat build-up in his suit was becoming intolerable, and condensation was collecting inside his helmet. But he could tell he had managed to pull Dave a good hundred yards. At this rate, he might just make it by the launch deadline. He decided to switch on his comms receive circuit. Three seconds later, CapCom's earnest voice came over his headset.

"Glad to have you back on line, Phil," he said. "The guys back here are a hundred percent behind you. I know you can hear me, so I'll give you the news. Dave's condition is critical but stable. He has enough O_2. You have precisely one hour five minutes to get to the LEV, and at your current rate of O_2 consumption, one hour ten minutes of that. We have pre-set the LEV to launch and rendezvous with Phoebe on overpass plus two, but with the take-off mass we have here, it's touch and go whether you can achieve rendezvous. We advise you jettison as much mass as possible before you take off. Leave the ramp behind; remove the sliding drawers from equipment lockers 4B and 4C and throw them out; they are the heaviest items you can get rid of easily. Finally, you probably realise you're not in Straker's best books any more, and may not be on the payroll by the time you get back, but you probably don't care about that now do you! Are you going to talk to us, Phil?"

Phil switched on his send circuit. "Shut up, rat face!" he jibed.

With six minutes to go before launch, Phil's lungs were bursting, his arm and leg muscles felt like he'd just spent two hours weight training, and his suit life support system was running on overload. He had got Dave's prone body to the foot of the ramp leading to *Argus*' air lock. He unhooked the strap from Dave's legs and fixed it round his chest under his arms. He then began climbing the ramp, dragging Dave behind him. He had to stand on the ramp and literally jerk Dave up it, inch by inch. As he did this, straining every sinew of his aching body, CapCom was feeding him countdown and other information through his head-set.

"Two minutes, Phil!" he heard as he got Dave to the top of the ramp. He stood inside the air-lock and began manhandling Dave's limp body over the rim of the outer door. It was a near-impossible task, but finally, all but Dave's legs were inside the air-lock.

"Sixty seconds! You must get to the console now!"

Phil leant out past Dave's recumbent body and removed the pins holding the ramp in place, then lifted it clear of its latches and let it fall to the ground. He grabbed Dave's legs and tried to move them inside the air-lock, but the make-shift splint caught on something and stopped him swinging them through the restricted opening.

"Thirty seconds, Phil. You must confirm the launch sequence now. Now!"

Phil knew that as a last resort, Dave could be left in the airlock during the burn. So long as he got to him before the weightless portion of the ascent, he wouldn't move. He clambered up through the already open inner airlock door and sat at the console. Red warning lights were flashing on about six switches, and the screen cursor was blinking on the "Confirm Firing Sequence Command" menu.

"Select Engine Ignition Execute," shouted CapCom.

Phil selected the command, and hit the Enter key.

"Now, flip every switch flashing red to the on position. Do it now Phil, for God's sake!"

Phil, his helmet visor now almost completely misted up, fumbled desperately with the switches. The red lights went off one by one. On the console screen, the countdown notched down to zero. But the engine did not fire.

"Christ! What's up with it?" he gasped. He realised it was getting difficult to breathe.

"The air lock!" shouted CapCom. "Close the goddamn air lock door. The interlock is still on. The main engine won't fire unless at least one of the doors is closed."

"But Dave's still in the air-lock. I can't!"

"Close one of the doors now, Phil, or stay on the Moon for two weeks!"

Phil leaned over, flung the inner door closed, and hit the lock button.

"Get back in your seat. Main engine firing."

As CapCom's words reached Phil, he felt the craft shudder, then accelerate upwards. At the same time, he realised that he was getting no oxygen from his suit supply. The cabin began to swim in front of him, his ears started buzzing, and a strange taste came into his mouth.

"Phil! Your O_2's gone. Tie in to the cabin supply!" he heard CapCom's voice coming to him as if he was calling down a tunnel. "Switch to cabin O_2! Cabin O_2!"

Phil, straining against the unfamiliar acceleration, unplugged his oxygen feed from his back-pack and connected it to the cabin supply. He didn't know how he did it, but the training drummed into him by Rob Klute's team paid off. Within seconds, a glorious cool stream of the life-giving gas was fanning over his nose and mouth.

His mind now back in top gear. He knew that the ascent burn would last just over three minutes. There would then be a long period of zero-g, followed by a short orbit insertion and rendezvous burn. Once the ascent burn ended, Dave could easily float out of the still open outer door. But the safety interlocks absolutely prevented the inner door being opened during the burn. He would have to wait.

He reached over, placed his hand on the airlock door, waited for the burn to end, and concentrated on CapCom's calm voice constantly reassuring him that everything was going to be okay. When the burn did end, it was in fact easier than he thought, opening the door and grabbing Dave. He pulled him inside, closed the airlock doors, and changed Dave's O2 supply. Mercifully, he was still unconscious, and just floated serenely in the cabin, like a baby in the womb. Phil placed him in his seat, strapped him down, and waited for the rendezvous burn. It was once he was calm again, that CapCom came over his headset once more.

"I'm afraid we have a slight problem, Phil."

Phil could not imagine anything worse than the experience he had just gone through, so he didn't feel too shaken by this news.

"What is it, Keith?"

"The delay, Phil. The lift-off delay."

"Yes? Those few seconds? Well?"

"That's put you that many seconds behind Phoebe. The navigation and control computers have already tried to compensate, but to catch up with her, you need more fuel. And you haven't got any more."

"You don't mean .....?"

"No. Don't worry. You're going to make it. But at the end of the rendezvous burn, you'll be in orbit but about three miles from Phoebe, with no fuel left. You are not going to make rendezvous."

"So how the hell do I get home, Keith?"

"Svetlana can use the LTV to come and get you. Just one thing - the LTV and Argus can each dock to Phoebe but not to each other. You haven't had any zero-g EVA training yet have you, Phil?"

"You mean a spacewalk!"

"Training starts today, Phil," said CapCom with irritating calm.

***

At the end of the rendezvous burn, Phil stared longingly out of the cockpit of his stricken craft. Three miles ahead of him glided Phoebe, with its warmth, its comfort, and its safety.

"I couldn't use the hypergolic docking jets to get me over there could I?" he said to Houston. "Surely, there's enough juice in those."

"Possibly Phil," said CapCom, "If you were a trained LEV pilot. But without that training, you haven't a prayer. You could end up spinning the thing all over the place."

"So what about Svetlana using Phoebe's attitude thrusters to bring the station to me?"

"No can do either, Phil. Too massive. Not enough fuel to do it in the time. I'm sorry Phil. It's the spacewalk or nothing. Don't worry. It'll only be a short hop."

As CapCom switched Phil into direct contact with Svetlana, he saw a small dot of light separate from Phoebe.

"Coming to get you both!" called Svetlana. "I'm a bit rusty with Artemis controls, but hang on. Okay on the EVA, comrade?"

"Do I have a choice?" he said ruefully.

"No, Major."

After a number of attempts, Svetlana managed to get the LTV stationary alongside *Argus*, with about fifteen feet between the outer airlock doors. Phil moved down to the LEV outer airlock door, opened it, and looked out. Below him, with absolutely nothing between him and it, was the surface of the Moon. He gripped a hand-hold and froze with terror.

"Don't look down, Phil," came Svetlana's calm voice. "Look over here. Concentrate on LTV."

He looked across the void to see her - fully suited - in the LTV airlock. She floated a tether rope across to him. They secured the rope at each end, then, paying out a second rope as she moved, Svetlana pulled herself across. Phil could hear her nervous breathing through his headset. When she got to his craft, she clutched his arm warmly, then helped him unbuckle Dave, manoeuvre him into the airlock, and tie him to the second rope. She then returned to Artemis, gripped a handhold inside, and gently pulled Dave across. Both she and Phil were praying that Dave would not recover consciousness during this manoeuvre, or he would probably have died of shock.

"Now you, Phil," she said encouragingly. "And don't forget item!"

As Phil reached into the locker to remove the container, Svetlana was already making her way across once more. She tied the second rope to Phil's waist belt, took the key from him, tucked it under her left arm and made her way back to Artemis using her free right hand. Phil's heart was in his mouth each time she let go of the tether rope to move her hand further along it. She eventually disappeared inside, stowed the container, then appeared once more in the airlock and pulled him across.

"Nearly there," she panted, before making the trip one final time, to unhitch the rope at the Argus end. She then tied it to her own waist belt, and pulled herself back to Artemis.

Once the craft was sealed, Svetlana and Phil removed their and Dave's helmets. Svetlana held Dave's head in her hands and kissed him tenderly on the forehead.

"I heard what he said before he passed out," she said. She leaned over to Phil and kissed him on the cheek. "I owe you greater debt than I can ever repay."

"That makes two of us," he said.

"Let's go home," she said thankfully. Phil gazed at her in admiration as she headed the craft back to the comparative safety of Phoebe.

***

Three days after their return to Phoebe, it was clear that Dave was going to die unless they got him to a hospital quickly. He had a compound fracture of the tibia and fibula, a crushed knee joint, his left hand had frozen solid and was gangrenous, and now he was suffering from septic shock. Phil and Svetlana - under instruction from Houston - had done everything they could, including giving injections of morphine and anti-biotics, and even setting up a zero-g pumped intravenous drip. Dave had been drifting in and out of consciousness and having bouts of shaking interspersed with hallucinating. But today, he had become very drowsy, and his skin was turning an awful yellowy sludgy colour. Houston diagnosed liver failure. Svetlana became frantic. The thought of waiting another seven days, and watching Dave die was quite unbearable.

"We have got to get him to Earth," she demanded to Houston. "If we wait up here for another week, he'll be dead. We have to come back now."

Whilst she waited for Houston's response, she outlined her plan to Phil. The 5,500 ft/sec velocity of Phoebe's polar orbit would be of no help to the LTV returning to Earth unless the orbital plane lined up with the Earth. Without that assistance, Artemis would have to use much more fuel to leave lunar orbit, and would consequently not have enough fuel for the retro burn to rendezvous with the ISS. But to allow the LTVs to double as ISS emergency rescue vehicles, they had a thermal protection system - like the tiles on the shuttle - and could return directly to Earth using aero-braking in the Earth's atmosphere, then use parafoils for landing at low speeds on land or sea. Svetlana's plan was to use their LTV to go directly to Earth without an ISS rendezvous. But nobody had ever done it from the Moon, from which the re-entry speeds were much higher. It would be a first, and Svetlana was not an experienced Artemis pilot.

"What do you think?" she asked Phil. "Do you trust me? Do you like idea of going home a week early?"

To Phil, everything Svetlana had done so far, had been completed with consummate perfection. There was no doubt in his mind that she had the guts and ability to get the spacecraft back to Earth safely. But even if that had not been the case, Dave's situation was critical, and there was no way Phil was going to give up on him now.

"You are the *only* person I would trust with our lives," said Phil, pressing his hand round her arm. "Go for it!"

Houston was not happy.

"It couldn't be a worse configuration," they said. "It'll mean a 90 degree orbital plane change. And if your aero-braking isn't on the button when you get here, you could fry or bounce back into space. The risks are very high."

But when Phil told them that Svetlana was going to do it whether they liked it or not, they capitulated. This mission had been unusual in many respects, not least the determination and stubbornness of the crew. Flight Planning came up with a flight profile in record time, and that evening - Friday 14th December, exactly one week early - Artemis undocked from the now deserted Phoebe, and completed a successful Trans-Earth Injection.

As Phoebe and the crippled Argus craft disappeared from view, and the surface of the Moon fell away behind them, Phil turned to Svetlana.

"Any regrets?" he said.

"No, Phil." She turned and gazed lovingly at Dave, lying strapped in one of the seats behind her, his eyes barely open, and his face totally drained of colour. She reached out and lightly touched his cheek. "I've found what I was looking for."

A lump came to Phil's throat as he thought of Jo-Ann and the children.

***

On Monday 17th December, the retro-burn using their remaining fuel completed, Svetlana yawed Artemis round into its re-entry attitude. The Earth, looking as fresh as a spring salad and seemingly larger than he'd ever seen it before, filled Phil's view through the cockpit windows. They were coming in at about 20,000 mph. This was slower than the Apollo capsules, but faster than the shuttle, and certainly faster than any LTV had ever re-entered. Their flight profile brought them down into the Atlantic just off Nova Scotia. Recovery ships were already on station in an elliptical splash-down zone running parallel to the coast. If they undershot, it was pointless worrying about recovery - they would have burned up.

At 200,000 feet, Phil began to feel a slight braking force, and just the hint of g. Svetlana sat in the pilot's seat, and both she and Phil were bombarded with information and advice from Houston. In front of them, displayed on the high resolution computer screen, was the flight profile. It showed a series of dips into the atmosphere, reminiscent of a stone skimming across water. The actual and theoretical paths were displayed simultaneously.

Half way through the first dip, it was clear that something was wrong. Their re-entry velocity was not reducing as quickly as it should. The first bounce was going to take them much further downrange than anybody had allowed for. Someone had fouled up. In the last minute dash to produce a return flight plan, something had been misjudged.

"Where the hell are we going, Houston?" said Svetlana anxiously.

"Sorry!" replied the ever-temperate voice of Keith Smith. "But you're okay. Next entry will be steeper than predicted, but quite tolerable."

"Well we're pleased to hear that, Keith!" said Svetlana.

Houston then detailed the new craft attitude parameters, which Svetlana keyed in to the guidance computer. Phil could feel the air drag reducing, and weightlessness returning.

"And new splash-down zone?" she inquired.

"Bit of a tricky one that," replied CapCom. "Mightn't be an actual splash - could be a dull thud."

"Not a ground landing, Keith!" gasped Svetlana. "Where? Apart from tip of Newfoundland, there isn't any land downrange."

"Yes there is," replied Houston.

"For pity's sake, Keith," she said, "How far downrange are we going to be?"

"Scotland."

"What!" Svetlana turned to Phil, disbelief in her eyes.

"Your reconfigured first bounce will put you in the middle of the north Atlantic," said CapCom. "Obviously, we don't have anybody there to recover you. But if we push it, we can get you to the west coast of Scotland. There's a north-westerly surface wind blowing in the area, so if you execute a 150 degree turn to port once you get over land, that should bring you down safe and sound with a low ground speed."

"And what about Dave?" said Phil.

"We're contacting local hospitals right now," said CapCom confidently. "They're quite used to coping with helicopter ambulances - what with all the oil rigs around."

Some minutes after that, Phil felt the drag returning, though this time more strongly. At 35 miles up, the fireworks started. Out of the windows, pinks and oranges and flashes of bright white light enveloped the craft, the g force began to feel like a ton of bricks on his shoulders, and the vibrations and buffeting made it almost impossible to talk. The cabin began to get hot, and Dave chose that moment to drift out of unconsciousness. All Phil could do was to lean over, clutch his arm and give him the 'thumbs up'.

The deceleration phase of the re-entry lasted for nearly thirty minutes, during which they travelled - like a fireball - nearly 6,000 miles. To Phil, this was like a nightmare with no end, but at last, at 40,000 feet, the buffeting stopped, the view from the windows cleared, and they were surrounded by glorious blue sky. The guidance computer placed them over the Outer Hebrides, and as Phil looked out, dead ahead, the snowy peaks of the North West Highlands rose up to greet them. From now on, it was Svetlana's piloting skills that were going to be needed.

"Helmets off," she commanded, calmly. They were now low enough to not rely on their launch-and-entry suits for air pressure and oxygen. She turned round for a moment and touched Dave's hand.

"Nearly home, Golubchik," she said

At 25,000 feet, the drogue chutes deployed, and slowed the LTV to under 100 mph, then the main parafoil unfurled. There was a series of jolts, then a swinging motion as the craft hung from its massive controllable wing. Servo motors linked to a small joystick allowed Svetlana to turn or vary the glide angle and airspeed, which was currently some 30 mph. They were now crossing the North Minch channel. Phil could even see the white horses of wave crests scattered below him. As they approached the far side, he suddenly spotted the tiny port of Ullapool.

"There!" he shouted excitedly to Svetlana. "Put her down there. I know that place!"

Svetlana turned out to be far more competent pilot than she had made out. After checking the wind speed and direction, she flew down Loch Broom, then executed a perfect 180 degree turn into the wind, and put the craft down less than a mile upwind of the harbour. She cut loose the parafoil, and the craft settled into the water, rolling slightly in the gentle swell.

They were alive! They were back! They were home!

Svetlana, totally exhausted, collapsed over the controls. Phil, his hands shaking, his legs like jelly, and feeling as if he was wearing a lead waistcoat, struggled to his feet and flung his arms round her.

"Brilliant!" he said, realising his eyes were filled with tears of joy and relief. "You got us back damn-it. We bloody did it!"

"I can't move. I feel so heavy," she said. Phil tried to imagine how Svetlana must be feeling, after two years in zero-g. It could take her weeks to re-adapt to normal gravity.

He reported their splash-down to Houston.

"There's an Air-Sea Rescue helicopter on its way to you from RAF Lossiemouth," said CapCom, "But it won't be there for another ten minutes or so. We can't contact the authorities on the shore. The line's permanently engaged. If the sea state is calm enough, suggest you open the top hatch and fire off a distress flare."

Phil needed no second biding to open the hatch. He had been breathing spacecraft air for two and a half weeks. He disarmed the safety lock, reached up and swung the heavy door to one side. As it opened, his senses exploded into life as an avalanche of sights, sounds, smells and tastes assailed him.

"Listen to that, Dave!" he called down inside, as seagulls shrieked overhead and cold salt spray blew into his face. He filled his lungs, wiped his face with his hands and licked his fingers. Never again would the taste of salt produce such sweet rapture. As he turned his head to the wind, and felt its freshness tugging at his hair, he finally understood the unspoken bond that existed between everyone who had been into space. It was the revelation - only really experienced after an extended trip - that the magic and mystery of life on Earth was something to be revered.

But he had not only left Earth; he knew what it was like to *be without it*. He had experienced the empty loneliness and indescribable terror of the wilderness, and the exquisite joy of coming home.

Now, he felt he had touched the hand of The Creator.

11

Eve

His first sensation was that they were accelerating. But how was it so smooth? Why no vibrations from the engines? And how come they were in a burn while he was still in his sleep station? He opened his eyes. Silhouetted against the half light filtering through near-closed Venetian blinds was the outline of a woman's head and shoulders. How strange, her hair was hanging down, not floating. A hand touched his cheek, then her head came nearer and hair fell about his face. The touch and scent of her was unmistakable.

"Welcome back, darling," said Jo-Ann.

Phil reached up and wrapped her in his arms. She dropped down onto the bed beside him and rocked him to and fro like a baby. He closed his eyes. It was sheer heaven.

"Never again!" he said, as they slowly unwrapped themselves. He sat up, rubbing his eyes. It was then that he saw Nick and Tess standing by the other side of the bed. They leapt onto him, and squeezed and hugged him until he could hardly breathe.

"You're in all the papers, Dad!" said Nick excitedly. "Not just here, but all over the world!"

It took a moment to recall where 'here' was. They were in the Quarantine Facility of the Lunar Receiving Lab back at the Johnson Space Centre in Houston. It had not been used for the reception of astronauts since the Apollo missions, when nobody was quite sure whether there was a risk of extra-terrestrial contamination. But now, its original function was being utilised to the full. And an added bonus was that it was secure. No-one could get into the building without a Codax coded access card for the electronic entry system.

"And you've already had eight proposals of marriage by FAX," said Tess, giggling.

"I thought we were keeping all this hush, hush," said Phil.

"Hush hush!" exclaimed Jo-Ann. "You must be joking! From the moment your first launch was abandoned, the press have been watching your mission like hawks. They're dying to know what's happening. And you don't think you can defy the Secretary of Defense, drag somebody from the jaws of death, and land in the wrong continent without causing one helluva rumpus do you?"

She took his hand tenderly.

"You'd have been a world hero anyway, without the incident at Ullapool," she said, "But a hero with a magic holdall... that's *really* got 'em going!"

Phil thought back. That had been three days ago. To the residents of Ullapool, *Artemis* and its huge multi-coloured parafoil must have been a dramatic sight as it glided majestically down the loch. And by the time it executed the turn and lowered itself gracefully onto the water not a mile from them, many of the townsfolk were gathered along the waterfront. Angus McLeod, the resolute full-bearded harbourmaster, finding his phone jammed by incoming calls, contacted air-sea rescue by radio, then commandeered a fishing boat. When he returned with an English astronaut, a devastatingly beautiful Russian cosmonaut too weak to walk, and a man on an improvised stretcher who looked as near to death as anyone would care to be, the landing assumed an altogether more newsworthy significance. It was not long before the silent and wide-eyed spectators along the harbour walls began to connect the events unfolding before them with the snippets of news they had heard about some sort of incident, or rescue, on the Moon.

Within minutes, the first Sea-King helicopter had whisked Dave and Svetlana off to a hospital in Inverness, but Phil had remained on the quayside to organise the recovery of the LTV and the transport of himself and his precious cargo to a military base. Mrs Partridge, a homely woman from the Loch View restaurant, had brought over an empty tea trolley onto which Phil had loaded various items including, in a small holdall, the key container. It was when one of the trolley wheels caught on the uneven ground and the trolley pitched its cargo onto the roadway, that it happened. To everyone's amazement - not the least Phil's - the holdall, instead of falling to the ground, remained stationary in mid air. Its straps hung downwards, and it seemed as if it was being held up by whatever was inside it. Cameras clicked; videos whirred; people pointed in disbelief. Horrified, Phil reached forward and grabbed hold of the straps, whereupon the holdall reverted to normal behaviour.

"This sometimes happens to things after a long period of weightlessness," he said unconvincingly. But the explanation didn't wash. The onlookers knew - something very odd was afoot. By the next morning, newspapers across the globe carried pictures of the returning trio and the miraculous holdall, and TV news footage showed amateur film of Phil wresting the thing to the ground.

"Are they still working on it in the lab next door?" he said, as Jo-Ann opened the blinds a little. Tess went to fix them all some coffee.

"Well, they've got it," said Jo-Ann wryly. "I wouldn't say they were working on it. Apparently it hasn't moved an inch since you left it with them."

"Can we go and see it, Dad?" asked Nick.

"Why not," said Phil, getting up and throwing on some clothes.

He used his Codax card to let them into the adjacent laboratory section of the building. There, absolutely motionless and floating some four feet off the ground, was the key. It was surrounded by a complex array of sensing and recording devices. A gaggle of scientists were in animated conversation next to a white-board covered with mathematical equations.

"Oh, Major Newheart. Could you move it for us now the kit is set up please."

Phil recognised the figure - in his usual well-worn jeans and check shirt - of Richard Connolly, NASA's senior materials physicist. He was a tall strong-looking man with a high polished forehead, arms like a truck driver, and a deep tan.

"You mean there's nothing you can do to move the thing?" said Phil.

"No Sir. It's rock solid. Like it's cemented to the spot. We've even wrapped chains around it and ....."

He turned to a colleague nearby.

"How many tons, Jim?

"Four point eight, Dick."

"We've hung four point eight tons on it, and it just sits there. It didn't even move a thousandth of an inch."

"No magnetism, electric charge, hidden gyros, radio-activity?" said Phil.

"Nothing. It's completely inert. We can see it and feel it, but the sensors say it doesn't exist!"

"It's miraculous," said Jo-Ann, sweeping her hand round and under the key, as if she could not believe it wasn't somehow supported.

"It certainly looks that way, Mrs Newheart," said Connolly, but I believe that somewhere, somehow, we can explain its seemingly supernatural behaviour in terms of the laws of Physics."

"But is it supernatural?" said Phil, "It hasn't actually broken any of the laws of Physics."

Some of the men in the room raised their eyebrows. Dick Connolly was the sort of man you thought twice about before challenging.

"Well, take the hovering for instance," he continued. "No energy is required; just a force. It's not actually doing any work. It's just sitting there, like .... like that coffee pot on the bench there."

"But in that case, the bench is supplying the upward force needed to overcome gravity," said Connolly. "Where's the force keeping the key up?"

"Either from the key itself - maybe a force we haven't discovered yet - or ......" Phil started pacing to and fro as he gathered his thoughts. "Or, maybe it draws on any force acting on it, and uses that against itself as it were - a sort of force mirror."

Connolly's eyes widened. He turned to the others.

"Now we sure didn't think of *that* one did we!" he exclaimed.

"We mustn't allow pre-conceptions to blinker our ideas," Phil went on. "Maybe it's not even an 'object' as such at all. Maybe it's an *entity*, organised somehow."

Connolly began to show signs of discomfiture. Phil sensed that he felt in danger of being out-classed, toppled from his pedestal. That had not been his intention. But being back in a laboratory had triggered the old skills. He thought of his battery research labs. in England. Strange, he wasn't missing them as much as he thought he would.

"Can we get on please," said Connolly, irritably. He ushered Phil towards the key.

Phil resisted the urge to continue with the speculation, and kept quiet. The men dispersed to their various instruments and stood, waiting.

"Okay. Now." said Connolly.

Phil stepped forward, reached out and closed his fingers round the handle on the end of the key. Immediately, it became free, and allowed him to move it about normally. He walked across the room and placed it carefully on a bench.

"Incredible!" said Connolly. "Any readings anybody?"

The men shook their heads.

"It sure knows you, Dad," Nick piped up, with just the hint of an American accent. He had obviously totally embraced his own scanning theory, and partly embraced his host country.

"What I don't understand, is how you didn't notice this behaviour before you got to Ullapool," said Connolly.

"In zero-g, how could I notice," he said, "And on the Moon, only I ....."

Then he remembered he had handed it to Dave to put in the container on his back-pack, and he'd also passed it to Svetlana. They hadn't experienced any problems. It crossed his mind that it not only recognised him, but also sensed his intention, but he thought better of introducing such an outrageous theory. He picked up the key again.

"I wonder what happens if I actually give it to someone," he said, turning and handing it to Connolly, who grasped it by the handle. Phil let go.

"It's solid as a rock again," said Connolly. "Damn it!"

He began tugging at it in frustration, as if trying to yank open a stuck door. Phil smiled to himself that he hadn't really wanted Connolly to be able to move it. He was beginning to get quite attached to the thing.

"Seems I'm its favourite handler," he said. Out of the corner of his eye he saw Jo-Ann grinning to herself.

"One thing's for sure," said Connolly. "There's no way anybody's going to steal it."

"That's true," said Phil. "Though I'd feel better with it near at hand. He picked up the key and ushered his family back into the living quarters.

That evening, with Nick and Tess safely asleep in a nearby room, Jo-Ann's arm curled out from the half-open bathroom door and dimmed the lights in the bedroom. She then appeared, and walked slowly and purposefully towards Phil, lying on the bed. She was wearing the skimpiest of see-through negligees, and her breasts bounced enticingly as she approached him.

"And what have I done to deserve this?" he said, looking up at her.

She sat on the edge of the bed next to him, and began to run her fingers through his hair.

"Followed your heart for once, not your head."

"The Dave thing?"

Jo-Ann gazed at him admiringly and nodded.

"That was a courageous and wonderful thing you did up there, Phil. I wish my father was still alive. He'd have made you an honorary brave for sure. I know one thing, you're *my* brave."

She had never used that expression before. She really sounded as if she meant it.

"And defying the Secretary of Defense like that... We'll make an activist of you yet!"

"That was nothing. He made a mistake. I just put him right."

"Oh come on, Phil. Don't pretend. You can't tell me it didn't feel great. *Now* do you understand? I need you to feel like I do sometimes. Forget your goddamn lists. Listen to your soul."

He had to admit, she was right. His trip to the Moon had not only tried him physically, but had been a emotional roller-coaster ride, forcing him to come to terms with the forces which really drove him. For too long, he had distrusted his emotions, suppressed their effect on him, leant too heavily on logic, on facts. But now, those emotional forces could not be ignored. They were part of him, and he had to learn to listen to them, control them, and use them. He began to see what it must have been like for Jo-Ann, living with him. Why was he like this? It hadn't always been this way. There was a time...

"It's difficult to let go," he said. He began to shake a little as he realised that for the first time in years, he might be able to open up about his childhood. "I loved this country once - trusted it. Like a child trusts its parents. And look what happened...."

Jo-Ann started kissing him on the face.

"Honey, Honey. That wasn't the whole of America. I don't know who was responsible for that plane crash, but it wasn't me, wasn't Dave, wasn't Rob Klute or Ted Beemish, or any of the great guys we've met. Don't take it out on us."

She gently removed the quilt, then lay back on the bed next to him.

"Just *take* us," she purred. Then, mischievously, "Well, *me* anyway!"

As he feasted his eyes on Jo, he realised that memorable though his encounter with Svetlana had been, sex without love was like taste without food - sensation without fulfilment. Deep in his soul was a hunger that could only be satiated through the love of his wife. He bent down and began kissing her face tenderly.

"I love you, Mrs Newheart," he whispered.

But there was a niggling distraction. Something about the situation kept reminding him of Svetlana. Then he realised that although Jo's negligee had a line of silk bows all the way down its front, there was something familiar about the style.

"This is new. Where did you get it?" he said, intrigued.

"Victoria's Secret. Actually, Svetlana told me about it."

It? She couldn't mean..... No, she had to be talking about the shop.

"You've been talking to Svetlana!"

"She phoned from Inverness while you were having lunch with Rob Klute. Dave's okay. He's lost his hand but they've saved his leg. They've got the infection under control and he's out of danger."

"Oh, thank God!" exclaimed Phil. He permitted himself a pat on the back. It wasn't every day one had the opportunity of saving someone's life.

"I was going to tell you this afternoon, but then .... I went to the Galleria. Thought you'd like me and the good news together. Sort of Christmas stocking!"

The look in her eyes said that for him at least, Christmas had come a few days early.

"And they're engaged," she continued. She began squirming around, as if scratching her back on the sheet she was lying on.

"That's wonderful! I wonder where they're going to live."

Jo-Ann looked as if she was going to say something, but didn't. Phil realised what a daft thing it was to say. Jo and he could do without being reminded of their most intractable problem. But it was she who saved the situation. Feigning anger, she sat up, pushed him down onto his back, and sat astride his middle.

"I don't know and I don't care!"

She began grinding her hips into him. He reached up and stroked the silky material covering the front of her body.

"So how come you and Svetlana started talking about ... you know?"

"Oh, just girl talk. She's some lady. We were talking about temptation actually."

She looked at him wistfully. There was a message there somewhere, but now was not the moment to indulge his curiosity. And in any case, more tangible matters were demanding his attention.

"Temptation eh," he said, lustily. He lifted her up, rolled her onto her back, and started untying the line of silk bows, as if he was undoing a Christmas parcel.

"Who needs it. I prefer unwrapping presents!"

In the darkness across the room, the key glided, imperceptibly slowly, to a more effective scanning location, its motion in stark contrast to the writhing bodies below it.

***

It took a superhuman effort of will for Phil to unwrap himself from the warmth and comfort of Jo-Ann's recumbent body and take the call. He glanced at the clock. It was 7:15 a.m..

"Phil. Ted Beemish here. Are you well?"

"You will never know how well," he said smugly, gazing down at his beautiful wife. Her breathing sounded like the soft sighing of a Galveston breeze.

"Great! Well I've just come from an early morning strategy meeting of the Sesame Group..."

"Sesame Group?"

"Yeah. Bit corny I know, but that's the name they've come up with for the committee responsible for co-ordinating all activities relating to the door, and getting into it."

"Who's in it?"

"It's headed by Vice President Powell. Then there's Secretary Straker, Governor Cranford, myself of course, Generals Miller and Norman, Pulanski, and Sheriff Collins."

Phil felt uncomfortable. Apart from a single concession - Pulanski - the committee lacked apolitical objectivity.

"And what about a scientist or two, an anthropologist, astronomer, geologist, biologist, and what about me?"

There was an awkward silence.

"We didn't think you should be bothered with policy, Phil. You've done your bit. Fact, you've contributed more than anybody could be expected to. Once you put the key into the door, I think we can let you go."

"Bullshit!" said Phil. He got up and went to the bathroom. "Who says I want to be let go! You're not making me redundant. Anybody'd think I wasn't a player. I'm on that committee, General."

"I thought you might say that. I'd like you on there myself to be honest, but this thing's getting big. Straker's worried about security. If the truth gets out, we'll have to go international - the UN, the whole works. Then God knows where we'll end up."

Phil believed him. Beemish's genuine tone was enough to stop him saying what he was about to say: No Phil - no key, no open sesame.

"Anyway," Beemish continued. "I phoned to say we're going in on Christmas eve. You need to get back up here by the day after tomorrow. Meet the team. Sort out what's what."

"Fine. I'll be there of course. We'll fly up tomorrow afternoon."

"There's something else," said Beemish more seriously. It almost sounded as if he was whispering. "The bomb, on the first launch. There wasn't one. It was a hoax."

"Go on."

"But whoever it was knew a lot about the mission, and the spacecraft, and felt strongly enough to try to prevent you getting to that key. That same person probably also knows where you are, and that we've only got five days left."

"And you're saying he might try again."

"Yes, I am. But this time, all he can do is take you out or try to destroy the key. I've sorted out a bodyguard for you, but NASA tell me you've got the thing in the bedroom with you. That right?"

"Yes."

"Best store it in another room - preferably as far away from you as possible. If our friend pays you a call, we don't want to make it easy for him, now do we?"

Phil smiled to himself as he imagined a thief trying to take the key, but then realised Beemish was right. If that didn't work, he'd be next. Still naked, he returned to the bedroom. Jo-Ann had woken up.

"You're right, Ted. Thanks."

"And I will do everything to get you on the committee. Bye, Phil."

Jo-Ann looked at him questioningly. Phil just shook his head, and indicated it wasn't important. He didn't want to worry her.

And in any case, they had a lot of catching up to do.

***

The remainder of the morning had been fully occupied conducting more tests on the key. They had him pulling it with cords, holding it whilst he was weighed, and even trying to project it away from him. That test was the most rewarding, as the key simply decelerated and came calmly to rest in mid-air. To the investigating scientists, the key offered a fascinating challenge. But when it stubbornly refused to react or respond in any way unless Phil was involved, disillusionment began to set in, and by mid afternoon, many had returned to their normal places of work.

Rob Klute had phoned around lunch time to invite Phil and the family to a farewell drinks party in his office at 6pm.

"I think it would be appropriate if you wore your Air Force uniform," he said. "There'll be one or two officials there who'll expect it."

Phil had never even tried it on. He had been measured for it shortly after he arrived at Houston nearly three months ago; it had been delivered since, but had just hung in its bag, untouched. By the time he tried it on, Jo-Ann had pressed it, he had tried it on again and received her final approval, it was nearly four o'clock.

"You look absolutely fabulous," she said, standing back and looking him up and down admiringly. "Now, Tess and I need to get ready. Out, out, out."

"I'll show Nick the mock-ups and simulators."

"Yeah!" called Nick, bounding in from the next room.

"Don't mess up your uniform. Don't let Nick touch anything he shouldn't. Don't encourage him to be an astronaut, and be sure you come back for me by quarter to six," said Jo-Ann.

Phil and Nick grinned at each other.

"No sweat!" said Nick, winking at him. "Come on, Dad."

As he left, he checked the laboratory. The key was there, hovering as usual, but the lab was deserted. Everyone had given up. As they walked out into the late afternoon sunshine, neither he, Nick, the guard on the door, nor his personal bodyguard, noticed the black Buick parked amongst the other cars some distance away.

Jo-Ann stood waving her fingers to and fro as they came in.

"Don't touch me! Nail varnish," she said, backing off as Phil went to kiss her.

"Oh Mum! You should've seen this place!" said Nick excitedly. "It's ginormous! It's got exact copies of the ISS, Phoebe, the Shuttles, and all the vehicles Dad's been in. And then there's the...."

Tess glared at him from behind her mother's back. She knew - as Phil did - that Jo-Ann had heard enough about spacecraft to last a lifetime. Nick shut up, and contented himself by digging in his pocket and proudly examining - yet again - the moonrock Phil had brought him.

"Was there anybody there you knew?" she said.

"Actually no. Whole place seems a bit quiet actually."

Jo-Ann just smiled, mysteriously.

"Come on," she said. "Let's get it over with."

They set off to walk the four hundred yards or so to Rob Klute's office. The only people they saw were all heading off towards Building 2, where the large auditorium was.

"Must be a do on," muttered Phil as they opened the door to Building 45.

To his surprise, Rob was waiting for them by the lifts. Phil hardly recognised him. Gone were the baggy trousers and short-sleeved shirt with ink marks on the pocket. In their place was a designer suit and tie and immaculate polished shoes. He walked towards them with outstretched arms, beaming. Nick and Tess stood, expectantly. Jo-Ann just smiled that smile again.

"What's going on?" said Phil. There was a smell of collusion in the air.

"You, Phil," said Rob. "Follow me please."

It had been almost too easy for Snake - the name he used when negotiating contracts like these. He already had a forged NASA ID badge, but he needed a Codax card for the Receiving Lab's entry system. The group of men he followed from there at lunch time were heading for the restaurant. He sat near to them, pretending to read a paper. One of them was obviously single, and intent upon bedding some girl he knew would be at the Gulfstream Club that evening. He was going to take the afternoon off and clear up his apartment. Perfect, thought

Snake. Nobody would miss him until the next day. As the man got up from the table, Snake was already on the phone to Whistler in the Buick. They followed him as he drove out of the Centre and headed for Pasadena. At the apartment, the man didn't even lock the door behind him. Snake followed him and knifed him silently in the kitchen. The Codax was still on a chainlet round his neck. He took that and his wallet, left the man's ID badge, ransacked the flat, and walked back out to Whistler.

Back on station outside the Lab, they had watched the Newhearts leave. At 6 o'clock, a lone night guard took over. All Snake had to do was see to him, then he would have the building to himself. If he couldn't steal or destroy the key, he would go through and wait in the accommodation section and kill Newheart when he came back.

Snake opened the Buick's trunk, and took out the standard issue NASA equipment box he had found in a store room that morning. He walked up the ramp towards the laboratory entrance, holding the box with both hands. It was obvious to the guard that it was heavy.

"Would you mind?" said Snake, glancing down at the Codax hanging round his neck. "It's a bit awkward."

He looked the guard squarely in the face, smiling. He was banking on him not checking the box, and if he did, he would just have to take him there and then.

"Certainly, Doctor," said the guard, noting the name on the ID badge. He unlooped the chainlet, inserted the card into the electronic lock, held the door open and returned the card.

"Wish me luck," he said to the guard. "This'd better work first time, otherwise I could be here all night!"

"Tell me about it," said the guard woefully.

"Well, probably see you when you do your rounds," said Snake nonchalantly.

"You don't think they'd actually let me *in* there do you," said the guard contemptuously. "Oh no. I just sit out here or walk around outside. Make sure no-one breaks in or nothin."

That'll save me the bother of killing you, thought Snake, as he let the door close behind him and made his way to the central laboratory. He had to go through three sets of air-tight biologically sealed doors, to get to the inner room where the key was held. There was no way, he realised, that the sound of a small explosion or gunshots would be heard through that lot.

Rob Klute led the way to the Teague Auditorium.

"What is this?" said Phil.

"I'm sorry, Phil," said Rob, panting slightly as he walked. "I wasn't sure it was definitely on until the very last moment. I didn't want to tell you in case it didn't happen."

"What didn't happen?"

"Your presentation."

Phil turned to look at Jo-Ann. "You knew! You ... You rat!" Jo-Ann just smiled again and squeezed his hand.

As they entered the 800 seater room from the rear, Phil could see it was packed. A spotlight picked them out as Rob escorted them down the long aisle towards the stage. The whole audience rose to its feet, applauded and cheered. The aisle was lined with what seemed to Phil to be the entire astronaut corps - many of whom had been, though courteous, rather cool towards him on his arrival. Now, they were smiling broadly and offering their hands. As they got to the front row, Rob introduced two of the original Apollo astronauts - now in their eighties - who had come in specially to honour him. Jo-Ann and the children sat down next to them.

Phil was led onto the stage, where a number of distinguished looking men were standing smiling.

"Sir, this is Major Philip Newheart," said Rob proudly. "Phil, meet Stan Silverman, Head of NASA. Mr Silverman has just got in from HQ, Washington."

The applause subsided. Overcome, Phil sat down in the chair offered to him.

"Phil," began Silverman, warmly, "NASA owes you a debt of gratitude that can never match the determination and bravery you displayed last week. As a direct consequence of your actions, Dave Gentry will live. Rarely in the history of this organisation has an individual made their mark so swiftly, so effectively, and so honourably."

And to peals of laughter and much applause, he continued.

"As to the small matter of the lost Lunar Excursion Vehicle, if you can go back and find it before we get into next year's budget period, we won't have to dock it from your pay!"

"The bastard won't budge!" said Snake over the phone. He was breathing hard. Whistler had never heard him so unnerved before. He was usually so cold and clinical. If he hadn't known him better, he would say Snake was actually frightened.

"I don't know how they've done it, but they've got the sonofabitch in some sort of magnetic lock or something. I can touch it but I can't move it."

"What ya gonna do, Snake?" said Whistler. His voice sounded like slime flowing from a broken pipe.

"The plastic won't stick to it, and neither will the limpet. I'm going to have to try the explosive dumdum."

He reached down into the NASA box, pulled out and donned the flak jacket and the face guard, then took out and screwed together a specially converted large bore sawn-off shotgun. Carefully, he took one of the two special shells from a foam-filled box and inserted the shell into the breech. He was very wary of these shells. The projectile comprised a lead casing surrounding titanium shrapnel mixed with explosive jelly. The armour-piercing percussion cap at its tip detonated on contact, and would even set it off if it was dropped on the floor.

"Can you see the guard?" said Snake.

"Yeah. He's just sitting there."

"Okay. Keep on the line. Soon as I've fired the thing, I'll pick up the phone. You tell me quick whether he heard it. If he did, I'll have to come out straight away and take him. You ready?"

"Sure."

To protect his lower half from possible back splatter, Snake stood behind one of the benches. The special mirror sights on the gun allowed him to fire the heavy gun from the waist. He lined it up. He could clearly see the key in the sights. He pulled the trigger.

Stan Silverman's speech at an end, he picked up a medal from the table next to him. It had the NASA motif in its centre, and a long two-tone blue ribbon attached to it. He indicated to Phil that he should stand. Silverman hung the ribbon round Phil's neck.

"So finally, Major Philip Newheart, it gives me the greatest pleasure to award you NASA's highest and most prestigious honour. For your courage, and in recognition of your most distinguished contribution to the Astronaut Corps, the NASA mission, and the United States of America, I hereby award you the Distinguished Service Medal. Major, we thank you."

Snake did not see the shell coming back at him. When it hit him and drove straight through his jacket, the real centre of the explosion was somewhere near the top of his stomach. Some of the shrapnel got up as far as his throat, and a lot came out through the front of his lower pelvis. But what he did see in that last half second of his life was the flak jacket bulging outwards and a strange yellow and red putrescence spraying from a large hole in the centre of it.

Three miles beneath the windswept Wyoming plains, the incident did not pass unnoticed.

12

Descent

Phil peered downwards as the helicopter skimmed low over the snow-covered landscape on its final approach to the door. Jo-Ann gripped his hand as the massive temporary cover - a geodesic dome filling most of the small bay between the two headlands - came into view. The scene below had totally changed in the three months since September. Surrounding the dome were ranks of field guns, tanks, missile launchers, communication dishes, helicopters, vehicles of every description, and temporary buildings. Their helicopter put down on a pad just outside the dome, to a swirl of dry snow and dust. Beemish led the way through a huge plastic weather door. Phil followed, carrying the key. Military guards held the heavy material to one side for Jo-Ann and the children.

Inside, the feeling that he was in a theatre was overwhelming. At the far end, dominating the scene and looking even more like a proscenium arch, was the door. Leading up to it, a wide concrete roadway had been laid, either side of which were banks of equipment, floodlights, cameras, and more guns. Round the edge were mobile offices, a laboratory, a small canteen, and washrooms. Officials, scientists, and military personnel stood in groups, speaking in hushed tones. A knot of men were waiting outside one of the huts as they walked in. Governor Cranford stepped forward and extended his hand.

"Ah! The hero of the hour," he said, disingenuously. Phil recalled how his knee-jerk reaction to Cranford's offer of an illicit import licence had triggered Jo-Ann's divorce action. "Let me introduce you to Vice President Powell and Secretary Straker. I think you know the others in the reception party."

Phil recognised the Vice President. There had just been a presidential election, and during his stay in Houston hardly a day had passed without Powell appearing alongside the President on TV. As for 'Reception party', he wondered whether this was misplaced arrogance - were they assuming the aliens were going to come out to them?

In the flesh, Richard Powell was even smoother than his television image. He was taller than Phil had expected - probably because the presidential PR men ensured he always looked shorter than the President - and his beautifully tailored suit perfectly complemented his clean-cut features and intense brown eyes. Phil contented himself that it was simply money which allowed a man the same age as himself to look younger, but at the same time exude an air of experience and mature authority.

"Pleased to meet you, Major," he said politely, in the cultured tones for which he was so well known. He shook Phil firmly but briefly by the hand. The introduction was not helped by the body language of the older, stocky figure of Rod Straker. He swept his hand over his balding head, as from behind half-moon spectacles, he watched, bristling with disapproval.

"Last time we spoke, you were on the Moon," said Straker, without offering his hand. "I trust that now you are back in the USA and part of Vice President Powell's team, you will not see fit to act unilaterally."

His expression was severe. He obviously wanted the last word on the Moon incident. The fact that Dave's life had been saved was not mentioned.

Before Phil had a chance to reply, Ted Beemish diplomatically cut in, explaining he needed to brief him about the immediate arrangements.

Phil realised that during his time with NASA, he had become part of a community largely protected from the real world. Yes, there had been times when this protection had been breached - not least the sickening incident in the receiving laboratory - but on the whole, he had been in good company. Now however, the old pressures, insecurities, distrust and suspicion crowded in on him like the clouds of a gathering storm.

"I think we are ready, Sir," said Beemish eventually.

Phil walked over to Jo-Ann and hugged her. She was standing proudly, but her eyes betrayed her deep concern. Tess and Nick clung to him for as long as they could. Although Phil was the key player and had been preparing for this moment for nearly three months, now it had finally arrived, he felt strangely distant, numb even. Now, he was a passenger on a ship - destination unknown - an unseen hand at the helm.

Jo-Ann and the children were led away, to watch from the protection of a bullet-proof observation room. Phil mouthed, I love you, as Jo-Ann's fingertips slid out of his hands.

"Positions," boomed a voice over the loudspeaker system, with the tone and authority of a film director.

"I'm right behind you, Phil," said a reassuring voice. It was Beemish. He was carrying a 44 Magnum in his right hand.

The reception party arranged themselves into a slender phalanx with Phil at its apex, then walked to within twenty yards of the door and stopped. An expectant silence filled the dome. The only sound was the wind, moaning softly beyond the canvass. Phil, the key in his right hand, was facing the door and staring steadfastly at the hexagonal hole. He could feel his pulse building up and his breathing getting rapid. He raised his left hand, indicating he was going in.

"Proceed," boomed the voice.

With Beemish five yards behind him, Phil walked the last few yards and stopped. The door towered menacingly over him, as if daring him to try something. For a moment, he was paralysed, as fear and curiosity played tug-of-war with his right arm. Finally, he raised the key and placed it into the hole. It fitted exactly, and glided in smoothly and silently. As it was drawn away from his hands, Phil let go and took two steps backwards. He stood there, teeth gritted, eyes wide, waiting, ready. For an agonising few seconds nothing happened, then a movement to his right caught his eye.

"It's opening!" called Beemish, "There, to the right."

Near the right hand column, a small section - no larger than a normal door - had silently opened. A warm yellow light flooded out. To a man everybody moved back. Some men donned dark glasses. Phil could feel the hairs on the back of his neck rising as he - along with the others - waited for something to emerge. But nothing did. Beemish walked over, and stood peering into the opening.

"Can't see inside," he said quietly into his radio microphone. "I think one of us should try going in."

"Okay," replied the controller. "But easy does it, General."

Beemish stepped forward, and extremely slowly, moved his left hand into the door opening. But Phil could see that he had touched an invisible wall.

"Something in the way." Phil could hear the tension as he spoke. "Feels like glass."

Phil joined him.

"It may have to be me, Ted.

Beemish stood to one side, gun at the ready.

Phil took one look back towards the wide-eyed onlookers. The floodlights were dazzling, but he waved towards where he knew Jo-Ann and the children were, then turned and walked into the glow. Almost without realising it, he was inside.

He swallowed hard, as he realised the doorway had closed behind him.

***

He was in a small room. The wall ahead of him was a featureless charcoal grey except for a rectangular panel - perhaps a control panel - embedded into it. To his left was the outline of what, despite its generous proportions, could have been a doorway. The remaining walls and ceiling comprised illuminated panels, and it was from these, in an even glow, that the light was emanating. There appeared to be nothing in the room except a traditional wing-back easy chair and a coffee table. Phil blinked. What he had not expected to see was something familiar. On the table was a glass decanter with orange-coloured liquid in it, and one drinking glass. He walked over to the chair and stood by it, holding its back for comfort and support. He could feel the moquette under his fingers.

"Greetings, Major Newheart. I honour and welcome you."

The voice came from somewhere in front of him. He guessed there was some sort of speaker built into the wall. He was surprised to realise that it had not given him a shock - perhaps the chair had helped him to expect the familiar. But what was strange was the quality of the voice. Never, even in the most eloquent of public speakers, had he heard a voice of such clarity, such benevolent authority, such presence. It was not obviously male or female, but somehow made him feel like a child being welcomed into his aunt or uncle's stately home.

And those first words. It knew his name. The very first time an alien civilisation had spoken directly to a member of the human race, and it was to him. Phil realised how Neil Armstrong must have felt, the day he stepped onto the lunar surface. Here now, was an even more significant moment in Earth's history. He struggled to manufacture a suitably memorable response, but settled for something rather more mundane.

"How did you know my name?"

"You spoke it to the Sheriff the day you revealed the lock," came the reply. "Since then, your name and assumed rank have been used in numerous communications, verbal and otherwise."

There was something about the clinical logic of the reply, which told Phil he was talking to a computer.

"Who are you?" said Phil.

"In your parlance, I am Maximum Intellect Neural Databank, or MIND, for short - a hybrid entity comprising original brain material and nucleic processors. I am responsible for the protection and day-to-day running of this facility, and for monitoring events outside. I was going to introduce myself, but you followed my greeting with a question. Please excuse me."

So, it is a computer, thought Phil. He wondered about the 'protection', and whether that fact had been dropped into the conversation deliberately. He also detected the merest hint of a reprimand for his sudden second question. It was as if someone of intellectually high stature had been interrupted by an idiot, yet apologised to the idiot for presuming to carry on speaking. He decided to pause, and await MIND's next move.

"Major," it began. "Please sit down. The drink is iced orange juice, to which you are very welcome."

Trembling slightly, Phil sat down and poured a little of the drink. It smelt like orange juice, and the glass started misting up. It crossed his mind that it might be poisoned or drugged, then dismissed the idea. If they had wanted a human specimen, they could have taken him long before this. He sipped at it then took a long draft. It was undoubtedly the most refreshing orange juice he had ever tasted. MIND continued.

"I have notified the Commander and others of your arrival. Currently, they are learning your language, and will be in a position to converse with you this afternoon. In the meantime, you and some of your colleagues are welcome to enter and explore what we have here. But before that, I imagine you have some questions."

The polite and disarming tone of the voice gave Phil the impression that he was being invited to look round an ocean-going Royal Yacht of some interstellar potentate. He fought to marshal his thoughts.

"How is it you speak English?" he said.

"There have been ample opportunities for me to listen to and learn your language since I started monitoring," said MIND. "Your radio, TV, satellite, and cellular telephone communications provide a rich source, as do the conversations in the proximity of this door."

"You've been monitoring us?" said Phil. He was beginning to comprehend the scale of their activities.

"Yes. My monitoring capacity includes all electro-magnetic transmissions, local air and ground-borne vibrations, data highways through your primary international cables, and visual inspection from the Moon."

Phil was stunned. The concept that most human activity was now under the microscope was unsettling to say the least.

"Cables?" he said. "How? What sort of information have you gained access to?"

"As you will soon see, Major, our expertise in underground habitation is unparalleled. Remote monitoring devices were despatched to your primary cable systems in late September. As for the information, that includes banks, corporations, government and military institutions, centres of learning, libraries, newspapers, literary and musical publishing, telephones, and of course, the Internet. I have recently completed a total on-load of that information. Now, it is simply a matter of updating as changes occur."

Phil's jaw dropped and his eyes opened wide. He couldn't believe what he was hearing.

"Are you trying to tell me that you have now got a copy of everything stored on every major computer system in the world? What about security, passwords, firewalls?" he said incredulously.

"Yes, Major. At least, all systems which are not totally isolated. Your security systems are, with respect, extremely primitive. Think of me as an ever-expanding receptacle, into which you drop the presents of human knowledge and activity."

If they can read it, they can probably write to it too, thought Phil. The prospect of the world's economic systems being manipulated by this all-powerful electronic brain sent a shiver down his spine. But perhaps it was a bluff. Dare he test it?

"What is Sysadmin's password at Newheart Electric Vehicles?" he said.

"Equinox," came the immediate reply. "And understand I am only divulging it because it is clear from the files that it is your own password."

It was right. Phil closed his eyes. The feeling in the pit of his stomach was almost a physical pain. Nobody else knew that password - not even Jo-Ann. God help us, he thought, if this thing turns nasty.

Recovering from the effects of MIND's revelations, Phil returned to the all-important question of what was behind all this. It wasn't at all clear whether it was MIND itself, or some beings that had come with it. It had mentioned a Commander and others.

The question and answer session that followed, solicited that there were creatures, they were anxious to make contact, but where they were from and what their mission was would be explained later.

"And their names?" said Phil.

"There is no direct translation, but I think 'The Cryons' is a suitable appellation," said MIND. "You will come to understand why I use this word, later."

The *Cryons!* At last, a name. The word conjured images of some sort of ice warriors. Phil was beside himself with curiosity as to what they looked like.

"Your friends are worried about you," said MIND suddenly. "May I suggest you report back to them now, before they launch the rescue attempt they are planning. A party of twenty are welcome to return. I would provide transport, but I think you would prefer to use your own. There will be a nine mile drive. It would be inadvisable for you to bring weapons, but I will not stop you if you would feel more comfortable carrying them. Go now in peace, Major."

With that, the small doorway opened once more, and Phil - to the considerable relief of Jo-Ann and the others - emerged, to face the barrage of questions from the now changed world.

***

In addition to Phil, the entry party - now clad in military coveralls and waiting nervously in five Humvees - comprised Vice President Powell, Secretary Straker, Governor Cranford, Beemish, Generals Miller and Norman, SETI's Pulanski and his wheelchair, Sheriff Collins, BJ, four government scientists, and six military guards. Beemish, under Straker's direction, was in charge of tactics and deployment, but overall command was assumed by Powell.

Despite the recommendation passed on by Phil that weapons should not be carried, every man had been issued with a shoulder holster and automatic pistol. Phil had overheard an argument in which General Miller had proposed that nobody go in, but rather, they should besiege the aliens and force them to come out. General Norman had tried to persuade Straker - over Beemish's head - that they should go in by tank. Neither suggestion had been well received, but Straker had been persuaded that if they were to go in, then at least, weapons should be carried. The guards carried machine guns and grenades. Phil was left wondering what the Cryons would make of their squabbling and their primitive attempts at self-protection.

Phil was in the back seat of the lead vehicle. A guard sat next to him. Beemish and Powell sat up front. On Beemish's command, the five vehicles drove in convoy towards the door. As they approached, a large section in front of them opened, and they drove inside.

Straddling the route ahead were a series of semi-circular hoops, glowing deep blue in the subdued light. The convoy stopped, and the door closed behind them.

"Drive slowly through the hoops," boomed MIND's voice over the sound of the growling engines.

Beemish hesitated, and turned round to Phil.

"What do you reckon?" he said.

Phil stood up and called out. "MIND. May I ask why this is necessary. What are the hoops for?"

"For your own protection," came the reply. "You are going to have to trust me. There will be occasions when you may be asked to co-operate without understanding why. Whilst you are welcome to ask, it will serve only to delay the contact you so desire. Please believe me. No harm will come to any of you by anything we do."

'We', thought Phil. That was the first time MIND had used that word. There was also the implication that harm might befall them from their own hands. Perhaps that was why weapons were ill-advised.

"I don't think we have a choice," said Phil. He could see the guard literally shaking with fear. He was gripping his gun and staring all around him, his finger quivering over the trigger.

Powell tried his mobile, but got no signal. Beads of perspiration dotted his forehead. "We're on our own," he said, shakily.

"Send the guard through," came Miller's voice over the walkie-talkie from the last vehicle.

Phil saw through the rear-view mirror, the contempt in Beemish's eyes. He engaged 2nd, and drove through.

After the hoops, the tunnel opened into the tip of a wedge-shaped chamber of gargantuan proportions. From Phil's position, the floor of the tunnel seemed to vanish. All he could see was the dimly-lit roof. The party halted, and everyone climbed out. To their amazement, in front of them, resembling the rim of some subterranean canyon, was the lip of an extremely wide ramp which ran downwards into the ground at a slope of about one in three. Above this, the roof of the chamber continued horizontally for at least 1000 ft before following the ramp downwards. The result was a steeply-inclined tunnel, whose proportions - some 500 ft wide by 300 ft high - brought gasps of disbelief from the party. Phil peered down into the distant gloom, but the tunnel extended before them as far as the eye could see. He tried to conceive the type of vehicle which would need such an enormous entry shaft; it was easily large enough to accommodate an ocean liner.

There was no question of the 200 horse power 4WD Hummers not making it back up the slope, so the decision was made to continue. As the vehicles lurched over the edge and started their precipitous journey, it felt to Phil as if they were driving down the side of a mountain. He studied the tunnel walls. They had the appearance of fused glass, and were glowing with a dim yellow light. As they travelled, a brighter band of soft light kept pace with them, showing the way several hundred yards ahead. Behind, unfathomable blackness followed, like some gigantic beast in pursuit of its prey.

With the odometers reading nine miles, and the scientists exclaiming the party was at a depth of three miles, the tunnel became horizontal and emerged into a huge intersection. From it, the main tunnel continued, and smaller tunnels, each the same width and height as the door at the surface, led off to each side. They stopped; the engines were cut, and the awe-struck party dismounted. The rattle of equipment boxes being unloaded and the sounds of boots against the steel-hard ground, reverberated off the walls and echoed down the tunnels.

The air was not unpleasant, but Phil thought he sensed a slight mustiness about it, and strangely, it was humid.

"The temperature should be about 150 centigrade at this depth," called one of the scientists, "But it's only just over thirty!"

"Pressure should be way up," said another, "But it ain't."

BJ walked over to Phil and Beemish.

"Do you realise we are a mile deeper than the deepest mine man has ever sunk," he said. "It's quite incredible. I'd love to know what the walls are made of."

MIND spoke once more, its voice coming from somewhere high above them.

"Please feel free to explore," it said. "No visible avenue, hall, exhibit or device is excluded, and you may operate any machine you encounter. I repeat, there is nothing here that can harm you, save what you yourself may have brought in. Light patterns indicate the route back to here. The Commander will be ready to receive you at 1530 hours."

Beemish consulted with Powell and Straker, then addressed the party from his open-topped vehicle.

"This place shall be designated, 'The Hub'," he said. "Initially, General Norman and Sergeant Harris will remain here as anchor-men, and collate information which individual sorties provide. Parties may group by personal preference. Nobody who wishes to remain here will be forced or pressurised into going further. Notify party personnel to Hub control before you leave, and report by radio to the Hub on channel one every fifteen minutes. Re-assemble here by 1500 hours. No heroics please. Whatever you encounter, stay calm, and behave as if you were honoured guests in a foreign land. Good luck to you all."

He climbed down and walked over to Phil and BJ.

"One electrical engineer and an Earth scientist. Could be a good mix," he smiled. "Shall we take Mr Powell and start down that tunnel to the left? Sir?"

Whilst Beemish was logging details of his party with General Norman, Phil was analysing what MIND had just said. No visible avenue. Perhaps there were invisible ones. Exhibits, devices, machines? What was this? They were clearly being watched, but by whom? By what? For what purpose?

Beemish had returned and was ready for the off. Soon, the massive tyres were purring along the super-smooth surface once more. After a short distance, the tunnel brought them out into an enormous hangar-like hall. The roof was about 100 ft high, and the area would have dwarfed a football stadium. The floor of the hall was covered with row upon row of massive blocks. Each block measured fifty by ninety feet, and was perhaps forty feet high, with smooth, mirror-like sides. The grid pattern of broad aisles between the blocks seemed to extend indefinitely. Looming down from the half-light of the roof space were strange grappling devices reminiscent of industrial beam cranes. Beemish turned the Humvee down one of the aisles and pulled up at an intersection.

"This is like Central Stores at DC," he said, "But the size!"

That was it, thought Phil. It was a warehouse. He got out of the vehicle and walked over to the nearest block. He could see himself reflected repeatedly between its mirror surface and that of the block across the aisle. Powell and BJ followed him, bewildered.

"How the hell did they get all this stuff down here?" said Powell. "And why? This is no temporary base."

Beemish was standing studying a four foot high pillar next to the block. Phil joined him. The top surface of the pillar was inscribed with symbols resembling the petroglyphs along the top of the door. Below the symbols was something remarkably like a lever switch. He and Phil eyed each other.

"Shall we try it?" he said. His eyes glowed, like a small boy who had found a secret passage in a gothic mansion.

Powell and BJ retired to a safe distance. Phil found himself automatically weighing up the pros and cons, then realised it was pointless.

"You're the boss," he said warily, and took two steps backwards. Beemish gingerly touched the switch, then moved it towards him and jumped back to join Phil.

Phil heard an almost imperceptible hum from somewhere near the base of the block. The four men watched in amazement as the mirror surface slowly faded, and the block took on the appearance of a hollow glass tank. Inside, illuminated by an unseen sun, but motionless as if frozen, was a scene so lifelike - so incredibly detailed in every degree - that for a moment Phil was convinced he was part of it. In front of him, surrounded by vegetation glistening in the wetness of a recent shower, was a huge hairy orange-coloured beast with long tusks, larger than an elephant. Across its back and over its head were crude ropes, which looked as if they might have been made of rushes or flax. Tugging at these ropes, were men. They were short, hairy about the face and arms, and wrapped in furs. Some were brandishing spears with rough-hewn shafts and chipped stone heads. They were all in a state of great agitation, and their expressions - emphasised by their large protruding jaws - ranged from anger, through determination, to unmitigated terror.

"That's a Woolly Mammoth!" exclaimed BJ, "And those guys are Homo Erectus!"

It was like an exhibit in a natural history museum. But these were no models or taxidermed specimens. They were real! Then Phil realised that on the other three sides of the tank, where its walls should be, the scene extended into the distance but on a two-dimensional plane, as if the tank was bounded by cinema screens. He started walking round the tank, and in so doing was able to gain a 360 degree perspective of the environment from which the tank's contents had obviously been plucked.

"This is the most incredible and priceless record of pre-historic life I have ever seen," said BJ rapturously. He was standing with his nose touching the tank wall. The needles of a conifer tree were inches from his eyes. "Look at the scene. Cold, a bit boggy, lakes, Spruce, Mammoths. I'd say this was brought here from Europe."

But Phil was thinking of the implications, as were the other two.

"What era in Earth's history was this?" asked Powell.

"Oh, probably the Mindel ice age, middle Pleistocene. About half a million years ago," replied BJ.

"My God!" said Powell. "The Cryons have been visiting us since then."

"And taking specimens and storing them down here," said Beemish.

"Since then?" said Phil. "We don't know this was the first. There are hundreds of these things. I think we should check some of the others."

They dragged BJ away from the tank and flipped the switch back to its original position. Instantly, the tank reverted to its mirror-box appearance and the humming stopped.

Beemish checked the route back. In the centre of the aisle, rows of small lights could be seen rippling, wave-like, towards the Hub.

"Lets go on," he said.

They drove deeper into the hall of blocks, stopping occasionally to examine the specimens. It soon became clear that the blocks were in groups of thirty two, each group representing an earlier period in Earth's history. But in every case, the contents of each block were as fresh and lifelike as the day they were taken. They moved further into the hall, drawn on by the fascination of peering further back in time.

The hall turned out to be 2/3rds miles wide and 1½ miles long. The penultimate group of blocks - the 130th - had contained specimens from the beginning of the Tertiary period. BJ was beside himself with excitement as they approached the end of the hall, and the last group.

But Powell's face had taken on a shocked expression. He had stopped getting out of the Humvee, and was just sitting in it, motionless.

"Sixty five million years!" he kept repeating.

The end wall loomed ahead of them. They approached one of the blocks in the final group. Like a man possessed, BJ ran to the switch and flipped it on. Inside the tank, five dinosaurs, some seven feet tall, their scaly skin caked in the mud from the banks of a nearby stream, were caught, running towards him. He jumped back in horror at the ferociousness of their appearance.

"Those are Utahraptors!" he exclaimed. "Oh God! They're magnificent!"

Speechless, Phil peered into the tank, and began his usual circumnavigation. From another side, he heard Beemish shouting.

"Come round! Look at this!"

Phil and BJ ran round to join him. He was standing frozen to the spot, staring into the distance. Phil followed his gaze. There, less than three hundred yards away within the cinema-like image, and near the banks of a meandering river, was a structure. It was a huge glistening dome with a series of windows running along a balcony some fifty feet above the ground. Parked outside it was a metallic craft on six legs, looking remarkably like a gigantic silver ant. At the front of the craft - presumably its cockpit - were three windows.

"Look," said Beemish, his voice trembling with emotion, "In the cockpit."

It was too far away to see clearly, but behind the cockpit window, just visible through the sunlight reflecting off it, was the head of a creature.

From sixty five million years in the past, two large yellow eyes were staring at them.

***

By lunch time, as they arrived back at the Hub, it was clear that other parties had encountered similarly dramatic experiences. There was talk of huge machines the nature of which could not be established, vast stores of minerals, and specimens of marine life. The members of one party were hardly able to remain coherent as they described a library in which it had been possible to view 3D sound film of life on Earth, millions of years ago.

Some of the men were in the Humvees, totally bewildered and obviously in deep shock, and there was a queue for the portable toilet. Phil noticed General Miller, sitting hunched up as if he was cold, and quivering like a jelly. Powell, Straker and Cranford were clearly agitated, and kept walking off out of earshot, muttering to each other quietly.

The most profound discovery, and the one it was now decided that all should investigate, was what had been designated, 'The Dream Factory'. Sue Pickard, a bio-chemist, and Sergeant Chas Patroni, were the only two people who had tried it. They were in ecstasies. Pickard was clutching a roll of paper-like material on which was printed a series of highly complex equations. Apparently, the paper described the solution to a research problem she had been working on for over ten years.

"I just sort of asked for it," she said, "And out it came!"

Patroni was walking around grinning like a Cheshire cat, and turning his head this way and that as if listening for something.

"It just went - just like that!" he said. "I'm due for my next medical in two months, and I was shit scared. Now, I'll sail through it."

"What was wrong, Sergeant?" said Beemish.

"Oh, Tinnitus Sir. You know - ringing in the ears. It was getting so bad, I was going to be pensioned off. But I just drank the liquid, and it went! I can hear everything - clear as a bell! It's a miracle!"

The Dream Factory was a circular room off one of the main tunnels. As Phil walked in, he could see it was dominated by a central metallic cylinder some twenty five feet in diameter running from floor to ceiling. Arranged round and facing it were sixteen open-ended booths. Within each booth was a chair of unconventional design, in front of which was a bench. Each chair back comprised a broad curved structure, at the top of which were two flanges. Phil sat, uncomfortably, on one of the chairs, and noticed that the flanges came almost level with the top of his head. Within seconds however, the chair seemed to change shape in response to his body. It became perfectly comfortable, and the flanges ended up level with his ears. He realised why this uncanny suppleness did not unnerve him - it was just like the door material moulding itself round his palms. He was aware of some of the others from the entry party also taking up places round the cylinder.

"Hello again," said the voice of MIND. It seemed to be coming from just in front of him. Phil guessed that the others would also hear MIND speaking to them, and that it was probably capable of holding a multitude of simultaneous conversations.

"You have seen some of the treasures we have collected over the years," it went on. "And now, as a token of our friendship, we would like to offer you one or two of the things you most desire - if it is within our power."

As MIND was speaking, Phil realised that the booth, the chair, and indeed his very awareness of his surroundings seemed to be fading from his consciousness. All he could hear was MIND's soothing voice. Soon, a pleasant feeling of total relaxation overcame him, coupled with a desire to pour out his inner soul.

'One or two of the things you most desire,' seemed to repeat and channel his thoughts. He quivered momentarily as he thought of Jo-Ann, and the intensely pleasurable feeling when they made love. But that desire - if he managed to keep in her good books - was catered for. Briefly, Svetlana came to mind, then Dave. Dave .... Poor bastard. If only he could have got to him in time. If only .....

"You would like it if Dave could have his hand back would you, Phil?" came a voice from inside his head.

He didn't have to answer. He just thought his response.

"I see from Raigmore Hospital's Electronic Patient Record System, that the amputation was towards the base of the radius and ulna. I can provide a replacement hand and wrist, along with grafting instructions for the hospital. Would you like that, Phil?"

Trance-like, Phil calmly asked, "You can do that okay?"

"Oh yes. Our nano-technology is unsurpassed. Within three days of the graft, Dave's hand will look and feel - to himself and others - exactly like the original. The hand I will give you will remain inert until the graft is completed. Activation will then be automatic."

Thank you, thought Phil.

"And what about something for yourself, Phil?"

"You couldn't help with the vehicle battery design could you?"

The Holy Grail of the electric vehicle industry was a light, compact battery, with the power of a petrol engine and enough storage capacity to give the car a range of over 300 miles. If he could crack this, he would be able to change the world.

"I suggest you have a look at this," said MIND.

Phil was shown a solidly-built container, roughly the size of a large kitchen sink. Running across inside it were numerous rods of two different metals. A close-fitting reinforced lid was then fitted. The lid had a filler valve at its centre, through which was piped a fluid of unknown description. When the container was full, shown by a small quantity of the liquid seeping out of the filler valve, it was sealed with a simple twist of the hand.

"It's important that no air remains in the cell," said MIND.

Phil then noticed that the container had, built in to one side of it, a cylinder, so arranged that a piston could exert pressure on the fluid within.

"The rods inside act as catalytic collectors," said MIND. "One set positive and the other negative. See. The ends of each set are connected together here. I will now connect each set to the terminals of the artificial load. The voltage and power produced can be seen on these readout panels."

Phil watched, entranced. The voltage panel was flickering around the 1 Volt mark, and the power, zero Kilowatts.

"Now press on the piston," said MIND.

Phil obliged. As he pressed and released the piston, the voltage and power gauges rose and fell, the peak power achieved being 2.4 Kilowatts.

That's over three horse power! He said. And with just hand pressure on the piston!

"That's right, Phil. It's a piezoelectric rechargeable liquid. If you want a good name, try LIQUECS or LIQUEX - Liquid Electrical Charging System. Its energy storage capacity is very high. With a unit this size, about one hundred and twenty horse power is easily achievable using a basic hydraulic pressure system."

That's equivalent to a normal car engine! And the capacity?

"Enough to provide the range you seek."

"Recharging time?"

"Whilst it is perfectly feasible to recharge it in situ, it could take overnight using the entire capacity of a domestic power supply. By far the easiest way is to discharge the flagging LIQUEX into a communal container, and re-fill with a fresh supply, just like .filling up with petrol. The LIQUEX station then recharges the LIQUEX in bulk, ready for dispensing to the next day's customers."

Even within his trance-like state, Phil could feel the euphoria building up inside him. A rechargeable, recyclable liquid, with an energy storage capacity far exceeding petrol! Clean power, environmentally friendly, convenient! Such a system would be of inestimable value to the world - a technological advance beyond his wildest dreams. The internal combustion engine would be thrown onto the scrap-heap of history. Exhaust gas pollution would be a thing of the past. The planet itself, and everything on it would benefit. And he would become the richest man in the world!

"Would you like a print-out of the LIQUEX manufacturing process, and the design specifications of the power cell and recharging system?" said MIND, in its warm, calm manner.

"Yes please!" said Phil out loud, almost exploding with elation.

As he became aware of his surroundings once more, he realised he was still sitting at the chair in the Dream Factory. He hadn't been anywhere at all, but his memory was so clear. He had been shown the LIQUEX power unit. He had *touched* it. The unusual smell of the liquid was still in his nostrils; the feel of the piston lever still on his right palm. Surely the whole thing couldn't have been only mental. He glanced around him and began to hear the others in the room, then realised that on the bench in front of him was a small box. He leaned forward, opened it, and recoiled at the sight of a human hand wrapped in transparent material. In a slim pocket within the box were instructions for grafting it.

So it wasn't a dream, he thought. As he closed the box, out from a slot in the main cylinder, emerged a print-out containing the information about the LIQUEX and power unit. He read it avidly. Everything was there - everything he needed to go into production. He quickly folded it up and hid it in the inner pocket of his coveralls.

He stood up, to see Beemish walking towards him. He was clutching a small bottle of turquoise liquid.

"They've given me something for Louise's spinal injury!" he exclaimed. "My wife, she's a paraplegic. I can't believe it. If this works, it'll change our lives!"

The room was now ringing with the sounds of exclamations and mutual congratulations. Excited voices could be heard exalting the gifts bestowed upon them. Some people shed tears of relief as a long-term problem was solved, or a burden lifted from their shoulders. Suddenly, Phil saw one of the scientists walking backwards, videoing the scene in front of him. Round from behind the central cylinder appeared Sheriff Collins. He was gripping someone by the arm, steadying him, helping him. The man was crying out in wonderment and rapture. He raised his head. Tears of joy were streaming down his face.

It was Pulanski. He was walking.

***

As the party re-assembled at the Hub, the general mood was one of euphoria. But Phil could see that not everybody shared this emotion. In particular, Governor Cranford and General Miller were far from happy. Unlike the others, neither of them was clutching a gift; neither of them looked any better for their experiences. If anything, Cranford was more worried and Miller more distressed than before. Clearly, not all dreams came true in the Dream Factory.

It was half past three. MIND's voice echoed through the Hub once more. This was the moment when it had said that 'The Commander' would be ready. The party listened expectantly.

"Ladies and gentlemen. We have been pleased to be able to help many of you, and through our simple gifts, allow you to benefit from our experience and some of our discoveries. The Commander is now in a position to receive you, but before he does, he has asked me to reveal to you, the first of the Great Truths."

The members of the party stared at one another, intrigued. The scientists stood spellbound. They were clearly hoping for a major pronouncement concerning the nature of the universe. The military personnel - unused to having to deal with such a perplexing 'enemy' - peered about them suspiciously. The politicians were as usual, the most disconcerted group. It crossed Phil's mind that of all the issues they had to deal with, truth was not high on their agenda.

MIND continued.

"If you would follow the lights please, it is a short walk to the conference rooms. You may leave your belongings with the vehicles. They will be quite safe."

Once again, lights appeared along the ground leading to one of the tunnels. Driven by the curiosity which now overcame any reticence or fear, the party followed them. Phil began to feel uneasy. Not only did he hate being led anywhere in a party - he could never stand coach tours - but he was convinced they were being observed. He didn't like the idea that they might be being studied, as one might study an insect discovered on a field trip. And there was something else. Every now and again, there was a whiff. It was just the merest hint of a smell, but smell there was. He couldn't place it, but it triggered a long-lost memory of a hospital. Was it gas? Wasn't it in the concentration camps that prisoners were told they were going to the showers, only to be gassed? The gifts and miracles that had just occurred seemed too good to be true. Why should this intelligence - these Cryons - be so altruistic? But on the other hand, why would they not be? If destruction or invasion was their aim, they could surely achieve that without these theatricals. It had to be that they genuinely sought contact, and had come offering gifts, as did the early European explorers.

Up ahead, the comparative gloom of the tunnel was pierced by shafts of light from two side chambers. MIND announced that they had arrived at the conference rooms. It was at that point that Phil realised why he was so dubious about explorers bearing gifts. He knew what had happened to natives all over the world who had been visited by explorers bearing gifts.

They had been invaded.

13

Revelation

"It would be of benefit," came MIND's voice, "And assist us during the contact phase, if each of you would join one of two groups. The first group will be your executives, and the second will comprise the investigators and the military assistants."

MIND then named Powell, Straker, Cranford, Beemish, Miller, Norman, Collins, and Phil himself to be in the first group, invited them into the nearest side chamber, and the others into the second.

Phil's group paused at the entrance to the room. It was clear that he was not alone in feeling uneasy. Ever since they arrived - in fact ever since the door had been discovered - a thread of manipulation had been woven through everything they had done. They were no longer in control, and they didn't like it.

"We don't have to go in there," called Miller from the back. "I've seen enough."

"I agree," said Cranford. "The only Great Truth I care about right now is whether those Hummers are going to make it all the way back, up that damned tunnel!"

"Gentlemen," said Powell, "We've come this far. We can't turn back now. We have to go in. I don't think we have a choice. The opportunity for contact is within our grasp."

An animated discussion ensued. Finally, it was agreed - reluctantly by some - that to demonstrate solidarity, strength, and a willingness to co-operate, all should enter. Along the corridor, the other group had obviously come to the same conclusion.

The room was well lit, and dominated by a large circular table of indefinable material. Twelve silver strips - arranged like the hour marks of a clock face - were inlaid into the table top. Nine high-back winged chairs - of similar design to those in the Dream Factory - had been placed, one per segment, round the table.

Phil was curious about the remaining three seats, and walked round to look at them. They were low stools, their upper surfaces curved in a way that would render them virtually impossible to sit upon. Even more strange was that between each stool and the table was a slender 'T' shaped structure some four feet high. The cross bar of the 'T' was slightly concave, as if designed to accept something leaning or resting on it.

The walls of the room were as usual, glass-like, and diffused a soft light. But behind the strange stools, the wall was dark. Phil stared at it. Its resemblance to a two-way mirror was undeniable.

"Please sit down," said MIND. "Make yourselves comfortable."

Hesitantly, the eight men took their places round the table. Phil found Secretary Straker and General Norman either side of him. He could see every face clearly. They looked like members of a Board of Directors who were meeting for the first time, and waiting awkwardly for the Chairman.

As before, Phil felt the seat and winged back adjust itself to match his body, but this time, there was no feeling of relaxation. Rather, he began to feel strangely alert. It was as if his mind was being tuned and supercharged - like a racing car engine before a Grand Prix. In addition, he began to feel the strangest but not unpleasant sensation that all his senses were increasing in their perceptivity. As he looked around him, the other men's faces became much clearer. He began to notice fleeting changes of expression, facial features, imperfections, eye colours. Strange, he hadn't noticed these before. He could hear them breathing, and faintly in some, another sound was detectable. Then he realised it was their teeth touching each other. He became aware of that smell again, but much stronger now. And he recognised why it had reminded him of a hospital. It was a cross between acetone and ether. The men around him smelt too - of after-shave, shower splash, hair gel, body odour, under-arm sweat, and bad breath. He even imagined he could taste some of those smells as he breathed in the air around him. He found himself exploring the surface texture of the table-top and the sides of his chair with his fingertips, which now seemed like 'touch microscopes' capable of detecting the tiniest grain of dust. Even his sense of balance - something he wouldn't normally notice when not in space - was informing him of every microscopic change in the position of his head and body.

And over and above all these enhanced stimuli, he began to be aware of something else - something new - something he had never experienced before. He felt that a veil was being lifted from his mind. Now he knew how people felt who, having been blind all their lives, were operated upon and given their sight. Vision can never be truly described to those who have never seen, but once they gain their sight, they recognise its power and wonder instantly. He tried to describe this new sense to himself, but failed. What he did know however, was that Powell was about to ask a question about the Great Truths.

"Could you tell us please," said Powell suddenly, "What are the Great Truths, and what is the nature of this, the first one?"

How had he known what Powell was about to say?

"The Great Truths," replied Mind, "Are the understanding we have of the universe, its laws and its reason, from the Self, right up to The Hierarchy."

"The Hierarchy?" replied Powell. Phil realised that the thought of any chain of command which did not lead to the President, would unsettle Powell.

"Do not ask about the ultimate," said MIND. "Before any of the other Great Truths can be understood, you must understand the Self."

"Are you saying that the first of the Great Truths is an understanding of the Self?"

"Almost, Mr Vice President," said MIND. "The first of the Great Truths is an understanding of the truth about yourselves."

As MIND spoke those last words, Phil recognised what it was that he was sensing. It was as if he was able to see into the minds of the others. He glanced round the table. As his eyes lighted upon this man, then that, it was as if he was removing a mask, and exposing each subject's inner thoughts. Their very souls were laid bare.

For a moment, Phil lowered his eyes, avoiding the others. What had MIND meant by 'yourselves'? Did it mean the group collectively, or did it mean oneself? Could it be that somehow, by seeing others for what they really were, one began to truly understand and accept one's own psyche?

The answer came sooner than he thought, and hit him like hammer blow from hell. He suddenly realised that he himself was being studied. He looked up, to see Cranford gazing at him from across the table. The feeling was the worst and most disconcerting terror he had ever experienced. It felt like the mental equivalent of standing in a public place and having one's clothes removed completely. Nothing was sacred, nothing hidden. It got worse. As others glanced his way, more and yet more defenses were breached. Mental fingers began probing into his most secret places. Nobody had been there before. This was violation of the worst kind. He fought to protect himself but it was useless. The sickening feeling became all-consuming.

His mind was being raped.

What were they finding out about him? What would others think? Yes, when his father and brother were killed, nobody shouldered the blame. Yes, he distrusted the US Government and all its agents. Yes, and all Federal institutions, especially the Federal Aviation Authority. The cold which prevented him from flying? Yes, his fault - he'd not worn a jacket when his mother told him to. Yes, he should have been on the plane too but was saved because he'd been disobedient. Of course he loved his wife. Yes, he desired other women too. What did he want from life? To be loved, to provide for his children, to be admired and respected, to grow the business until he was the world's number one. How? He could use the knowledge MIND had passed on. The world would beat a path to his door. Of course he told lies sometimes. Yes, he'd been unfaithful - once.

Phil couldn't tell who it was who was doing this to him. It could have been everybody. But what he began to feel was a strange sort of relief, now it was out. He recalled a similar unburdening when, as a child, he confessed to some misdemeanour. The act of confessing took guts and was unbearable at the time, but afterwards, the freedom from fhe need to continue the deception was ample compensation.

Humbled, but now no longer fearful of further disclosures, he raised his head and began studying the others round the table. He soon discovered that eye-to-eye contact was unbearable. By nature, men are not at ease with admitting vulnerability, and in their transparent state, that was what was happening. The technique - soon acquired - was to scrutinise either someone whose eyes were lowered or someone who was already watching someone else.

He started with Powell. He was sitting motionless, an expression of helplessness on his face. Gone was the New Englander's squeaky clean mantle of lofty family values and loyalty to his country. Underneath, was a power-hungry hypocrite, and the leader of a clandestine Washington group whose primary aim was to unseat the President. He was toughing it out. To him, family values were a thing of the past anyway, and many believed his quest for the Presidency justified.

Straker's mind divulged that over the last few years, America's defense strategy was one of destabilization or covert manipulation of every country who could pose even the hint of a threat. America's so-called allies - including the UK - were treated as mere tools of the United States, and that the principle behind all agreements was one of total US self-interest. Delving deeper revealed that Straker's eldest son had for years been exporting arms to a neighbour of Borumbia, the war with whose drug barons had cost hundreds of American lives. Floyd Straker knew perfectly well that the ultimate destination of the arms was Borumbia, but his father turned a blind eye. What father wouldn't, he appealed.

As Phil cast around the table for further interesting subjects, he began to sense an increase in the level of tension. It was clear that many of the men had experienced - and come through - the confessional phase, and were now hell bent on unashamedly discovering as much as they could about the others around them. Three of the men opposite were staring at Miller, a mixture of pity and contempt on their faces. Phil followed their gaze, to see Miller, stone-faced and in total denial. Major General Nathan Miller - the man in charge of the most powerful nuclear weapon fleet in the world - was sexually inferior, a coward, and a Fascist. He compensated for his inadequacies with sexual sadism. He had even been a member of a private audience on at least two occasions during which abducted non-white women had been publicly gang-raped in the most sickening and deviant manner imaginable. After that, it came as no surprise that it was Miller's 'Free America cell' who had arranged the Cape Canaveral bomb hoax. He was so frightened of the prospect of encountering the aliens that he would do anything to sabotage contact. It was he who sent Snake and Whistler. Miller, sensing the eyes burning into him, attempted to get up and leave the table, but could not. As a test, Phil tried to rise, but he too could not move. His arms and legs felt as if they were paralysed.

He realised that if he studied Miller for a moment longer, he would be physically sick, so sat for a moment staring down at the table. He now understood exactly what MIND had meant about knowing the truth about themselves. It was turning into an extremely unpleasant experience. He began to wonder what 'normal' people were like inside. Did everyone have dark secrets? Was everybody play-acting the whole time?

It was while he was pondering this that he glanced up, to see Beemish staring back at him, pleading. Jo-Ann was a very desirable woman. His own wife was a cripple. Phil had disregarded Jo-Ann's wishes for years - no wonder she wanted a divorce. She had been very upset in Cheyenne whilst Phil had been in Houston, and he had been around. A woman like that deserved attention. He was so sorry, but he couldn't help himself - he had tried, gently, to seduce her. No red-blooded man could fail to try, given the opportunity. Jo-Ann had not resisted his first approaches, but in the event, had not succumbed.

It clicked suddenly, what Jo-Ann had meant when she mentioned temptation back in Houston. Perhaps both Jo and himself needed to experience someone else, for them to learn the real value of their marriage. Beemish had actually done him a favour. But then, Phil recoiled at the thought of another man touching Jo-Ann. The smarmy two-faced bastard! He felt the blood drain from his face, and his arms and legs turn into coiled springs. He wanted to leap across the table and smash his fist into Beemish's face. He tried to move but couldn't. He opened his mouth to speak, but no words came out. It was then that he realised that for this entire session, no-one had spoken or moved anything but their head and eyes. Obviously, they could not.

Then he looked at Cranford.

Cranford was sitting, his head bowed in contrition. From his mind, Phil was bombarded with images of corruption, deceit, and duplicity, all fired by a need for sexual gratification and a desperate desire to be admired by others. Cranford knew he was no academic, and accepted he was not exactly God's gift to women. But with influence, power, and money, he could indulge his peccadilloes, gorge himself on the fruits of life, and *be* someone. Yes, his brother had raped that girl, but if he hadn't suppressed the evidence against him, he would have lost everything. She was a nobody anyway.

As Phil delved deeper into Cranford's mind, he was able to peel back layer upon layer of hidden truths. A sense of dread began to take hold of him as he became aware of Cranford's earlier connections and business dealings. So he used to be big in aviation. Commercial airlines. Trans-American!

The realisation exploded in his mind like a bomb-shell. That name - Cranford. Now he knew where he had heard it before. It was his mother. During those terrible months after the crash, it was Cranford his mother had been campaigning about. It was Cranford who controlled the airline.

Robbed of any form of defense, Cranford's mind was now totally exposed to Phil's ruthless explorations. He sat there, his eyes boring into Cranford's head, and his mind ripping and tearing through his memories like a machete through undergrowth. Cranford had chaired secret meetings in the late seventies, at which, following two crashes, the cost of safety improvements had been discussed. He had fired the man who was pushing for more service and safety staff and more rigorous checks. To underbid the competition to secure lucrative government contracts, he had actually reduced the fleet maintenance budget, and cut corners on servicing. The airline bought replacements for failed components from aviation factors, but they were second-hand. They were components which had failed the rigorous checks of other airlines. They were lethal.

Phil discovered Cranford had been personally involved in the blackmail of the chairman of the FAA inquiry board, and then saw, through Cranford's eyes, the pages of the NTSB crash report. His blood ran cold. There, in black and white, he saw the words 'detectable fatigue crack' being changed to 'undetectable fatigue crack', and a paragraph pointing out that the crack should have been spotted during a routine maintenance inspection being removed completely. Cranford had caused that crash. As surely as if he had put a knife into them, Cranford had killed his father and brother.

In that moment, the cause of his mother's pain, her alienation with America, his own wariness of the US and its agencies, and his own guilt could be attributable to the actions of one man. For over thirty years, he had had no father to lean on, learn from, respect, live up to, show off to, or love. To fund his base desires and bolster his ego, Cranford had robbed him of a normal childhood, robbed him of the most important man in his life, and left him with a deep distrust of his own emotions. He sat staring at the ceiling, tears rolling down his cheeks, as, reliving the lost years, wave after wave of grief engulfed him. His anguish turned to bitterness, hate, burning rage, then blind fury. He stared at Cranford, his eyes glowing like a wild animal. His breathing was rapid and his pulse thundered in his ears. All he wanted to do was kill him. Every sinew was straining for action. He gripped the edge of the table. Oblivious to all else, he felt himself stand up, run round the table, and leap at Cranford. He had him by the throat, and was squeezing ... squeezing that podgy flesh between his iron-strong fingers. He felt Cranford's windpipe collapse under his thumbs, and saw his eyes bulging and his face turning bright scarlet. He could even smell Cranford's under-arm sweat as his arms went up to try to wrench Phil's hands from his neck. His mouth opened wide and his tongue darted out as he struggled desperately for air.

"You lousy rotten bastard!" Phil heard himself saying over and over again as he shook Cranford like a terrier shakes a rat. In that moment, the years of pent up grief and pain were released in one primeval act of raw vengeance. He could feel a tangible and deep physical satisfaction, as if he were purging his body of sorrow via his hands. Cranford's head lolled backwards and forwards, and his legs began to buckle. He was dying, and Phil was killing him.

As he sank slowly towards the floor, he gazed up at Phil. His eyes, no longer fearful, took on a look of total submission and acceptance of his fate, yet, in the few seconds remaining to him, appealed to Phil for mercy.

Phil stared down at the pitiful face, its eyes starting to blink as life ebbed away from it. His instinct demanded he finish the job; his body craved total satisfaction.

Suddenly, the enormity of what he was doing came home to him. He had no right. Revenge was certainly sweet, but not sweet enough to justify this ultimate act of retribution.

He loosened his grip on Cranford's throat, and let him fall to the floor like a sack of flour.

Chastened, and deeply shocked by the power and ferocity of his feelings, Phil found himself back at his place at the table. He slumped backwards in the chair and sat staring blankly in front of him. He felt totally drained and exhausted. MIND's words, 'The first of the Great Truths is an understanding of the truth about yourselves,' came back to him. Now he understood. Now he knew the real truth about his fellow man, and about himself. He knew that behind the faces, beneath the paper thin facade of civilisation, ran the dark and terrible chasms of their primeval past.

He had seen with the eyes of the beast within.

As he came round from his mental experience, he glanced about him. The others were still sitting at the table as before. He had to look carefully at Cranford before convincing himself that what had happened had only taken place in his own mind. It was clear that nobody had moved - nobody had been injured or nearly strangled - but it was also apparent that most of the men had undergone similar experiences. He could see that they too were traumatised by the import of what had been revealed to them. They too sat as he sat, eyes focused only inwards, faces wan, and completely exhausted.

All that is, except Miller.

"I don't accept it!" he exclaimed. His eyes stared wildly about him.

The room had been silent for so long, that the sound of a real voice came as a shock, bringing Phil back to reality with a jolt. Also, the unseen bonds which had prevented him from getting up seemed to have fallen away.

Miller rose to his feet and started fumbling for his gun as he backed towards the wall. But Collins, already anticipating pandemonium, fired a shot into the ceiling then levelled his gun at Miller's chest.

"Move a muscle and you're a dead man," he commanded. "Now, hands in the air!"

The gunshot was deafening in the echowy room, and, backed by the unmistakable authority of the Sheriff's tone of voice, had the desired effect.

"Your gun please, General," said Collins. "Easy does it. Now turn around. Hands on the wall."

Miller, his face an ashen grey, handed over the gun and complied. Collins frisked him then walked round to a position behind the three stools.

"Sit down, General," he ordered.

Miller obeyed.

Very slowly, and without taking his eyes off the men round the table, Collins bent down and laid Miller's gun on the floor near the wall behind him.

"Right, everyone," he barked. "Foreheads on the table, hands clasped behind your back. Now!"

From this prone position, Phil could just see, by squinting sideways, Collins relieving General Norman of his weapon, then heard him walk over and place it next to Miller's. Phil's own gun was next, then Straker's, and so on round the table.

"Stay down. Don't move," he said, as he walked back to the stools.

Out of the corner of his eye, Phil noticed the light in the room change slightly. There was a hint of amber. At the same time, Collins started to speak again.

"We may be three miles underground, but we're still in my County," he said. "And if there're any scores to settle, it'll be within the law. Now slowly, heads up, sit normally, and let's all stay calm shall we."

As Phil and the others raised their heads, the source of the amber light was obvious. Behind Collins, in the wall of their room was a transparent partition of some sort, and beyond that was a well-lit room.

And in that room, staring at them with huge yellow eyes, were five creatures.

***

Collins, too street wise to fall for the, 'Look out behind you!' trick, kept his eyes firmly fixed on the men round the table. But when he saw that to a man, their faces displayed unbelievable horror and their eyes were focused on the same point behind him, he permitted himself one glance rearwards.

"Oh, Jesus!" he exclaimed. He stood transfixed. The creatures were only ten feet away.

"Well handled, Sheriff Collins," came a disembodied voice. "Now, your gun too please. It will be returned to you later."

The voice was completely different to MIND's. It was sonorous, and had a strange musical quality about it, reminiscent of a Jew's harp - but of variable pitch.

Collins hesitated for a moment, then laid his gun on the ground and sent it skidding towards the partition with his foot.

"Sit down please," said the voice.

Collins, unable to take his eyes off the grotesque sight in front of him, stumbled backwards and felt his way back to his seat.

Three of the creatures were a good seven feet tall, and the other two, about five. The first impression Phil had was that of a giant Preying Mantis. They had massive triangular-shaped heads, atop bodies divided into three segments. The most striking feature of the head were the two yellow eyes, each some three inches across. They were not compound eyes like those of an insect, but forward-facing, with lenses. There was no iris. Instead, the corneas seemed capable of darkening or lightening depending upon the brightness of what was being observed. There was no nose as such, and the mouth comprised two side-hinged mandibles similar to those of some insects. On each side of the head were bulges, the open ends of conical tubes running backwards into the head. Phil thought these might be some form of ears. On the top of the head, and also forward-facing, was a third opening, in which could be glimpsed two parallel comb-like structures. From each side of the top of the head, sprang short segmented antennae, strengthening further the impression that these creatures were like giant insects

Phil could feel the hairs on the back of his neck rising as the creatures began slowly moving behind their partition. The upper of the three body segments was clearly the equivalent of a chest, as it served as the fixing point for two long arms, at the end of which were four multi-segmented chelae, serving as the creature's fingers. The central body section - angled at about 45° - held two pairs of articulated legs, the front pair of which were much larger and obviously stronger than the rear pair. The creatures were maintaining an essentially upright but stooped posture using their front legs as primary support, the rear pair seemingly being used to maintain balance or adjust position. It occurred to Phil that these creatures might be able to run quite quickly, by leaning further forwards and keeping their shorter rear legs and stubby body section off the ground. There was no sign of any sort of clothing, but one of them - incongruously - was wearing an amulet.

As they moved, Phil could see that their exoskeletons glistened in the light, and were a pinkish white on all upward-facing surfaces, but more of a greeny yellow on all downward facing surfaces. Their heads, apart from the crown, were golden brown, and at this moment, were all turned towards the horrified onlookers.

"Do not be afraid," said the same voice. None of the creatures appeared to be moving their mouths, but Phil could tell that it was the central figure who was addressing them.

"We will be coming in to join you. Stay in your seats. It will be necessary for us to increase the temperature and humidity in your room to a level half way between our and your preferred conditions. This will cause us all discomfort, but for the limited duration of this contact, be just tolerable."

Within a few seconds, Phil could feel the temperature of the room rising. Simultaneously, the air around him acquired a soft humid feel, reminiscent of a sauna. He lowered the zip of his coveralls as beads of perspiration began to form on his forehead. Some of the men round the table began wiping their hands on their trouser legs and mopping their brows as they waited nervously for the next stage.

The partition opened to a swirl of mist. Clearly, the air behind it was hotter and more humid than that within the conference room. The two smaller creatures walked out and gathered up the weapons lying on the ground, and carried them to the recesses of their own quarters. As this happened, the ether-like smell returned, but much more strongly. The smell, though slightly nauseating, was not intolerable. Phil could not stop himself wondering whether to the creatures, humans also smelt.

With the guns now out of reach, the two small creatures took up positions each side of the partition, and the three larger ones came forward. Their gait was slow and deliberate, and their bodies rocked gently from side to side as they walked. Their heads, whilst remaining upright, moved from side to side as do some animals when studying a potential prey. Phil swallowed hard as they approached the table and lowered themselves onto the three stools, the creature with the amulet between the others. The stools were clearly their equivalent of chairs, as they then rested their upper bodies on the 'T' shaped structures in front of them then leant on the table with their crab-like elbows. It was a macabre and unnerving sight to see creatures who looked so like insects, behaving like human beings.

Now at close quarters, Phil could see that their arms, indeed their entire bodies, were covered in cilia-like hairs - sensilla - which wafted to and fro in waves like undersea grass. On most of the surfaces, there were about a dozen half inch long sensilla per square inch, but on their chelae, the sensilla looked like short soft fur. It was clear that this covering served as the organ of touch. Phil recoiled at the thought of actually being touched by such creatures, with their formidable and totally alien appearance.

From the creature on the central stool, came the same complex twanging sound. Now they were nearer, Phil could see that the voice emanated from the central opening on top of its head. The comb-like structure was vibrating.

"We are Cryons," it said. "I am Senior Councillor Vorkan, Commander of Solara, and in charge of all our activities here. On my right is Councillor Entorik. He is responsible for all monitoring operations and is our chief scientist. On my left is Councillor Valaasor. She is responsible for the maintenance and safety of the entire facility, its infrastructures, and everything we have stored down here, including our fellow Cryons."

So one of them is a female, thought Phil. She ... it, looked identical to the other two. She was certainly no beauty!

"The two attendants are my neutant siblings, Charis and Nitra," continued the central creature. "They have not been able to learn your language, so will not be participating in our discussions."

Up to this point, the men round the table had sat transfixed and speechless. Phil guessed that like him, they had expected something strange, but not giant insects. The shock and instinctive revulsion that all felt was clear to see on every face. But it was not only that. It was the idea that creatures which we consider so lowly could have evolved to a level which allowed them to design, build and operate spaceships, travel between the stars, and present themselves as a superior race.

Powell, his voice croaking with fear, managed to compose himself and address the Cryons.

"You are welcome as our guests," he said.

Doubtless, nothing in Powell's experience had ever warranted less of a welcome than these creatures, but the moment demanded diplomacy, and Powell was making the best of an impossible situation.

"This is indeed a momentous occasion," he continued. "May I extend the hand of friendship across the miles to you, and ask, where is Solara?"

The central creature, the one calling himself Vorkan, looked left and right at his companions and uttered a series of complex sounds of an eerie and unearthly timbre. Simultaneously, all three creatures' sensilla rippled, causing fascinating patterns of light to flash and dance off their bodies. Phil gazed spellbound at this display. With their faces so inflexible, this was obviously a form of communication equivalent to our facial expressions. It occurred to Phil that it might even have been laughter.

"Solara," said Vorkan, "Is the name of this planet - what you call Earth. And may I say that you too are welcome, as *our* guests."

Powell was totally non-plussed by Vorkan's reply. The implication that Vorkan was not only Commander of the Earth, but that the humans were guests on their own planet was obviously the last straw. He slumped back in his chair, utterly speechless.

Beemish took up the cudgel.

"May we ask please, why are you here? What is your mission?"

The three Cryons, disconcertingly, repeated the previous procedure.

"I think that we should explain everything, from the beginning," said Vorkan. He settled himself more comfortably onto his body rest.

"Sixty five million of your years ago, we discovered that our planet, Cryon, was doomed. The reason need not concern you. Suffice it that we had to leave, or die. We conducted a thorough search and analysis of all planets we knew about at the time, to seek a suitable uninhabited planet to which we could migrate. We found none. The only suitable planets were already colonised by highly advanced creatures."

Beemish, seemingly growing accustomed to the Cryons' presence, and suppressing his revulsion, leaned forward slightly.

"Are you saying .. er .. Commander, that there are numerous inhabited planets?"

"Yes. One of the things you may come to understand is that life is the norm in the universe rather than the exception."

Phil was fascinated. Here was the answer to one of man's most fundamental questions.

"So," Vorkan went on, "We then sought a suitable planet inhabited by only lowly life forms. Unfortunately, still, no planet was found. Our only recourse was to select a planet with lowly life forms that, though not immediately suitable, would respond to an imposed climate adjustment. We found only one such planet - this one."

A ripple of concern ran round the table. Many were now following Beemish's lead, and allowing their curiosity to overcome their repugnance of the Cryons.

"Climate adjustment?" interjected Straker, suspiciously.

"Yes," said the Cryon. "We need a mean atmospheric temperature of one hundred and eighteen degrees Fahrenheit and almost one hundred percent humidity. Nowhere on this planet, are conditions anything like those."

Phil tried to imagine what such conditions would be like. The worst he had experienced - during a trade exhibition in the Middle East - were the hot fogs of the Persian Gulf, when the mercury touched eighty during pea-soupers. In such conditions you could lose litres of water per hour sweating, but to no avail; the sweat couldn't evaporate so it didn't cool you down. You could die of dehydration in less than a day. But 118°F and saturation humidity; that was a sauna!

"But you say this was sixty five million years ago," said Beemish incredulously. "What have you been doing since then? Where have you been? How have you kept going for so long?"

"Please, General," replied Vorkan. "All will be revealed. This planet, Solara - the one you call Earth - was therefore selected. Sixty five million years ago, we came. We arrived here then. We have been here ever since."

To Phil's surprise, Cranford found his voice.

"Do you mean that you discovered Earth before we discovered America?" he said, with child-like naivety.

"Yes we did, Governor. And not only that. Had we not come, you - the human race - would not be here now." The sensilla were rippling again.

Powell looked as if he was going to faint. Many of the others stared at each other in disbelief.

"Would you explain that please," said Beemish.

"When we came," Vorkan began, "Solara was inhabited by large numbers of reptiles - dinosaurs. Many of these were very aggressive, and some, notably the ones you call the Troodons, displayed considerable intelligence. It was clear to us that these creatures, given time, had the potential to evolve to a highly technical level. If we had let them, there is no doubt whatsoever that they - the Troodons - would have overrun Solara, and by now have spread to surrounding star systems. Clearly, under such circumstances, the small mammals from which you the human race evolved - your distant ancestors - would have fallen prey to the Troodons and been wiped out."

Phil began to put the pieces of this fantastic jigsaw together, but many were still missing. He listened, spellbound.

"I mentioned," continued Vorkan, "That we would have to adjust the climate of this planet. But we needed to check that the results of our proposed adjustment method matched our predictions. We needed a test adjustment. Bearing in mind that once we achieved the climate transition, the dinosaurs would not be able to tolerate the new conditions, and that even if they could, we could not possibly share the planet with such dangerous creatures, we decided that our test adjustment should be powerful enough to eliminate them. So that is what we did. You will now appreciate that your very existence is a direct result of our timely intervention."

The enormity of what had just been revealed defied comprehension. Phil was aware of many theories which explained the extinction of the dinosaurs, but deliberate intervention by aliens had not been one of them. He wondered whether in the next room, BJ and the other scientists were being told the same thing, and what they would think.

"You . . . . deliberately caused the extinction of the dinosaurs!" said Straker, his voice trembling. "How?"

"I should point out, Mr Secretary, that our survey showed that with a few exceptions - notably the Troodons - most of the dinosaurs were heading for extinction anyway. All we did was precipitate what for them would have been their ultimate fate. As to how we did it, with a very large explosion - an iridium-based device detonated in what you now call the Yucatan Peninsula in Mexico, and a magma plume accelerator under what you now call the Deccan Traps in India. Your geological documents show that you are familiar with these events, but attributed them to the impact of one or more meteorites and natural volcanism. There had been a meteorite impact in the Yucatan, which formed the Chicxulub crater, and our explosion was detonated within the crater. The detonation of our devices marked the boundry between the Cretaceous and Tertiary periods"

The K-T boundary. That was what had brought him and the family to this part of Wyoming in the first place. The Cryons had actually caused it!

But things were still not right. There was the question of what had happened in the intervening 65 million years, and why had the Cryons not changed the climate already. Beemish was already there.

"So why," he said, "If the Chicxulub explosion - your test adjustment - worked, why did you not go on and finish the job? Why did you not modify the planet's climate to suit you?"

The three Cryons looked at each other again, and emitted those uncanny twanging noises that were obviously their language. Vorkan replied.

"Because we had to wait until a number of factors, including long-term cosmological ones, were conducive to the imposed change being permanent. You do not know this, but the Sun is a long period variable star. In a cycle which lasts many millions of years, it increases its brilliance slightly but suddenly, then slowly returns to its normal brightness level. In addition, the powerhouse at the centre of the galaxy exhibits a similar cycle in its emission of high energy particles - the galactic flux - which lasts even longer. Finally, the clarity of the interstellar medium - the space between the stars, which absorbs or transmits the galactic flux - varies as the solar system revolves round the galactic centre. Only when all three combine, along with the shorter period factors linked to the planet and its orbit, will we be able to adjust the whole planet's climate and make that adjustment permanent."

"And are you telling us you have been waiting for sixty five million years?" said Beemish, the disbelief in his voice even more pronounced than before.

"We have, General," said Vorkan. The Cryon seemed to be eyeing Beemish strangely, as if he expected him to come back immediately with another question.

Of the multitude of questions still clamouring to be answered, two stood out from the rest in Phil's mind. One concerned the 65 million years, but as he considered the other, he could feel that all too familiar chasm open up in the pit of his stomach. He couldn't wait for Beemish.

"When will the factors combine?" he blurted. "When will you be wanting to change the climate?"

The three Cryons turned their heads towards him. They had a strange way of staring, as if their eyes were focused on a point some distance behind his head. They glanced briefly at each other again before Vorkan replied. His sensilla were waving again, but this time the pattern was different; the ripples seemed to be directed towards him, and something about their soft rhythmical motion suggested harmony, fellowship - even friendliness.

"Before I answer that," said Vorkan, "We wish to take this opportunity of congratulating you, Major Newheart, for the manner in which you have conducted yourself throughout, since you discovered our doorway - and particularly your behaviour on the Moon. Honour be upon you."

Phil felt embarrassed. Being singled out for praise by one of these creatures was not guaranteed to help him make friends and influence people! But now he was actually conversing with the Cryons, he felt a sort of thrill - like as a little boy, the first time he used a telephone.

"Thank you," he said, politely. "But I think you owe us an answer to my question."

Vorkan's head moved forward slightly as he scrutinised Phil with those massive eyes.

"Quite right, Major," he said. "Actually, we are nearly there. The factors will combine in two hundred thousand years time."

'Nearly there', thought Phil. Compared to 65 million, I suppose two hundred thousand is nothing.

"But now," continued Vorkan, "There is something else to consider. I will explain. I will also explain what we have been doing and where we have been over the last sixty five million years, and lastly, what we propose to do next."

With the exception of Miller, whose eyes had remained firmly fixed on the centre of the table since the Cryons appeared, everyone sat forward, waiting expectantly.

"We have developed a state of existence - initially to facilitate the long-term storage of food - called cryostatic encapsulation. Your existing technology, cryogenics, is the first step along a similar road. In cryogenics, the subject or item in question is cooled to extremely low temperatures; in metals and other materials, strange things happen such as superconductivity; in biological specimens, deterioration is virtually halted. The trouble with cryogenics however - and this applies particularly to living organisms - is that the cooling process can damage cells and other structures. So can the subsequent thawing process. What is needed are two things: an instantaneous change of state, and the equivalent of an absolute zero storage temperature. We have achieved both. Cryostatic encapsulation can be performed in an instant, and within the cryostatic encapsulation frame, nothing - not even the component parts of the atoms - moves at all. The subject is in effect sealed into a time capsule which will last forever without the slightest change or deterioration. And when the encapsulation is terminated, the specimen, or subject, carries on as before, not even aware that the encapsulation has taken place."

"Are those huge blocks in one of the halls we looked at encapsulation frames?" asked Phil.

"They are, Major," replied the Cryon on Vorkan's left - the female. Her voice was almost identical to that of Vorkan. This was the first time she had spoken.

"Those frames hold specimens taken during the sorties we have been doing once every half million years since we arrived. The ones at the far end - the dinosaurs - were of course taken prior to the test explosion. You realise from what the Commander has just told you, that should we wish to, we could transport those frames to the planet's surface, de-encapsulate them, and the creatures would instantly come back to life. Apart from their surroundings having changed, they would be completely unaware of what had happened to them."

After he dismissed the vision of dinosaurs being let loose in Central Park, Phil marvelled at the concept of extinct creatures being brought back to life. The hall of blocks was a wonderful and irreplaceable record of the evolution of life on Earth.

Then he homed in on the mention of sorties.

"You have been monitoring all along?" he said.

The Cryon on the other side of Vorkan answered this time.

"Our teams - myself included - have been out there for thirty days at a time," he said. "It has been fascinating."

That was it. The sixty five million year wait was, to the Cryons, simplicity itself. But the thought of it was breathtaking.

"Are you saying," he said, "That you yourselves have also been in cryostatic encapsulation all this time, except for thirty day outings every half million years?"

"Almost completely correct, Major," said Vorkan, rippling his sensilla once more. He turned and pointed towards the doorway. "The bulk of our people - some eighty million citizens - are in fact in permanent and undisturbed cryostatic encapsulation chambers, the nearest of which are not far from this chamber."

Eighty million! Phil could hardly believe his ears. Secretary Straker looked horror-struck; the Vice President went white as a sheet.

"But we have automatic systems which de-encapsulate the monitoring teams every half million years," it continued calmly. "Encapsulation to us, is imperceptible. We walk into the encapsulation chamber, blink as it were, and walk out again half a million years later. Encapsulation is, to all intents and purposes, forward time travel. The monitors, including the three of us, have aged by less than eleven years since we arrived."

"We have even walked amongst the dinosaurs," said the female.

"And for the most recent three or four million years - the last eight sorties - we have watched you, the human race, evolve from a hairy ape-like creature to how you are today," said Vorkan.

A stunned silence descended upon the room as the men round the table absorbed the full implications of what had just been revealed. The heat and humidity of the room were affecting everyone, and the thought that they were sitting only a few yards away from some vast and macabre storage facility holding eighty million aliens did little to alleviate the situation. Beemish was the first to recover enough to continue the exchange.

"So this is the latest - and last - of your sorties before the factors conducive to changing the climate come together, in two hundred thousand years time?" he said, tentatively.

"I'm afraid not, General," said Vorkan. "This is not a sortie. The last proper half million year sortie - the ultimate one prior to the climate adjustment - was two thousand years ago, in 12 A.D."

"You will have seen the Roman empire at its peak then," said Beemish. "How fascinating. What an experience!"

The three Cryons started communicating with each other again. Phil could sense that something was up.

"An experience it certainly was, General," said Vorkan. "The time before that, we saw a few primitive hunter-gatherers living in harmony with the land. Next time, we saw the Romans and their empire in Europe and North Africa, the warring tribes in Mesopotamia and the Indian sub-continent, and the Han Chinese in their countless millions."

"Magnificent progress," said Powell, suddenly finding his voice again. "And something of which the human race can feel justly proud."

Unexpectedly, Vorkan rose to his feet. The two others followed suit.

"You think so do you?" he said, dramatically. "Then your and my concept of magnificent progress are I fear, at odds."

He peered searchingly at each man round the table, his huge eyes glowing strangely.

"The time has come for us to look closely at this so-called progress," he said. "Because we have a problem - a not inconsiderable problem."

***

It was clear to Phil that the real reason the Cryons had revealed themselves was about to be explained. And the signs were not good.

Vorkan obviously wanted the floor to himself, because he indicated to the others to lower themselves again. His seven foot stature dwarfed the men round the table as he addressed them.

"It is your very rate of progress - indeed your very existence - which has given us cause for concern, and presented us with a problem we did not foresee. You will have gathered from what I said earlier, that we are not an insensitive race. It is against our beliefs to appropriate planets and dispossess creatures on those planets, and it is certainly abhorrent to us to kill any living thing, unless we have no choice in the matter."

Sounds good, thought Phil, but doesn't quite square with wiping out the dinosaurs.

"As I explained," Vorkan continued, "We attempted to find somewhere to which we could migrate which would not involve the disruption or destruction of life, and particularly advanced life. But when it came to weighing our survival as a race, against the survival of lowly reptiles, there was no question - it had to be ourselves."

Vorkan paused for a moment. He looked suddenly detached from his surroundings. He seemed to be staring at the floor.

"Having said that," he went on, "The day we detonated the thermatron was the worst day of my life. I observed the event from a scout ship hovering near the surface of the planet. I myself triggered the explosion. The effects were more terrible than you can imagine. I have no desire to go through that again."

"Well that's kinda comforting!" came a voice into Phil's right ear. It was General Norman - the first time he had spoken since they entered the room. Vorkan immediately looked up and directed his gaze at the General. He had obviously heard him.

"But I would do, if necessary. I would go through it again," said Vorkan, holding Norman's startled stare.

Here we go, Phil thought to himself.

"We believed," Vorkan went on, "That once we had eliminated the dinosaurs, that no group or species could evolve to an advanced stage in the time available. And apart from the last half million year period, we were right. But two thousand years ago, suddenly, there you were, not only in your millions, but becoming technically competent. We decided that a change of plan was necessary. If we went back into encapsulation and emerged two hundred thousand years from then, your development and expansion would doubtless have changed Solara completely; there would be even more of you, and we would have a major problem on our hands about modifying the climate and taking over. We decided therefore, that the honourable course of action was to inform you of our intentions, to allow you adequate time to make the necessary arrangements."

Necessary arrangements, thought Phil. These creatures are either our undertakers, or our landlords.

Powell had obviously assumed the latter.

"And we'd always thought we held the freehold of our own planet," he said, somewhat pointedly.

"Come come, Mr Powell," said Vorkan. "As an American, you must surely recognise that occupation of a piece of land at any particular moment in time does not necessarily give you right of tenure for ever more."

Powell looked distinctly uncomfortable. Vorkan raised himself to his full stature, and addressed every man at the table.

"You should understand," he said, "That you, the human race, do not own this planet. You don't. We don't. Nobody does. This planet is a priceless island resource - a jewel in the crown of the cosmos - that we should all feel privileged to use as a haven, as tenants, as we ply our evolutionary course. You just happen to have tenure of its surface now. We will have it later, when we emerge, after you have moved on."

"Moved on!" echoed Powell, seething with indignation.

"But of course," said Vorkan. "As in family life, you do not have to stay living all your life in the house in which you were born. Although you may look back at your childhood home with fond memories, life moves forward. Families move from house to house. Civilisations move from planet to planet."

In a few simple sentences, Vorkan had catapulted his audience from a state of blissful ignorance into one which brought them face-to-face with the stark reality of survival amongst the stars. No longer was Earth sacrosanct. It was just one of many islands in the hazardous river of evolution. And the Cryons - indeed any race who could travel between the stars - were the navigators of this river, using the islands as staging posts, and when necessary, occupying them.

"We realised however," continued Vorkan, "That at a time when your greatest technological achievement in the field of aviation was the flying of kites, that presenting you with the news that you would have to vacate, would be treated with derision and anger. We thought it would be kinder - less of a culture shock - if, before we made contact, we waited until your technology demonstrated an understanding of some of the laws of physics, a knowledge of the universe, and a real ability to travel in space. We decided therefore, to get MIND to test your technological progress and invite contact once every thousand years. In 1012 A.D. you did not respond. Now, in 2012, you have responded, successfully. MIND therefore de-encapsulated us, told us all about you, and now we must talk about the future."

So the door was a test, thought Phil. And having to go to the Moon to get the key, that was all part of the Cryon assessment of us.

"Unfortunately," continued Vorkan, "In the two thousand years since our monitoring sortie, you appear to have increased your numbers to what can only be described as infestation levels. Further, some of the directions in which your technological advances have been made leave much to be desired; your recent stewardship of the planet can only be described as scandalous; and finally, I am afraid to say that our in-depth study of the human character - concluding with the mind probes you have all just experienced - gives us cause for grave concern. In fact, if you continue in the direction you are going, it is highly likely that not only will you render the planet uninhabitable for yourselves, but even jeopardise our adjustment plan."

Phil scanned the faces round the table. He could see that without exception, each person knew exactly what Vorkan was referring to. Mankind was its own worst enemy.

Nobody spoke. Nobody could muster a defense against Vorkan's accusations. He was right. It was as if they were being scolded by a firm father. Phil felt a shiver run down his spine as he tried to anticipate what Vorkan was going to say next.

"I am gratified," said Vorkan eyeing each person in turn, "That not one of you has attempted to justify your seemingly headlong descent towards self-destruction. There may be hope for you yet."

Powell, evidently vexed by the direction events were taking, spoke up.

"These last two thousand years - if MIND has been monitoring us so closely, what was the point of testing whether we could get to the Moon or not? You must have known we could. And why didn't you warn us about our numbers earlier? You wait until our population displeases you, then you complain!"

Vorkan directed his inscrutable gaze at the Vice President.

"Mr Powell, I did not say that MIND has been monitoring you closely. MIND, like ourselves, has been encapsulated. We could not possibly justify keeping MIND on line continuously for two thousand years - it would deteriorate. No, we employed a simple timer device which triggered the door manifestation and seismic signal every millennium. When the door lock was revealed - only then was MIND de-encapsulated."

"So, if I understand you correctly," said Powell - and Phil got the impression that he was deliberately avoiding the use of the term Commander - "You've observed us from down here for three months, and now, you are giving us two hundred thousand years notice to quit, on the assumption that by then we will have worked out how to, and that in the meantime we should be a little more thoughtful in our use of our planet. Is that it, basically?"

Vorkan's sensilla began moving in a way they had never moved before - in a staccato bristling motion. And as one instinctively senses danger from certain brightly-coloured creatures, Phil could tell from this motion, that it was anger.

"No that is *not* it," said Vorkan. "*This* is it. You - the human race - are the uninvited occupants of our planet. Your presence here offends us. You will be tolerated only if you agree to come under the jurisdiction of the Cryon High Council sitting as it does from time to time in this place. You will obey the laws and edicts issued by the Council in so far as they apply to your tenure of Solara and your exploration of and relationship with nearby planets. You will be required to reduce your population, reduce your pollution of the planet and its åtmosphere, reduce your use of irreplaceable natural resources, totally eliminate all weapons of mass destruction, remove from the hands of ordinary citizens the arms and other weapons which make them a danger to others and themselves, and move immediately towards a zero growth world economy."

He paused, to allow this diatribe to sink in. His huge eyes bored into Powell, like lances. Powell's face was deathly pale; he just sat, blinking.

"None of these are unreasonable demands," he continued, "But we accept that to you, they will seem - in the short term at least - disaccommodating. So in return for your co-operation and demonstrable compliance, we will, subject to your willingness to use them sensibly, pass on to you some of the discoveries we have made over the last six hundred thousand years. Rest assured, we have no desire to frustrate or restrict individual freedoms or ways of life, so long as these do not conflict with the global interest. However, if powerful individuals attempt to put into effect decisions which would have an adverse effect on the planet, those attempts will be frustrated. As for enforcement, you will understand that we - individual Cryons - have no intention of wasting non-encapsulation time in personally monitoring your adherence to our demands. Instead, we will disperse amongst you, automatic mobile monitors, who will respond as necessary to any deviation from the correct behaviour. There will be a global review meeting in one hundred years time, here, when your progress up to that point will be assessed. I now advise you to explain the situation to the rest of the world. We will be available here for the next few weeks, during which we will deal with any points requiring clarification. Take the key with you when you leave, and through Major Newheart, whom we now appoint as liaison officer, use it to visit us as often as you like. I think that is all, and see no reason to detain you further gentlemen."

With that, the two other Cryons rose, leaving the men round the table stunned and open-mouthed.

Powell called out as the Cryons headed back through the partition.

"And if we do not comply?"

All five of them stopped. Vorkan turned round, very slowly, then walked to where Powell was sitting. He lowered his massive head to within inches of Powell's face, and stared intently into his eyes. Vorkan's sensilla were rigid but quivering slightly, and all pointing straight at Powell.

"Then join the dinosaurs, Mr Powell," he said.

14
Christmas

An impenetrable wall of silence surrounded the twenty men and women who, late that Christmas eve, emerged haggard, exhausted, and in a state of deep shock, from the Cryon stronghold. On Powell's insistence - and to howls of protest - the lower ranking military personnel, all the scientists, and even Sheriff Collins, were unceremoniously bundled into helicopters and flown to Fort Carson in Colorado for de-briefing. There, they would be told that this year at least, their Christmas had been cancelled. They were to be kept in total isolation.

Powell had wanted Phil to be taken to Fort Carson too, but Beemish had dissuaded him. So Phil found himself with the Vice President, the Secretary of Defense, Cranford, and the three generals, inside a locked portacabin within the dome. The tension was unbearable as each man tried to come to terms with not only the Cryon ultimatum but with the debilitating realisation that every other man knew their most private, embarrassing and damming secrets. Instead of sitting round the table, the men sat facing away from it, or paced up and down or just stood gazing out of the window. It had to be the Vice President who broke the silence, and in the end, he did. He drew a chair up to the table, sat down, and indicated to the others to do the same.

"Gentlemen," he said, thoughtfully. "What we have seen and heard today, and particularly the Cryon ultimatum, is *dynamite.* If this gets our - even the smallest whisper - whoever talks is going to be personally responsible for the greatest mass panic the world has ever seen. It is therefore *essential* that you say nothing - to your boss, your best friend, your husband, your wife, your lover, nobody - not even the goddamn cat."

He scanned the faces round the table, waiting for acquiescence. The six men stared equivocally towards him. Nobody had the energy to argue or comment. He continued.

"Mr Straker and I will be flying to Washington tonight to inform the President. He will obviously handle the ultimatum issue, and involve other world leaders as necessary. But before we leave this room, I want personal guarantees from each of you about the other matters."

"Which particular matters, Sir?" said Straker, cautiously.

"The gifts, solutions and cures, and that ridiculous attempt to set us against each other with hallucinations."

Powell very pointedly engaged each man round the table in earnest eye-to-eye contact. "I mean, they obviously were ... hallucinations."

My God, he's going to deny it, thought Phil, as he himself scanned the other men's faces. Miller's eyes narrowed to slits as he clutched Powell's lifeline. General Norman was about to lace his coffee with a tot from his hip flask, but recognising that his alcoholism could remain unofficial after all, wisely returned the flask to his pocket. Cranford's eyes opened wide, as if he had just received divine inspiration.

"Of course! Obviously none of us believed any of that stuff," he blustered. He looked from man to man inanely. "Well, I mean ..."

Phil regarded him impassively, his bitterness and anger spent. Now he had had time to reflect upon Cranford's mentality, he even found a tiny spark of understanding in the void that represented his feelings for him. And to a certain extent Phil could see that every man, whatever he had done or not done, had acted with what he at least deemed to be a justification. Some justifications may have been shaky - such as not finding the strength or motivation to temper one's desires - but justification there always was.

"I think the best thing we can do with those last experiences is to completely forget 'em, for *all* our sakes," said Powell. "Are we agreed, gentlemen."

He cast round the table once more. Phil and Beemish looked askance at each other, but said nothing. Powell's solution was brilliant. He had recognised that at least for the people with the real power, self-interest would override any urge to start whistle blowing.

One by one, each man confirmed his acceptance. Phil recognised that he and Beemish had little choice. Now was not the moment to insist the administration be rocked to its foundations.

"What about the fights?" said Straker after a pause. "They weren't hallucinations."

In the other group, some plagiarism between two of the scientists had been revealed, and there had been adultery within the military personnel. After the truth session, a sergeant had suffered a severe head wound at the hands of one of his corporals, and the aggrieved scientist broke the other one's jaw. But as the party returned through the hoops, the two injured men were miraculously healed, though afterwards, they could remember nothing of their subterranean experiences.

"Hoops sorted those out," said Norman with a satisfied expression. "Like it never happened."

"But if we could get access to that sort of technology ... Well, it's incredible," said Beemish.

"General Beemish," said Powell sternly. "The President will decide whether the gains are worth us losing control. Far as I'm concerned, these critters are trouble, magic hoops or no goddamn magic hoops. Now, can we get back to the point. I want to be sure we keep the lid on this thing. That's what's important."

Straker glowered at Beemish. Obviously, neither Straker nor Powell was in any sort of mood to capitulate. Beemish glanced at Phil - he obviously had misgivings on what appeared to be a hardening attitude to the Cryons displayed by the men from Washington.

"Finally," said Powell, "Any of us who have gifts - especially ones which can't be explained using existing technology - should keep them secret and in a safe place for the time being. Wait until official announcements are made, or you are contacted by me. Now, do you all agree to absolute secrecy, until this thing's sorted? It has to be everybody."

Drained faces stared listlessly around. No-one objected.

Powell then insisted that one by one, each of them affirmed out loud that they would keep the secret pact. All obliged.

"Then I now suggest those of us who are able, get back to our families," he said, "And have as happy a Christmas as we can."

By the time the helicopter carrying Beemish, Phil, Jo-Ann and the children arrived at the F.E. Warren Air Force Base, it was 2 a.m. on Christmas Day. The flight had been completed in absolute silence, with Phil and the family curled up together in the back, and Beemish up front with the pilot.

After he had got Jo-Ann and the children into the waiting car, Phil placed the Cryon key and the now securely taped-up box containing Dave's new hand into the trunk, then returned to where Beemish was standing. Beemish turned and faced him. His arms were by his side, and he was shivering slightly in the cold night air. He had a look of dignified bravery on his face, as if he were standing as the accused in a Court Martial.

Phil looked into his eyes, temporarily suppressed the disconcerting regard he was forming for the man, began to turn away rightwards, then swept around with a right uppercut to Beemish's chin that split the skin on two knuckles. Beemish went down like a felled tree, blood dripping onto the snow from the side of his mouth.

"I never did believe in hallucinations," said Phil, as he stood over him, breathing hard. He reached down and helped him to his feet. "That's for trying it with my wife."

Beemish stood silently for a moment, wiping away the blood with his hand. Suddenly, Phil felt himself falling backwards. Beemish had replied with a forehand jab to his face.

"Neither do I, Phil," said Beemish, "And that's for trying and succeeding without her."

It was Beemish's turn to help Phil up. There was a stinging pain in his nose, the taste of blood on his tongue, and an embarrassing realisation that his holier-than-thou mantle had slipped from his shoulders.

"Don't worry," said Beemish, smiling grimly. "There's no contest. Just wanted to put the record straight."

The two men searched each other's faces. The mutual respect each was forming for the other was almost a physical sensation.

Phil wanted to say something, but couldn't find the words.

"Good night then, Major" said Beemish.

He saluted, walked to his car, and drove off into the night.

***

In the silent communications chamber, Vorkan settled onto his front-rest and flipped the cerebra-sensor units forwards. He had come directly from the monitors' review meeting, and now, wanted to speak to MIND in private.

To Vorkan, it was only yesterday that he had chaired a similar meeting, when the date on Solara was 12 A.D. They had been worried then about the sudden human infestation, but nobody - not even MIND - had foreseen the amazing explosion in numbers that had occurred since then. Had that been predicted, the plan to test human advancement every thousand years would never have been proposed, let alone adopted.

After MIND had de-encapsulated them this foreday, and passed on a compacted version of what it had learned over the three months since the door had been activated, they had been shocked and saddened. Worse still, some of the monitors were now expressing grave doubts regarding the entire Solara solution, and Vorkan's own credibility was beginning to be questioned.

"Hello, Faro," came MIND's liquid voice inside his head.

"What do you think? The meeting with the humans - do you think they'll accept our demands?"

Vorkan had never had to deal with such primitive and unpredictable creatures. He had met one or two Meerians - his neutant sibling Charis used to know one - but at least they were benign. The human males, even the most sensible ones, were all physically and emotionally aggressive.

"You successfully communicated with them in terms they understood, Faro. I think you struck a good balance between reasoned argument and human-like threats."

Vorkan recalled the fear shown by the humans during their visit. It had never been his intention to cause them distress, but quite obviously, it was their nature to distrust, to fight, to subjugate, and many of them saw the Cryons as a threat rather than an opportunity to benefit.

"My main regret, was that the one they call Powell - the Vice President of the local country - asked me what would happen if they did not comply."

"He forced you into a corner, Faro. That was very unwise. If he had not asked, you would not have had to answer."

"I assume you supported my answer. If the humans do not modify their behaviour, our entire Solara migration will be put in jeopardy. They must comply or be eliminated."

"That would certainly solve our problem," said MIND. "You would of course have to gain the full Council's consent for such an action. However, I believe they would grant you the power to exercise that option were it to become necessary. Would you like me to de-encapsulate the Councillors now?"

Vorkan's breathing tubes began to itch. The last time the full Council had convened was - measured in Vorkan's unencapsulated time - eleven years ago, when he had been able to escort them round Solara after the planet had recovered from the dinosaur elimination. They had been impressed. The Master had hinted at the possibility of succession. At the time, Vorkan had expressed confidence that the councillors' encapsulation would not need to be disturbed until Solara was finally theirs. He viewed it as a personal failure, having to go to them prior to this. It was important to him that his nation-saving plan, the one to which he had totally devoted the last fourteen years of his life, went without a hitch.

But there was something else which was contributing to his discomfiture. Although, before this latest de-encapsulation, he had only been able to study modern humans for some thirty days, he could see in them an energy, an industry, and a zest for life which he could not help admiring. Despite their cruel and self-destructive nature, there was something about them that attracted him. They were a complex breed. Deep inside them was still the vicious beast of their primeval ancestors, but beginning to form outside this - and in some, suppress it - was a cortex of amazing potential. How was it for instance, that the Roman Augustus could so highly value the works of his architects, poets and artists, yet embrace the campaign of slaughter being carried out by his heir Tiberius? And what was it that drove the man Newheart, to risk his own life to save another?

Eliminating Solara's dinosaurs had been bad enough, but the prospect of ending the lives of thousands of millions of creatures with such potential, filled him with an awful dread.

"If only they weren't so aggressive," said Vorkan.

"And so numerous," replied MIND. "No other planet known to us is so blighted. The Meerians for instance, were over-populated and terrible polluters. The Saarbrons turned their planet into a desert by using up all its natural resources. The Karlags worshipped their weapons, but this particular combination of behavioural characteristics - this syndrome - is unique to Solara."

What is it about this place, thought Vorkan, that engenders such behaviour in its inhabitants? This syndrome, as MIND called it, had to be dealt with, or the plan - and his credibility - would be in tatters.

"Faro!" MIND's voice was urgent. "I repeat, do you want me to de-encapsulate the Master and Councillors now?"

"Yes, MIND," he replied sadly. "Inform them that I seek their permission to execute, if necessary, a bio-level 5 de-infestation."

***

During that extraordinary Christmas - spent with Jo and the children in the house on the air base - Phil tried to come to terms with the dramatic events he had experienced. He knew he was recovering from a dizzying ride on an emotional roller-coaster and needed a little time to adjust, but what was clear was that he now enjoyed a raised level of emotional reaction to things. It was like being given another sense. Everything he thought about now had another facet. His logic and analytical skills had not deserted him, rather they had been put in their place.

The revelations from Cranford had brought about a total re-assessment of his attitude to the USA. For the first time since the plane crash, his feelings and love for his home country were returning. Now he knew the reason for the crash, and the individual personally responsible, the doubt and mistrust were evaporating. He found he was regarding America with new unclouded eyes, and the relief and joy this brought about in his general demeanour was summed up by Jo-Ann on Boxing Day evening.

"I don't know what you're on, Honey, but next time you go down there, can you get me some?"

She had in fact, been amazingly understanding. Once he convinced her that if he hadn't sworn a vow of silence, he wouldn't be with her but locked up in a Colorado army base, she stopped plying him with questions. Neither of them liked the secrecy - nor did the children - but at least they were together as a family for Christmas.

But during quieter moments, Phil could not stop thinking about the Cryons. He could not get them - and particularly their leader - out of his mind. He found himself agonising over the conflict between the instinctive revulsion he felt for Vorkan, and the disarmingly reasonable manner in which he had presented his demands. And how, once the world was presented with them, would it react? What was Vorkan really like, inside, as an individual? Did he have hopes, fears, problems, emotions? What made him tick? Who were these Cryons? Where did they come from? What could they tell us?

He sat for hours on end, staring out of the window at the other houses in the circle, watching the different state flags fluttering in the breeze, and dwelling on how totally unimportant these territorial demarcations would become in the new world order. To Tess's delight, he found himself taking a more than common interest in programmes on the Discovery Channel dealing with environmental issues and global conservation, and began analysing the insidious pressures being generated within society by the constant stream of TV adverts. After all, it's difficult to take seriously, claims that Banish grey hair treatment is essential for mature modern man, when the future of the entire human race is in doubt.

By the morning of the 27th December, Phil had heard nothing from any source about events surrounding the Cryons. Only one TV station had briefly mentioned that the archaeological dig on the banks of the Seminoe reservoir had been shrouded in secrecy, and that no reporters had been given access to the site. The station had promised to keep people posted if any discoveries were announced, but other than that, the world seemed totally unaware of the gathering storm that would surely engulf them all.

The need to maintain secrecy, and the lack of answers to his ever-mounting list of questions, was becoming almost too much to bear, when events abruptly moved forwards.

At about 11 o'clock that morning, two of General Miller's men arrived, armed, and demanded that the 'item' Phil had in his possession be lodged in the General's safe in his office over at 20th Air Force headquarters on the base. Unable to get Beemish on the telephone, he had no option but to comply, and accompany them with the key. The safe was an ancient device with a mechanical combination lock. Phil was told to stay back whilst it was opened. Only when the shocked security guard failed to move the key one millimetre towards the safe, was Phil allowed to place it inside himself. As he was driven back to the house, it was obvious from the constant to-ing and fro-ing of helicopters, that something was up. There were goings on around the briefing room building, and he thought he caught a glimpse of some stretched limos with blacked-out windows - rare in Wyoming.

It was about 6 p.m. when the door bell rang again. Phil opened it to find Secretary of Defense Straker, with Ted Beemish standing behind him. The two National Guard men at the end of the pathway had been replaced with Miller's Air Force security staff. Beemish looked strained and anxious. Phil got the impression that he was distinctly unhappy about something, but could not speak out.

"May we come in, Major?" said Straker, brushing past him and walking into the hall. "Is there somewhere ... ?"

"The others are in the kitchen," said Phil, and fired a glance at the lounge door. Straker strode over to it and stood waiting.

"Come in please, General," said Phil to Beemish, who was still waiting politely on the doorstep. For a fleeting moment, Beemish's eyes spoke volumes. Something was seriously wrong.

Phil led the way into the lounge. Straker closed the door behind him, and the three men stood round the fire.

"We'd like you to go in again," said Straker, unemotionally. "Tomorrow morning. Think you can do that for us, Major?"

Phil looked at Beemish, but he was standing staring at the floor.

"Who'll be with me?" said Phil.

"We rather thought ... well, it would be better if you were on your own. The critters seem to trust you."

Straker was a good liar, but not that good. He was hiding something, but Phil couldn't put his finger on it.

"What for?" he said, suspiciously. "What do you want me to do?"

"Liaise," replied Straker innocently. "They've nominated you as liaison officer, so we'd like you to liaise. Find out precisely what they want. Get them to specify their demands in more detail. Find out as much about them as you can. They seem to know all about us, well let's know all about them."

He stared at Phil keenly. "You will do it?"

On the surface, the request sounded reasonable. The misgivings Phil had were overpowered by his realisation that here at least was an opportunity to find out more, and talk to someone, even though it would be a Cryon.

"Yes, okay" he said, guardedly.

"Good man! But whatever you do," went on Straker, "Don't give any sort of impression that we won't comply. Be nice. Be diplomatic. Treat it as a fact-finding and clarification exercise. Got it?"

Phil just nodded. The demands of his curiosity had overcome his suspicions, although he knew he was being manipulated.

To what end, he would doubtless discover.

15

With Alien Eyes

Phil shivered slightly as the door to the small Cryon ante-room closed behind him once more. It had been bitterly cold outside and in the dome, but he had come lightly dressed, knowing that behind the door, the environment was tropical. Comfortingly, the chair, coffee table and orange juice were there as before.

"Welcome once again, Major. How can I help you," came MIND's disembodied voice. It sounded like a reception clerk at a Citizens' Advice Centre.

"I would like to speak with Commander Vorkan."

"Certainly, Major. I will let him know you are here. If you would care to step through the door in front of you and wait by the side of the ramp, the Commander will be with you shortly."

Silently, the door-shaped panel opened. Beyond it loomed the cavernous chamber behind the main doors. He walked through, stood at the top of the tunnel, and stared down into the inky blackness below. Soon, faint sounds echoed up to him from the depths, their strangeness emphasised by the reverberations within the tunnel. Then he spied a pinpoint of light. It looked like an orange star surrounded by a phosphorescent blue glow. It grew in brightness rapidly, hurtling up the tunnel towards him like a ack-ack tracer bullet. It reached him within seconds, decelerating dramatically only in the last few hundred yards. As it approached, he realised that the orange light was a powerful headlamp, and the blue glow some form of ion discharge from the rear of the craft. As it came to rest some thirty yards from him, then turned to face down the tunnel, he could see it was a blue and silver bullet-shaped object the size of a small bus, with a curved front windshield. And at the controls, sat a Cryon.

The craft glided silently towards him, sideways, then stopped, hovering about a foot off the ground. A door opened and the Cryon stepped out. It was wearing an amulet. It was Vorkan.

"Good morning, Major?" he said. "Welcome back."

"That's an amazing vehicle you have there, Commander!" said Phil. It was the only thing he could think of to say.

Vorkan's sensilla rippled softly in the eerie half-light of the tunnel. Phil could smell him. He was standing only feet away.

"Would you like a ride?" he said.

Phil had a fleeting memory of greasy-looking stranger in an old van, who had driven up to him in Richmond Park one day when he was flying his kite as a child.

"I don't think my body could take the accelerations," he said.

"Neither could mine," retorted Vorkan, "But inside, you do not feel it. The drive accelerates your atoms along with the shuttle."

He held out one of his long ant-like arms towards Phil, as if to help him to board. Phil gazed at the fur-covered claws, realising this was yet another first in the history of mankind: physical contact with an alien. He swallowed hard, then extended his own shaking hand, and gingerly at first then more firmly, made contact with this extraordinary creature from outer space.

He had expected an unyielding lifeless shell, but was amazed to feel that under the velvety hairs, the underlying carapace gave subtly as he tightened his grasp; and it was hot! Standing this close to Vorkan, he realised the creature was like a walking hot water bottle.

"This is where I say, 'How do you do', is it not?" said Vorkan. "I have never in my life before, touched claws with an alien."

Phil was too preoccupied with the feel of Vorkan's chelae to pick up on which one of them was the alien.

"What is your normal body temperature?" he blurted. He couldn't help himself.

"One hundred and eleven to one hundred and fifteen Fahrenheit," replied Vorkan, "And I am getting cold standing here."

Phil was sweating. The contrast between the temperature in the tunnel and the dome outside was remarkable.

"But I thought proteins de-natured at those temperatures," he said.

"Not if they are based on silico-carbons," said Vorkan. "You have much to learn, Major."

They climbed aboard the shuttle. The inside was starkly utilitarian, the main compartment seemingly designed for stowing equipment. A number of rings, not dissimilar to the hoops by the tunnel doors, encircled it. It was obviously designed to carry six passengers - four in the back amongst the cabinets, and two up front either side of a small control panel. The seats were like the strange stools in the Conference room; Phil did not attempt to sit; they looked far too uncomfortable.

Instead of sitting in the cockpit as Phil expected him to do, Vorkan stood by him in the back.

"Ready?" he said. "You will not need to hold on."

At that, he spoke a few words in his strange twanging tongue. Two seconds later, the door closed, and as Phil looked out in amazement, the tunnel - not apparently the craft - accelerated past them at breakneck speed. There was no sense of motion whatsoever, but the view through the windscreen was like standing in a flight simulator. He stared forward wide-eyed, instinctively reaching out to steady himself as the bottom of the tunnel flew towards them. A crash seemed inevitable, but then, in the twinkling of an eye, they were through the hub, down a side tunnel, and had stopped dead alongside a personal door. The nine mile journey had taken less than a minute.

"I should have told you to close your eyes," said Vorkan, "But I am sure a veteran astronaut such as you can take it."

The droll comment sounded remarkably like good-natured sarcasm. Was it possible that Cryons had a sense of humour?

Vorkan led Phil out, and into a small side chamber arranged in a similar fashion to the Conference room. As he followed him, Phil noticed that a small metallic device was attached to the nape of Vorkan's neck, but he did not mention it.

"Please sit down," he said, indicating one of two chairs next to the central circular table. Vorkan moved over to the wall, produced two cylindrical containers of liquid which he placed on the table, then lowered himself onto a stool nearby.

"As before," he said, "The environment in here will be just tolerable to both of us. Please ... Drink."

Phil's vessel held an unfamiliar but pleasant-smelling liquid. He sipped it. The taste was not unlike concentrated fruit juice. Vorkan lowered his head, his jaws opened slightly, and out from between them uncurled a narrow prehensile tube through which he sucked the liquid.

"Now, Major," he said, resting against the cross-bar, "What can I do for you?"

There followed the most extraordinary conversation. Phil learned about the Cryon's home star system, the reason for their sudden departure, their anatomy, their way of life, and their social organisation. He was fascinated to hear that Cryons could see in the infra-red, hear through their feet as well as the hearing organs on the sides of their head, and smelt and detected the relative humidity with their antennae. Their exoskeleton was permeable and they breathed through it, and though they had one primary heart, a number of important secondary units pumped their equivalent of blood to the different organs. They had evolved to exist in conditions of near 100% humidity in air temperatures higher than their own body temperature. In such conditions, cooling by evaporation of water was impossible. Instead, they secreted - from most upward-facing surfaces of their body - a liquid organic compound like ether, whose evaporation was unaffected by humidity. As a result of the body being cooler than the surrounding moist air, water vapour condensed upon it, and was absorbed through the exoskeleton. Cryons, even though they would ingest nutrient-bearing liquid through their mouths, needed the exoskeletal absorption route to survive. In lower ambient temperatures or humidity - or worse still, both - exoskeletal water absorption ceased.

Phil discovered how over the millennia, the Cryons had reached a stage of technological progress which was difficult to better. There had also been a long period of growth and territorial expansion, followed by a period where just the opposite occurred. Interestingly, despite their level of advancement, they had reverted to a calmer unsophisticated lifestyle, based round village life. Housing predominantly comprised groups of six to eight residences backing onto a central courtyard in which communal and social pursuits were followed, and mutual assistance was provided.

"Would you say you had everything you could desire?" asked Phil. "I mean, you seem to have achieved Utopia. Factories and food production units run themselves; machines do all the tedious jobs; they even make and service other machines; no acquisition or technical innovation is beyond the reach of the ordinary citizen; you have access to unrivalled sport and leisure facilities, and repositories of knowledge beyond our wildest dreams. You want for nothing."

Vorkan moved his great head slightly left and right. He seemed to studying Phil closely. "Do you think that wanting for nothing is the ultimate goal of existence?" he said.

It was a profound question. Until recently, Phil would have found little difficulty in answering in the affirmative.

"It is something we all appear to be striving for," he said. "But whether it should be the final goal, I'm not so sure. What I am beginning to recognise is that the satisfaction gained during the struggle to achieve is rarely sustained once the goal has been reached."

"You accept then, that the real pleasure derives from the striving. So what are you going to do for pleasure when you have everything you want?"

"Me, personally?"

"No, humanity. Let us say that all this effort - all this feverish activity by so many people - leads ultimately to a state of nirvana. You reach Shangri La, your Utopia. What are you going to do next?"

Phil was non-plussed, caught unawares by the depth and quality of Vorkan's questions.

"I have no idea," he said. "What you're suggesting is an impossible dream. We've been far too busy down at the striving stage to worry about that."

"But you should," said Vorkan, slowly and deliberately. "What is the point of striving towards something if you don't know what you are going to do afterwards?"

"I don't know," said Phil. "Once we're there, we'll stop and think, Where next?"

"And what if there is nowhere left to go? What happens if you have reached a dead end?"

Phil had to think hard about that one.

"You're implying that at any given point in time, there is a choice of goals, and that this pattern forms a tree structure, with some branches leading to dead ends."

"Yes I am, except that the tree has a straight and true trunk - if the traveller did but recognise it - guiding him ultimately to the leading shoot, the only ultimate aim. Follow any side branch, to its tip on the edge of the tree, and you will reach light, space and air. You will think how wonderful it is, but then you will see the leading shoot above you, in an even better position, and forever climbing. To reach it, you will have to backtrack to where you left the trunk. This can be painful."

"You have experienced this pain?"

"Certainly. For instance, we wasted many thousands of years proliferating, and acquiring possessions and land, only to discover that in the long term, nothing of real value was achieved. We have reverted to the simple life - much more pleasant."

"It's all very well preaching that once you've got everything!" said Phil. "But tell me, what *do* you do? What do the members of a race who have everything, do next? What is this ultimate aim you are telling me I should go for?"

"Before I tell you," said Vorkan, "You will need to accept the principle that if an aim is achievable, it cannot be the ultimate, because a time will always come - the time one achieves it - when one says, What next?"

"You are suggesting that the ultimate aim is one which we know right from the beginning, is impossible to reach! What then is the point of even trying?"

"Because we agreed that it is that very trying - the endeavour itself - which gives the greatest satisfaction. The ultimate aim should therefore be one in which the effort is itself fulfilling but never ending. It should be like striving to keep up with the leading shoot. We get there, but then the shoot climbs even higher. In the process, the whole tree is growing beneath us, majestically, higher, stronger. The aim is to help the whole tree to stay healthy and alive. The ultimate aim is to guide the leading shoot itself."

Phil had got it. It was so blindingly obvious.

"The ultimate aim is to help others!" he cried.

Vorkan sat up straight, his sensilla waving serenely.

"You learn quickly, Major," he said. "But helping others before helping yourself - that is not good. One must be strong first. We believe that it is the primary responsibility of every creature to provide for its own survival. Once this is done, the ultimate and on-going aim of any creature, group of creatures, nation, civilisation, or planet, should be to help others *to help themselves*. If this aim is pursued, it is amazing what progress is made. Instead of struggling on your own, for yourself, you find that everyone else is struggling for you. You realise you have nothing left to do other than to use your abilities to help others."

The notion was so simple, so beautiful, so ... perfect.

Phil gazed at Vorkan's huge eyes. The more he talked with him, the more he began to distinguish slight changes in his facial appearance. There was expression there, and right now, there was a warmth, an understanding, a benevolence. It was unsettling, but from this alien, from this unpleasant-smelling, physically repulsive creature, there came something Phil never expected.

There came love.

"I think we have some way to go before we can aspire to such ideals," said Phil ashamedly. "We're far too busy helping ourselves, never mind others."

"You have certainly provided more than adequately for your own survival, Major," said Vorkan accusingly, "The time has come - in fact it is long overdue - that each of you thought for others. But most of you humans are driven by needs and desires which are to say the least, misguided."

"So what do you think drives us?" said Phil.

Vorkan paused for a moment before replying.

"Some of you, but not many, seem genuinely to concern yourselves with helping others. But the vast majority are driven by the need to acquire possessions, wealth and property, the need to show off and impress others with those acquisitions or physical prowess or power, the need for such physical pleasures as are gained from travel, exciting sports, or by eating, drinking, taking drugs, or being violent to others, including animals, and last but not least, you are driven by sex."

Phil could not help himself thinking what a stimulating kaleidoscope of experiences Vorkan's list had conjured up in his mind.

"Are you telling me you don't feel any of those things?" said Phil.

"None."

"Not even sex?"

"To us, sex as you call it, and by that I assume you mean any physically pleasurable sensations we derive from the instigation of the procreation process, happens so rarely, that it is of no consequence to us in our daily lives - unlike yourselves, who seem to think of nothing else most of the time. In my opinion, your preoccupation with sex - and in particular men's preoccupation with women - is the cause of many of the problems which beset your race."

"You don't know what you're missing, Commander," said Phil cheekily.

"You are wrong there," said Vorkan, his sensilla rippling strangely. "I know exactly how you feel."

"You can't do. You have to do it to understand."

"You seem to forget," said Vorkan, "That I have seen into your minds - during the truth session. In addition, I have watched film of you and Mrs Newheart making sex together, and we have a short recording of you and your Russian colleague."

Phil was horrified. He felt his face flush.

"What!" he said indignantly. "How? And it's making love, not making sex by the way - well, at least with my wife that is."

"In Houston. The key. It transmits continually to MIND, and earlier, your spacecraft flew within sight of our lunar station."

"You've got a bloody nerve!" said Phil, blushing. "Is nothing sacred?"

Vorkan sat up straight, as if taken aback. His sensilla assumed a pendulous appearance.

"I am very sorry, Major," he said. "Many of your films show this being done, and your nature programmes include studies of animals copulating. I did not realise you were sensitive about it."

"I'm not sensitive Commander," retorted Phil irritably, "It's just that, well, it should be private. How would you like it if I watched you making love to ..."

He suddenly realised he didn't know whether Vorkan had a partner, or indeed how the Cryons did it.

"I would not mind at all," said Vorkan. "In fact, I will show you now."

Phil felt a little nauseous. He had a vision of Vorkan wheeling in some Cryon concubine, and the two of them giving him a demonstration.

"Show me?" he exclaimed.

"I can do better than that," said Vorkan. "I can make it possible for you to experience what I felt at the time." He turned the back of his neck towards Phil, and tapped the metallic object fixed onto it.

"We always wear these for unusual or important events. Like you might video it, we brain-rec it. It is a device which records our brain activity - sights, sounds, smells, feelings, everything. We can play it back to ourselves, or MIND can convert it to match anybody's brain receptors. They then experience what we did."

"And you've got a brain-rec of er ....?"

"Yes. And it is Jasoma - my partner," said Vorkan. "As I said, coupling happens very rarely. Cryon females are only fertile for three days every two years. Coupling is only necessary once during those three days, and is invariably successful. We usually produce only two viable offspring in our 140 year life. So you see, we only make sex .. excuse me, make love, twice in our whole lives. I have done it once. I brain-rec'd it. I will show you. You will be especially interested because we were here on Solara when we did it. It was in the early morning, the day of the bomb."

"Are you telling me that on the morning of the day you wiped out the dinosaurs, you and Mrs Vork ... Jasoma, made love?"

"We had to, Major. It was Jasoma's time. She woke me up, and we did it up on the surface." He spoke some words in his own language, presumably to MIND. "But let the brain-rec speak for itself. I have asked MIND to convert the conversation and feelings into your equivalent. Just sit back in your chair and relax while MIND tunes you in."

Phil was absolutely fascinated and intrigued by the idea that not only was he going to experience something from someone else's viewpoint - brainwise - but that someone else was an alien, and it was going to be 'making sex'!

Within seconds, he felt as he had done when he was being shown the battery. It was like a waking dream. Soon, the room faded into insignificance.

"Of all the days!" he thought, as he clicked the brain-rec unit into place, it would have to be today! We've been on Solara for six months; specimens have been collected and stored deep underground; the survey is complete and the results confirm the initial findings from the probe. The bomb has been positioned and primed to explode at midday. In six hours, our five ships will emerge from the caverns and return to orbit; the entry points to the underground complex will be sealed. From midday onwards, Solara will change - dramatically - never to return to its present state. And now, today, it's Jasoma's time!

But I do want a son.

As he lay trembling, imagining the awful devastation he was about to wreak on the planet, the poignancy of the moment overcame him. He would be the agent of untold death and destruction, yet amidst that terrible event, he had the opportunity to create new life, new hope.

"Okay," he said. "We'll do it. But not here. Not down in this dismal place. I want to see the surface. I want us to do it at the surface."

"We can't!" protested Jasoma. "Where? Where can we go that's safe, away from the dinosaurs?"

"At the upper dome entrance," he replied. "We'll do it there. I want our child to start in the light."

He got up, and led the protesting Jasoma out and through the labyrinth of underground passageways to the hub chamber. The complex was deathly quiet. They boarded one of the parked shuttles. As he started up its drive unit, the noise echoed off the walls and reverberated up the main tunnel towards the surface.

At the main blast doors at the far end, they parked the shuttle alongside the only other vehicle there, and got out. He knew there would be a guard on the other side, in the dome or patrolling round its upper balcony. He led Jasoma through the personal access hatch to the side of the main doors, and up the winding staircase the final thirty feet or so to the outer hatch. He opened it and they emerged onto Solara's surface and into the vast echoing dome. For six months, in an artificial climate within it, this had been where they had lived and worked and conducted their experiments. But now, the dome was empty and silent, the quarters and equipment stowed miles underground, and the dome prepared for auto-collapse.

They looked up, and saw the guard sitting in the east balcony alcove. He stood up, obviously surprised to see anyone so early in the morning.

"Commander Vorkan?" he called down. "Madam Vorkan."

"I'll take over here," he said, motioning to the guard to leave. "Go back to the shuttle station. I don't want anybody coming through into the dome until after 0530. We wish to be alone. You return here at that time. Understood?"

"Yes Commander," replied the guard obediently, starting down towards them. As he passed them, he said wistfully, "It's very beautiful out there, Sir. First light."

He disappeared through the hatch, closing it behind him. Then there was silence.

"Shall we go up to the east balcony?" he said, leading her across the dome.

"Yes," she said quietly. "We can watch the dawn."

They climbed the stairs up the inner surface of the dome, and walked to the balcony alcove, from which there was an unobstructed view through the dome surface barrier field.

"It's humid enough for us to go through to the outer balcony," he said. "It'll be cold, but from what I've been told, we'll probably not be too bothered about that."

Jasoma just nodded, coyly.

He de-activated the barrier field, and they walked out into the cool, dank, half-light of a Solara foredawn. He checked the bio-sensors were on, then re-activated the barrier field behind them. From this position, some fifty feet above the ground, they could see and become part of the world outside, but remain safe.

They stood there together, watching the orange light creep over the horizon; two lonely figures against the brightening sky. Below them stretched the tropical forest, glistening and dripping with dew. In the dimly-lit clearings, they glimpsed strange animals lumbering slowly towards their water holes by the muddy riverbanks. It felt as if they were watching the dawn of creation.

Jasoma gently nudged him into a position behind her, then wrapped her arms backwards round him and drew him close. Instinctively, he responded by wrapping his arms round her upper body. She smelt different. Her secretion glands were exuding a film of moisture which filled the air around her with an inviting, exciting aroma. He felt his antennae extend and stiffen, and their cillia fan much more quickly than usual. The sensation was exquisite as he soaked up more and more of Jasoma's body perfumes. Jasoma's sensilla were quivering and fluttering; his were becoming ultra-sensitive. He felt his whole body responding to this signal. Deep down, in the soft crevice between his central and lower sections, a duct began dilating. Now, Jasoma was moving with a slow rhythmical gyration, round and round, pushing backwards into him. He began to feel her snake-like seed collector worming its way into the duct. It dilated even further, and now he could feel suction within him. He wanted her further inside. He felt he should try to envelope her completely, and respond to this primeval demand. He pulled her even closer, his right arm moving down to her lower thorax, and his left arm across her chest. She threw her head back next to his, and they pressed their mandibles together. Their eyes widened, and their long tongues began darting in and out of their mouths, eventually twining round each other as their free-flowing juices interacted in an explosion of intimate chemistry. He became aware that he too was now exuding a liquid from his cuticle. It ran down his head, arms, legs, and body, collected on Jasoma's dorsal thorax, and trickled round the base of her seed collector, triggering her final response to this ultimate union. Their two fluids reacted together, sending both of them into a shuddering spasm of pleasure. Deep inside him, he felt Jasoma drawing his very being into her. They crushed each other together as if they were trying to fuse their bodies into one, and finally, as the first rays of sun slanted across the valley, both let out a frenzied howling cry into the still morning air.

As the brain-rec ended, Phil found himself back sitting at the table next to Vorkan. His T-shirt was soaked with sweat and he was panting hard. He had the strangest impression, albeit briefly, that somewhere below his abdomen, a part of his body was missing. There was also a pleasurable sensation, as if in the missing part, a long satisfying sneeze had just been induced.

"Did you find that interesting?" said Vorkan.

"Er, yes. I did," he replied. In fact, he had never experienced anything remotely like it before. It had been absolutely incredible.

"So now you understand," said Vorkan, "We do appreciate what you humans feel regarding sex. It is just a pity that it so often seems to dictate your entire lives. It, along I must say with your predilection for violence, drives your actions, to the exclusion of more constructive pursuits."

"Such as?"

"Understanding and accepting the Great Truths would be a good start. If you understood, you would modify your actions. Your lives - the entire planet - would benefit."

"Go on."

"Take the Truth about Life, for instance," said Vorkan. "We have come to realise that all life forms, however apparently lowly, must be respected and treated as if they had the potential to evolve. Just because, at a given moment in time, a thinking species has the power to control or eliminate another, that in itself is no justification for it doing so. There is no pinnacle of evolution. It is an ever-branching network, where, from any single point may spring - by luck or adaptation - the seed of a magnificent race of beings who do nothing but benefit their fellow creatures. You Humans make the arrogant assumption that all other species - all other branches of the tree of life - are lowlier than yourself, and have somehow been provided for your benefit. You are very wrong."

"So how do you defend your elimination of the dinosaurs, along with many other species?" said Phil.

"As I stated earlier, we believe our primary responsibility is to survive. Given that, we had no choice but to invade somewhere. Where there is a clash of interests, the criterion for judgement is, 'Which decision or life form is, from now through to the predictable future, likely to be of most benefit to the total life force within the system as a whole? We had a choice between eliminating a highly aggressive group of reptiles likely to eat or subjugate all other species, and invading an advanced and peace-loving civilisation. The decision was clear. It was not that the dinosaurs were lowlier than the Saarians. It was not that they were an easy target. It was that they were not *as* beneficial. We had to run the test, the bomb. Nobody wanted to do it, least of all myself. I had to trigger the explosion. It was the worst experience of my life."

Phil felt naturally suspicious. Vorkan would say that, wouldn't he.

"You do not believe me do you Major," said Vorkan, sadly. "I know that it may not be proof positive, but you could experience another part of that same brain-rec, recorded during the bomb detonation. You will at least know how I felt myself. Would you like to? I warn you, it is not pleasant."

Whether or not it proved Cryon fair-mindedness, Phil jumped at the chance. To experience at first hand, the event which changed the course of Earth's evolution so dramatically - the K-T event itself - was something that could not be missed.

"Yes Commander. Run it please."

Vorkan was silent for a moment.

"I think I will sense it with you," he said. "It was such a distressing experience, I have never replayed the recording before. It is only right that I now summon the courage to re-live it."

There was something about Vorkan's tone and posture which suggested apprehension. He regarded Phil, earnestly.

"Ready, Major?"

"Ready, Commander."

Phil knew that there would only be a few precious seconds during which he was still conscious of the present, yet beginning to experience the past. It was uncanny, knowing that soon, he would be Vorkan, and the date would be 65 million years BC.

The underground chamber began to fade. He began to make out windows.

***

From his location in a parked lander south of the tunnel entrance, he would have a good view of the launchings. The dome had gone, and already, some of the more adventurous animals had begun, tentatively, to reclaim their territory. But as he watched, they scurried for cover as the five great space cruisers emerged one by one from the depths of the planet below him. It was a magnificent sight, as each craft accelerated into the sky on a column of light. The last to appear was *Stallustra*, an incredible half mile long cylinder, gleaming in the morning sunshine. Immediately after it cleared the entrance, the blast door closed behind it, leaving the entire installation completely sealed off from the outside world.

Stallustra climbed to an altitude of one mile then stopped. Kraadin's voice came over the intercom to his lander.

"Last chance, Commander. Are you still determined to remain?"

"Absolutely, Captain. Go. Take up your position in orbit."

"So be it, Commander. May the Great One protect you."

And with that, *Stallustra* tilted skywards and accelerated upwards, the glow from its drive unit lighting the sky with an ever diminishing radiance as it disappeared from view.

Silence returned once more to the landscape. Unaware of their imminent fate, the animals began to break cover again. Directly in front of the lander, he saw a small furry creature with a long whiskered snout emerge from a burrow in the ground and sniff the air suspiciously. Its fur was a beautiful mixture of reds, browns and greys, and it stood on its hind legs surveying the scene around it. As he moved nearer the window to get a better view, it spotted him, spun round and shot back into its hole, kicking dust back towards the lander with its rear legs.

He sat in the lander cockpit and surveyed the scene around him. He realised that never in the history of Solara, would this place ever be the same again.

Kraadin's voice came over the intercom.

"Fleet now in parking orbit, Commander. You have control."

"Thank you Captain," he said. "I have 5 minutes 20 seconds on my timer. Do you confirm?"

"I confirm. You realise Commander that a split second after you command the detonation, the electro-magnetic pulse will render your craft's local position sensors inactive for at least thirty seconds?"

"I do. As a safety precaution, I will remain parked on the ground until sensing is re-activated."

"Yes," replied Kraadin, his voice rising slightly as detonation time drew near. "But you must take to the air before the ground shock gets to you. It would be extremely dangerous to remain in contact with the ground. I advise a climb to at least a hundred feet once the sensors come back on line. And don't forget - maximum anti-impact shields as soon as you lift off."

"Understood, Captain.".

The countdown timer now read sixty seconds. He lifted off for a brief moment and re-oriented the lander so it faced south, the direction of the bomb. After it came to rest, he powered off the drive unit and stole one final lingering look at the exotic landscape he was about to devastate. He switched on the lander's flash shields, then moved his right foreclaw towards the detonate button. His hands were shaking, and he had to rest them on the panel next to the button to keep his claw in the right position. He began to feel physically sick.

At ten seconds to go, Jasoma's voice came over the intercom.

"My life is yours, Faro," she said. "Whatever happens, may you be in peace."

Five seconds to go. In a final moment of self-doubt, he raised his head to the sky.

"If this is wrong, stop me now," he cried.

One second.

He depressed his foreclaw an eighth of an inch.

A quarter of a second after that, the sky to the south lit up with a piercing violet light, and simultaneously every warning bell, buzzer and flasher on the lander demanded his attention. The intercom exploded into an ear-splitting crackle, matched in volume only by his own scream of terror as the enormity of what he had just done bore upon him.

The lander's EMP shield had protected its electrical systems from the pulse, and one by one, they were reporting normal status and re-contact with the world outside. Eventually, the warning signals ceased. For a moment, silence surrounded him. The brilliance in the sky faded considerably, so he switched off the window flash shields. Then the intercom came back on line.

"Commander Vorkan. Please respond," came the urgent words. It was Kraadin.

"Vorkan here, Captain. All's well down here," he said, feeling sick with remorse as he gazed about him at the animals in the valley.

The curvature of Solara's surface had protected them all from the direct and searing light from the actual fireball, but they had all turned to look at the intensely bright sky to the south. Now they were beginning to move away from it, but many - still apparently dazzled - started bumping into trees and each other as they went.

Something on the ground in front of the lander caught his eye. It was the furry animal. For some reason, it had decided to emerge from its burrow again. He watched in horror as it was followed by a second, obviously female, and heavily pregnant. They started out across the open ground, but had barely got two yards when a Stygimoloch dinosaur ran straight into one of the lander's legs and fell senseless in front of them. They both stopped dead, then cowered, shaking with fear as the huge creature's multi-horned head struck the ground a few feet from them.

"Move!" he shouted, standing up and banging on the lander's window. "Get back into your hole!"

But the creatures would not move. He looked at them desperately. He was imagining the terrible fate about to overtake them.

Kraadin's voice came over the intercom.

"Commander. Take off. Take off now!"

He glanced at the timer. Three minutes after detonation. Four minutes before the ground shock arrival. He still had time to save the creatures.

"Just about to lift off, Captain," he said. "Don't worry."

Driven by some primeval instinct, he leapt through the cockpit bulkhead door and ran back to the lander's loading bay. He pressed the controls which opened the rear door and lowered the ramp. While he waited, he grabbed a freezer gun and a padded specimen box. It seemed to take an eternity for the doors to open. He jumped down to the surface while the ramp was still lowering and ran towards the creatures. They were still there, frozen to the spot. As he stooped towards their defenseless forms, the reptile's eyes opened and it started to struggle to its feet. He floored it with a perfect aim to the head, the beam of intense cold turning its eyes instantly white. Then he gently picked up the soft furry bodies. He could feel the rapid beating of their hearts as he cradled them in his hands. He laid them in the box, looped the strap over his head, and ran back to the ramp. As he climbed it, the sounds of distressed animals and the first signs of mass panic spread across the valley.

As he clambered back into the lander and closed the doors, he could hear Kraadin's urgent voice on the intercom.

"Commander! What is the matter? Take off! Take off!"

He threw the freezer gun to the floor, ran to the cockpit, and flung himself into the pilot's seat. There was less than a minute to go. He hit the drive button, and was airborne within seconds. He energised the lander's impact shields and rose to one hundred feet, then remained hovering at that height.

"All okay down here, Captain," he reported, trying to sound calm and collected. "Holding at one hundred feet."

Kraadin fed him images and data from the remote sensors and monitoring satellites. At the detonation site, the flash and fireball from the explosion had vaporised everything within a radius of five hundred miles. A supersonic blast wave was searing objects at a greater distance. The explosion, concentrated by the existing caldera, had hit the ground like a blow from a gigantic hammer. Most ground material was being ejected straight through the atmosphere at thousands of miles per hour, and some had reached velocities of up to twenty five thousand miles per hour - Solara's escape velocity. In the sea, a tsunami travelling at five hundred miles per hour was spreading outwards, creating a gigantic wave hundreds of feet high.

As the blast wave spread out from the explosion, shock heating of the atmosphere was causing its nitrogen and oxygen to combine to form nitrous oxide, a gas which would eventually return in the form of nitric acid.

The explosion had vaporised sulphur-rich rocks into sulphur dioxide, which would later return as sulphuric acid rain. The carbon-rich rocks had been converted into millions of tons of carbon dioxide.

In the ground itself, the primary shock wave was travelling outwards at four to five miles per second, and the surface wave, at just over one mile per second. He was two thousand miles from the explosion. These waves would take seven and twenty seven minutes to get to him.

He was facing southwards and concentrating on the distant ground, when he became aware that the sun was getting dimmer. He looked up, to see a wall of blackness rising and obscuring it. He got the impression that the leading upper edge of this wall consisted of thousands of individual dark dots.

Then without any warning at all, the ground below burst into life. The primary shock wave passed under him at the speed of an orbiting spacecraft. The initial noise was a series of deafening thuds which continued for many seconds. These were followed by an uncanny twanging noise as the sound of the wave reached him from an ever increasing distance in all directions. At the sound, in every direction, thousands of birds and other flying creatures took to the air, looking from above like a storm of leaves in a sudden squall. The ground below did not move up and down, but became blurred as the near-horizontal vibrations shook the very life out of it. Trees snapped off at their bases and came crashing down. Animals and anything else not rigidly attached to the ground remained stationary whilst the ground beneath them shook thirty feet to and fro. Nothing could remain in contact with such a dynamic platform, and many creatures were killed or injured as this crazy wobble smashed rocks and tree stumps into them. The rivers and streams looked like they were boiling, and many creatures who had been near them were overwhelmed by the sludge which erupted from their banks. Fortunately, their frantic cries were almost drowned out by the awful sounds from the straining rocks below.

As he looked around him, mudflows began surging through the undergrowth and slopping round the base of the trees, carrying before them a chaotic mass of intertwined vegetation and small animals. The desperate creatures thrashed, struggled and gasped for breath before they were overwhelmed by the sickening slime.

"The primary shock front has just passed under me," he shouted into the intercom. He had to lean very close to the microphone to be heard over the awful din outside.

"What's it like down there?" replied Kraadin.

"Indescribable destruction," he yelled.

Shortly after the shock front passed by, the sky started to grow very much darker. The sun was now totally obscured, and the main light source was the sky to the north.

The oscillations began to subside. The creatures that had not been killed, crippled, drowned or swept away, began to struggle to their feet, their eyes wide with terror. Instinct would be telling them to run and hide, but there was no sanctuary. Some of the offspring of the larger beasts tried crawling under or climbing on top of the prone bodies of their parents, but it was useless. Most of the parents were dead.

He sat, overwhelmed by the extent of the destruction and the degree of distress around him.

The intercom crackled into life once more, and he could hear Kraadin yelling something, but could not tell what he was saying. He caught a glimpse of the time. Seventeen minutes after detonation. He knew the surface waves had not got to him yet, and was considering whether to increase the lander's altitude when he realised it was nearly pitch black outside.

Then, without any warning, the sky above him lit up with a brilliant yellow light, and an incandescent object fell like a meteorite and smashed into the ground a few hundred yards in front of him. As it hit, it exploded like burning shrapnel, and formed a crater at least twenty feet across.

This rock was closely followed by another behind him, then another over to the right. Above the explosions, he became aware of a continuous roaring sound. The only other time he had heard anything like this was just prior to a violent hail shower a few months back, when hailstones one inch in diameter fell from the sky. But this sound was different. Not only was it far louder, but mingled with the general roar were high pitched whistles and screeches.

Along with the roaring, the sky began to light up all around him, and blazing rocks of every size and shape began raining down. As each fell, it too exploded, sending sheets of flame and shrapnel across the already devastated landscape.

The lander took some large and many small hits, but the missiles were reflected harmlessly in the direction from which they had come as the retroflective shields did their work. As each missile hit one of the shields, he was glad to hear the low pitched hum of the impact-induced current being instantly generated by the responders. The protection afforded by the shields would only be jeopardised if the lander took a series of very large strikes in rapid and prolonged succession. He prayed that this highly unlikely event would not occur.

The creatures who were still alive ran to and fro in blind panic, stumbling and falling over the split and shattered trees, and impaling themselves on their edges. He saw one desperate animal jump to one side to avoid a smouldering meteorite crater, then take a direct hit which smashed through its backbone like a cannonball.

The landscape all around was now beginning to catch fire. Firstly in isolated clumps, then gradually in increasing numbers, the trees and bushes began to spontaneously ignite. He could see the red glow from hundreds of fires waxing and waning as thick black smoke drifted across in front of them. Even the flying creatures, who had up to now saved themselves by taking to the air, were now succumbing to the smoke and heat. He watched with horror as a large bird, it wings on fire and cawing desperately, tried in vain to stay airborne, falling eventually into the furnace below like a stone into a volcano. The smoke began to enter the lander. It had a choking acrid sulphurous smell, of burning wood mingled with burning bone, flesh and feathers. He could see wisps of smoke inside the cockpit, and had to switch to sealed running.

The worst of the meteorite storm - the ejecta from the explosion falling back from hundreds of miles beyond the atmosphere - had now passed. Apart from the occasional distant 'thump', the sky was becoming free of these deadly missiles. But above him, it was pitch black. Below, all he could see was fire and smoke. He strained to glimpse a sign of life, but to no avail.

He was checking his altimeter and clock, when he realised the lander was going down. But he had felt nothing. The fiery ground to the south was moving up towards him at an alarming rate. Warning buzzers started sounding. The ground got nearer and nearer. A clump of blazing shattered tree trunks came to within feet of the lander's legs. He grabbed the controls and climbed a hundred feet. The ground fell away, then rose again, then fell again. The on-board control system advised that he climbed a further hundred feet. As he did so, he looked down again and realised what was happening. To this indescribable hell was now added the rolling surface waves from the explosion. The ground itself was behaving like the water of a great ocean. But the waves were travelling at over four thousand miles per hour, and were one hundred and twenty feet high.

Kraadin's voice could now be heard once more.

"Are you all right, Commander? I've been trying to warn you that though our prediction of the average height of the surface waves was correct, at certain places, including your location, their amplitude can be much greater."

"Thank you, Captain," he said ruefully. "I've just worked that one out for myself!"

"Haven't you had enough, Commander? When are you returning to *Stallustra*?"

He looked around him. Like a wounded animal, the planet he had grown to love over the last few months was screaming in agony. And this terrible act had been inflicted upon it by his own hand. He had wanted to witness his 'adjustment', and now he had done so - at least in part.

He knew that if he chose to wait at least another two hours, he would experience the air-borne blast wave with its hurricane force winds, initially surging forwards then sucking backwards. It did not take much imagination to visualise what that would do to anything which by some miracle, had survived until then. He also knew that the gigantic tsunami which was at this moment spreading outwards across the ocean would in part enter the inland sea to his east from its southern end, and as the wave encountered increasingly shallow water in a narrowing channel, its height would increase dramatically. To anything in its path, it would appear as a three hundred miles per hour mountain, destroying and overwhelming everything in its path. And these two phenomena were only the last of the direct and immediate effects of the explosion.

As he surveyed this awful vision of hell, he was distracted by a tiny squeak from the specimen box. The furry animals! He had completely forgotten about them. He gently took the box and looked inside, to see not two but eight of them. The female had given birth to six tiny pink babies, who, completely unaware that their home had been destroyed, were now busy jostling for position as they suckled on her four nipples. He was entranced. As Vorkan, he had never seen mammalian activities in the raw before. There and then, he decided to give them to Charis and Nitra to look after. If the morning's activities were anything to go by, he and Jasoma would soon have a son, but Charis and Nitra could never have such a gift. The little family saved from certain death would be a sort of consolation present.

"I'm naming you Therma, and you, Tron," he said out loud to the creatures, "In memory of all your friends that I have killed with my thermatron device."

He placed the specimen box on the co-pilot's seat, reached back and poured himself some enerjuice. He drank most of it, then poured the remainder into the cup lid and placed it inside the box. To his delight, Tron sniffed at it for a few seconds, decided it was good, and drank, his eyes constantly darting around him to ensure he was not about to be eaten. Therma could not move, and he got the strangest impression that Tron was trying to push the lid towards her. Could we have underestimated the intelligence and potential of these diminutive creatures? he thought to himself.

The intercom crackled into life once more. This time it was Jasoma.

"Faro. Please come up to the ship now. It must be horrible down there. We can see what's happening from here, and it can't be doing you any good staying there dwelling on it all. Please come. This is where you are needed. Not there."

She was right, and there was something in the emphasis on 'This' which told him her message was very personal as well as eminently sensible.

"Returning to *Stallustra* now," he said; as he slowly powered the lander vertically upwards.

As he climbed above five miles altitude, the smoke cleared and he was able to see around him. Over to the west, the line of volcanoes which normally signalled their presence with innocuous columns of white smoke were now in full eruption. Their cones were spewing out angry billows of black ash, the ugly towering clouds emphasising still further how Solara had been sickeningly wounded.

As his lander cleared the atmosphere, and the sky around him reverted to the inky blackness of space, he gazed upwards to see the five cruisers glowing pink in the reflected light of the hellish scene below. They looked like the fingers of some gigantic metal hand, stained with blood.

In the now silent cabin, he relived the events of this most extra-ordinary day. He had created life, saved life, and destroyed life. It occurred to him that if his action of coming to Solara and detonating this terrible explosion had been against Universal Law, and the Great One really did exist, then somehow He would have stopped him. Perhaps the Great One did not exist; or perhaps He did, but condoned the bomb. Perhaps there were no such things as deities. Perhaps there were only beings like himself, with awesome power at their disposal, totally mysterious to those over whom the power was exercised. Either way, the burden of responsibility for the evolution of an entire planet for the next sixty five million years rested firmly on his shoulders.

He sat and pondered the desperate fate of the creatures down there, and wondered which ones would claw there way out of the yawning chasm of extinction. He could only speculate on how life would evolve from then on, and wonder how, when the time came for the final explosion - the ultimate and cataclysmic adjustment - he would find the strength to trigger it. But trigger it he must. Even now, with the blood of millions of defenseless creatures on his hands, and his spirit in a nadir of grief, he knew he must carry out the plan to the end. The future of his race depended on him.

Strangely, now he had the degree of absolute power he had craved for so long, he felt humbled rather than satiated. In the absence of guidance from a higher authority, he would wield this power with all the wisdom at his command.

But as he sat in the darkness, idly clawing the amulet from his mother, he knew there was something else, something intangible, something out of reach. Something was still missing from his life. Deep within his soul, he was still not at peace.

***

Back in the underground chamber, Phil became aware that tears were running down his cheeks. He had seen films of the aftermath of disasters before, but nothing could have prepared him for the harrowing gut-wrenching horror he had just witnessed.

Vorkan was sitting motionless, his head bowed, and his arms hanging loosely by his sides. He was emitting a strange desolate low-pitched moan. Eventually, he stopped, and raised his head.

"It was the worst day of my life," he said. "You must have felt it. I need you to believe that it was not a callous act. We do not do such things lightly."

Phil regarded him closely. For the first time, he saw an alien gentle giant, robbed of his home, the future of his race depending upon him, trying to act responsibly and make the best of an almost impossible situation.

But he also saw a creature who once - perhaps misguidedly - craved absolute power but who now needed Phil to believe in him. A creature who, though superior in intellect and ideals, was not perfect. A creature who, whilst obviously mature, still fiddled nervously with an amulet from his mother.

Vorkan had a soul.

"I believe you," said Phil. "I understand."

Vorkan's posture changed. He looked strong again. He produced a thin document from a slot below the table.

"The demands," he said, passing Phil the document. "These are the demands I put forward at the meeting with you and your colleagues. They still need to be met. You must understand this. Do not misconstrue our sympathy with you and our regard for your well-being. You *must* comply. We will help you to help yourselves, but the price you will pay for non-compliance is extinction, just like the dinosaurs."

"I understand," said Phil. There was no doubt that Vorkan meant it.

"And the benefits you would gain by complying are beyond your wildest dreams," said Vorkan. He leant towards Phil. "The demands are reasonable. Do you agree? I need you to believe in those too. Do you, Major?"

He had been weighing these up since Christmas eve, and had reached the conclusion that the Cryon ultimatum was possibly the only way that humanity was going to survive. There seemed little point in denying what he felt: that to a reasonable person, Vorkan's demands were indeed eminently sensible.

"Yes, I do," he replied.

"And do you think that you can persuade your various governments to set the changes in motion?"

"I promise faithfully that I will try."

Vorkan studied him closely.

"If we can start by trusting each other, progress will be swift and enormously beneficial to all of us. I have let you into my innermost thoughts. I trust you. Do you trust me, Major?"

There was no question. Phil was convinced of Vorkan's goodwill.

But as he sat, bathed in the almost palpable benevolence radiating from this amazing creature, he was thinking about the men of power, up there on the surface above him, and whether he trusted them.

Now that was a different matter.

16

Rendezvous at Ruby's

As Phil emerged from the door into the cold and the glare of the dome floodlights, he was relieved to see the silhouette of Ted Beemish waiting for him. He removed the key from its hole, and walked down the ramp towards him.

"Welcome back, Major," said Beemish loudly, handing him his flying jacket. The warning message in his eyes did not match the greeting. "I'm afraid I have work to do here. General Miller will escort you back."

As he said this, Phil saw the gaunt figure of Miller close behind, as silent as a statue.

"The Cryon leader gave me this," he said, handing Beemish the document. "It's a written version of their demands. I promised them I would do my best to......"

But Beemish's expression told him to shut up. Out of sight of Miller, Beemish lightly tapped his own jacket, pointed surreptitiously at Phil's, and mouthed, "Pocket."

Phil zipped up the jacket, turned to Miller and forced a smile. It was not returned.

He had expected there to be more activity within the dome, and at the very least, some form of de-briefing, but there was none. Without a word, Miller led him to an Air Force helicopter, which he piloted himself. Phil sat on his own in the back, and when Miller and the co-pilot were pre-occupied with the flight, he reached into his inside pocket, and felt a piece of paper. Keeping it well hidden, he unfolded it, and read it.

House bugged.
Essential we meet off base.
8 pm Ruby's Steak Bar tonight.
You will be followed.
Must seem normal. Bring Mrs Newheart.
Beemish

***

Ruby's Steak Bar, a typical glass-fronted establishment just off Cheyenne's West Lincolnway, was easy to find. Phil parked in the well-lit street just opposite, and walked Jo-Ann across, protecting her from the brunt of the snow-laden wind with his body. They paused outside to read the menu, but focused their eyes on the reflection of the black sedan that had followed them from the base and which had pulled up a few car lengths behind them. Once inside the dimly-lit bar, they could see that the two men in the sedan were staying in their car. Its doors did not open.

Beemish had chosen the rendezvous wisely. It was a friendly place, arranged into loosely-defined booths. The lighting - from dim lamps high above each booth – was atrocious. Most of the clients were wearing broad hats, and it was impossible to see any of their faces. As Phil and Jo-Ann stood peering into the darkness, a tall man in a black Stetson who looked as if he had left his horse tied up outside, rose to his feet and headed towards the bar.

"Plenty of room at my table, folks," he said, in an over-emphasised drawl.

But as he squeezed past them, he glanced up briefly and winked.

"But these cowboy boots are damned near killing me!" he whispered.

It was Beemish.

Whilst keeping an eye on the door and checking adjacent tables for eavesdroppers, the three of them, feeling much like conspirators in an assassination plot, leant inwards towards the centre of the table.

"I have to break the vow of silence," said Beemish hoarsely. "Your trip in there today, Phil - just a ploy. A diversionary tactic. What they're going to do is madness, sheer madness. What's the point of secrecy when there won't be anyone around to keep the secret!"

Phil stopped him.

"Jo-Ann doesn't know anything," he said. "It's been agonising, but I've told her nothing."

Beemish smiled at them both.

"You're a good man, Phil," he said warmly. "But tell her. Tell her about Christmas eve. Tell us what you found out today if you like, then I'll tell you both what's happened. The whole goddamn world is going to know about it soon enough anyway."

He took over door watching, and sat nervously sipping his beer as Phil unburdened himself and described the extraordinary events below ground to an increasingly incredulous Jo-Ann. By the time he had finished, her tourniquet-like grip on his left wrist was in danger of depriving his entire hand of its blood supply. She eventually let go, and called the waitress over.

"I need a drink," she said. "Two double brandies and a large Jim Beam please."

"Comin' up," said the waitress, eyeing her strangely.

Phil then saw an expression of horror come over Jo-Ann's face. At the same time, he realised who the Jim Beam was for. Brandy had always been his and Jo-Ann's favourite drink. There was only one way she could have known what Beemish's was.

"It's all right," he said. "I know what happened when I was in Houston. I know everything. There are no secrets left."

Jo-Ann's jaw dropped and the blood rushed to her face. She stared down at the table in embarrassment.

"Oh God!" she said.

Phil closed her hand in his and kissed her on the cheek.

"We were all under stress... And it's not going to happen again, is it, Ted!" He grimaced at Beemish, who smiled back ruefully as he wobbled his own jaw with his hand.

"Have you two been... ?" she said, eyeing them suspiciously. She turned to Phil. "Christmas eve. Slipped on the snow my ass! I knew it was bullshit."

"History," said Phil.

The drinks arrived, and the three collaborators quietly touched glasses. But then, Beemish's face took on a deadly serious expression. He got up, checked the men were still in the sedan outside, and returned to the table.

"*They're going to nuke the Cryons*," he whispered.

Phil felt as if he'd been punched in the solar plexus.

"What!" he blurted out so loudly, that everyone else in the restaurant stopped talking.

Once the conversation level around them returned to normal, Phil stared at Beemish in disbelief.

"For Christ's sake, how? Why?"

"The why is easy, Phil. America accept the rule of a higher authority? No way. Lower our standard of living by reducing use of resources? No way. Emasculate our men-folk by taking their guns away from them? No way. Zero long-term growth? Heaven forbid we should consider something so eminently sensible. What about making our bucks now? That's far too fucking important!"

He glanced at Jo-Ann. "Sorry," he said.

Even in the poor light, Phil could see Beemish's face flushing with anger. The Jim Beam tossed and rippled in his shaking hand as he took a swig.

"Has the President okayed this?" said Phil sceptically. "Surely .."

"Powell and Straker saw him over Christmas. One of the options they considered was a pre-emptive nuclear strike. The President flew down here yesterday, very hush-hush... "

"So *that's* what all the fuss was about."

"He saw the door in the morning. He was in the briefing room for most of the afternoon. That's when it was finally decided."

"So when you and Straker came to the house... "

"We'd come straight from the President. Sorry. No way I could tell you."

"Who else was there? What happened? How the hell are they planning getting a bomb down in there?"

"Powell, Straker, Cranford, Norman, Miller and myself. No-one else," replied Beemish, desperation in his voice. "The President was all for meeting the Cryon commander."

"So why didn't he? I could have taken him in there."

"Powell, Straker and Cranford persuaded him it was too dangerous."

"Couldn't you do anything?"

Beemish looked up, his eyes weary.

"Do you think I didn't try? I was the only voice against. They really laid it on thick. Miller's obviously quite mad, and old Doug Norman - well, this could be his last stand. He's been busting for a good scrap ever since Desert Purge. And the others, they've got far too much to lose if the Cryons take over and start their truth revealing antics."

"And what about other world leaders? The UN? Don't they get a say?"

"Discussion with them is not an option, Phil. What if the President did tell them, and they decided to capitulate? No. Powell and Straker painted a gruesome picture to the President, and convinced him that we can zap the Cryons with this strike. If it works, America can boast it's saved the world. If it doesn't, then what the hell, we're doomed anyway. Might as well go down fighting. That's the logic."

"But we wouldn't necessarily be doomed," said Phil. "All Vorkan said made sense to me. It's just a pity it had to come from a bloody alien. I think they're right. And since I've been into space, I'm totally convinced we've got things wrong. The Cryons might have come in the nick of time."

Beemish eyed him closely.

"You're preaching to the converted, Phil," he said wearily. "But it's all academic now. They're going to hit the Cryons, and if it doesn't work first time, and knock them all out, I reckon we've had it."

"How the hell are they going to do it?"

Beemish peered round furtively, then got up and checked the sedan once more.

"Have you heard of the Hell Hole?" he whispered.

"Oh yes, I have actually. BJ told me about it the day I discovered the door. I'd forgotten all about it. It's all that's left of the GEGA project - a bore hole three miles......"

Phil stared at Beemish in horror.

"Don't tell me, the Hell Hole goes straight down to the Cryon facility."

"Ends right on top of it," confirmed Beemish. "The mileage we drove in the jeeps, and the direction - exactly right. When we were in that room with the Cryons, we were just below the bottom of the Hell Hole."

"Oh God!" said Phil. "Not an H-bomb down the hole?"

"Twenty."

Twenty hydrogen bombs! Phil and Jo-Ann stared at each other in disbelief.

"Three hundred kilotons each," said Beemish. "They're in the arsenal on the base. When we reduced our strategic holding for START II in 2003, we kept two Peacekeeper ICBM warhead clusters. There are ten warheads per cluster, each small enough to be lowered down the bore shaft."

"And they'll detonate simultaneously?" said Phil.

"Miller's techies are rigging up a multiple trigger which will be lowered down the shaft along with the warheads. It'll be a pre-primed stand alone system. Once it's down there, they'll plug the shaft above the bombs."

"A six megaton underground explosion!"

"Three hundred times more powerful than Hiroshima," said Beemish. "They've called it Operation Groundstorm."

"Groundstorm," echoed Jo-Ann. "What an awful name. What will happen at the surface? The ranchers?"

"According to the experts, the largest underground nuclear explosion we've ever detonated was a five megaton device, back in '71, on Amchitka in the Aleutian islands. Apparently, this bomb was down 1800 metres, and just shook the ground a bit only a mile from ground zero. The Atomic Energy Commission chairman at the time was so confident of its safety that he had his wife and kids on the island with him when it went off! Miller's bomb will be two or three times as deep. The theory is that nobody'll get hurt."

"But the tunnel," said Phil. "The blast could come out of that like a nuclear cannon."

"I think they're hoping that the angle will direct any effects up into the sky, but sure as hell, that door and everything around it is going to get blown away."

"They'll have to warn the people along the blast line," said Jo-Ann.

"No chance," said Beemish. "Their idea is to just do it. No warning. Nothing. Any other way, you lose the element of surprise. Start moving people out and the Cryons will get wind of it."

"But people could be killed!" said Jo-Ann.

"Necessary sacrifice if it saves the world," replied Beemish. "There's a sort of warped justification in there somewhere."

The three sat in silence, trying to come to terms with the potentially devastating consequences of such a strike. Phil couldn't see Groundstorm actually working, but even if it did, and wiped out the Cryons, he was rapidly coming to the conclusion that that was the worst thing that could happen. The Cryons were clearly not bent on the destruction of humankind, or they would have done it two thousand years ago. Admittedly, they had given humanity notice to quit, but two hundred thousand years in advance. Ample time to find somewhere to move to. All they asked is that we look after the Earth in the meantime.

"We have to stop this," said Phil. "It's not right."

"Oh, sure!" said Jo-Ann, patronisingly.

"We've got two choices," said Beemish. "Persuade the President to abandon Groundstorm, or sabotage it."

Phil studied him closely. "You would do that?" he said.

"I've thought of nothing else over the last twenty four hours," he replied, gravely. "If the President has been misled - which we know he has - I can justify sabotage."

Phil considered the issues.

"If we show our hand and try the persuasion option, we're stymied if it fails," he said. "After that, we'd be under close guard or even imprisoned. We'd have no chance to fall back on sabotage."

Beemish suddenly placed a hand on Phil's arm.

"I've been so concerned about my news, I haven't asked you what you found out today. Don't suppose Vorkan said anything which we could use to persuade the President? I mean, the annihilation thing, he couldn't have been kidding could he?"

Phil smiled, as he thought back.

"No way," he said, shaking his head. "Vorkan's reasonable but ruthless. If we don't comply, he'll do it."

He sat and thought for a moment.

"So we're left with sabotage," he said, reluctantly.

"We!" exclaimed Jo-Ann. "Goddammit Phil, you're not James fucking Bond. What's come over you."

Phil began analysing the question, then realised he couldn't be bothered with analysis. He *had* changed. Now, he felt more alive, more aware, more empowered.

"New me," he said disarmingly, smiling at her. Then, turning to Beemish, "How long have we got?"

"A week. They're aiming for detonation at midday Friday 4th January."

"Bloody hell!"

But week or no week, Phil was coming to the conclusion that neither persuasion nor sabotage was a solid bet. He sat, rested his head in his hands, and tried to come to terms with the solution that was clammering for his attention. He could feel a sense of dread as he raised his head and addressed the others.

"We have to warn the Cryons," he said.

Jo-Ann and Beemish stared at him, wide-eyed. For a while, neither spoke. They just sat, their changing expressions betraying their inner agony. Eventually, Beemish looked up.

"That would be treason," he said. "It's curtains if we're caught."

"If those bombs don't wipe out the Cryons completely," said Phil, "It's curtains for all of us anyway."

He drained his glass.

"Look, I really don't think the bombs are going to work. And we don't know if the Seminoe site is the only place the Cryons have anyway. If the bombs fail, then sure as hell, we'll have totally convinced the Cryons we're just a tribe of barbarians. They won't give us a second chance; they won't be bothered; they'll just exterminate us. If we warn them, the worst that'll happen is that we strengthen their hand, but as it's overwhelmingly strong anyway, what difference does it make? At best, it'll convince them we're not all mindless killers, and prevent them reacting to our pathetic warmongering effort by wiping us out."

"And what if they react to the news that some of us are trying to wipe them out, by immediately wiping *us* out?" said Beemish. "It's a hell of a gamble."

Phil suddenly realised that all through their conversation, he had assumed that Jo-Ann was of the same mind as himself. But he hadn't actually asked her. Old habits die hard - that was going to have to change too.

"What do you think, Jo?" he said, turning to her. "Do you think we should accept the Cryon ultimatum, or do you think we should fight?"

Jo-Ann looked at him with surprise.

"You really have changed haven't you," she said.

She sat back in her seat. It looked as if she was searching her soul for an answer to Phil's question. Eventually she came back, and addressed them with her eyes.

"Indian chiefs have faced this dilemma for hundreds of years," she said solemnly. "When I was young, my brothers would grab their guns and knives and pace up and down and say to my father, 'Why don't you let us fight for our rights? How can you tolerate these impositions?' And he would calm them, point out the overwhelming superiority of the forces against them, and impress upon them that when no other options remain, it is better to work with your enemy from within, rather than die in a futile gesture of defiance. He even made us memorise some words spoken by Chief Seattle in 1854. 'Revenge by young men is considered gain, even at the cost of their own lives, but old me who stays at home in times of war, and mothers who have sons to lose, know better'."

"That explains the distinction you pointed out to me," said Beemish, "That you are an activist, not an anarchist."

No wonder she nearly found solace in Ted, thought Phil. He obviously listened to her.

"Exactly," said Jo-Ann. She turned back to Phil. "I believe it would be suicide to attempt to defeat the Cryons. We must accept their ultimatum."

"And what about warning them?" said Phil.

"Wouldn't be surprised if they knew about it already," she replied. She paused before continuing. "But if persuading the President or sabotage can't be guaranteed, then yes, the only way is to warn them. I'm with you."

Beemish drained his glass.

"This could be the final decision of my career," he said, "But I agree."

They ordered more drinks, then sat silently, absorbing the implications of what they had decided to do. Phil looked around him at the other customers in the restaurant, and wondered how they would react if they knew that at one of the tables, three relatively insignificant people were making a decision that would affect the future of mankind.

"How do we warn them?" he said.

"Could try just talking to the key," said Beemish. "If it transmits to them all the time, it'd be like phoning them."

"But it's in Miller's safe," said Phil. "How do we get it out, and somewhere private, without arousing suspicions?"

"No good," said Jo-Ann. "For a start, you'd have no way of knowing for sure whether the Cryons were tuned in, you wouldn't know how they reacted, and anyway, you can't tell somebody that sort of news on the telephone for Christ's sake!"

Jo-Ann suddenly realised what she had said.

"Oh shit! Me and my big mouth. No! Phil... you can't." She slumped back in her chair, cursing herself.

"I have to, Jo. I have to go back down in person. It's the only way."

"You would do that?" said Beemish.

"I think a personal approach, an appeal, an explanation, might appease them. Vorkan trusts me."

"You'd better be right, Phil!" said Beemish, "For sure as hell he ain't going to be over the Moon when you tell him."

The two men exchanged sick-joke grimaces.

"It's going to be one helluva job getting the key," said Beemish. "Miller's men are tightening their grip. My authority is questioned now. His isn't."

"We need a diversion," said Phil. "We need to set up something which gets Miller out of his office, then convinces his goons that the key should be moved. They'll take orders from you, Ted, surely?"

"Only if Miller isn't there."

"What if he thought the base was under attack? What would he do?"

"The only things he cares about after his own hide, are his precious warheads - and now, Groundstorm. One thing's for sure, he wouldn't stay in his office. He'd high-tail it over to the arsenal or take a chopper to the Hell Hole. I wouldn't worry though. He's already set up a mobile office at the shaft. He'll be there most of the time from now on."

"So," said Phil, "What we have to do is give the impression the base is being attacked, get the key, pretend we're taking it to a place of safety... "

"Like Fort Carson,"

"Okay, but then we take it to the Seminoe instead," said Phil, eyebrows raised.

"Miller's men will want to accompany it. There is the small matter that Fort Carson and the Seminoe are in opposite directions! If we go north-west, they'll be on to us immediately."

"Then we'll have to fool them. Some sort of switch. What do you say, Ted?"

Jo-Ann, who had been listening to this conversation with increasing disbelief, suddenly grabbed Phil by the arm.

"Phil! I don't believe this. You're really going to do it aren't you. You're both crazy, d'you know that?"

"Are we, Jo? Maybe. Maybe we should leave the job to someone else," said Phil, provocatively. "Any ideas, luv?"

She looked at him long and hard with those big brown eyes. Her expression changed from frustration through admiration to resignation.

"Okay, this switch..." she sighed.

17

Pure Hell

The strains of Auld Lang Syne drifted through the crisp night air as Beemish set the timer on the last bomb. He clambered into his Cherokee, started the engine, and blew onto his frozen fingers. It had been at least twenty years since he had been so frightened, so stimulated, so alive.

The three bombs under the propane tanks had been easy - they were deliberately sited away from buildings. Nobody would be anywhere near them when they blew, but they'd light up the whole base.

The single device at the warhead storage building had not been so straightforward. There was no way, even if he had wanted to, that he could get anywhere near the doors of the place - it was far too well guarded. But round the back in an adjoining service building, he found an unused storeroom, one of whose walls was common with the main building. It would not be considered inconceivable when that one went off, that sabotage of the missile storage was being attempted. The device could not actually do any harm or hurt anybody, but it would certainly put the wind up Miller. He was understandably touchy about his nuclear warheads.

He placed the last two devices in the generator rooms which served the 90th Missile Wing headquarters and Miller's office - one under the main generator, and the second under the backup machine. By the time they hooked up the power to another generator, he and Phil would be well away.

All six bombs were primed to go off at 6:30 pm. It would be dark; most personnel would be on New Year's Day leave; the base would be almost deserted.

Now back in the comparative safety of his Jeep, he wiped the dirt off his hands, removed the overalls he had been wearing, donned his general's cap and drove calmly out of F.E. Warren via the main gates.

At precisely 5:15pm, as daylight faded across the shivering base, Captain Sam Palmer and Lieutenant Nichols, a trusted junior National Guard officer from Laramie, drove up to Gate 3 of F.E. Warren in Palmer's private car. Gate 3 was at the north-west corner of the base, isolated, and little used, except by those living along Horse Creek Road. It was through this gate that Phil and Beemish intended to escape, later, after dark, by impersonating Palmer and Nichols. Beemish knew that though passes were always checked on the way in to F.E. Warren, they were seldom checked on the way out.

As they pulled up at the guard hut, the bored Corporal was relieved to have something to do. He glanced at Palmer's windscreen sticker and saluted as the car pulled up.

"I'll need a two hour pass for Mr Perry here," said Palmer, showing the guard his own ID badge. "He's from the university, doing some research on military historic buildings. I'll be with him all the time."

Nichols leaned forward, a little uncomfortably, and made sure the guard got a good look at his vivid green windcheater. He smiled at the guard, his bright orange baseball cap clashing strikingly with Palmer's Captain's uniform.

The guard returned mechanically to the hut, wrote out the pass, stamped it and handed it to Nichols through the window.

"Enjoy your visit, Sir, Mr Perry" he said, saluting Palmer once more.

"So far so good," said Palmer, breathing a sigh of relief. "He obviously got a good look at your clothes."

He drove away from the gate and headed for the car park outside Miller's office.

Jo-Ann and the children had been edgy all day. Phil had agreed with Jo-Ann that she take them into town before the action started. He could understand Jo-Ann acting strangely, but not the kids as well. After all, they knew nothing about the plan.

As 5:30pm approached, he tried to grab a few moments with Jo-Ann before she left. He wanted to hug the children too, and ask them to look after their Mum if he didn't come back. But he couldn't risk it.

Chuck and Charlie had not appeared since Christmas, and Jo-Ann was bustling about clearing up after tea. Phil stood nervously in the kitchen, passing her things when asked, and watching her pluckily carrying on as if nothing untoward was happening. Everyone had been strangely silent. Phil wondered whether this was the last time he would see them.

"Come on then, gang," she called, as she swept out to the hall.

Phil moved towards them. He limited himself to giving them pecks on the cheeks, but his heart was aching to hug them.

"See you later, Honey," called Jo-Ann, as she closed the door behind her. Phil wondered how she could be so cool.

Waiting for the explosions for the next hour was agonising. He drifted round the house like a spectre; he tried relaxing in a chair; he paced up and down like a caged animal. He turned on the TV, then turned it off when he realised it might stop him hearing when the action started.

He needn't have worried.

At precisely 6:30pm, the house was plunged into darkness. Less than half a second afterwards, the muffled thuds of the generator bombs echoed across the silent base. The sound had hardly ended when the west-facing windows of the house lit up with an eerie red light, then shook violently in their frames as the shock waves from the exploding gas tanks hit them. Acting naturally, as per the plan, he flung open the front door and peered out into the cold night. The white painted wood of the houses in the circle was now pink in the light of the pillar of fire from the tanks. He could hear men shouting in the distance, and the wail of sirens starting up.

"What's happening?" he called out to the guards, feigning shock.

They were panicking. The base had never been attacked before. One of them was fumbling with his radio and trying to prime his weapon at the same time. The other ran towards him gesticulating, and shouting that he should go back into the house. He withdrew inside, put on .the jacket and NASA baseball hat that had become his trademark since he returned from the Moon, and waited for Beemish.

Absolutely on time, at 6:40pm, the lights of Beemish's Cherokee swung round the circle road outside. Within seconds, he was hammering on the door and ordering the guards to follow him and Major Newheart in their jeep to 20th Air Force

HQ. It was important they did not think he was trying to take Phil away from them.

"Come with me, Major," he said in a loud voice, then softly, "The bastards are jumping like they've got ants in their pants!"

In the privacy of the Cherokee, Phil could see that Beemish was on a high. His face was glowing, and his movements were those of a man half his age. He slammed the car into gear and headed for the HQ building.

"Outstanding!" he exclaimed. "The tanks going up have really got 'em going."

"Where's Miller?" said Phil anxiously. "Any news?"

"It's okay. He is up at the Hell Hole," panted Beemish, "But we have a problem. They're ahead of schedule. Getting the bombs down the shaft took less time than they thought. The goddamn things are set to go off two days early."

Phil's stomach went cold.

"But that's tomorrow!"

"Yep. Midday. Still game?"

The thought of standing only a short distance below a six megaton nuclear bomb less than eighteen hours before detonation, and telling the Cryons that the only way to prevent the explosion was for them to somehow get to it, did not fill him with relish.

"Piece of cake!" he said, shaking.

Beemish swung the Jeep into the headquarters car park. Palmer's car was there, exactly as planned, nose-first in a parking bay between two trees. Beemish backed the Cherokee up to it, left the engine running and the headlights on full beam. They were pointing at the entrance to the building.

"Ready?" he said, teeth gritted. "Don't forget your cap."

Phil's pulse was racing. He yanked his NASA cap even more firmly onto his head, then grasped the door handle.

"Okay, now!" he said.

The two men jumped down and started running towards the entrance. Inside, Beemish's flashlight shone up the darkened stair-well leading to Miller's office. As they climbed the stairs, the sounds of men shouting to each other echoed down to them and along the corridors. At the second floor, Beemish strode purposefully towards Miller's office.

"Sergeant Haxby?" he called. "The General in? Major General Beemish here. Hurry up, man!"

Two flashlights shone at them out of the darkness.

"General Beemish, Major?" Haxby sounded suspicious.

"We've got to get the item in the safe to Fort Carson," said Beemish authoritatively.

"Sir? It can't leave the office. General Miller's orders, Sir." Haxby sounded panicky. He was obviously torn between obeying his own General, and Beemish, one rank higher. Phil could hear the other man in the room, trying unsuccessfully to get Miller on the radio.

"Quite right, Sergeant, but I don't think he imagined the base coming under attack. Now, open the safe. And I want you and a couple of your men to provide an escort. Two jeeps - Now, Sergeant. We haven't a moment to lose."

There was a momentary silence. Haxby was obviously extremely loyal to Miller. But the ploy was a good one. Beemish asking him to provide an escort should allay his fears. At least that way, he would be able to keep tabs on where the key was going - or so Haxby thought.

"Yes Sir," said Haxby.

It had worked.

He opened the safe. Phil reached inside and grabbed the key.

"All right," said Beemish urgently. "Keep with us, Sergeant. When we get downstairs, you take the lead jeep. We'll follow in mine, and your second vehicle can take up the rear. Main gate."

As they ran downstairs, Haxby shouted orders to his men. But Phil's heart was pounding; the real sting, the all-important switch, had yet to come.

In the blacked-out car park, the lights from Beemish's Jeep were dazzling. Phil and Beemish ran towards them, one each side of the car, then opened its wide front doors, and stood behind them looking back towards the building. They could see Haxby peering at them, trying to shield his eyes from the glare. Phil gave his NASA baseball hat to Nichols, who was sitting in the front passenger seat, and Beemish gave his two-star-general flight cap to Palmer, in the driver's seat.

"All okay?" said Beemish.

"Okay, Sir. Good luck." replied Palmer.

With the Jeep doors still open, and hiding their actions from Haxby and his men, Phil and Beemish crouched down and moved along the sides of the Jeep, and on to Palmer's car behind, opened the doors, slid inside, and quietly closed them. Palmer and Nichols closed the Jeep doors, then drove off, accompanied by Haxby's vehicles.

Phil and Beemish sat for a moment, panting, watching the tail lights of the three vehicles as they headed down the road towards the main gate. When they got there they stopped. Phil held his breath. Haxby might walk back to the Cherokee to have a word. The game would be up.

"It's the explosions," said Beemish, tensely. "They'll be checking every car."

But after an agonising moment, the lights moved on.

"They've made it!" he said, jubilantly.

But already, Phil was thinking about the next move. They still had to get out of the base.

He felt down the side of the steering column, found the ignition key, started up Palmer's car, and drove quickly away from the HQ building, stopping in a deserted side road. They both got out. Phil donned Nichols' baseball cap and windcheater which had been left for him, and was relieved to find the two-hour pass in its pocket as arranged. Beemish put on Captain Palmer's flight cap and ID badge, and changed his shirt shoulder boards. They changed places, and Beemish headed the car towards Gate 3.

Back on the central avenue, they were constantly passed by fire and security vehicles, lights flashing, sirens wailing. Attention was divided between the still-burning gas tanks and the distant warhead storage building.

Suddenly, a security guard jeep pulled ahead of them and flagged them down. They were only five hundred yards from the gate.

"Shit!" said Phil, feeling behind his seat for the Cryon key. It was in the foot-well. There was a blanket on the rear seat.

He hurriedly pulled the blanket over it. The guard got out and started walking towards them. Phil swallowed hard. He could feel his throat clamping up. Beemish rolled down the window.

"ID please," said the guard, then, "Oh sorry Captain. Where ya headed Sir? We've had to seal off all this area over here - the bombs an' all."

"I'm taking Mr er..."

"Perry," whispered Phil, glancing at the pass.

" ...Perry home," continued Beemish. "This is no place for a civilian. Say, could you just escort us to Gate 3 please, and hand Mr Perry's pass in for me."

He gave the pass to the guard, then rolled up the window.

"Don't give 'em time to think. That's the secret." said Beemish boyishly.

The guard's vehicle led the way to Gate 3, stopped by it, and within seconds, the barrier was lifted. Phil and Beemish drove out into the darkness and headed north, towards the clearing in the woods two miles away, where Beemish's helicopter was waiting.

"We bloody did it, Ted!" exclaimed Phil triumphantly.

But as Ted Beemish drove through the darkness, he was silent. He was wondering which would get him first: a hit by one of Powell's agents, a Court Martial, or the Cryon annihilation. Right now, passing away quietly in old age did not seem very likely.

The National Guard Black Hawk was, as arranged, sitting in a clearing in the woods, engine purring. Phil and Beemish jumped from the car, ran across the frozen ground, and clambered inside.

"I'm sorry, Sir!" yelled the pilot, in a hopeless tone. "I couldn't stop them!"

Phil peered into the darkened cabin, to see Jo-Ann and the children sitting belted in, ready to go.

"What the...!" he said.

"They know everything," said Jo-Ann, a determined expression on her face.

Nick and Tess beamed excitedly at him.

"This time, we're in it together," she went on. "I'm not letting you go off again without me, and there's no way I'm leaving the children."

Phil felt a wave of love surge through him. Now, he understood Jo-Ann's behaviour earlier.

"But..."

"No buts, Honey. You're not going without us."

"Sir?" The pilot's tone was urgent.

"Have you any idea what you're getting into?" said Beemish. "There could be trouble at the door. I can't guarantee your safety."

Jo-Ann and the children just nodded. Phil knelt down and hugged them. His eyes were watering.

"Sir!" the pilot repeated. "ATC. They're asking where we are. We gotta go now."

Beemish stared at Phil. Phil gave him a helpless look.

"Go!" said Beemish to the pilot, shaking his head.

The engine roared into life, and the helicopter rose quickly, turned, and headed for the Seminoe reservoir.

Beemish sat down next to them, now huddled together like Bush Babies. Concern and admiration were etched on his face.

"You are a wonderful family," he said, smiling wistfully. "I only wish..."

"Don't wish," said Jo-Ann, "It's the future that matters now."

Beemish bit his lip.

"Just before I left, I gave Louise the bottle of liquid I got from the Cryons," he said. "At least, if I don't make it back ..."

"Of course you'll make it back, Ted," said Jo-Ann. "You and Louise are going to start living again. It'll be wonderful."

Beemish seemed to be staring into the distance.

"I hope," he said, then focusing his gaze, "Did you get your stuff off okay Phil?"

"Special air freight to Inverness yesterday," he replied. "Put a note in to Dave: Thought you could do with a hand!"

Beemish grinned.

"And the electric vehicle stuff?"

"Posted to England - special delivery. Legal will do all the international patent stuff."

"So everybody's sorted," said Beemish, standing up and heading for the cockpit. He turned and faced them. He was ready for action again.

"All we have to do now, is prevent the end of the world!" he said.

***

Under the harsh light of arc lamps, their beams turning the passing snowflakes into dazzling fireflies, Nathan Miller stood alone, hunched like a vulture at a kill he was watching the last convoy of massive earth-moving trucks queuing up and dumping their cargoes of sand down the Hell Hole shaft.

He felt proud. This had been his operation. At last, he had been proved right; the Peacekeeper warheads he had hidden away were needed after all. He had always been opposed to the START II agreement. He deeply resented America agreeing to the reduction in nuclear weapons. We must be strong, he had always said. Power, control, an iron fist. That was the way to get what you wanted. That was the way his father had done it; he should know; the scars on his buttocks and thighs from his father's strap - still there after all these years - were a constant reminder.

And he would be performing the greatest act of purification the world had ever known. He thought back to Lisa, the Mexican maid his father had taken in after his mother died, and how his father had made him watch whilst he tried to purify her.

And he had learnt from his father about his race - the chosen people - and how the women of other races should be purified and the men purged. He had tried to emulate his father, but lacked his potency. But he had discovered other ways in which he could prove to the world that he was a man. Guns were good - the bigger the better, and the intimacy of knives was heavenly. Fast cars - particularly ones with really long hoods - were thrilling, but best of all, were rockets. That's why he had tried to join NASA. If he could ride those rockets, it would be the consummation of his dreams. But the fools had turned him down. He, Nathan Miller, the perfect candidate for astronaut training - who's great uncle Axel had worked on V2s at Peenemunde - had been rejected. But the Air Force had more sense. They recognised his strength. And when, in the nineties, they gave him command of the most potent fleet of missiles the world had ever known, he knew that secretly, they were honouring his body and racial purity.

But he had never had the opportunity to launch those missiles - the Peacekeepers, the ultimate manifestation of his masculinity, the essence of his inner drive. From their tip, from a split in their perfectly-rounded nose-cones, would emerge - into the sterile blackness of space - a spray of ten pods, carrying his seed down to mother earth, and ending ultimately in the white-heat of an orgasmic purification.

Yet tomorrow, he would be satiated. His milk of purity - the pods from the only two Peacekeepers left on earth - had passed smoothly down the black shaft and were already lodged, deep in the womb of the filthy alien whore. At midday, they would explode within her, in a concentration of power the like of which the world had never seen. Tomorrow, he, Nathan Miller would purify the Earth itself.

"Sir! Sir! General Miller Sir." The urgent voice was unreal for a moment. "Your personal radio, Sir. It's not on. We've been trying to reach you for ages!"

Miller turned. His face was white as a marble slab, and his grey eyes were rimmed with red. Snow was caked on the fir of his high turned-up collar.

"Yes," he said. The icy tone of that one word sent a shiver of fear through the Airman's veins.

"There's been an attack on the base, Sir. Sergeant Haxby. The radio hut."

Miller's eyes widened into a manic stare, and his mouth twisted into a snarl. He pushed the Airman aside and bounded towards the radio hut.

Haxby was calling from the Interstate south of Cheyenne. Miller strode up and down the hut like a leopard in a cage, occasionally banging the walls with his fist in frustration.

"What do you mean, no real damage?"

"Warhead storage okay! So what did they do?"

"General Beemish!"

"Newheart!"

"Jesus Christ, Haxby. Can't you see the whole thing's designed to get the key! You obey *me*, Haxby. *Me*!"

"I don't give a fuck what he said. Stop them. Stop them now! I want General Beemish on this line immediately!"

There was a long pause. Miller strained to hear what was going on at the other end. Then he started shaking. He had undone his trench coat. His hand went down and started fingering his pistol.

"You idiot! You're finished, Haxby! You're a dead man!" he screamed.

There was agony in his eyes as he smashed down the phone in frustration.

"ATC. Get ATC now!" he yelled at the terrified communications officer. "Any flights headed this way from Cheyenne? Come on! Come on!"

The officer fumbled desperately with the frequency switches before getting through.

"Just one, Sir. Low flying unregistered aircraft. Could be a helicopter. Wait.... They lost contact with a National Guard Black Hawk near Cheyenne a while back. Could be that one."

"Its Beemish! And that sonofabitch Newheart!"

The pitch of Miller's voice rose to a scream. A crazed expression came to his face, and his head started jerking uncontrollably.

"Where's it going? Where's the bastard going?"

"The Seminoe, Sir. It's about 20 miles east of the door."

Miller drew his pistol, kicked open the door and firing wildly into the air, ran across the snow-covered ground to his helicopter. Men came pouring out of the other huts towards him.

"Out, out!" he screamed, tugging at the locked pilot-side door.

The pilot got to him first.

"Sir? What's the problem, Sir?" he said. His tone was calm, but laced with just a hint of reprehension.

Miller stared at him insanely for two seconds, then shot him.

The pilot fell backwards into the snow, the helicopter keys still clenched in his hand. Miller dropped to his knees, grabbed the keys, and still waving his gun at the unarmed men now surrounding him, clambered aboard.

***

In the Black Hawk, Beemish's pilot had his radio tuned to military Air Traffic Control, and was manfully refusing to respond to their requests for identification and flight details. Beemish was more concerned with the civilian broadcast from Radio Cheyenne, and what they were saying about the explosions at F.E. Warren. The early evening phone-in show was crackling with tension, with eye-witness accounts of the pandemonium at the base interspersed with reports coming in of unusual military activity from around the State. There were rumours of a missing National Guard helicopter, and folks in Seminoe were demanding to know what the fleets of trucks were doing, and why a large area of the prairie down by Coal Creek had been sealed off.

The pilot's voice broke in, on his head-set.

"ATC are bursting a blood vessel!" he said. "Apparently, there's an Air Force helicopter heading towards us from the north west."

"Keep going!" ordered Beemish.

"Sir! It might be armed. We still haven't identified ourselves."

Beemish thought quickly.

"Okay," he said. "It's pointless maintaining radio silence. They're obviously onto us. Tell 'em who we are, and that you've had trouble with the radio. Then, hail the Air Force chopper and tell it to stay out of our flight path. Then tell my guys guarding the door that we're coming in."

They were only five miles from the door. Beemish thought he could see the lights of the other helicopter ahead of them.

"Go back, Phil," he said. "Belt up. Heads down. As soon as we touch down, unbuckle and get ready to run for the door. Tell the others."

"The Air Force chopper's not responding, Sir," yelled the pilot. "But I've got you Colonel Reynolds at the door."

"General!" The Colonel's voice was charged with emotion. "The guys at the Hell Hole have been on to me. General Miller's gone berserk, shot his pilot and is headed this way in a helicopter. Wait a minute..."

Beemish could hear the sound of engines in the background.

"Reynolds!" shouted Beemish. "General Miller must be arrested as soon as he touches down. That's an order. Do it. I'll be there in one minute. Do it!"

"He's here! He's coming in..... What the.... Where's he going?"

The engine noise subsided. For a while, Beemish could hear nothing. Then, the unmistakable sound of gunfire.

"He's landed over by the Abrams Sir!.... Oh God!..."

Beemish stared out. The lights from the door complex were now rising up all around them. Dry snow and dust began flying about as the pilot put down on the pad in front of the dome. Over to the left, Miller's helicopter blades were still turning, and grinding slowly towards him from that direction, was an Abrams M3 tank.

"He's in the tank!" yelled Reynolds. "General Miller's in the goddamned tank!"

"Swing it round!" shouted Beemish to the pilot. "Block the way with the tail."

They were on the ground. Beemish clambered out of his seat and threw open the door nearest the dome.

"Okay. Out! Out! Out! Run for your lives!"

Phil jumped down, and caught hold of Jo-Ann and the children as they got out. They began running towards the plastic dome entrance doors. The tank was yards from the helicopter. Beemish and the pilot jumped down and were heading for the dome as the muzzle of the gun made contact with the chopper's tail rotor. The rotor disintegrated, spraying shards of steel up into the air. Phil and the family were through into the dome. Beemish looked back in horror as the tank ground mercilessly onwards, crushing the helicopter's tail section in the process and toppling it over. Its main rotor blades hit the ground, their broken ends flailing the tank, then the helicopter fuel tank went up. Beemish and the pilot were thrown to the floor by the blast, and Beemish could feel the heat from the fireball scorching the back of his neck. He rolled over instinctively to smother any flames on his back, but he was okay. But so was the tank. It was heading towards him - towards the dome entrance.

"Go straight for the door!" he shouted to the others ahead of him. Then to his pilot, "Get out of here. I'll handle Miller."

The pilot ran off to the side. Beemish got up and barrelled through the heavy plastic dome doors. Phil was putting the key into the hole. Beemish's men were crouching, helpless, back from the roadway leading to the Cryon door. Behind him, the tank crashed through the dome doors, ripping the plastic like it was tissue paper. The sound of the tank engines suddenly grew very loud as the 65 ton machine entered the dome itself. But no part of the Cryon door was opening. Jo-Ann and the children were cowering down at the right hand side and Phil was shouting up at it. Beemish, his lungs bursting, ran up the ramp to join Phil, who was trying the key again. Beemish turned. His back was to the door. Miller's tank had stopped forty yards from them, its engines growling and throwing out angry black smoke. It looked like a wild beast, crouching before the attack. Its gun muzzle started to lower towards them. Then, a brilliant flash of red light blinded his left eye. Simultaneously, the small doorway opened, Phil leaped towards it and started pushing his family through into the glow. Beemish knew the red flash was the gun's laser range finder. The tank's automatic firing system was being employed. It would fire in five seconds.

"Good luck!" was all he had time to shout.

Then he remembered the properties of the door, and what Phil had told him about Snake and the key. The shell would rebound. It would hit the tank. He instinctively started waving his arms, pointing at the door, then the tank. He realised that for some inexplicable reason, he was trying to save Miller's life.

The time was up. He flung himself to the ground, and covered his head with his arms.

Inside the Abrams, Miller half lay, half sat in the driver's position at the front of the hull, a place from which he had indirect control of all the tank's systems.

The enemy must not reach his milk of purity. He would stop them. He *must* stop them. The purity of the Earth depended upon him. *Free America* was relying upon him.

Beemish was in his sights, and Newheart was next to him. His half-cast bitch was trying to get through the door. He engaged the auto-fire mechanism. Newheart dived to the right.

"No! No!" he screamed.

Then Beemish was waving at him. Trying to stop him. The stupid bastard! As if those frantic gesticulations - the last twitches of a man who was about to die - made the slightest difference. The 150mm plasma-jet armour-piercer would pass straight through him.

His face twisted into a manic snarl. His eyes widened. The gun fired.

When the shell hit the tank, a hole appeared in the forward-facing armour above Miller's feet. It rapidly grew larger, and from it, a searing lance of plasma entered the compartment and atomised his lower torso. This was immediately followed by the main charge, which vaporised everything which was non-metallic, and expelled it from the compartment and out of the turret top hatch. The roaring white-hot pillar of fire passed through the dome and flung itself skywards like an incandescent geyser.

Nathan Miller's purification was complete.

18

One Voice

After the din, the drama, and the action in the dome, the total silence of the Cryon ante-room was strangely unsettling.

"Everybody okay?" said Phil, as he bent down, hands on knees recovering his breath.

The others gathered round him, gasping and nodding. Jo-Ann gave him a look which spoke volumes, but said nothing. Tess reached out nervously for her mother's hand. Nick, ever positive and totally convinced of his father's ability to walk on water if he had to, gazed admiringly at him.

"Well done, Dad," he said. "So what happens now?"

Phil knew what he had come to do, but at this moment had not the faintest idea of how to do it. It wasn't every day, one was expected to save the world.

"We wait," he said.

The chair, coffee table and fruit juice were nowhere to be seen. The featureless room felt less welcoming, and it was still silent. MIND did not speak.

After a few minutes, Nick produced a yo-yo from his inside pocket, and started playing with it. It was the sort with a battery, and it flashed and sparkled as it spun up and down the cord.

"What the hell did you bring that for!" barked Tess suddenly. "Can't you act your age! That's really annoying!"

"Oh yeah!" retorted Nick, "So you jangling your bracelets is..."

But then, Nick stared open-mouthed at something behind Phil. He spun round, to see the door to the tunnel had opened. Beyond it was a Cryon shuttle, and standing by its door, one of the smaller Cryons. It was beckoning them.

Even though Phil had described the Cryons to Jo-Ann and the children, actually seeing one at close quarters in all its repulsive detail, was a test of the stoutest heart.

"Oh my God!" rasped Jo-Ann, gripping Phil's arm. She was rooted to the spot.

Strangely, Tess didn't seem bothered.

"It's a cross between a Preying Mantis and a giant ant," she said, clinically. "We did those in biology."

"Oh wow!" said Nick. "Just wait 'till I tell the guys back at McCormick High!"

Phil ushered Jo-Ann towards the shuttle. She stifled a cry as she gazed, terrified, down the cavernous tunnel, and was most concerned to keep Phil between her and the Cryon as she boarded.

As the children climbed in, the Cryon seemed more interested in Nick's yo-yo than anything else. Nick smiled innocently at it, but it didn't respond.

"Roller-coaster freaks: eyes open and hang on," said Phil. "The rest: eyes closed."

He was trying to lighten the atmosphere, but inside, an ever growing feeling of foreboding was taking hold of him. He began to regret he had allowed the others to come with him.

There was another Cryon in the cockpit. No sounds were exchanged. The door closed, and the shuttle pursued its mercurial flight into the bowels of the Earth.

"Oh boy!" cried Nick. "Wait till the guys hear about *this*!"

It was obvious, thought Phil, that the entire student body at McCormick Junior High was going to be treated to account after account of Nick's adventures. Of course, that assumed that the school would still be there. But Nick knew the score. He knew why they were down there. Tess knew too. They were either eternal optimists, or they had total faith in him. He might never know which.

The shuttle came to rest outside a room Phil recognised. It was the Conference room where the truth session had taken place. His blood ran cold as he imagined Jo-Ann and the children being subjected to the same mind analysis he had undergone. They would never be the same. Children and their parents deserved some privacy from each other. He wanted to call out - ask MIND not to try it.

The two Cryons' movements made it plain that they should alight and enter the room. With a sinking heart, Phil led the way. It was the total lack of any conversation that was so disconcerting. On the three other occasions he had visited,

MIND's calm voice had provided a reassuring anchor. But today, nothing.

They sat at the central table, and the two Cryons left via the panel in the wall. Sounds - clanking, purring machinery, and occasionally the twanging of distant Cryon speech - filtered through into the room from the echowy caverns.

"I don't like it here," said Jo-Ann. "What's happening, Phil?"

Before he could answer, the temperature and humidity of the room began to rise.

"They're coming to join us," he whispered. "Stay calm. Hang your jackets on the back of the chairs. There'll be a smell. You'll get used to it."

Jo-Ann and the children sat transfixed as the now transparent wall panel opened. Vorkan and two others entered the room, then the panel closed again. Behind it, more Cryons could be seen, standing, watching them.

"Yes, Major," said Vorkan, mechanically. Clearly, something was wrong. Phil hoped it was simply the business with the tank.

There was no point beating about the bush. He had to tell Vorkan what he had come to tell him. This was the moment he was to become a traitor or saviour of the human race. His mouth was dry. How do you tell someone that your countrymen are about to blow him and his race to kingdom come?

"I have come to warn you about a decision that has been made by a small group of powerful, but misguided people," he said, swallowing hard.

"Yes?" said Vorkan. He was staring steadfastly at Phil. His sensilla were completely motionless.

"I wish to make it clear that this decision was made without reference to other world leaders, and without seeking the support of the general population."

"Yes, Major. I am waiting."

Phil took a deep breath. He could feel his knees actually knocking together under the table, and all of a sudden he was desperate for a pee.

"This group, fearful of the unknown, and anxious to protect their people from what they perceive as a threat to their safety, have planted a very powerful bomb, just above this chamber. The bomb is due to explode in....." He consulted his watch. " ... fifteen hours time."

Phil could feel his lower lip quivering as he held Vorkan's inscrutable stare. Vorkan turned his head very slightly to the left and right, regarding his colleagues, but said nothing.

"I have brought my family," continued Phil, "To convince you of my sincerity and my wish that this had not happened. The bomb's detonation cannot be prevented now - not by us at least. We have come to warn you, in case you can do something about it before it's too late."

After another agonising period of silence, Vorkan and the others turned towards each other and spoke briefly together. Vorkan then addressed Phil.

"You will come with me, Major. Mrs Newheart and the children will be looked after here." Then turning to Jo-Ann, "No harm will come to any of you while you are down here. Do not be afraid. Your husband will be returned to you shortly. Major ..."

He walked to a door in the wall that Phil had not noticed before, then stood waiting. Phil rose from his chair. Jo-Ann was trembling. She looked helplessly up at him, appealing. If ever there was a moment when his own judgement, and the strength of his family would be put to the test, it was now.

"We have to trust them," he said, with as much confidence as he could muster. Secretly, he was praying. He kissed Jo-Ann and the children lovingly, then walked from the room.

As the door closed behind him, Phil saw that he was inside a vast complex - the Cryon equivalent of offices and workshops. There were benches, control panels, gently humming machines, and screens displaying strange animated light patterns. Robot-like devices appeared to be operating these devices, occasionally gliding silently from place to place. In the distance, he thought he glimpsed two Cryons sitting studying a monitor screen. Then he realised that the heat and humidity of the place were almost unbearable. His clothes were clinging to him, and sweat began running down his face, into his eyes. Clearly, in this section, conditions were set to suit the Cryons.

Vorkan walked over to a wall locker and produced a small unit resembling a battery pack, which he strapped to Phil's waist. He then gave him something like a tube of toothpaste.

"You will need these," he said impassively. "Smooth the liquid over your face, ears and hands, then stand in there."

He was pointing to a cubicle with three transparent sides.

"What is it?" asked Phil nervously, as he applied the liquid.

"It is a personal environment controller. You will be coated - except where the barrier cream is - in a material which will keep you cool. You can set the temperature with the slider on the pack. I do not want you expiring before..."

He didn't finish his sentence. Before what? Phil thought, but decided against asking.

Phil stepped gingerly into the cubicle. Within seconds, he was enveloped in soft material. It felt like a two-piece lycra body suit, split at the waist. It covered him closely and comfortably, like the inner garment he had worn on his EVA, but better.

"Step out now," said Vorkan.

Phil walked from the cubicle and tried the controller. The response was instant and effective. NASA would give their eye-teeth for one of these, he thought.

Vorkan set off along a wide central aisle. His feet on the hard floor sounded like a large heavy crab on the march, and his peculiar gait was ostrich-like. Phil followed meekly. He had no way of knowing what Vorkan had in store for him, but the suit, he thought thankfully, was at least intended to keep him alive for a little while yet.

As he walked through Vorkan's subterranean stronghold, he became aware that other Cryons were about, busying themselves controlling strange machines. As he passed, each stopped what it was doing, and regarded him menacingly, with those large bodeful eyes.

They emerged into an area resembling a hangar. At one end, large doors led, Phil guessed, to one of the main tunnels.

But what was striking - what identified it as a hangar - was its contents. Phil gazed awe-struck at line upon line of what he presumed were aircraft, or spacecraft. The design was totally alien. Each craft was completely smooth, gunmetal in colour, and resembled a rather fat discus over 50ft in diameter. The periphery and lower surface - except for a circular space at the centre - were covered with a glassy honeycomb. It was difficult to tell, but above the honeycomb, on the sloping upper surfaces, may have been windows. There must have been at least a hundred of them, hovering silently and motionless - a sinister manifestation of Cryon superiority.

"Part of our scout fleet," said Vorkan, waving dismissively towards them. "Do not walk directly underneath."

He led the way to an open area, the centre of which was dominated by an elevated platform like a flat-bed trailer. Rising from the four corners and arranged over the platform was an open framework. The members of this framework and the four edges of the platform glowed a faint blue colour, and Phil got the impression that the faces of the box shape so formed shimmered slightly, like water.

But it was what was sitting on the platform that engaged his attention. On it, were a number of conical objects, each linked by a cable to a central box-shaped metallic unit which was definitely not of Cryon origin. He counted the cones. Twenty. With his pulse now thumping in his ears, he approached the platform to confirm his suspicions. There, on the side of the box, below the active countdown timer - which now read 14h:56m:12s - were the words, 'United States Air Force'.

"Avro Mark 21 re-entry vehicles," said Vorkan coldly. "Nuclear warheads. 300 kilotons each. First tested successfully June 17th 1983. Deployed in the late ninteen eighties. De-commissioned and destroyed in 2003."

And with that, Vorkan swung round and pointed a long arm straight at Phil.

"But they were *not* destroyed, were they Major!"

The tone and power of his voice took Phil by surprise. Vorkan had not displayed such emotion before. His sensilla looked like ten thousand needles.

"They are here, to destroy us!"

"That is the device I came to warn you about," said Phil, ineffectually.

"And do you think, Major, that your telling me makes the slightest difference! Do you expect me to say, Oh well, now you have told me, it is all right?"

At least, thought Phil, no-one back on the surface could accuse him of revealing the plan, if the Cryons knew about it anyway.

"You knew," he said.

"Of course we knew, Major," said Vorkan contemptuously. "We knew the moment you uncapped the Hell Hole shaft. Your childish bungling attempt at secretly lowering the bombs down the shaft would be laughable, if it was not so pathetic. You seem to underestimate our monitoring capability. Even without the coded transmissions between Washington and General Miller's office - which we decoded instantly - our subterranean sensors can unscramble noise and hear a footfall at two miles!"

Phil felt helpless. It was clear that Vorkan was in no mood to be pacified. He could hardly be blamed for his reaction.

"But if you hadn't known," ventured Phil, "At least please recognise that there are some people who tried to warn you. We are not all savages."

"But the people who matter *are*," said Vorkan. "Your leaders - those who represent the human race - deserve only contempt. You have a democracy. You the people are responsible for the actions of your leaders. You the people are as savage as they. And you the people will soon learn the price that must be paid."

Over the last three months, Phil had experienced fear of every sort. Now it was an overwhelming feeling of hopelessness. He stood, motionless.

"You were given the chance to help yourselves," Vorkan boomed, "And you were informed of the consequences of an inappropriate response. But not only have you dismissed our generous and eminently reasonable offer, you have responded with violence. We agreed to trust each other, Major Newheart, and this is the result. I have no intention of wasting further time with you or your kind. You do not deserve our help. You do not deserve our protection. The planet does not deserve the disease your race represents. You will be eliminated."

Vorkan was staring at him, eyes glowing. Phil felt as if a vice was being tightened across his head. He was in the presence of the Lord Chief Justice on the Day of Judgement.

No, he was in the presence of the Lord High Executioner.

***

From behind the transparent wall, Jasoma and her son Solex studied the three humans in the room beyond, and listened to their conversation.

"How strange they are," said Solex, "So soft-bodied. I suppose that's why they cover themselves, for protection."

"The two females are frightened," said Jasoma. "See how they touch each other for comfort."

"Mother and daughter," said Solex. "Why do the males and females look so different? It's almost as if they are different species."

"It's not that long since these creatures had to battle against the elements just to survive, Solex. The average life expectancy of a human might only have been a few years then. So only a small percentage of the offspring born to a particular female would survive to adulthood."

"The strongest ones."

"Yes. For them, it was important that each female produced many young, to increase the probability that one would survive."

"I still don't understand why they're so different."

"Well, for each female to produce many young, she had to make sure that she was fertilised over and over again by a male."

"Yes..."

"So she had to be attractive to him."

"Why?"

"Well, if she wasn't attractive, he wouldn't fertilise her."

Solex thought for a moment.

"Why couldn't she just ask him to fertilise her?"

"Asking's not enough, Solex. He has to want to."

"But what makes him want to?"

There's no escape! Jasoma thought. She chose her words carefully.

"When he notices the difference between him and her - that's what makes him want to."

"So the greater the difference, the more he wants to?"

"Well yes. I suppose so."

"But the differences are obvious all the time. That means that the males want to fertilise the females all the time. How very distracting that must be."

"It is, Solex. What's more, now these creatures have defeated most diseases and live their lives sheltered from the elements, many more of their young survive, but their bodies - their instincts to reproduce - are still how they were before."

"So they still fertilise each other over and over again?"

"Yes. They certainly do."

"But because the young don't die, their numbers increase."

"Exactly, Solex."

"Hmm... a great problem. Why are we not like that, Mother?"

"I think it is because our early evolution did not take place in such an unreliable environment. Our old planet - though it began to warm up towards the end - was much more stable, and our distant ancestors did not have to fight to survive. We have never had to fertilise each other over and over again. We don't want to. There's almost no difference between us. There's no incentive. The instinct is not there ... apart from rare occasions."

"So, I am the result of a rare occasion."

"Yes you are, Solex. The occasion was very special, but nothing like as special as you are to us."

"Strange, Mother. I wonder where I would be if that occasion had not happened. It is very good to be alive. I can't imagine what it must be like not to be."

He looked wistfully at the male human.

"It must be glad that its father and mother created it. It seems a pity it has to die. Does it have to, really? I mean, what would happen to them all if Father didn't wipe them out?"

"We think they'd increase so much that they'd use up the whole of Solara and wipe themselves out anyway. But worse, they'd take the planet with them."

"Why can't we warn them. Surely they'd understa......."

The male human had been sitting watching them for some time, but it suddenly got up and walked towards them. Solex noticed how - unlike Cryons - human faces were flexible; the human's mouth changed shape; it curled up at the corners. It then stood back from the partition, reached into a slit in its body covering, and produced a coloured object.

Solex and his mother watched, intrigued.

The human held the object, then let it fall towards the ground on a cord. It flashed and sparkled and rose up the cord again. It was obviously a primitive electrical device. Solex had never seen anything like it before. It was fascinating.

"I think it might be a form of generator," said his mother.

"But what for? If it is, it doesn't seem to do anything except flash. You don't think it could just be for that do you?"

"You mean, with no purpose, Solex?"

"Does it have to have a purpose, Mother?"

The human held the object in its outstretched hand towards him. It seemed as if it was showing it to them.

"They seem very friendly," said Solex. "I think I would like one. Better still, two or more. I could look after them, breed them."

"I don't think your father would allow that, Solex."

"Why not? Charis and Nitra have got Therma and Tron and all their offspring. Humans keep lowlier animals too. They call them - what is it? Oh yes, pets."

"You'll have to ask your father, but I really don't think ..."

"Then can I go into the room with them, Mother."

"Your father has not said you can do that, Solex."

"He hasn't said I can't either. He was in there with them. It's quite safe. They're obviously harmless."

Before his mother had a chance to invent any further objections, Solex opened the door, and walked slowly into the room.

***

Phil felt weak, helpless, and terribly alone. Vorkan had obviously made his mind up. He really was going to do it. He was going to wipe out humanity.

Phil could feel his strength of spirit ebbing away. He looked back over his life. Was there anything he should have done which could have prevented this? Vorkan was right. We get the leaders we deserve. Phil had known for the last twenty years that humanity was on the wrong track, but had he done anything about it? Had he bought a smaller car? Had he joined a pressure group? Had he written to his MP? Had he tried to persuade others that something should be done? No. Like so many people, he had accepted the benefits of the modern world, paid lip service to worrying about the environment, complained about the vanishing rain forests at dinner parties, but carried on anyway.

Along with most people in the developed world, he was guilty. Even his electric cars - promoted as being environmentally friendly - ran on electricity he knew perfectly well was generated primarily by the burning of fossil fuels.

And it wasn't that he could claim ignorance. He was intelligent, had a sound scientific education, and was well read. He knew the issues better than most. Yet he still did nothing. He was guilty of what he now realised was a degree of complacency bordering on the criminal, and now, he was going to pay the price.

He felt a yawning chasm open in the pit of his stomach. Strangely, fear was deserting him, and overpowering sadness was taking its place. His only duty now was to Jo-Ann and the children. He must ensure that they suffer as little as possible, and they must all be together at the end. He turned to Vorkan, who was still standing near the bombs, staring at him.

"How are you going to do it," he said, resignedly.

Vorkan paused for a moment. His sensilla relaxed a little, and he turned away slightly. It was as if he could not look Phil in the eye.

"Your bombs," he said, pointing at them, "Will be returned to you. They will detonate on time. But I thought the White House lawn would be a suitable place. As for the rest of you, these craft are already loaded with thousands of canisters of a lethal virus. The virus will only affect humans, is highly contagious, and is transmitted by breathing or by just touching something an infected person has touched. It can survive in the air or on surfaces for two weeks between hosts. The symptoms are lethargy, drowsiness, sleep, coma, then death. Ninety percent of the population will die within forty eight hours of the release, which will be by the way, tomorrow at noon. We then expect an on-going reduction of over ninety percent each day. By the end of the first week, the total world population should be down to six thousand. By two weeks, zero."

Phil trembled as he imagined the world succumbing to this... sleeping sickness. Industry, power generation, transport, would grind to a halt. Once people knew what was happening, some who had not yet been affected would rampage through the streets. There would be mayhem as armed gangs smashed, drank and raped their time away. It would be hell on Earth. He had to get the family to a place of safety. A mountain retreat perhaps. They could die together there, peacefully.

But then he imagined the world totally devoid of people. All the great cities, silent. Scientific and technical achievements, unused. Libraries - with their priceless store of knowledge - unread. Beautiful buildings, gardens, and works of art, unappreciated. Orchestral instruments, unheard.

And anger began to well up inside him. Anger born of indignation. Anger that fed on its own strength. Anger that surmounted any care for his own self-preservation. *What a waste!* What a terrible, wicked waste. The labours of innumerable generations, countless millions, rendered needless in less than a fortnight. He felt charged - empowered to speak out for the whole rotten and misguided world. It needed a voice - one voice.

His voice.

"How dare you!" he thundered, glowering at Vorkan. "How dare you stand as judge and executioner of the entire human race, because of the actions of fewer than ten people."

Vorkan twitched. He moved backwards as if he had been taken by surprise.

"You know perfectly well," continued Phil, "That had you presented the world at large with your demands, it might have replied very differently. You have not given us a real opportunity to respond. Those men - the men who were with me - they're only human. They all have reasons for behaving as they do. The reasons may be misguided and based on the need for personal gain, but we all do that to a certain degree. Even you, Vorkan."

"I have no hidden needs," said Vorkan, mechanically, "And my title is Commander."

Phil had the bit between his teeth. He was determined to get Vorkan going, even if it was a suicide mission.

"Commander, you say. You're no Commander. You're a cold-hearted, trumped-up beetle with a power complex that sticks out like a wart on a willy!"

There was a deathly silence. Vorkan's sensilla began to quiver. Phil wondered whether Cryons were capable of real anger, and what they did if they were.

"I realise that to your kind, such a remark would be offensive, Major Newheart, but to me, it is simply nonsensical. It achieves nothing," said Vorkan, disappointingly calmly.

"Maybe not, Vorkan, but it sure as hell feels good!" said Phil. He was actually beginning to enjoy himself - gain some satisfaction and self-esteem from the confrontation.

"When you can prove to me that you're worthy of your title, I will use it," he continued. "I say that you have hidden needs, and this monstrous decision is simply a pretext. The real reason is that you are as power-hungry as any of those men you condemn. Go on Vorkan. Prove me wrong."

"All my decisions are based on pure logic, and nothing else," said Vorkan. But Phil noticed he began to move in a strange way. I may be getting through, he thought. What I need is an impartial judge. Then he remembered MIND.

"I want MIND to listen to this," said Phil suddenly.

"MIND hears everything anyway," said Vorkan. "Don't you MIND."

"Yes." boomed MIND from somewhere above them.

It was a relief to hear MIND's voice. Somehow, Phil felt safer when it was communicating.

"MIND," called Phil, raising his head towards the hangar's lofty ceiling, "If Vorkan doesn't have any hidden needs, how come - in the brain-rec when he eliminated the dinosaurs - how come he felt that he had achieved the absolute power he had craved for a long time?"

His words echoed from the super-smooth ceiling high above them, and glanced off the sleeping craft, with their deadly cargoes.

There was no reply.

"MIND will not enter into conversation with you about me," said Vorkan, evasively.

"Bullshit!" said Phil. "If you tell it to, it will. Who's the boss around here anyway, you or MIND? Go on Vorkan. Tell it. Tell it to be honest with me. Or have you something to hide?"

Vorkan fixed him with a steady stare.

"Well," said Phil. "What are you waiting for? Go on. Tell it. Prove me wrong."

After another long pause, Vorkan spoke.

"Do what he asks, MIND," he said. "Answer his questions."

Got you, you devious bastard! thought Phil.

"Commander Vorkan," said MIND hesitantly, "Did go through a phase when he sought control over the destiny of the Cryon race."

"So any decisions he made could, possibly, have been influenced by this need, could they not?" said Phil.

"Possibly, but extremely unlikely," said MIND. "Commander Vorkan has one of the best brains in our long history."

"There," said Vorkan.

Phil disregarded Vorkan's interjection.

"But what you are saying, MIND," he said, "Is that there is a possibility, albeit remote, that Commander Vorkan's judgement may be influenced not only by the facts, but by personal feelings."

"In a purely biological brain," said MIND, "It is almost impossible to separate what the individual perceives as facts and what he recognises as feelings. Feelings are simply the individual's response to a group of so-called facts. The feelings themselves then become perceived as further facts."

"So are you saying that possibly, any decision Commander Vorkan makes could be influenced by his feelings, without his realising this? In other words, could he genuinely believe he was taking a purely objective decision, when in fact, that may not be the case every time."

"Yes," said MIND. "But in this, he is no different from any other individual."

Vorkan stood motionless, silent.

"After the explosion that ultimately wiped out the dinosaurs," continued Phil, "Commander Vorkan not only felt he had achieved the power he had craved, but it was clear he did not feel at peace, and he was fiddling with the amulet - the one he wears all the time - as if that gave him comfort. I want to know why he didn't feel at peace. Why did he - why does he still - fiddle with that amulet?"

"Silence!" boomed Vorkan suddenly. "Those are private matters I will not have aired in public, and especially not with you, Major!"

"But those private matters may have affected your judgement, Commander," said Phil. "They may still. If there is any doubt - any doubt at all - you owe it to the human race to open this to objective scrutiny. If you have nothing to hide, which you say you have not, what does it matter? You have seen into our souls. We have the right, before we die, to see into yours."

Phil realised the time had come to hit Vorkan below the belt. He knew he was not totally cold and devoid of emotion. Perhaps...

"Those furry animals you saved," he continued. "My wife and children - they evolved from creatures like that - they wouldn't hurt a fly. Please Commander. You have nothing to lose."

For the first time since they had arrived in the hangar, Vorkan's sensilla relaxed. Phil was learning to recognise the signs. He pressed his advantage.

"Any commander can issue orders," he said quietly. "But it takes an exceptional individual to have the courage to bare his soul."

Vorkan regarded him intently, turned and gazed at the hundreds of scout ships, then walked over to the platform holding the bombs. He spoke a few words into a control panel, then keyed in a code with his crusty fingers. The frame above the platform shimmered, then locked. Phil could see the countdown timer had frozen at 14h:12m:08s. It was a cryostatic encapsulation frame. For the moment, time - for the bombs at least - stood still.

"Come with me," said Vorkan.

***

As Vorkan made his way down towards the Nucleus - the chamber in which MIND had been installed - memories of the argument he had had with his father came flooding back. The human, Newheart, was right. He had craved power, and when he achieved it, he was not at peace. Why not? What was missing? He had pontificated to Newheart on the superiority of the Cryon race, and how they had acquired all they could ever want, and how now, their only role remaining was to help others to help themselves, but he himself, Vorkan - in loco parentis of his people - needed help himself. He was not complete.

He glanced behind him. Newheart was still there, padding along with his soft footfalls, panting as humans do. How could he have allowed himself to fall under the spell of this man, this primitive? Why did he exercise such a hold on him?

The door to the Nucleus was straight ahead. He had only been in MIND's physical presence twice before in his life. Once on Cryon just before he left on the advance party; and once more, on Solara, when he had overseen MIND's arrival and installation.

"Where are we?" said Newheart.

"We have come to speak with MIND direct," said Vorkan. "This is the only place - the only circumstance - where communication with MIND is, as you would say, 'Off the record'. Under the circumstances, I am prepared to allow you this privilege, but I do not want our conversation to be available to just anyone."

The massive doors slid open, Vorkan and Newheart walked in, and the doors closed quietly behind them. Even to Vorkan, an audience with MIND was a daunting prospect. In front of him, forming a sphere some hundred metres in diameter, were tier upon tier of neural databank processors - dark mysterious super-cooled cabinets interlinked with a network of connectors resembling the tendrils of some giant adventitious fungus. A catwalk led from the periphery of this great structure, towards its centre.

"Do not touch anything except the catwalk and the hand-rails," said Vorkan. "You will be killed instantly if you do."

As they walked through, they could see the cabinets were arranged in layered shells, like an onion, and Vorkan knew that the nearer they got to the centre, the deeper they were going into the heart - and the history - of this formidable entity. Feeder tubes ran along the sides of the catwalk, and fanned out into the darkness, supplying the nutrients MIND needed to keep its brain material alive. The whole thing was like a body, which needed energy, created waste products, evolved, grew, and repaired itself; but a body devoted to one function and one function alone: thought.

As they approached the kernel - the very centre, the pod of original brain material from which the entire structure was built - Vorkan began to feel apprehensive. He had never actually conversed with MIND in this way before. Few had.

"Oh my God!" he heard Newheart whisper, as they emerged into the central chamber. There before them, like a silver sea urchin with a translucent flexible shell, and suspended in space by thousands of spine-like threads radiating from it, was MIND's original brain. Since its creation, some fifty real-time years ago, it had grown from something the size of a normal Cryon brain, to its present size - a two metre diameter sphere.

Directly connected to this brain, and arranged on a biotic structure accessible from the balcony at the end of the catwalk, were two cybernetic eyes, a stereophonic listening device, a speech unit, an interactive tactile sensor unit, and an electronic scanner unit.

This, was the face of MIND.

"Welcome, Faro," came MIND's voice. "It has been ten years since you came into this chamber, and never have you come to my direct interface before."

MIND's eyes moved, and focused first on Vorkan, then on Phil. Vorkan could see that his companion's teeth were chattering.

"Don't be afraid," said MIND. "Come, Faro, touch me please. This is an experience I am normally denied."

Vorkan hesitated, then gingerly inserted his hand into the tactile sensor unit. It felt like the supple and soft resistance offered by a container of warmed mercury.

"That feels good," said MIND. "Can you feel me grasping you, Faro?"

Vorkan winced as his hand was gripped, softly, within the unit by what felt uncannily like a real Cryon hand. He had to keep concentrating on the unit - with only wires leading from it - to prevent himself imagining MIND possessed an actual hand.

Vorkan slowly withdrew his hand and studied it - a hand that had been touched by MIND.

"You know why we have come, MIND," he said, in English. "Please answer in English. Major Newheart here is worried that my feelings - my personal history perhaps - have coloured my judgement. Before we delve into that, I want to ask you some direct questions."

"I will do my best to answer them, Faro," said MIND.

"Are humans a dangerous species?"

"Yes," replied MIND without hesitation. "They are a danger to themselves, a danger to each other, but most importantly, a danger to Solara itself."

"How likely is it, that even if they had agreed to our demands, they would honour that agreement for 200 thousand years without their being monitored?"

"Infinitesimally unlikely. Had they agreed, I predict that without intimate and continuous monitoring involving hundreds of thousands of automated attendant monitors, their nature is such that at some point, they would break the agreement, with potentially disastrous consequences for the planet. Furthermore, as they advance technically, their potential to outwit the monitors would increase, requiring us to continually upgrade our sophistication and disturb this final period of encapsulation."

"So given their aggressive response to our demands, do you agree that our best course of action is to rid the planet of these creatures as soon as possible?"

"Yes, Faro. For us, that would certainly be the best course of action. However, I should point out that ..."

"I'm sorry to interrupt you, MIND, but your answer to my question was 'Yes', was it not?"

"Yes," said MIND.

"Thank you," he said, and turning to Newheart, "You could not have a clearer confirmation than that, could you Major?"

The human was studying him, suspiciously.

"Ask him about the amulet, Commander," he said.

"I don't have to," said Vorkan. "I know when I got it, and I know why it gives me comfort. It was my mother's."

"Are your parents dead now?" asked Newheart gently. "I mean, did they come on the advanced party with you, or did they stay behind on Cryon?"

"They stayed behind."

"So they are dead. They must be. The main party didn't leave until one hundred and eighteen years after you. I'm very sorry. It must have been a wrench, leaving them behind, knowing you were never going to see them again."

"Actually, Major, that is not what happened," said Vorkan. "My parents are here. They came with the main party."

"But, that's impossible!"

"No, it is not. The Council agreed that close relatives of all members of the advance party could, if they wished, enter into encapsulation on Cryon during that hundred and eighteen years. My father was quite resolved not to do that. He wanted to remain. In fact, he wanted everybody to remain. He did not agree with the migration. But the rest of the family knew, his real reason for giving up was a debilitating depression, brought on by the death of my elder brother."

Vorkan looked up, to see Newheart staring at him, open mouthed.

"I lost a brother too. I lost my father and my brother at the same time."

Vorkan knew that - from the truth session - but had never compared the loss of Maazak to Newheart's plane crash. He began to imagine how Newheart must have felt. It was bad enough losing his brother, but his father too. Somehow, recognising how Newheart had suffered similarly, made it easier for him to re-live the past. Now, he was gaining comfort just talking about it.

"My father's depression was so bad," continued Vorkan, "That it affected his attitude to me. I could do no right. He could not help comparing me to my brother, and I was never able to match him."

"Go on please, Vorkan," said Newheart calmly. "What happened about your parents' encapsulation?"

"My father doted on my mother, Meena. When I left, she could not bear the thought of not seeing me again, so she opted for encapsulation, alone if necessary. That finally persuaded my father. He could not live without her, knowing that she would just be a short distance away, but totally inaccessible. He agreed to join her."

"So have you spoken to your parents since their arrival. I mean, have they ever come out of encapsulation?"

"No. My mother left instructions that neither of them was to be de-encapsulated - other than in emergencies - until the new world had been established. That suited me perfectly. I want my father to walk out, and see the planet I have found for them - see what I have achieved. I want it to be perfect."

The human was regarding him knowingly.

"And we, the human race, are going to sabotage that perfection aren't we Commander Vorkan? That is what's driving you isn't it. *You're doing all this to impress your father.*"

The words drove into Vorkan's brain, and exploded like a heat-seeking missile. He closed his eyes and thought back. MIND had warned him about this, years ago, but old habits die hard. Newheart was right. Everything he had done - all he had tried to achieve - since Maazak's death, had been designed to gain the recognition, respect, and love of his father. He found himself instinctively fiddling with the amulet. He thought back to the day his mother had given it to him - the day of the argument - the day his father had dissociated himself from him. His mother's words came back to him, 'Nothing can change the past, but one day, you will come to understand'

With Newheart watching, wide-eyed, Vorkan unlatched the amulet, held it in his hand, and gazed at it.

"What did she mean, MIND, One day, you will come to understand?"

"Today could be that day, Commander," said Newheart. "May I ask, what is that crystal embedded in it?"

"I don't know," said Vorkan.

"May I see it please?" said MIND.

Vorkan held it up. The solaramine scintillated mysteriously as light from the crystal passed through it.

"Place it into my tactile unit please, Faro," said MIND.

After a moment's hesitation, Vorkan obliged. The amulet disappeared into the unit. Within seconds, it re-emerged.

"There are coded instructions in the crystal," said MIND. Its tone was different, almost child-like. "Put the amulet into the electronic scanner Faro, quickly!"

MIND had never behaved like this before. It had always shown complete self-control. But now, it was as if it was actually getting excited.

Vorkan placed the amulet in the scanner unit, and waited.

"There is a message from your mother, Faro," said MIND. "If when you hear this, she is still alive, she must be brought here. If she has died, the next part of the message is automatically unlocked."

She would have to be de-encapsulated. He had not seen his mother for eleven years. The last thing she had done was to walk into the encapsulation unit back on Cryon, nearly sixty five million years ago. The situation would need to be explained to her by someone she knew.

He instructed MIND to ask Jasoma to receive his mother, escort her to the door of Nucleus, and explain what was happening.

After what seemed an interminable wait, the door at the end of the catwalk opened, and a solitary figure walked slowly towards them. Meena's encapsulation period had been linked to his own. She had been eighty when they last saw each other. Now, they had both aged by eleven years. As she approached, he could see the difference. Her sensilla were a little less flexible, her exoskeleton had lost something of its earlier sheen, and her antennae were lower. But her eyes - those beautiful eyes that radiated love whenever she looked at him - were just as before. He moved to meet her, and they embraced.

"Oh Faro, Faro," she whispered, stroking his back tenderly, "It has been a long time. Too long, my son."

"How is my father?" asked Vorkan anxiously.

Meena gave him a look he did not understand.

"Patara was grumpy as ever when we went into encapsulation," she replied. "Nothing has changed of course. But Jasoma tells me you have given the amulet to MIND, and that you are troubled."

Vorkan explained about the humans, and, translating for his mother, introduced her to Newheart. He also asked MIND to keep the human informed of the gist of their conversation, now conducted exclusively in Cryon.

"What a strange, soft-bodied creature," she said. "But I do not feel uncomfortable in its presence. It seems calm, good almost."

"Newheart has unwittingly been the agent for my distress, Mother. He is a good creature. It is just a pity he is a human. But we have come to a crisis point. I must justify my decision to cleanse this our new home of these creatures, and him and his family with them."

Meena gazed into his eyes. She was obviously saddened by the news.

"Why are you doing this, my son?" she said, looking from him to Newheart and back again.

"Because my father - everybody - deserves a new home devoid of problems of this nature. I owe it to my race, to give them a fresh start, uncontaminated, clean."

"Your motives are beyond question, Faro," she said, "But based upon a fallacy. Your father, your real father, would not demand this of you. He would seek a solution which did not involve mass annihilation."

Vorkan was thunderstruck. He stood rigid, searching his mother's eyes for an answer.

"What do you mean, my real father?"

Meena took her son's hands in his, and stood before him.

"Faro," she began, "Before you were born, I used to work in the Electro-Neural research institute. We had reached a stage of being able to completely fuse biological material to electro-nucleic processors, and had designed what you now recognise as MIND."

"You helped to design MIND!" said Vorkan, astonished.

"I did, Faro," said Meena modestly. "Anyway, it was at that time that I met and partnered Patara. We loved each other completely, and when my time came, we coupled, and had Maazak, your brother. Patara loved Maazak to distraction. He would spend entire days with him, passing on his wisdom. So much so I'm afraid, that I felt excluded, relegated to the boundaries of his life - a peripheral. I found myself spending longer and longer at the Institute, immersing myself in the research, at the expense of our relationship."

Vorkan stood spellbound. "Go on, Mother," he said.

"There was a brilliant scientist - Farola was his name. We worked together, sometimes for days at a stretch with only snatches of sleep. We conducted the final tests of the MIND design. We grew close - very close."

"Mother?" said Vorkan in horror.

"The feeling - you must have experienced it or you would not have Solex - is so intense. After it has happened once - that was Maazak - you know it's extremely unusual for it to happen again within five years. But it did. It was so sudden and unexpected. I was unprepared. Patara wasn't there. Farola was. It seemed so right. Our work was all but completed. We were elated. Our physical consummation was a natural complement to our professional one. Do not doubt Faro, that Farola and I loved each other in a unique way. Your father, Farola, was a wonderful man."

Vorkan felt the world had been swept from under him. There was an awful, lonely emptiness. He who he had treated as his father, was not. He who he had striven to please, could never be satisfied. But along with the feeling of loss, came relief. At last, an explanation of his tortures.

"But Mother! What happened? What became of my father? How did Patara react?"

"He was understanding, philosophical, agreed to treat you as his son. He was wonderful."

"And Farola?"

"Devastated. Consumed by guilt. He resolved to pay his debt to society with the ultimate sacrifice."

Meena let go of her son's hands, and held her left wrist up in front of him. Her amulet - the one she had always worn - was still there.

"This amulet," she said, turning her left wrist round, "Is from Farola."

She unclipped it and held it near to MIND's scanner unit.

"For your sake Faro, and to ensure the project began with an untainted and objective knowledge base, Farola ensured that the truth about you would be removed and locked away in this band, and rendered inaccessible even to MIND from the moment it was switched on. He made me promise never to reveal the truth unless there came a day when it was in your interests to do so. That day has clearly come."

"Removed, Mother? What do you mean?" said Vorkan, now beside himself with apprehension. "Removed from what?"

"He also ensured that his own identity and events in his own life up to that moment would also be removed from the donor brain at the moment of switch-on. His brain - Farola's brain - is the seed from which this entire being grew."

She thrust the amulet into the electronic scanner unit.

"Faro. MIND is your father."

As her wrist band triggered the final unlock initiated by the amulet, MIND's massive form visibly shook. Ripples ran round the great brain, criss-crossing its surface like an unending spasm. It shivered and palpitated in its spiny threads, as wave upon wave of multi-coloured light travelled along them, dissipating ultimately in the surrounding shells of neural units. At the same time it let out a long low moan of heart-rending passion the like of which Vorkan had never heard.

He dropped to the ground, and placed his right hand into MIND's tactile unit. He could feel his mother's hand next to his, and his father, holding them both. A beautiful warm feeling spread from it throughout his body - a security, an unbounded all-enveloping love unsurpassed in his experience. In his mind, the crushing weight - the need for recognition - which had dominated his entire life, was lifted from him.

"Faro, my son!" came MIND's voice, from just in front of him.

"Father!" cried Vorkan.

Now, nothing was missing.

At last, Vorkan was at peace.

19
Countdown

From a specially constructed earthquake-proof bunker on the far side of the reservoir and two miles from the Cryon door, Vice President Powell, Secretary Straker, General Norman, and a hand-picked team of scientists and military observers waited nervously as the count-down ticked inexorably towards noon. A battery of cameras, binoculars and telescopes was trained on the doorway, which had been cleared of equipment, and the dome removed.

As agreed - through hand-written notes or direct person-to-person conversations - no mention whatsoever had been made over any communication circuit, of Operation Groundstorm. Up to this moment, security had been absolute.

Now, lines had been opened to the Joint Chiefs of Staff at the Pentagon, and the telephone Powell now held to his ear linked straight through to the Oval Office.

"Can you hear me, Mr President?" said Powell. "I have 30 left."

"Understood," replied the President.

Powell could hear his own breathing in the handset as he leaned forward and peered through the massive 40 x 150 military binoculars. Stretching out before him, its wavelets flashing in the sunshine, was the clean blue surface of the reservoir. On the far bank, jet black against the snow-covered headland behind it, was the door.

"Five," came a voice from behind him.

He stopped breathing. His eyes began to water but he was determined not to blink.

"Zero," said the voice.

Nothing happened.

No-one spoke for ten seconds.

"No tremor," reported the seismologist. "Should be here by now."

"Jesus Christ!" came Straker's voice. The anger was laced with fear. "That bastard Newheart."

Powell had to blink. As he re-focused, something had changed. There was a different blackness about the face of the door.

"Wait! Something's happening," he exclaimed.

"The sonofabitch is opening!" somebody shouted.

Powell strained to keep his eyes on the eye-cups without nudging the instrument. The door was open - wide open. Then, a large shell flew out from it - at least it was as fast as a shell - and disappeared out of his field of view within a split second. It was so quick, if he had blinked, he would have missed it. This was closely followed by another, then another.

"Goddamn flying saucers!" yelled one of the observers.

Speechless, Powell raised his head and stared directly out. From the door now emerged, like a swarm of hornets, hundreds of craft. They came out in groups of between eight and twelve - line astern and at near supersonic speed - and described tight arcs in the sky before climbing rapidly and heading off in all directions.

"Major attack! Major attack!" shouted the Air Force observer into his phone. "Code red! Scramble! Scramble! Unidentified aircraft! Hundreds of them!"

Some of the men in the bunker fell over themselves in a rush to get outside, and stood gazing skywards. There was an equally unseemly scramble to return, as one of the craft headed towards them, decelerated rapidly, hovered nearby for a moment, then flew away. The incident lasted only a few seconds, and was completed in absolute silence.

"It's got no engines!" called out one man.

"What's that glow?" shouted another.

As suddenly as it had begun, the emergence ended. The craft had vanished. The door closed. Tranquillity returned.

Powell was trembling. He gripped the handset tightly as he reported to the President.

"Detonation negative, Sir. Repeat, negative," he began wearily. "I think we may have a problem."

***

The first the world knew of the Cryon scout-ships were reports to local TV and radio stations of strange lights in the sky.

In the North and South American continents, daylight or cloud rendered the speeding craft unseen to the average person glancing casually skywards. But in Cold Bay, on the easternmost tip of the Alaska Peninsula, with the lifeless sun yet to struggle over the south-eastern horizon, Attu Tanaga, the Aleut native wildlife warden watched and wondered, as processions of tiny blue lights filed silently across the sky, heading west.

In Europe, it was already early evening, and dark. For many, it had been the first day back to work after the Christmas and New Year holidays. The first sighting came from Tarbert in the Outer Hebrides. June McCullough, a barmaid from the Harris Hotel had just set off for work when the lights appeared from the north-west.

“I’ve no’ seen anything like it! They were like strings of glowing sapphires,” she said, as she arrived somewhat flustered, at the hotel.

Reports began flooding in to local radio stations from mainland Scotland, and Donegal, County Mayo, and Connemara in Ireland. Only minutes later, switchboards across the United Kingdom were jammed by anxious callers as the lights crossed the country and headed on towards Europe - most of them, that is.

Within forty minutes of the original emergence, lights in the sky had been seen from every country in Europe, from the Pacific rim, and now, unconfirmed sightings were coming in from some African countries, from Russia, China, and the Indian sub-continent.

Reuters, and other international news organisations soon noted a pattern. There were clearly three ‘radiants’ from which the lights had come: North America, Africa, and somewhere in central Asia.

About half an hour after the first sortie, a group of six extra-ordinary craft emerged from the door. Whereas the original flight had resembled discuses, these were more like tankers. They only just cleared the 40ft high by 60ft wide door, and were about as long as a jumbo jet. Like the others, their sides and lower surfaces glowed with a blue phosphorescence as they moved. The six craft climbed to 50 miles, then headed east at orbital velocity - some 17,000mph. Within six minutes, they were over New York, and there they stopped.

At 2:40pm Eastern Standard Time on Wednesday 2nd January 2013, the Cryons arrived at Manhattan.

People on the waterfronts of Brooklyn and New Jersey got the best view. Out of a hazy grey sky, the six tanker craft dropped from space, then held steady at 2,000ft over the Hudson and East Rivers. One was just north of the Queensborough bridge - in line with East 60th St; the second, south of the Williamsburg bridge; the third, off Battery Park; the fourth, over the Hudson near the Freedom Tower; the fifth, near the West 30th St Heliport; and the sixth, in line with West 60th St. By all accounts, all six craft performed the same actions on arrival. Sam Sukauski, pilot of the Staten Island ferry heading for Battery Park terminal, had only a third of a mile to go when craft number three appeared out of nowhere high above him.

"I damn near messed my pants, I can tell you!" he said to waiting reporters on his return to Staten Island. "One minute, everything's normal. The next, this damn great machine's right there up in the sky in front of the boat. Then a sort of cylinder appears from its bottom surface, and a column of bright blue gas stuff comes straight down to the water, and I'm headed straight for it!"

"So it fired at you," suggested a reporter.

"Well, not really. There was just this blue pillar. And I can see that it goes on down into the water, real deep. Anyway, I threw the wheel over and brought her about. Then, I sees another one, 'bout a mile over to the left, and one over by the Williamsburg."

"Were you frightened?"

"What do you think, pal! Look at it!" He stared back across the water towards Manhattan. "Anyway, next thing that happens is this machine links up to the other two. Same blue stuff, but this time, like a rod across the sky. Then I see there's more rods, going up the Hudson and the East River from the others. I can tell you, I got the hell out of there."

What happened next was seen - and experienced - by thousands of people. Two minutes after all six craft linked up, translucent sheets of what some described as soft blue glass, began to lower from the aerial framework. The sheets descended slowly and inexorably towards the water and - along 60th Street - towards the ground. Drivers heading out of Manhattan on the four bridges affected and on the northbound avenues that crossed 60th Street, described driving through a vertical wall of fog which seemed to slow their vehicles down, as if they were being dragged backwards by an unseen force. The same thing happened underground in the Queens, Holland and Lincoln road tunnels, and train drivers of the last trains to get through reported the engines behaving as if they were climbing a steep gradient.

The vertical curtains - to the amazement of those intrepid souls who attempted to pass through them - soon became like walls of ice-blue treacle. Enormous queues of horn-blowing traffic backed up along all roads and bridges leading into southern Manhattan, and thousands of frightened and dumbfounded people gazed incredulously at the walls, now totally obscuring their view of the downtown area. Airline pilots reported a similar effect across the top of this vast sock-shaped, six sided box, entrapping an area of some 16 square miles.

At the same time, the control rooms of water, gas and power distribution companies surrounding Manhattan were experiencing an unprecedented fall in demand. As one electrical engineer put it, “It’s as if everybody downtown is pulling the plug!”

Telephone conversations and radio and TV broadcasts which had been in progress during the cloaking operation were cut dead, and computer systems outside the area reported data inaccessible and all network connections failed.

Then, at 3pm, the walls and top cover turned into a rock-hard and totally impenetrable mirror. Nothing - absolutely nothing - could get into or out of the box. Inside it, the heart of the most vibrant city in the world had stopped beating. Not a thing stirred; not a molecule moved - nothing.

The Cryons had encapsulated Manhattan.

Simultaneously, similar encapsulations - though on a smaller scale - were occurring all over the world. The London, Paris, Tokyo and Mexico stock exchanges were hit, as were the headquarters and main computer centres of hundreds of multi-national companies. Dealing rooms were thrown into chaos. National and international trading organisations went haywire as their in-house systems were deluged with wave after wave of incomprehensible data.

Arms manufacturers reported factories rendered inaccessible, their workers locked inside. A similar fate befell weapon storage facilities, arms dumps, and stocks of biological and germ warfare devices, again, on a world-wide scale.

Air defense radar systems had detected the craft but failed to launch any anti-ballistic missiles. By the time perplexed and frantic commanders had realised something was locking their systems, it was too late. The only casualties had been the crews of fighter aircraft and independent ground batteries who had been brave enough to launch attacks on the Cryon craft. In every case, the trajectories of the missiles and shells had been reversed, resulting in the destruction of the attacker. Once word got around, no-one tried it again. The Cryons were invulnerable.

Powell was in animated conversation with the President, as he flew towards a stunned Washington. They had been discussing Manhattan, the stock exchanges, and the weapons facilities.

"I suppose we must thank God that the Cryons haven't annihilated us," said the President, ruefully. "But they've done something almost as bad. They've hit us where it really hurts. They've stopped our heart, frozen our bank accounts, and paralysed our trigger fingers! Not to put too fine a point on it, Richard, "They have us. They have us by the nuts!"

***

In the hours following the encapsulations, the media - initially the American, but closely followed by the world - pieced together hitherto disconnected events over the last three months, and demanded answers.

Why had the American Government sought to silence seismologists who had reported unusual signals? What was so special about the 'Site of special archaeological interest' in Wyoming? How was it that someone who had been running a small electric car business in England, had suddenly become an astronaut? And how come that rookie astronaut had, with no acceptable explanation, participated in a hush-hush flight to the Moon? What had happened at F.E. Warren base? Why had a group of US Government scientists been imprisoned in Fort Carson, Colorado, and been prevented from even communicating with their friends and families? And last but not least, what did the American Government know about the UFOs, the encapsulations, and what were they going to do about them?

On Thursday 3rd January, an angry mob hundreds strong - egged on by journalists who had been unable to wring any sense out of Washington - besieged Fort Carson and demanded the release of the scientists. The guards, recognising that their choice was simple: a televised massacre to a global audience or capitulation, chose the second option. The scientists were released. The secret was out.

By the evening of that day, the entire world knew the whole truth. Domestic and international condemnation - with a vehemence unparalleled in its history - was directed at ever-higher echelons within the US Administration. The assault continued into the night. Their actions had been indefensible.

By Friday morning, at an emergency meeting of the United Nations in Geneva - the New York building remaining encapsulated - world leaders were tabling a vote of censure against the US, and demanding the President's resignation.

Then came the global message.

On every radio and TV in the world - spoken or appearing as text on the screen in the local language - and achieved without the knowledge or intervention of broadcasters, the following message was received.

We are the Cryons. Do not be afraid. No-one will be harmed. No-one currently locked within locations under the control of our ships is in any danger. Our only purpose in doing what we have done is to demonstrate to you and your leaders that we can do it, and to prevent ill-conceived or precipitate actions by yourselves. In one hour, New York, the stock exchanges, and the multi-national companies will be released. Personnel within those locations will be unaware that time has passed since their entrapment and will need counselling. Your arms manufacturers and supply facilities will also be released, but be closely monitored. Any attempt to use those arms will result in an immediate and permanent period of entrapment. Finally, we charge and require every country to despatch a representative - preferably one elected by the people - to the United Nations General Assembly in New York on Monday 7th January at four in the afternoon, when the future of mankind will be revealed.

The reaction to the broadcast ranged from total disbelief to country-wide panic, and depended to a large extent on national temperament, the nature of the regime, and whether the country was already a member state of the UN.

When as promised, Manhattan and the other locations were de-encapsulated and their occupants found to be in perfect health - though understandably much confused - a degree of confidence was restored. However, the nature of the message, with the sinister implication that the future of the world was no longer under the control of the human race, was sobering and though-provoking.

In the days that followed, churches, mosques, synagogues, temples and other religious meeting places became packed. People who had never shown any religious leanings before, flocked to them and queued for hours - sometimes in atrocious weather - to gain admittance and receive guidance. Across the world, stadia, concert halls, hillsides - anywhere that served as a gathering place - were used for prayers, services, and evangelical appeals.

And one of man's greatest questions: Are we alone? had been answered more dramatically and suddenly than anyone could have envisaged. The thought that for decades, man had searched the heavens for signs of life, only to find it - literally -

under its feet, caused not inconsiderable consternation and embarrassment in scientific and philosophical circles.

Across the world, people and their leaders began to stop and consider the implications of the alien visitation. There were many suicides. There were some who sought to profit from the situation. There were many who assumed smug expressions and went round saying, 'Something like this was bound to happen - I told you so'. But most people spent that week-end in deep introspection, applying their minds to the question of whether perhaps, after all, there was such a thing as the Day of Judgement.

They would have to wait until Monday to find the answer.

20
New York

"Major Newheart."

MIND's voice was calm and measured.

"Yes MIND," said Phil, with a mixture of relief and apprehension. He and the family had guessed that of all days, they would be involved today, Monday 7th January.

Since the episode at the Nucleus five days ago, they had been provided with comfortable quarters within the Cryon complex. Whilst they were unquestionably prisoners, their dungeon had been synthesised on MIND's command, and was a perfect copy of the Ritz-Carlton penthouse suite. They were not permitted to leave, but the sights and sounds from the virtual reality windows were amazingly authentic, and the food - supplied on demand by something akin to an articulated robotic hostess trolley - was excellent.

There were flat-screen TVs on the walls of every room. These were compulsive viewing, and had provided an unrivalled perspective on mankind's reaction to the unfolding events. Clearly, Vorkan had not carried out his plan to explode the Groundstorm bomb on the White House lawn, and each day that brought no reports of people dying of sleeping sickness bolstered their belief that their intervention had worked - or at least postponed the event. But the ever-present knowledge that they were prisoners, their inability to communicate with the outside world, and the total silence from MIND and Vorkan, were beginning to take their toll.

They had tried sitting down and discussing what they would do under this or that circumstance, but without any clues whatsoever on what was to befall the human race, this proved a thankless and impossible task. Phil had thought long and hard about how he could make up for his broken promise to Jo, and from what she and the others said, he could plan roughly what he was going to do under a variety of scenarios. But he could not bear to air his ideas - after all, some of the outcomes he was catering for were the stuff of nightmares. For the whole family, the uncertainty about the future was unbearable. They knew they had been condemned - but to what?

That day, live reports and comments from the UN building in New York had dominated all TV channels. There were interviews with diplomats, religious spokesmen, and commentators round the globe. Speculation was rife, and the atmosphere crackled with tension. World leaders had been arriving throughout the day; meetings were already in session; it was without question the most widely covered event in the history of the world.

"Please gather your belongings," said MIND. "You are to leave today."

Phil and the others looked at each other. No-one knew whether to cheer or cry. The global transmission had provided some comfort. If annihilation by the Cryons was imminent, what would be the point of telling the world beforehand? It would achieve nothing. But there was the undeniable fact - confirmed by both Vorkan and MIND - that the Cryons wanted to rid the planet of humankind. The only questions remaining were how, and when.

They grabbed the few items they had brought with them, then following MIND's instructions, filed out through a series of doors and passageways, and boarded an unmanned shuttle. Under MIND's control, it raced through the tunnels, eventually emerging into a hangar-like chamber of gigantic proportions. But it was not the chamber's size that made them all gasp in amazement - it was what it contained.

Towering above them was a craft of extra-ordinary size. Its length and beam were at least double those of a super-tanker. It was lying horizontally, its shape resembling a sharpened pencil. Apart from lines of what may have been hatches, and the strips of blue-glowing hexagons running along its lower-facing surfaces, its sides were completely smooth.

"Oh wow!" exclaimed Nick, as the shuttle rose the 150ft from the chamber floor to the tip of the craft's giant nosecone.

Protruding from the nosecone was a short transparent cylinder with a hemispherical end, some 30ft in diameter. As the shuttle approached it, they could see it contained two decks. On the lower deck, a number of Cryons were moving about within a circle of illuminated control panels.

"Our flagship, Space Cruiser *Stallustra*," said MIND. "This will be your transport."

Before Phil had a chance to say 'Where to?', the shuttle drew alongside the rearward section of the nosecone cylinder and docked. The hatch opened, and they stepped through into the cylinder itself. Once inside, its glass-like wall closed behind them, and the shuttle floated off and disappeared from view.

They were on the upper deck, in a transparent-walled air-conditioned room furnished with chairs, and providing an unimpeded view of the deck below. They stood wide-eyed. Despite what appeared to be a glass partition between the decks, they could hear the sounds coming from what was clearly the bridge of this great ship. One of the Cryons turned towards them and raised his arm. Phil recognised him as Vorkan. But he was no longer wearing the amulet.

"It is time," he said.

Phil felt Jo-Ann grip his hand tightly. Vorkan's turn of phrase suggested a finality that did little to calm their fears.

"Time for what?" said Phil apprehensively. "What's happening, Commander?"

"Do not be afraid," said Vorkan. "No harm will come to you or your family. We are going to New York, where I shall address the world leaders. I want you to be there."

"But why this ship?" said Phil. "What are you going to do?"

"You will see," said Vorkan mysteriously. "We have a little job to do first. Relax, Major. Enjoy the view."

With that, he turned away and began speaking in his own tongue to those around him.

The lights within the cylinder dimmed, giving them a clear view of the world outside the ship. Ahead, a tunnel led out from the chamber. The vast ship started moving slowly and silently towards it, then through it. They passed through the hub, then onwards and upwards towards the surface. As they emerged into the daylight, it was clear that the original door had gone. The full width of the main tunnel now broke the surface.

To gasps from Jo-Ann and Tess, and whoops of excitement from Nick, *Stallustra* accelerated upwards and out of the atmosphere, into space. The panoramic view was spectacular as they climbed to what Phil estimated was at least 1000 miles altitude. There was no sound, no vibration, no feeling of motion - just peace.

"Oh God! It's beautiful," whispered Jo-Ann.

She and the children were spellbound. Phil felt a lump come into his throat as he now shared this near spiritual experience with those he loved.

Stallustra came to rest high over the Atlantic. Then, silently and mysteriously began descending, whilst executing a series of vast circles in space, releasing as it did so a number of orange-coloured objects like ten-sided dice. By the time the operation was complete, the objects had formed a gigantic funnel shape, with the narrow end directed at their destination, now a mere 50 miles below them - New York.

Up to then, the Cryons on the deck below had worked silently at their control panels, but now, incongruously, Phil heard Vorkan speaking in English.

"Please confirm that all is ready for my arrival," he said.

"We are ready," came the nervous reply from the surface. "The special dais you specified is installed, and the area round the UN building is secure."

"The craft containing your bombs will be landing in thirty seconds," said Vorkan. "The countdown is in progress and has two hours to go. You do all understand that unless I return to my ship unharmed, and cancel the countdown, New York will be destroyed."

"We understand that perfectly, Sir."

Phil realised that Vorkan was using the Groundstorm bombs to ensure his safety. All it'll take is one misguided hero, he thought, but kept it to himself.

As they gazed out, a small craft launched itself from the main ship and fell rapidly towards the city, now only a few thousand feet below them. To the side, Phil could see *Stallustra*'s half-mile long shadow, darkening a wide swathe of north Queens.

After a few moments, Vorkan looked up at Phil.

"Let us go," he said.

He walked from the cylinder and disappeared into the main ship. Shortly afterwards, a door opened behind them.

"Please join me," said Vorkan from the doorway. "It is not far."

The stunned family followed him through sweltering passageways, out into a large landing bay, and onto a parked scout ship. The outer skin of *Stallustra* opened, and their craft flew out.

"Time to face the truth," said Vorkan.

***

It was five minutes to four as Vorkan's scout craft descended rapidly and noiselessly towards the jutting skyscrapers of Manhattan's East Side. From above, the buildings looked like long crystals of quartz as their glass sides glinted in the setting sun. Within seconds, the unmistakable form of the United Nations building rose up outside the windows. Phil could see that all the streets in the vicinity had been cordoned off by scores of blue and white NYPD vehicles, their lights flashing incessantly. The craft came to rest, hovering over a circular area just yards from the main doors of the building.

Still reeling after their exhilarating flight, Phil and the family stood in the exit cylinder at the centre of the craft. It was like a circular lift with a glass wall. Once lowered to the ground, the wall would part.

"Are you ready?" asked Vorkan. "I will follow once you are out."

It was not difficult to imagine what their reception would be like. It wasn't every day that an alien spacecraft landed in Manhattan! Phil checked with the others. They locked hands together, and took a deep breath.

"Ready," he said.

The cylinder lowered, then began to open. After the relative peace of the Cryon stronghold and the silence of the flight, the sheer volume of Manhattan's background noise took them by surprise. The sickly odour of Vorkan's acetone was replaced by the all too familiar smell of exhaust fumes. They did not need their eyes to tell them they were back with humanity.

They stepped out into the cold air and gazed around. Above them, a silent menace hanging like an anvil ready to fall, was the vast bulk of the space cruiser *Stallustra*. It dominated the sky, and dwarfed the skyscrapers reaching up towards it.

Phil could see that they were encircled by hundreds of heavily armed men, and behind them, occupying every conceivable vantage point, were cameras. He realised that his every movement was being relayed to what must have been the largest television audience the world had ever known.

A knot of men detached itself from the circle, and walked slowly towards him. They were all dressed in UN blue uniforms. One of them - a tallish man with greying hair and sunglasses - was clearly in charge, and as he approached, there was something familiar about his gait. He removed the sunglasses.

It was Beemish.

"Talk about arriving in style!" he said, shaking them warmly by the hand. "Thank God you're all safe. This is wonderful!"

Phil could have cried with joy and relief. If it hadn't been for the cameras, he would have hugged him.

"So what's happening, Ted?" he said. "Just another day's work for the National Guard!"

Beemish grinned.

"I'm not in the Guard any more," he said. "The Administration's in turmoil. Heads are rolling across the country. Miller's dead, Cranford's under arrest, Powell's out, and Straker's resigned."

"And you?" said Phil, fascinated.

"I get a promotion every few hours! They've put me in charge of this little get together today, and there's even talk I should run for President."

"President! Things that bad huh!" said Phil roguishly. "And your wife, Louise?"

"Fully recovered thanks. Amazing. She's here. You must meet her later."

Phil then brought Beemish up to date. They walked away from the scout ship and looked towards the square to the north of the building. The craft carrying the bombs had already landed there. Its bay doors were open, revealing its lethal cargo and countdown device. Phil could tell from the frenzied activity centred on that craft, that its portent was only too clear, but no-one could access the device to disable it.

Beemish issued strict orders to his lieutenants, who eventually returned with confirmation that everyone in the building, including the Secretary General and assembled delegates - and in particular every armed person - understood the situation.

"Okay. Let's get him inside as quickly as possible," said Beemish anxiously, scanning the windows of the overlooking buildings. "We can't rule out the possibility that some psycho up there could decide to take a pot shot."

Phil returned to the scout ship, then led Vorkan out. Beemish's men - despite their obvious revulsion - closely surrounded Vorkan for the quick walk to the front doors, but once inside, gladly stood back and gave him all the space he needed.

Flanked by UN police, greeted by cries of awe and fear, and accompanied by a barrage of flashguns, Vorkan's giant figure - all seven feet of it excluding his short antennae - made its way through the entrance lobby. Press and TV crews from across the globe fell over themselves to get their pictures as the party headed for the escalators. As Phil followed on, he realised what an extra-ordinary sight Vorkan was. Underground in his own environment his appearance was awesome enough, even when dwarfed by the sheer size of the caverns. Whereas up here, on the surface, suddenly seen against a purely human setting, he was incredible, freakish, terrifying.

Beemish led them along a wide hallway lined with flags of many nations, from behind which peered the incredulous faces of delegates and representatives from across the world. Phil could see some turning away in horror, and some barely able to stifle their cries. Many were visibly shaken. One man actually turned and was violently sick as Vorkan passed him, and at least two others keeled over like guards in a heat wave.

Finally, they entered the General Assembly hall itself. Vorkan paused in the doorway as a hush descended on the packed auditorium. Two thousand faces, of every form and hue, turned towards him and stared open-mouthed as he made his way slowly down the main aisle towards the rostrum. Beemish indicated a row of reserved seats at the front to Phil and the family. They sat down awkwardly. Sitting within thirty feet of him, Phil recognised the US and Russian Presidents, the UK Prime Minister, and the Heads of State of Japan and many European countries.

On the platform, the Secretary General coughed nervously into his microphone as Vorkan stepped onto his specially-designed rostrum. In the strong lights, Phil could see wisps of steam rising up from its circular periphery. Vorkan's form shimmered slightly, as if he was standing in a mirage.

"This assembly recognises the representative of the Cryon race," he stuttered, his voice trembling and his hands visibly shaking. "The floor is yours."

Vorkan turned towards his audience, and scanned the apprehensive faces in front of him, his huge eyes fixing on one, then another delegate. Phil got the impression that he had done his homework, and recognised most of the heads of state. It was noticeable that the leaders of the western world, and in particular the US President, came under particular scrutiny.

"Secretary General, leaders and representatives of the countries of the world," he began in his unmistakable timbre. Its power and quality sent gasps and exclamations rippling across the hall. He waited for silence.

"On the 24th December, I, Commander Vorkan, acting with the full authority of the Cryon High Council, communicated to your representatives that this planet, Solara, would be required by ourselves in two hundred thousand years time, that you would have to leave, and that we were giving you as much notice as possible. I also pointed out that your growth and many of your activities were giving us cause for grave concern. I made it quite clear that for your own sake, for ourselves, and for the planet as a whole, you must take immediate action to reduce your population, reduce pollution, reduce your use of natural resources, eliminate all weapons of mass destruction, disarm ordinary citizens, and move towards a zero-growth world economy. I also made it clear that in return for taking these actions, we would, at appropriate times, pass on to you the benefits of our technology and discoveries. There can be no doubt that under the circumstances, those demands were eminently reasonable."

Despite his less secure position after the vote of censure against the United States, the President, barely disguising his fury and indignation, rose to his feet and tapped his microphone impatiently with his pen.

"What right do you, an alien, have to dispossess us, and come here making demands?" he stormed. "Since the dawn of man, Earth - and I repeat, *Earth* - has been our birthright, our land, our home."

Many delegates applauded. The President nodded in acknowledgement. Vorkan slowly turned his head and stared menacingly at him.

"Firstly, Mr President," he said, stonily, "Your use of the term 'Come here' distorts the truth. As you know full well, we have been here for the last sixty five million years. You on the other hand have only appeared very recently. If anyone has come, Sir, it is yourselves. But secondly, even if we had just arrived, the right by which we shall dispossess you is based upon the same principle which you and your very people, Mr President, dispossessed the native residents of North America. It mattered little that they were here before you. You wanted their land, so you just took it. We have to remain on this planet, and remain we shall. So now, *we* will take *your* land. As you and many of the other nations on Solara are such experts at dispossessing each other, I feel sure you will recognise our actions as being perfectly normal!"

Phil glanced at Jo-Ann, who was clearly moved by what had just been said.

"At last!" she whispered. "Official condemnation. If only White Eagle could have heard this."

Vorkan's point had touched raw nerves in representatives from many a country They began calling and pointing to each other accusingly. The Secretary General restored order.

"Delegates!" he called. "This is not the moment to fight between ourselves. We appear to have little choice but to listen to what Commander Vorkan has to say. I suggest we conduct this session with the composure and dignity that becomes this institution. Let us hear him out."

He turned to Vorkan, indicating that he should continue.

"Thank you, Secretary General. As I was saying, under the circumstances, our demands were perfectly reasonable. I was asked at the time, what would be the consequences of your non-compliance with our demands. My response was unequivocal - annihilation."

At the sound of that word, from the creature who had the means to carry it out, cries and gasps came from all round the hall. Phil leaned over and gripped Jo-Ann's and the children's hands.

"And as we now all know," Vorkan continued, "Your response was absolutely typical of you humans. Attack! You attempted to wipe us out with the nuclear device which, I remind you all, is sitting not twenty yards from this building, and counting down to detonation."

Vorkan paused, and scanned his audience. The hall was deathly quiet.

"I now ask you to consider what you would do in my situation. My initial reaction was to waste no further time attempting to be reasonable. Even without your aggressive response, the crimes you have already perpetrated on the planet itself are sufficiently grave to justify our eliminating you completely. Were it not for the timely intervention of one man, Major Newheart - and his family - that is exactly what we would have done. We knew about your bomb days before Major Newheart came to us; the ships of our scout fleet were already charged with a lethal virus; humanity had less than a day remaining. You have Major Newheart to thank for saving you from total destruction."

Phil could feel the eyes of the entire audience directed at him. Some of the TV cameras moved from Vorkan to himself. The whole world was watching him. The blood rushed to his face. He gripped Jo-Ann's hand once more, and remained expressionless.

Vorkan continued.

"Whilst you may have been granted a temporary reprieve, the problem is still with us. Before your bomb was planted, we had even begun to investigate the feasibility of a short-term compromise solution, in which the planet was divided - by major atmospheric engineering - into two zones, one which would suit yourselves, and one which would suit us. But what we now know of the human character, and the fact that any solution must include the rich and powerful nations such as the USA - who would doubtless give us problems later on - has caused us to abandon that compromise solution. There will be no sharing."

"In our attempt to resolve what at first would seem to be an irreconcilable situation, we have sought to understand you, the human race, and to determine what are the root causes of your problems. We have come to the conclusion that those causes are greed, growth, and apparently, a total inability or disinclination to include a global or long-term view when prioritising your actions."

"Over the last few weeks, I have seen a divided planet. I have seen that some fifteen percent of you - the western world - enjoy rich lives, with access to thirty times the resources available to the remaining eighty five percent. And even within that exclusive group, a similar imbalance exists, with a small fraction of your people grabbing a large fraction of the wealth. These differentials result in irresistible forces within society. The greatest pressure is the rise of consumer expectations. Even within the western world itself those who have less, covet the prosperity of those who have more. The flaunting of wealth, coupled with covert persuasion and overt advertising, feeds a self-perpetuating demand for growth. But it also feeds resentment. The lower strata of this privileged group, apparently unaware of how fortunate they are in absolute terms and inured by TV and an irresponsible media, turn to crime, violence, sexual deviancy or drugs to feed their desires for instant gratification."

"And providing the processes which drive and feed these demands, reaping the rewards and disregarding the long-term consequences, are your multi-national companies. Western governments have done little to restrict their activities or the growth that they induce. You permit unrestricted growth - growth in possessions, growth in numbers, and growth in power. Growth seems to be your God. But you must know that growth in itself - growth without direction, growth for the sake of growth - is doomed."

All around him, Phil could sense that the delegates - particularly those from the developed countries - were squirming in their seats. No-one rose to defend themselves from Vorkan's attack. He continued.

"You blunder aimlessly onward, blind to the warning signs all around you, and fail to acknowledge that your planet is on course for disaster. You are as sleepwalkers who have left the safety of the bedroom and are now on the landing. The stairway to oblivion is but one step away."

***

No-one spoke; everyone in the hall was stunned into silence. And Vorkan had yet to reveal the Cryon's plans for mankind.

"Is it perfectly clear that you are totally incapable of managing the planet you call home. The remedy, which is defensible under interplanetary law, will be imposed upon you forthwith, and comprise three main components."

Every person in the hall was on the edge of their seat. In the uncanny silence. Phil could feel his heart thumping and an awful sense of dread came over him. Was he right to have warned the Cryons? What if Vorkan's 'remedy' was so bad that most people would prefer to die rather than accept it? Then he remembered Jo-Ann's words in Ruby's Bar, 'When no other options remain, it is better to work with your enemy from within, than die in a futile gesture of defiance'. He prayed that what he was about to hear was not going to create an exception to those words of Indian wisdom.

"The first component," said Vorkan, "Is that you will undergo - over the next hundred years - a dramatic drop in world population."

Thank God, thought Phil. At last. An indication that he does not intend to kill us all.

"Not only must it be reduced," he continued, "But in terms of distribution across the globe, it must reflect the ability of the world's arable land to support it. To this end, we have divided the planet into eighty zones. Each zone has the capacity - in terms of food production - to support the same number of people. The reason why it is eighty and why we are demanding an even distribution will shortly become clear when I present the third component. By the end of the hundred years, instead of the present imbalance, all eighty zones will contain roughly equal populations. The process of population reduction itself has already started. Our craft, which have been patrolling your skies since January 2nd, have released an airborne agent that by now will have been absorbed by the entire world population. The agent, based on our pico-molecular technology, has the effect of sterilising your females. Already, every human female is infertile. Existing pregnancies will not be affected, but without an antidote, no further pregnancies can occur."

From total silence, there now erupted howls of protest and despair from the hall, in a crescendo of anger. Delegates hammered on their benches. Women rose to their feet and shouted and gesticulated at Vorkan, who remained impassive. Phil turned to Jo-Ann, who was hugging Tess. Tears began to stream down their faces.

"Oh Mum!" wailed Tess. "How could he!"

Phil had expected something dramatic. He stared at Vorkan, who was holding his bony claw up, seeking silence. Eventually, the clamour died down and he was able to speak again.

"If you would hear me out," he said. "There is an antidote. Each antidote will permit one non-multiple pregnancy. Appropriate numbers of antidote ampoules will be despatched to each national government on an annual basis. The numbers despatched will depend upon the population reduction necessary that year, and the number of arable zones - or proportion of a zone - that apply to that country. One thing you are going to have to learn, is that the begetting of children is no longer a right - it is a privilege. National governments will be responsible for selecting those women who may be given an antidote, but we will oversee the fairness of the selection process and rigorously eliminate black market trading and corruption."

Tess brightened up a bit, and wiped away her tears. Delegates looked about them, murmuring to each other. The tension eased. The President of India, a majestic woman with an orange and green sari, rose to her feet.

"Commander Vorkan," she began. "It would appear that you have - overnight as it were - solved one of the greatest problems besetting our country: that of our rapidly growing population. Whilst I cannot condone your methods, there is no question that they will be effective."

A number of heads nodded in agreement. She continued.

"Currently, total fertility rate - the number of children born per woman - is running at 3.2 in my country. What will the rate be under your regime?"

"For the world as a whole," replied Vorkan, "It will begin at 1.0, gradually reduce over fifty years to a low point of 0.2, then over the next fifty years, rise to 2.0."

The President's eyes widened in disbelief.

"That means that at the low point, the fertility rate is equivalent to only one in five women having any children in their lifetime!" she exclaimed. "And that is for the world as a whole. I do not think I care to ask what the figure is for India! We, and many other nations, are going to need assistance to manage the ever-increasing proportion of older people this regime will generate, and to cushion the awful feeling of emptiness our childless women will experience. Without this assistance, I cannot accept your plan."

"You will receive assistance, Madam President," said Vorkan, "But with respect, even if that assistance was not forthcoming, you have no choice in the matter. You *will* accept it."

Vorkan paused for a moment and stared steadfastly at her.

"The only alternative is annihilation," he said icily.

The President sat down, stunned.

The Secretary General rose to his feet. He was fiddling with his watch.

"I am mindful of the time," he said anxiously. "We must allow Commander Vorkan to deliver his address and return safely to his ship and stop the countdown. You say there are three components to your solution, Commander. Please tell us the other two."

"The second component," said Vorkan, "Comprises a suite of measures, which include our original demands, and a few more. You will take immediate action on arms sales, economic and industrial growth, natural resource depletion, deforestation, over-fishing, biodiversity, desertification, pollution, degradation of fertile soils, the burning of coal, oil and gas for power production, and the reliance you place upon personal transport using the internal combustion engine. On that last point, you will design and effect an integrated transport policy which, over the next ten years, phases out gasoline and diesel engines and replaces them with electric vehicles. Power for those vehicles will be provided by electricity generated from renewable energy sources."

Cries of 'Ridiculous' and 'Impossible' rang out from the audience. Vorkan's voice cut through the clamour.

"If the will is there, it is perfectly possible," he said. "It only requires a change of attitude. What you fail to comprehend is that you can have progress without growth. With fewer people - with negative growth - each has a greater share of the whole; each is able to benefit more from the advances you make. You should be aiming at quality for all, not quantity for the few."

Phil found it hard to remain objective about Vorkan's negative growth dictum. He agreed in principle, but he also realised - with some relief - that because of the business he was in and the technology that had been revealed to him, his company would experience unprecedented growth. His and his family's futures would be assured; they would be multi-millionaires. But how could he justify this in the new world order? He was wrestling with these thoughts when he realised a hush had descended on the hall once more. Vorkan had not revealed how he intended to tackle the tenure issue. Phil checked his watch. Fifty-four minutes left. The agony had to be over soon.

"And finally," said Vorkan, "The third component."

Complete and utter silence descended upon the hall.

"You will appreciate that the state of affairs I have described can not continue indefinitely. We have neither the time nor the inclination to carry the burden of monitoring you for longer than the hundred years. We wish to return to undisturbed cryostatic encapsulation, in the sure and certain knowledge that never again will the security of our future home be threatened. The planet needs time to recover from the damage you have done. It must be allowed to revert to its natural state. If we could trust you to behave sensibly once the hundred years was up, and keep your numbers as low as they will be by then, we could let you stay. But we cannot."

He paused, and swept the whole hall with his eyes, then continued.

"By the power vested in me by the Cryon High Council, I now declare that in one hundred years from now, all humans under the age of fifty years - and that number will by then not exceed eighty million - shall be banished from this planet and deported to the planet Hetranova. Those of fifty and over - who we shall ensure are not capable of bearing children - shall remain here to live out what remains of their lives in peace, until no-one remains."

Over the other side of the hall, someone cleared their throat. That was the only sound.

It took some moments to absorb the implications of what Vorkan had just said. Once they sunk in, Phil knew that he was experiencing the most significant moment in the history of man. The realisation that the enormity of Vorkan's pronouncement was being experienced by upwards of a billion people became a palpable sensation. During that silence, it was as if he could feel the weight of the contrition of the world bearing down upon it. He leaned forward, closed his eyes, and covered his face with his hands. Never, had he felt such overpowering sadness.

He put his arm round Jo-Ann's shoulders. To her and her people, places - especially ones with sacred significance - were very important. Banishment would be a bitter blow. But it was the children who mattered the most. They must be given hope. He sat up, dragged a smile across his face, leant across to them and whispered, "Now there's a challenge. Like Australia in the old days, but a whole planet!"

The questions were beginning to form in his mind, and obviously in others' too. Soon, speakers from all parts of the hall sought attention. The Chairman of the People's Republic of China was the first to be acknowledged. He was a diminutive man, with an alabaster face and jet-black hair swept back over his balding head.

"We would like to know, Secretary General," he began, in an almost mechanical tone, "If the Cryons are going to devastate the planet later, in their ultimate act of adjustment, what difference does it make what we do in the meantime?"

The Secretary General, looking altogether like a drowning man clutching at a straw, indicated that Vorkan should reply.

"The difference, Sir," said Vorkan, "Is that our adjustment mechanism requires certain atmospheric and biomass parameters to be within definite limits. Even as we speak, these are in danger of being exceeded. I dread to think what they will be in 200,000 years time, given that China is determined to emulate the USA - a country which has already used more than its fair share of Solara's limited resources."

China's Chairman turned to his advisors for support, but before they could marshal a riposte, the German Chancellor rose to his feet.

"Commander Vorkan," he boomed authoritatively, and with an air of smugness, "If we can survive on Hetranova, why can't you? If you are so advanced, why don't you adjust that planet, and leave us to our own devices. Answer that."

Cheers rang out across the hall. The Chancellor looked around him, nodding in acknowledgement. Eventually, silence returned, and all eyes focused on Vorkan.

"This is not a game, Chancellor!" said Vorkan coldly. "You are not at the EU negotiating table now. You may be used to point-scoring and slick diplomatic manoeuvring there, but in case you are unfamiliar with the concepts, we are dealing here with truth, and facts. Hetranova's supplies of available water - and its potential for water manufacture - are insufficient for our needs. Further, even if there was sufficient water, the cosmological factors applicable to Hetranova are not the same as Solara. Adjusting Hetranova to suit us would be impossible."

Vorkan paused, then addressed the entire hall. The authority in his voice left no room for doubt.

"We are staying. That is that," he said.

The message sank in. Their spirits broken and accepting they had no choice in the matter, the delegates contented themselves with requests for clarification.

"And how," called out a woman with an Italian accent, "Will the over fifties who remain look after themselves when they grow old and there are no younger people to care for them?"

"Android carers," replied Vorkan. "They will have all they need."

The woman shook her head, and crossed herself.

"This place, Hellawhatever," blurted another, "Sounds like a penal colony to me."

"No. Hetranova is a second chance for mankind," retorted Vorkan. "It is a world some sixteen light years away, the fourth of seven planets orbiting within a binary star system in the constellation of Perseus. The central star is stable. Revolving round that at a distance further than Saturn is from the Sun, is a white dwarf star. This star was, until recently in astronomical terms, a red giant. During the course of its collapse, it blew off material into surrounding space that decimated the seven planets. Only now are they recovering. Hetranova has stabilised with Earth-like conditions and simple life forms, and is ripe for colonisation."

"And the transport?" called a voice.

"When we came here, we used eighty interstellar liners, each capable of holding - in encapsulation - one million passengers. These will be your transport. Each ship will depart from, and accommodate the people from, each of the eighty zones I mentioned earlier. The fleet, together with some supply craft, will travel and land under automatic control. Once the passengers - who will not age during the journey - disembark, the ships will return empty to Solara. Machines will be left to assist the migrants to establish themselves, but in essence, that is it. From that moment on, your people will be on their own. We are assuming that by that time, you humans will have learned the basic principles of planet management, and not repeat the disastrous mistakes you have made here."

Another delegate from China rose slowly to his feet.

"I am concerned with the lead-up to this migration," he said. "Are you telling us, Commander, that by 2113 AD, your population reduction programme will have reduced the world's population from its current value of seven billion to a mere eighty million? I would also like to know how many ships my country will be entitled to."

"There will be eighty million people under fifty - the migrants," said Vorkan, "But at the time of their departure, there will be more than 200 million who are fifty and over, to wave them good-bye. As for the number of ships each country has, I emphasise that this depends entirely on that country's ability to grow food - this was what we decided was the fairest method. The figures are: China: six ships; Russia: eight; India: ten; the rest of Asia: another ten; Australasia: three; Africa: eight; Europe: ten; South America: seven; and North America: eighteen."

The Chinese delegate sat down and began an animated conversation with his colleagues. It was well known that the Chinese population was over 1,000 million. Six ships meant six million.

All around him, Phil could see calculators and palm-tops being pressed into service. The Americans, Canadians and Australians kept quiet, but delegates from some of the more densely populated regions, including the Europeans, gasped in horror as it was brought home to them how dramatically their populations would have to be reduced.

But all this activity, all these questions and calculations were, Phil thought, avoiding the most painful and poignant aspect of Vorkan's pronunciations - the fact that humanity was to be banished from the Earth. In 100 years time, the youngest and second youngest generations would leave their parents and grandparents behind, and over the following fifty years, the ageing and ever-dwindling numbers who remained would witness a world without the innocent laughter of children, without the vibrancy of youth, without the driving force of hope, and without the march of man. Attended only by Cryon androids, they would die lonely, clinging to their memories, on an eerily silent planet inhabited only by the ghosts of the past. And eventually, the only people left would be a few centenarians – probably women – stubbornly clinging to life. One by one they too would die, until somewhere, in Russia perhaps, or South America or China, one old woman would be the last human alive on Earth. What would be her last words? Would she call out the name of her son, her God?

What would be her final cry?

Phil was suddenly aware that Vorkan was speaking again. There was only quarter of an hour left before the bombs would detonate.

"...so at long last in the history of your planet, two entire generations will work together with the *real* good of their descendants at heart. They will lay the foundations for a bright future, then make the ultimate sacrifice of standing back for their children's sake, and not participating in that future."

"And finally," said Vorkan, "I have arranged a small demonstration. It may be seen from the east terrace once we switch off the city lights. It seems a pity to waste the power of your bomb, so we will allow it to explode - in space I hasten to add - but capture its energy to form a temporary nucleonic lens, which will... Well, you will see for yourself."

And with that, Vorkan stepped down from the rostrum and made his way towards the exit. As he passed Phil and Beemish's row, he stopped, and spoke to them.

"You will lead your country well, General," he said to Beemish. "The future of mankind now rests with you and your people."

Then he turned to Phil. His amazing eyes seemed to have warmth about them that Phil had never seen before.

"We have learned much from each other, Major, " he said. "That is how it should be. The role you have played in moulding your and our civilisations' histories will never be forgotten. The Great One is surely within you, my friend."

He reached out and touched Phil's shoulder gently with his claw, then turned and walked out of the hall.

***

On the crowded terrace, Phil, Jo-Ann, Nick and Tess were joined by Beemish, who proudly introduced his wife Louise. She was an elegant woman who, despite the drama of the events unfolding before them, displayed an impressive air of serenity.

"I am delighted to meet you, Major Newheart," she said, as she removed her glove and offered her hand. "It isn't often I get the opportunity to shake the hand of someone who has been instrumental in changing my life. You know I hope, that wherever Ted and I are, you and your family will always be welcome as honoured guests in our house."

"We're alive again," said Beemish joyfully, putting an arm round Louise's waist and pulling her to him. "We have a new start. It's as if we were married last week."

Louise blushed. Phil could see she was in heaven.

Phil and Jo-Ann looked at each other searchingly. It was obvious to Phil that they were both thinking the same thing. The drama was over, now came the future. The time had come for Phil to honour his promise.

"What are you folks going to do now?" asked Beemish, providing the perfect cue.

Phil began to glow with pleasure. Of all the possible scenarios he had catered for, the one Vorkan had presented them with was the best.

"Go home, I suppose," he said wistfully, staring eastwards, across the river.

Jo-Ann regarded him with disbelief.

He turned round, and pointed in the opposite direction.

"Laramie," he said firmly, grinning mischievously. He reached for Jo-Ann. "I gather that's the favoured location for our new home."

Relief and delight followed each other across Jo-Ann's face. Tears of joy welled up in her eyes, and she flung her arms round his neck. Nick and Tess were beside themselves with excitement.

"Will you come skiing with me, Dad?" piped Nick, staring at him with spaniel eyes.

"Just you try and stop me!" said Phil, "And that's a promise."

"And I'll be able to go to the university, and keep seeing Michael," said Tess, "Oh Dad, you're wonderful!"

Jo-Ann waited until the children unpeeled themselves from Phil.

"But what about the business?" she said. There was genuine concern in her voice. "I know it means the world to you, Honey. What are you going to do?"

"I think that'll look after itself," he said, confidently. Then, he addressed both Jo-Ann and Beemish. "However, I do have a proposition which each of you should jump at. You, Ted, as President - or at least Governor - and you, Jo, as heroine of the Shoshone."

They looked at him, intrigued.

"Yes?" said Beemish guardedly.

"I don't think it's right that my company retain world patent rights on the LIQUEX vehicle propulsion system," he said. "But before I share these rights, I want the US government to build the first vehicle assembly plant this side of the Atlantic in the Wind River reservation - if the tribes want it that is - and lay a branch line to it from Cheyenne."

Jo-Ann was staggered. Beemish just stood there, blinking.

"The components can come in and the finished cars can go out by rail," he continued. "And I want the first model to be called 'The Eagle'. The tribes will run the plant, and its profit will go to them. I'll be around to advise if required. How's that?"

"Brilliant!" said Jo-Ann.

"Once that assembly plant is up and running, and all the legal stuff is copper-bottom guaranteed for the Indians, then I'll relinquish the world patent rights to the power unit and rechargeable fuel."

"You would do that?" said Beemish. "You could be the world's richest man if you retained them."

Phil drew Jo-Ann and the children close to him.

"I didn't see it, but I've been the world's richest man for years," he said, pecking Jo on the cheek. He glanced at Beemish. "Now, Ted, do we have a deal?"

Beemish looked at him warmly then extended his hand. "You bet we have," he said.

As the two men shook hands, the lights of New York were suddenly and silently blacked out. From their waterfront vantagepoint, it was clear that the whole of Manhattan - and Queens across the river - had been thrown into darkness. For the first time since the power outage of 2003, stars could be seen from the city. Gasps went up from the crowd, and there were some stifled screams as, yet again, the awesome power wielded by the Cryons was eerily demonstrated.

Vorkan's scout craft had returned to the cruiser, which was now accelerating straight upwards. It stopped eventually, miles above them, a small blue strip in the clear, dark sky. Then the bomb transporter took off, carrying its lethal cargo with it. It headed in the direction of the constellation of Perseus, now hanging majestically, high over the East River.

"Isn't that where Hetranova is?" said Nick excitedly.

"Well, he did say Perseus," replied Phil. "That's Perseus up there for sure."

Phil checked his watch. Only seconds to go. The transporter was now only a pinpoint - no brighter than the stars. It stopped, and leaving a tiny yellow dot behind it, accelerated sideways and disappeared. Then, a brilliant flash of white light filled the sky with a dazzling radiance, and brought whoops and gasps from the crowd. As the light faded, where the yellow dot had been was an expanding band of pearly phosphorescence, like a smoke ring. It grew and grew until it was at least 30 degrees in diameter, at which point it seemed to make contact with - or energise in some way - a ring of hundreds of tiny orange lights. Phil realised it was the funnel laid out by *Stallustra* earlier, but from their position, its conical shape looked like a hoop. Then, to the amazement of the onlookers, the stars inside the hoop flickered and disappeared.

"What's happening?" said Jo-Ann.

"He did say he was going to make some sort of lens," Phil replied.

As he spoke, inside the hoop, an image was forming. It was the shape of the gibbous moon, but very much larger. It boiled and shimmered as if seen through the heat from a bonfire, but it was unmistakable in form. It was a planet. It was mainly sandstone in colour, but there were numerous blue lakes ringed and interlinked with green areas, and vast snow-covered plateaux. Lines of what were obviously cloud formations lay across the otherwise sunlit surface.

"It's Hetranova!" Phil called out. "It has to be. Vorkan's created a gigantic telescope!"

The crowd reacted as if they had seen a miracle. Some fell to their knees, mumbling supplications; some turned away, cowering in fear; one or two reached upwards with their arms as if to embrace the extraordinary orb hanging before them. But most people just stared, open mouthed.

The family stood, deep in thought, gazing at the rippling image. There was a strange magnetism about it, like a mist-shrouded island on the horizon of a tropical ocean.

"The future of mankind," said Phil, wistfully.

"I wonder what it'll be like there," said Nick. "I wish I could go, but I've worked it out - it's only people who are born later than fifty years from now who'll be going. It'll be my great-grandchildren who'll be the first to explore it."

"The first, you think?" said Phil, pensively. "Maybe..."

"Honey?" whispered Jo-Ann into his ear suspiciously. "What are you up to?"

"Oh nothing, darling," he said, looking at Hetranova then back to her. He met her gaze, took her hands in his, and smiled innocently.

"I was just wondering..."

One hundred billion billion miles away, the sands of Hetranova lay, waiting.

The End

7. Natural Law and Political Philosophy

In our selections from Section IV of the fourth treatise, Hutcheson comments that treatment of the 'particular laws of nature, or even of civil laws… is the largest field, and the most useful subject of reasoning, which remains upon every scheme of morals'. It is therefore fitting that the anthology turns from Hutcheson's discussion of reason's role in morality to his attempt in the *Short Introduction* to construct a natural-law-based political theory from his moral-sense-based moral psychology. *Prima facie,* this is a rather odd project to undertake. Hutcheson's own moral theory seems to constitute an *attack* on the natural law framework he inherited from his teacher and the man he replaced at Glasgow, Gershom Carmichael, who introduced Hutcheson to the long and complicated natural law tradition through the work of Samuel von Pufendorf (1632–1694). Hutcheson prioritizes concepts like virtue over central natural law concepts like rights and duties, and he frequently criticizes the tendency some members of this tradition have of linking moral motivation with consciousness of divine sanction. It is unsurprising, then, that the relationship between Hutcheson's moral-sense-based moral psychology and his natural law theory has attracted scholarly attention.

Successfully or not, Hutcheson derives a natural law theory from his moral sense theory in roughly the following manner. First, he uses the moral sense to establish the concept of a natural moral right: we all have a natural moral right to do anything of which the moral sense approves or does not disapprove. Then, he (somehow) extends the moral sense's approval of benevolence to the approval of that which promotes the end intended by benevolence, *i.e.* the common good. Thirdly, he uses the first two steps to show that the moral sense grants God alone a natural moral right to rule us because of his supreme willingness and ability to promote the common good. The fourth step combines steps two and three to establish the concept of rational rules for promoting the common good that have the status of natural moral *laws* because they reflect the intentions of the being with a natural moral right to rule us. The rest of the project applies to several areas of human life the now-established normative concepts of natural rights and natural laws. Even though these concepts are ultimately grounded upon the moral sense, they can be used to evaluate human institutions independently of it.

The first group of selections, which is taken from Book II of the *Short Introduction* (Book I provides an overview of Hutcheson's moral psychology), traces out this derivation. The selections also include Hutcheson's version of traditional natural law distinctions between perfect, imperfect, and external rights and between alienable and inalienable rights (some brief passages from the first treatise that provide helpful examples illuminating the first distinction are included here). Additionally, these selections include some brief excerpts from his discussion of the obligation to keep contracts, which forms the very basis of political society. (This discussion occurs within the context of Hutcheson's treatment of several other rights and obligations that emerge from basic forms of human interaction. The list of topics he discusses includes property, the right of recompense for injury—which he eventually uses to ground international laws of war—and rights that arise in cases of extreme necessity. Unfortunately, Hutcheson's treatment of these topics is not included in the anthology.)

The next two groups of selections come from Book III of the text, which deals with the rights and obligations that arise not in natural situations but in ones that are founded upon human institutions. We start with Hutcheson's discussion of the domestic state. The selections include his analyses of husband-wife and master-servant relations (his chapter on parent-child relations is not included). Given that Hutcheson is writing in the first half of the 18th century, his views on the former are striking for their emphasis on equal friendship between husband and wife, and his views on the latter are striking for their emphasis on the rights of the servant.

Next, we turn to Hutcheson's discussion of government. These selections include his discussion of both the actual and just causes of civil authority. He argues that the legitimacy of this authority can be derived from nothing but a contract between the rulers and the people, who enter into it solely for the sake of the common interest. These selections also include excerpts from Hutcheson's argument that a form of government combining elements of aristocracy, democracy, and monarchy is most likely to possess the institutional wisdom, honesty, concord, and efficiency requisite for promoting and protecting the common good. The anthology concludes with complementary selections from Hutcheson's discussion of the right to resist abused state power, from his discussion of the right to maintain one's own judgment, and from his discussion of the contract-based obligation to obey just laws on pain of suffering punishment.

Questions for Further Reflection

In its attempt to prepare beginning readers of Hutcheson to engage with his writing on their own, this editorial introduction mentioned a few specific questions that he left for us to answer. Here are a few broader ones:

1) Is Hutcheson's account of human nature too optimistic? He more or less denies the existence of disinterested malice, but aren't there people who are just mean? And what about psychopaths and sociopaths? How do they fit into Hutcheson's theory?

2) It seems that benevolence cannot possibly be the only virtue. We also seem to place intrinsic non-benevolence-derived value on traits like prudence and self-control. Is Hutcheson's point, then, that this value is different in kind from that which what we assign to benevolence? If so, wherein lies the difference?

3) If the moral sense grants authority to calm universal benevolence, then it seems that we are justified in valuing our local affective ties, such as those to family and friends, only insofar as they are consistent with the ends of universal benevolence. But is this view consistent with our intuitions regarding the special obligations we might have to those with whom we are especially close?

4) The way in which Hutcheson occasionally runs together the moral sense with a basic concern for others suggests that we might be able to explain moral judgment solely in terms of the latter. If we make this move, then we might be able to preserve Hutcheson's basic insights about human nature without acknowledging a special, naturally authoritative

moral faculty. A view like this one would likely be attractive to those looking to explain morality in evolutionary terms. What kind of case could Hutcheson make on behalf of maintaining his teleological, moral-sense-based view?

5) To what extent does the attention Hutcheson pays in his natural law writings to the common good amount to a move towards utilitarianism? Maybe we do or should morally value benevolence only insofar as it promotes the common good, rather than vice-versa. How would he respond to this suggestion?

6) Modern moral philosophers like Christine Korsgaard echo Burnett's dissatisfaction with Hutcheson's view that we make the moral judgments we do because it is, just as a matter of brute fact, in our natures to do so. But is any other explanation available?

Bibliography

Primary Sources

Facsimiles of 18th-century editions are easily available online. As of the printing of this book, critical editions of almost all of Hutcheson's major works are available from the Liberty Press. An edition of the lone exception, *A System of Moral Philosophy*, is scheduled for release in November of 2014.

Secondary Sources

The editorial introductions to the Liberty Fund editions of Hutcheson's works are excellent (they were of great assistance in preparing this text). Here is a brief list of other helpful secondary sources. Since it is by no means exhaustive, consider it a place to start.

Bishop, John D. 'Moral Motivation and the Development of Francis Hutcheson's Philosophy.' *Journal of the History of Ideas* 57.2 (1996): 277–95.

Gill, Michael. *The British Moralists on Human Nature and the Birth of Secular Ethics*. Cambridge: Cambridge UP, 2006.

Haakonssen, Knud. 'Natural law and Moral Realism: The Scottish Synthesis.' *Studies in the Philosophy of the Scottish Enlightenment*. Ed. M.A. Stewart. Oxford: Oxford UP, 1990, 61–86.

—. *Natural Law and Moral Philosophy: From Grotius to the Scottish Enlightenment*. New York: Cambridge UP, 1996.

Hope, Vincent. *Virtue by Consensus: The Moral Philosophy of Hutcheson, Hume, and Adam Smith*. New York: Oxford UP, 1989.

Kivy, Peter. *The Seventh Sense: Francis Hutcheson and Eighteenth-Century Aesthetics*. Oxford: Oxford UP, 2003.

Mautner, Thomas. *Francis Hutcheson on Human Nature*: Reflections on Our Common Systems of Morality *and* On the Social Nature of Man. Cambridge: Cambridge UP, 1993.

Moore, James. 'The Two Systems of Francis Hutcheson: On the Origins of the Scottish Enlightenment.' *Studies in the Philosophy of the Scottish Enlightenment*. Ed. M.A. Stewart. Oxford: Oxford UP, 1990, 37–60.

Norton, David Fate. 'Hutcheson's Moral Realism.' *Journal of the History of Philosophy 23.3* (1985): 397–418.

Scott, W.R. *Francis Hutcheson, His Life, Teaching and Position in the History and Philosophy*. New York: Kelley, 1966.

Turco, Luigi. 'Moral Sense and the Foundations of Morals.' *The Cambridge Companion to the Scottish Enlightenment*. Ed. Alexander Broadie. New York: Cambridge UP, 136–56.

Winkler, Kenneth. 'Hutcheson's Alleged Realism.' *Journal of the History of Philosophy 23.2* (1985): 179–94.

Editor's Notes

Since all selections in the anthology are from the latest editions published in Hutcheson's lifetime, they present what he would have taken to be the most mature expressions of his thought. Many outdated features of the texts have been silently altered, including the use of '*f*' for 's' sounds, the (rather random) employment of capitalization and italics, and some old-fashioned spellings. Some minor inconsistencies have also been silently rectified (e.g. an in-text shift from '*Illustrations on the Moral Sense*' to '*Illustrations upon the Moral Sense*'). With some exceptions, the anthology maintains Hutcheson's punctuation. The guiding aim behind all these decisions was to minimize unnecessary distractions for the modern reader in a way that also avoids altering the rhythm and content of Hutcheson's prose.

Omitted sections of text (including omitted notes) are indicated by an ellipsis. Editorial changes and notes are indicated by square brackets. Many of these changes and notes involve modifications of Hutcheson's own references. Within these references, 'T1', 'T2', 'T3', and 'T4' respectively refer to

Of Beauty, Order, Harmony, Design; An Inquiry Concerning Moral Good and Evil; An Essay on the Nature and Conduct of the Passions and Affections; and *Illustrations on the Moral Sense.* Where applicable, these references will use the following shorthand decimal method: Treatise.Section.Article.Paragraph (Hutcheson sometimes refers to but rarely numbers the lattermost category). Thus, 'T2.II.iii.1' indicates that the passage to which Hutcheson refers is from the first paragraph of the third article of the second section of the second treatise. The mechanics of references to texts other than these four Dublin treatises should be evident from context.

Most of the location details of Hutcheson's references to other authors have been maintained, with the exception of those made to exact page numbers in the editions with which he worked. Some of Hutcheson's scattered Greek and Latin quotations of classical authors have been omitted.

The anthology consists of seven parts, each dealing with a distinct topic indicated by its title. Thus, the selections that make up these parts are thematically and often logically linked, in that one selection often deals with a question left open by the previous one; this is especially the case when the anthology bounces back-and-forth between texts.

One

The Sense of Beauty

From *Of Beauty, Order, Harmony, Design*

Sect. I.
Concerning some powers of perception, distinct from what is generally understood by sensation

To make the following observations understood, it may be necessary to premise some definitions, and observations, either universally acknowledged, or sufficiently proved by many writers both ancient and modern, concerning our perceptions called sensations, and the actions of the mind consequent upon them.

[I.] Those ideas which are raised in the mind upon the presence of external objects, and their acting upon our bodies, are called sensations. We find that the mind in such cases is passive, and has not power directly to prevent the perception or idea, or to vary it as its reception, as long as we continue our bodies in a state fit to be acted upon by the external object.

II. When two perceptions are entirely different from each other, or agree in nothing but the general idea of sensation, we call the powers of receiving those different perceptions, different senses. Thus seeing and hearing denote the different powers of receiving the ideas of colours and sounds. And although colours have great differences among themselves, as also have sounds; yet there is a greater agreement among the most opposite colours than between any colour and a sound: hence we call all colours perceptions of the same sense. All the several senses seem to have their distinct organs, except feeling, which is in some degree diffused over the whole body.

III. The mind has a power of compounding ideas, which were received separately; of comparing objects by means of the ideas, and of observing their relations and proportions; of enlarging and diminishing its ideas at pleasure, or in any certain ratio, or degree; and of considering separately each of the simple ideas, which might perhaps have been impressed jointly in the sensation. This last operation we commonly call abstraction.

IV. The ideas of substances are compounded of the various simple ideas jointly impressed, when they presented themselves to our senses. We define substances only by enumerating these sensible ideas. And such definitions may raise an idea clear enough of the substances in the mind of one who never immediately perceived the substance; provided he has separately received by his senses all the simple ideas which are in the composition of the complex one of the substance defined: but if there be any simple ideas which he has not received, or if he wants any of the senses necessary for the perception of them, no definition can raise any simple idea which has not been before perceived by the senses.

V. Hence it follows, 'that when instruction, education, or prejudice of any kind, raise any desire or aversion toward an object, this desire or aversion must be founded upon an opinion of some perfection, or of some deficiency in those qualities, for perception of which we have the proper senses.' Thus, if beauty be desired by one who has not the sense of sight, the desire must be must be raised by some apprehended regularity of figure, sweetness of voice, smoothness, or softness, or some other quality perceivable by the other senses, without relation to the ideas of colour.

VI. Many of our sensitive perceptions are pleasant and many painful, immediately, and that without any knowledge of the cause of this pleasure or pain, or how the objects excite it, or are the occasions of it; or without seeing to what farther advantage or detriment the use of such objects might tend: nor would the most accurate knowledge of these things vary either the pleasure or pain of the perception, however it might give a rational pleasure distinct from the sensible; or might raise a distinct joy, from a prospect of farther advantage in the object, or aversion, from an apprehension of evil.

VII. The simple ideas raised in different persons by the same object, are probably some way different, when they disagree in their approbation or dislike; and in the same person, when his fancy at one time differs from what it was at another. This will appear from reflecting on those objects, to which we have now an aversion, though they were, formerly agreeable: and we shall generally find that there is some accidental conjunction of a disagreeable idea, which always recurs with the object; as in those wines to which men acquire an aversion, after they have taken them in an emetic preparation, we are conscious that the idea is altered from what it was when that wine was agreeable, by the conjunction of the ideas of loathing and sickness of stomach. The like change of idea may be insensibly made by the change of our bodies as we advance in years, or when we are accustomed to any object, which may occasion an indifference toward meats we were fond of in our childhood; and may make some objects cease to raise the disagreeable ideas, which they excited upon our first use of them. Many of our simple perceptions are disagreeable only through the too great intenseness of the quality: thus moderate light is agreeable, very strong light may be painful; moderate bitter may be pleasant, a higher degree may be offensive. A change in our organs will necessarily occasion a change in the intenseness of the perception at least; nay, sometimes will occasion a quite contrary perception: thus a warm hand shall feel that water cold, which a cold hand shall feel warm.

We shall not find it perhaps so easy to account for the diversity of fancy about more complex ideas of objects, in which we regard many ideas of different senses at once; as some perceptions of those called primary qualities, and some secondary, as explained by Mr. Locke:[1] for instance, in the different fancies about architecture, gardening, dress. Of the two former we shall offer something in sect. VI. As to dress, we may generally account for the diversity of fancies from a like conjunction of ideas: thus, if either from anything in

---

1 [John Locke (1632–1704), philosopher. For an explanation of his distinction between primary and secondary qualities, see page 8 of the editor's introduction and T1.I.xvi, this section.]

nature, or from the opinion of our country or acquaintance, the fancying of glaring colours be looked upon as an evidence of levity, or of any other evil quality of mind; or if any colour or fashion be commonly used by rustic, or by men of any disagreeable profession, employment, or temper; these additional ideas may recur constantly with that of the colour or fashion, and cause a constant dislike to them in those who join the additional ideas, although the colour or form be no way disagreeable of themselves, and actually do please others who join no such ideas to them. But there does not seem to be any ground to believe such a diversity in human minds, as that the same simple idea or perception should give pleasure to one and pain to another, or to the same person at different times; not to say that it seems a contradiction, that the same simple idea should do so.

VIII. The only pleasure of sense, which many philosophers seem to consider, is that which accompanies the simple ideas of sensation: but there are far greater pleasures in those complex ideas of objects, which obtain the names of beautiful, regular, harmonious. Thus everyone acknowledges he is more delighted with a fine face, a just picture, than with the view of any one colour, were it as strong and lively as possible; and more pleased with a prospect of the sun arising among settled clouds, and colouring their edges, with a starry hemisphere, a fine landscape, a regular building, than with a clear blue sky, a smooth sea, or a large open plain, not diversified by woods, hills, waters, buildings: and yet even these latter appearances are not quite simple. So in music, the pleasure of fine composition is incomparably greater than that of any one note, how sweet, full, or swelling soever.

IX. Let it be observed, that in the following papers, the word beauty is taken for the idea raised in us, and a sense of beauty for our power of receiving this idea. Harmony also denotes our pleasant ideas arising from composition of sounds, and a good ear (as it is generally taken) a power of perceiving this pleasure. In the following sections, an attempt is made to discover 'what is the immediate occasion of these pleasant ideas, or what real quality in the objects ordinarily excites them.'

X. It is of no consequence whether we call these ideas of beauty and harmony, perceptions of the external senses of seeing and hearing, or not. I should rather choose to call our power of perceiving these ideas, an internal sense, were it only for the convenience of distinguishing them from other sensations of seeing and hearing, which men may have without perception of beauty and harmony. It is plain from experience, that many men have, in the common meaning, the senses of seeing and hearing perfect enough; they perceive all the simple ideas separately, and have their pleasures; they distinguish them from each other, such as one colour from another, either quite different, or the stronger or fainter of the same colour; when they are placed beside each other, although they may often confound their names when they occur apart from each other, as some do the names of green and blue; they can tell in separate notes the higher, lower, sharper or flatter, when separately sounded; in figures they discern the length, breadth, wideness of each line, surface, angle; and may be as capable of hearing and seeing at great distances as any men whatsoever: and yet perhaps they shall find no pleasure in musical compositions, in painting, architecture, natural landscape; or but a very weak one in comparison of what others enjoy from the same objects. This greater capacity of receiving such pleasant ideas we commonly call a fine genius or taste: in music we seem universally to acknowledge something like a distinct sense from the external one of hearing, and call it a good ear; and the like distinction we should probably acknowledge in other objects, had we also got distinct names to denote these powers of perception by.

XI. We generally imagine the brute animals endowed with the same sort of powers of perception as our external senses, and having sometimes greater acuteness in them: but we conceive few or none of them with any of these sublimer powers of perception here called internal senses; or at least if some of them have them, it is in a degree much inferior to ours.

There will appear another reason perhaps hereafter, for calling this power of perceiving the ideas of beauty, an internal sense, from this, that in some other affairs, where our external senses are not much concerned, we discern a sort of beauty, very like, in many respects, to that observed in sensible objects, and accompanied with like pleasure: such is that beauty perceived in theorems, or universal truths, in general causes, and in some extensive principles of action.

XII. Let one consider, first, that 'tis probable a being may have the full power of external sensation, which we enjoy, so as to perceive each colour, line, surface, as we do; yet, without the power of comparing, or of discerning the similitudes or proportions; again, it might discern these also, and yet have no pleasure or delight accompanying these perceptions. The bare idea of the form is something separable from pleasure, as may appear from the different tastes of men about the beauty of forms, where we don't imagine that they differ in any ideas, either of the primary or secondary qualities. Similitude, proportion, analogy, or equality of proportion, are objects of the understanding, and must be actually known before we know the natural causes of our pleasure. But pleasure perhaps is not necessarily connected with the perception of them: and may be felt where the proportion is not known or attended to: and may not be felt where the proportion is observed. Since then there are such different powers of perception, where what are commonly called the external senses are the same; since the most accurate knowledge of what the external senses discover, may often not give the pleasure of beauty or harmony, which yet one of a good taste will enjoy at once without much knowledge; we may justly use another name for these higher and more delightful perceptions of beauty and harmony, and call the power of receiving such impressions, an internal sense: the difference of the perceptions seems sufficient to vindicate the use of a different name, especially when we are told in what meaning the word is applied.

This superior power of perception is called a sense, because of its affinity to the other senses in this, that the pleasure is different from any knowledge of principles, proportions, causes, or of the usefulness of the object; we are struck at the first with the beauty: nor does the most accurate knowledge increase this pleasure of beauty, however it may superadd a distinct rational pleasure from prospects of advantage, or may bring along that peculiar kind of pleasure, which attends the increase of knowledge [see T1.I.vi].

XIII. And farther, the ideas of beauty and harmony, like other sensible ideas, are necessarily pleasant to us, as well as immediately so; neither can any resolution of our own, nor any prospect of advantage or disadvantage, vary the beauty or deformity of an object: for as in the external sensations, no view of interest will make an object grateful, nor view of detriment, distinct from immediate pain in the perception, make it disagreeable to the sense; so propose the whole world as a reward, or threaten the greatest evil, to make us approve a deformed object, or disapprove a beautiful one; dissimulation may be procured by rewards or threatenings, or we may in external conduct abstain from any pursuit of the beautiful, and pursue the deformed; but our sentiments of the forms, and our perceptions, would continue invariably the same.

XIV. Hence it plainly appears, 'that some objects are immediately the occasions of this pleasure of beauty, and that we have senses fitted for perceiving it; and that it is distinct from that joy which arises upon prospect of advantage.' Nay, do not we often see convenience and use neglected to obtain beauty, without any other prospect of advantage in the beautiful form, than the suggesting the pleasant ideas of beauty? Now this shows us, that however we may pursue beautiful objects from self-love, with a view to obtain the pleasures of beauty, as in architecture, gardening, and many other affairs; yet there must be a sense of beauty, antecedent to prospects even of this advantage, without which sense these objects would not be thus advantageous, nor excite in us this pleasure which constitutes them advantageous. Our sense of beauty from objects; by which they are constituted good to us, is very distinct from our desire of them when they are thus constituted: our desire of beauty may be counterbalanced by rewards or threatenings, but never our sense of it; even as fear of death may make us desire a bitter potion, or neglect those meats which the sense of taste would recommend as pleasant; but cannot make that potion agreeable to the sense, or meat disagreeable to it, which was not so antecedently to this prospect. The same holds true of the sense of beauty and harmony; that the pursuit of such objects is frequently neglected, from prospects of advantage, aversion to labour, or any other motive of interest, does not prove that we have no sense of beauty, but only that our desire of it may be counterbalanced by a stronger desire.

XV. Had we no such sense of beauty and harmony, houses, gardens, dress, equipage, might have been recommended to us as convenient, fruitful, warm, easy; but never as beautiful: and yet nothing is more certain, than that all these objects are recommended under quite different views on many occasions: 'tis true, what chiefly pleases in the countenance, are the indications of moral dispositions; and yet were we by the longest acquaintance fully convinced of the best moral dispositions in any person, with that countenance we now think deformed, this would never hinder our immediate dislike of the form, or our liking other forms more: and custom, education, or example, could never give us perceptions distinct from those of the senses which we had the use of before, or recommend objects under another conception than grateful to them [see T1.I.v]. But of the influence of custom, education, example, upon the sense of beauty, we shall treat below [see T1.VII].

XVI. Beauty, in corporeal forms, is either original or comparative; or, if any like the terms better, absolute, or relative: only let it be observed, that by absolute or original beauty, is not understood any quality supposed to be in the object, which should of itself be beautiful, without relation to any mind which perceives it: for beauty, like other names of sensible ideas, properly denotes the perception of some mind; so cold, hot, sweet, bitter, denote the sensations in our minds, to which perhaps there is no resemblance in the objects, which excite these ideas in us, however we generally imagine otherwise. The ideas of beauty and harmony being excited upon our perception of some primary quality, and having relation to figure and time, may indeed have a nearer resemblance to objects, than these sensations, which seem not so much any pictures of objects, as modifications of the perceiving mind; and yet were there no mind with a sense of beauty to contemplate objects, I see not how they could be called beautiful. We therefore by... absolute beauty understand only that beauty which we perceive in objects without comparison to anything external, of which the object is supposed an imitation, or picture; such as that beauty perceived from the works of nature, artificial forms, figures. Comparative or relative beauty is that which we perceive in objects, commonly considered as imitations or resemblances of something else. These two kinds of beauty employ the three following sections [T1.IV not included here].

Sect. II.
Of original or absolute beauty

I. Since it is certain that we have ideas of beauty and harmony, let us examine what quality in objects excites these ideas, or is the occasion of them. And let it be here observed, that our inquiry is only about the qualities which are beautiful to men; or about the foundation of their sense of beauty: for, as was above hinted, beauty has always relation to the sense of some mind; and when we afterwards show how generally the objects which occur to us are beautiful, we mean, that such objects are agreeable to the sense of men: for there are many objects which seem no way beautiful to men, and yet other animals seem delighted with them; they may have senses otherwise constituted than those of men, and may have the ideas of beauty excited by objects of a quite different form. We see animals fitted for every place; and what to men appears rude and shapeless, or loathsome, may be to them a paradise.

II. That we may more distinctly discover the general foundation or occasion of the ideas of beauty among men, it will be necessary to consider it first in its simpler kinds, such as occurs to us in regular figures; and we may perhaps find that the same foundation extends to all the more complex species of it.

III. The figures which excite in us the ideas of beauty, seem to be those in which there is uniformity amidst variety. There are many conceptions of objects which are agreeable upon other accounts, such as grandeur, novelty, sanctity, and some others, which shall be mentioned hereafter [see T1.VI.xi–xiii]. But what we call beautiful in objects, to speak in the mathematical style, seems to be in a compound ratio of uniformity and variety so that where the uniformity of bodies is equal, the beauty is as the variety; and where the variety is equal, the beauty is as the uniformity. This will be plain from examples.

First, the variety increases the beauty in equal uniformity. The beauty of an equilateral triangle is less than that of the square; which is less than that of a pentagon; and this again is surpassed by the hexagon. When indeed the number of sides is much increased, the proportion of them to the radius, or diameter of the figure, or of the circle, to which regular polygons have an obvious relation, is so much lost to our observation, that the beauty does not always increase with the number of sides; and the want of parallelism in the sides of heptagons, and other figures of odd numbers, may also diminish their beauty. So in solids, the eicosiedron surpasses the dodecaedron, and this the octaedron, which is still more beautiful than the cube; and this again surpasses the regular pyramid: the obvious ground of this, is greater variety with equal uniformity.

The greater uniformity increases the beauty amidst equal variety, in these instances: an equilateral triangle, or even an isosceles, surpasses the scalenum: a square surpasses the rhombus or lozenge, and this again the rhomboides, which is still more beautiful than the trapezium, or any figure with irregular curve[d] sides. So the regular solids surpass all other solids of equal number of plain surfaces: and the same is observable not only in the five perfectly regular solids, but in all those which have any considerable uniformity, as cylinders, prisms, pyramids, obelisks; which please every eye more than any rude figures, where there is no unity or resemblance among the parts...

IV. These observations would probably hold true for the most part, and might be confirmed by the judgment of children in the simpler figures, where the variety is not too great for their comprehension. And however uncertain some of the particular aforesaid instances may seem, yet this is perpetually to be observed, that children are fond of all regular figures in their little diversions, although they be no more convenient, or useful for them, than the figures of our common pebbles: we see how early they discover a taste or sense of beauty, in desiring to see buildings, regular gardens, or even representations of them in pictures of any kind.

V. The same foundation we have for our sense of beauty, in the works of nature. In every part of the world which we call beautiful, there is a surprising uniformity amidst an almost infinite variety. Many parts of the universe seem not at all designed for the use of man; nay, it is but a very small spot with which we have any acquaintance. The figures and motions of the great bodies are not obvious to our senses, but found out by reasoning and reflection, upon many long observations: and yet as far as we can by sense discover, or by reasoning enlarge our knowledge, and extend our imagination, we generally find their structure, order, and motion, agreeable to our sense of beauty. Every particular object in nature does not indeed appear beautiful to us; but there is a great profusion of beauty over most of the objects which occur either to our senses, or reasonings upon observation: for, not to mention the apparent situation of the heavenly bodies in the circumference of a great sphere, which is wholly occasioned by the imperfection of our sight in discerning distances; the forms of all the great bodies in the universe are nearly spherical; the orbits of their revolutions generally elliptic, and without great eccentricity, in those which continually occur to our observation: now these are figures of great uniformity, and therefore pleasing to us.

Further, to pass by the less obvious uniformity in the proportion of their quantities of matter, distances, times, of revolving, to each other; what can exhibit a greater instance of uniformity, amidst variety, than the constant tenour of revolutions in nearly equal times, in each planet, around its axis, and the central fire or sun, through all the ages of which we have any records, and in nearly the same orbit? Thus after certain periods, all the same appearances are again renewed; the alternate successions of light and shade, or day and night, constantly pursuing each other around each planet, with an agreeable and regular diversity in the times they possess the several hemispheres, in the summer, harvest, winter, and spring; and the various phases, aspects, and situations, of the planets to each other, their conjunctions and oppositions, in which they suddenly darken each other with their conic shades in eclipses, are repeated to us at their fixed periods with invariable constancy: these are the beauties which charm the astronomer, and make his tedious calculations pleasant. 'Where the excitement pleasantly beguiles the hard toil.'[2]

VI. Again, as to the dry part of the surface of our globe, a great part of which is covered with a very pleasant inoffensive colour, how beautifully is it diversified with various degrees of light and shade, according to the different situations of the parts of its surface, in mountains, valleys, hills, and open plains, which are variously inclined toward the great luminary!

VII. If we descend to the minuter works of nature, what great uniformity among all the species of plants and vegetables in the manner of their growth and propagation! How near the resemblance among all the plants of the same species, whose numbers surpass our imagination! And this uniformity is not only observable in the form in gross (nay, in this it is not so very exact in all instances); but in the structure of their minutest parts, which no eye unassisted with glasses can discern. In the almost infinite multitude of leaves, fruit, seed, flowers of any one species, we often see a very great uniformity in the structure and situation of the smallest fibres. This is the beauty which charms an ingenious botanist. Nay, what great uniformity and regularity of figure is found in each particular plant, leaf, or flower! In all trees and most of the smaller plants, the stalks or trunks are either cylinders nearly, or regular prisms; branches similar to their several trunks, arising at nearly regular distances, when no accidents retard their natural growth: in one species the branches arise in pairs on the opposite sides; the perpendicular plain of direction of the immediately superior pair, interfering the plain of direction of the inferior, nearly at right angles: in another species, the branches spring singly, and alternately, all around in nearly equal distances: and the branches in other species sprout all in knots around the trunk, one for each year. And in each species, all the branches in the first shoots preserve the same angles with their trunk; and they

---

2 [From Horace (65–27 B.C.E.), Roman poet. Book II of *Satires,* Satire II, line 12. Translation from H.R. Fairclough's *Satires, Epistles, and Ars Poetica* (Cambridge: Harvard UP, 1970).]

again sprout out into smaller branches exactly after the manner of their trunks. Nor ought we to pass over that great unity of colours which we often see in all the flowers of the same plant or tree, and often of a whole species; and their exact agreement in many shaded transitions into opposite colours, in which all the flowers of the same plant generally agree, nay, often all the flowers of a species.

VIII. Again, as to the beauty of animals, either in their inward structure, which we come to the knowledge of by experiment and long observation, or their outward form, we shall find surprising uniformity among all the species which are known to us, in the structure of those parts, upon which life depends more immediately. And how amazing is the unity of mechanism, when we shall find an almost infinite diversity of motions, all their actions in walking, running, flying, swimming; their serious efforts for self-preservation, all their freakish contortions when they are gay and sportful, in all their various limbs, performed by one simple contrivance of a contracting muscle, applied with inconceivable diversities to answer all these ends! Various engines might have obtained the same ends; but then there had been less uniformity, and the beauty of our animal systems, and of particular animals, had been much less, when this surprising unity of mechanism had been removed from them.

IX. Among animals of the same species, the unity is very obvious, and this resemblance is the very ground of our ranking them in such classes or species, notwithstanding the great diversities in bulk, colour, shape, which are observed even in those called of the same species. And then in each individual, how universal is that beauty which arises from the exact resemblance of all the external double members to each other, which seems the universal intention of nature, when no accident prevents it! We see the want of this resemblance never fails to pass for an imperfection, and want of beauty, though no other inconvenience ensues; as when the eyes are not exactly like, or one arm or leg is a little shorter or smaller than its fellow.

As to that more powerful beauty in countenances, airs, gestures, motion, we shall show in the second treatise, that it arises from some imagined indication of morally good dispositions of mind [see T2.VI.iii, not included here]. In motion there is also a natural beauty, when at fixed periods like gestures and steps are regularly repeated, suiting the time and air of music, which is observed in regular dancing.

X. There is a farther beauty in animals, arising from a certain proportion of the various parts to each other, which still pleases the sense of spectators, though they cannot calculate it with the accuracy of a statuary. The statuary knows what proportion of each part of the face to the whole face is most agreeable, and can tell us the same of the proportion of the face to the body, or any parts of it; and between the diameters and lengths of each limb: when this proportion of the head to the body is remarkably altered, we shall have a giant or a dwarf. And hence it is, that either the one or the other may be represented to us even in miniature, without relation to any external object, by observing how the body surpasses the proportion it should have to the head in giants, and falls below it in dwarfs. There is a farther beauty arising from that figure, which is a natural indication of strength; but this may be passed over, because probably it may be alleged, that our approbation of this shape flows from an opinion of advantage, and not from the form itself.

The beauty arising from mechanism, apparently adapted to the necessities and advantages of any animal; which pleases us, even though there be no advantage to ourselves ensuing from it; will be considered under the head of relative beauty, or design [see T1.IV.vii, not included here]...

XIII. Under original beauty we may include harmony, or beauty of sound, if that expression can be allowed, because harmony is not usually conceived as an imitation of anything else. Harmony often raises pleasure in those who know not what is the occasion of it: and yet the foundation of this pleasure is known to be a sort of uniformity. When the several vibrations of one note regularly coincide with the vibrations of another, they make an agreeable composition; and such notes are called concords. Thus the vibrations of any one note coincide in time with two vibrations of its octave, and two vibrations of any note coincide with three of its fifth; and so on in the rest of the concords. Now no composition can be harmonious, in which the notes are not, for the most part, disposed according to these natural proportions. Besides which, a due regard must be had to the key, which governs the whole, and to the time and humour, in which the composition is begun: a frequent and inartificial change of any of which will produce the greatest, and most unnatural discord. This will appear, by observing the dissonance which would arise from tacking parts of different tunes together as one, although both were separately agreeable. A like uniformity is also observable among the bases, tenors, trebles of the same tune.

There is indeed observable, in the best compositions, a mysterious effect of discords: they often give as great pleasure as continued harmony; whether by refreshing the ear with variety, or by awakening the attention, and enlivening the relish for the succeeding harmony of concords, as shades enliven and beautify pictures, or by some other means not yet known: certain it is, however, that they have their place, and some good effect in our best compositions. Some other powers of music may be considered hereafter [see T1.VI.xii].

XIV. But in all these instances of… beauty let it be observed, that the pleasure is communicated to those who never reflected on this general foundation; and that all here alleged is this, 'that the pleasant sensation arises only from objects, in which there is uniformity amidst variety': we may have the sensation without knowing what is the occasion of it; as a man's taste may suggest ideas of sweets, acids, bitters, though he be ignorant of the forms of the small bodies, or their motions, which excite these perceptions in him.

Sect. III.
Of the beauty of theorems

I. The beauty of theorems, or universal truths demonstrated, deserves a distinct consideration, being of a nature pretty different from the former kinds of beauty, and yet there is none in which we shall see such an amazing variety with uniformity: and hence arises a very great pleasure distinct from prospects of any farther advantage.

II. For in one theorem, we may find included, with the most exact agreement, an infinite multitude of particular truths nay, often a multitude of infinites: so that although the necessity of forming abstract ideas, and universal theorems, arises perhaps from the limitation of our minds, which cannot admit an infinite multitude of singular ideas or judgments at once, yet this power gives us an evidence of the largeness of the human capacity above our imagination. Thus, for instance, the 47th proposition of the first book of Euclid's[3] elements contains an infinite multitude of truths, concerning the infinite possible sizes of right-angled triangles, as you make the area greater or less; and in each of these sizes you may find an infinite multitude of dissimilar triangles, as you vary the proportion of the base to the perpendicular; all which infinites agree in the general theorem. In algebraic, and fluxional calculations, we shall find a like variety of particular truths included in general theorems; not only in general equations applicable to all kinds of quantity, but in more particular investigations of areas and tangents: in which one manner of operation shall discover theorems applicable to many orders or species of curves, to the infinite sizes of each species, and to the infinite points of the innumerable individuals of each size.

III. That we may the better discern this agreement, or unity of an infinity of objects, in the general theorem, to be the foundation of the beauty or pleasure attending their discovery, let us compare our satisfaction in such discoveries, with the uneasy state of mind when we can only measure lines, or surfaces, by a scale, or are making experiments which we can reduce to no general canon, but are only heaping up a multitude of particular incoherent observations. Now each of these trials discovers a new truth, but with no pleasure or beauty, notwithstanding the variety, till we can discover some sort of unity, or reduce them to some general canon...

---

3 [Euclid, ancient Greek mathematician who lived around 300 B.C.E.]

Sect. V.
Concerning our reasonings about design and wisdom in the cause from the beauty or regularity of effects

I. There seems to be no necessary connection of our pleasing ideas of beauty with the uniformity or regularity of the objects, from the nature of things, antecedent to some constitution of the author of our nature, which has made such forms pleasant to us. Other minds may be so framed as to receive no pleasure from uniformity; and we actually find, that the same regular forms seem not equally to please all the animals known to us, as shall probably appear hereafter. Therefore let us make what is the most unfavourable supposition to the present argument, *viz.* that the constitution of our sense so as to approve uniformity, is merely arbitrary in the author of our nature; and that there are an infinity of tastes or relishes of beauty possible; so that it would be impossible to throw together fifty or a hundred pebbles, which should not make an agreeable habitation for some animal or other, and appear beautiful to it. And then it is plain, that from the perception of beauty in any one effect, we should have no reason to conclude design in the cause: for a sense might be so constituted as to be pleased with such irregularity as may be the effect of an undirected force... But then, as there are an infinity of forms possible into which any system may be reduced, an infinity of places in which animals may be situated, and an infinity of relishes or senses in these animals is supposed possible; that in the immense spaces any one animal should by chance be placed in a system agreeable to its taste, must be improbable as infinite to one at least: and much more unreasonable is it to expect from chance, that a multitude of animals agreeing in their sense of beauty should obtain agreeable places.

II. There is also the same probability, that in any one system of matter an undirected force will produce a regular form, as any one given irregular one, of the same degree of complication: but still the irregular forms into which any system may be ranged, surpass in multitude the regular, as infinite does unity; for what holds in one small system, will hold in thousand, a million, a universe, with more advantage, *viz.* that the irregular forms possible infinitely surpass the regular. For instance, the area of an inch square is capable of an infinity of regular forms, the equilateral triangle, the square, the pentagon, hexagon, heptagon, &c. But for each one regular form, there are an infinity of irregular, as an infinity of scalena for the one equilateral triangle, an infinity of trapezia for the one square, of irregular pentagons for the one regular, and so on: and therefore supposing any one system agitated by undesigning force, it is infinitely more probable that it will resolve itself into an irregular form, than a regular. Thus, that a system of six parts upon agitation shall not obtain the form of a regular hexagon, is at least infinite to unity; and the more complex we make the system, the greater is the hazard, from a very obvious reason.

We see this confirmed by our constant experience, that regularity never arises from any undesigned force of ours; and from this we conclude, that wherever there is any regularity in the disposition of a system capable of many other dispositions, there must have been design in the cause and the force of this evidence increases, according to the multiplicity of parts employed.

But this conclusion is too rash, unless some farther proof be introduced; and what leads us into it is this. Men, who have a sense of beauty in regularity, are led generally in all their arrangements of bodies to study some kind of regularity, and seldom ever design irregularity: hence we judge the same of other beings too, *viz.* that they study regularity, and presume upon intention in the cause wherever we see it, making irregularity always a presumption of want of design: whereas if other agents have different senses of beauty, or if they have no sense of it at all, irregularity may as well be designed as regularity. And then let it be observed, that in this case there is just the same reason to conclude design in the cause from any one irregular effect, as from a regular one: for since there are an infinity of other forms possible as well as this irregular one produced; and since to such a being... void of a sense of beauty, all forms are as to its own relish indifferent, and all agitated matter meeting must, make some form or other, and all forms, upon supposition that the force is applyed by an agent void of a sense of beauty, would equally prove design; it is plain that no one form proves it more than another, or can prove it at all; except from a general metaphysical consideration, that there is no proper agent without design and intention, and that every effect flows from the intention of some cause...

VI. And let it be here observed, that there are many compositions of bodies which the smallest degree of design could easily effect, which yet we would in vain expect from all the powers of chance or undesigned force, after an infinity of re-encounters; even supposing a dissolution of every form except the regular one, that the parts might be prepared for a new agitation. Thus supposing we could expect one equilateral prism of any given dimensions should be formed from undirected force, in an infinity of matter some way determined to resolve itself into bodies of a given solid content (which is all we could expect, since it is infinite to one after the solid content is obtained, that the body shall not be prismatical; and allowing it prismatical, it is infinite to one that it shall not be equilateral), and again, supposing another infinity of matter determined to resolve itself into tubes, of orifices exactly equal to the bases of the former prisms, it is again at least as the second power of finite to unity, that not one of these tubes shall be both prismatic and equiangular; and then if the tube were thus formed, so as to be exactly capable of receiving one of the prisms, and no more, it is infinite to one that they shall never meet in infinite space; and should they meet, it is infinite to one that the axes of the prism and tube shall never happen in the same strait line; and supposing they did, it is again as infinite to three, that angle shall not meet angle, so as to enter. We see then how infinitely improbable it is, 'that all the powers of chance in infinite matter, agitated through infinite ages, could ever effect this small composition of a prism entering a prismatic bore; and, that all our hazard for it would at most be but as three is to the third power of infinite.' And yet the smallest design could easily [affect] it.

VII. May we not then justly count it altogether absurd, and next to an absolute strict impossibility, 'that all the powers of undirected force should ever effect such a complex machine as the most imperfect plant, or the meanest animal, even in one instance?' For the improbability just increases, as the complication of mechanism in these natural bodies surpasses that simple combination above-mentioned.

VIII. Let it be here observed, 'that the preceding reasoning from the frequency of regular bodies of one form in the universe, and from the combinations of various bodies, is entirely independent on any perception of beauty and would equally prove design in the cause, although there were no being which perceived beauty in any form whatsoever': for it is in short this, 'that the recurring of any effect oftener than the laws of hazard determine, gives presumption of design; and, that combinations which no undesigned force could give us reason to expect, must necessarily prove the same; and that with superior probability, as the multitude of cases in which the contrary might happen, surpass all the cases in which this could happen': which appears to be in the simplest cases at least as infinite does to unity. And the frequency of similar irregular forms, or exact combinations of them, is, an equal argument of design in the cause, since the similarity, or exact combinations of irregular forms, are as little to be expected from all the powers of undirected force, as any sort whatsoever...

X. The combinations of regular forms, or of irregular ones exactly adapted to each other, require such vast powers of infinite to effect them, and the hazards of the contrary forms are so infinitely numerous, that all probability or possibility of their being accomplished by chance seems quite to vanish. Let us apply the cases in art. vi in this section about the prism and tube, to our simplest machines, such as a pair of wheels of our ordinary carriages; each circular, spokes equal in length, thickness, shape; the wheels set parallel, the axletree fixed in the nave of both, and secured from coming out at either end: now the cases in which the contrary might have happened from undirected concourses, were there no more required than what is just now mentioned, must amount in multitude to a power of infinites equal to every circumstance required. What shall we say then of a plant, a tree, an animal, a man, with such multitudes of adapted vessels, such articulations, insertions of muscles, diffusion of veins, arteries, nerves? The improbability that such machines arising daily in such numbers in all parts of the earth with such similarity of structure, should be the effect of chance, is beyond all conception or expression.

XI. Further, were all the former reasoning from similarity of forms and combinations groundless, and could chance give us ground to expect such forms, with exact combination, yet we could only promise ourselves one of these forms among an infinity of others. When we see then such a multitude of individuals of a species, similar to each other in a great number of parts; and when we see in each individual, the corresponding members so exactly like each other, what possible room is there left for questioning design in the universe? None but the barest possibility against an inconceivably great probability, surpassing everything which is not strict demonstration...

XVIII. Hitherto the proof amounts only to design or intention, barely, in opposition to blind force or chance; and we see the proof of this is independent on the arbitrary constitution of our internal sense of beauty. Beauty is often supposed an argument of more than design, to wit, wisdom and prudence in the cause. Let us inquire also into this.

Wisdom denotes the pursuing of the best ends by the best means; and therefore, before we can from any effect prove the cause to be wise, we must know what is best to the cause or agent. Among men who have pleasure in contemplating uniformity the beauty of effects is an argument of wisdom, because this is good to them; but the same argument would not hold as to a being void of this sense of beauty. And therefore the beauty apparent to us in nature, will not of itself prove wisdom in the cause, unless this cause or author of nature be supposed benevolent; and then indeed the happiness of mankind is desirable or good to the supreme cause; and that form which pleases us, is an argument of his wisdom. And the strength of this argument is increased always in proportion to the degree of beauty produced in nature, and exposed to the view of any rational agents; since upon supposition of a benevolent deity, all the apparent beauty produced is an evidence of the execution of a benevolent design to give them the pleasures of beauty.

But what more immediately proves wisdom is this; when we see any machine with a great complication of parts actually obtaining an end, we justly conclude, 'that since this could not have been the effect of chance, it must have been intended for that end, which is obtained by it'; and then the ends or intentions being in part known, the complication of organs, and their nice disposition adapted to this end, is an evidence 'of a comprehensive large understanding in the cause, according to the multiplicity of parts, and the appositeness of their structure, even when we do not know the intention of the whole.'

XIX. There is another kind of beauty from which we conclude wisdom in the cause, as well as design, when we see many useful or beautiful effects owing from one general cause. There is a very good reason for this conclusion among men. Interest must lead beings of limited powers, who are incapable of a great diversity of operations, and distracted by them, to choose this frugal economy of their forces, and to look upon such management as an evidence of wisdom in other beings like themselves. Nor is this speculative reason all which influences them; for even beside this consideration of interest, they are determined by a sense of beauty, where that reason does not hold; as when we are judging of the productions of other agents about whose economy we are not solicitous. Thus, who does not approve of it as a perfection in clock-work, that three or four motions of the hour, minute, and second hands, and monthly plate, should arise from one spring or weight, rather than from three or four springs or weights, in a very compound machine, which should perform the same effects, and answer all the same purposes with equal exactness? Now the foundation of this beauty plainly appears to be a uniformity, or unity of cause amidst diversity of effects.

XX. We shall hereafter [see T1.VII] offer some reasons, why the author of nature may choose to operate in this manner by general laws and universal extensive causes, although the reason just now mentioned does not hold with an almighty being. This is certain, that we have some of the most delightful instances of universal causes in the works of nature, and that the most studious men in these subjects are so delighted with the observation of them, that they always look upon them as evidences of wisdom in the administration of nature, from a sense of beauty.

XXI. The wonderfully simple mechanism which performs all animal motions, was mentioned already [see T1.II.viii]; nor is that of the inanimate parts of nature, less admirable. How innumerable are the effects of that one principle of heat, derived to us from the sun, which is not only delightful to our sight and feeling, and the means of discerning objects, but is the cause of rains, springs, rivers, winds, and the universal cause of vegetation! The uniform principle of gravity preserves at once the planets in their orbits, gives cohesion to the parts of each globe, and stability to mountains, hills, and artificial structures; it raises the sea in tides, and sinks them again, and restrains them in their channels; it drains the earth of its superfluous moisture, by rivers; it raises the vapours by its influence on the air, and brings them down again in rains; it gives a uniform pressure to our atmosphere, necessary to our bodies in general, and more especially to inspiration in breathing; and furnishes us with a universal movement, capable of being applied in innumerable engines. How incomparably more beautiful is this structure, than if we supposed so many distinct volitions in the deity, producing every particular effect, and preventing some of the accidental evils which casually flow from the general law! We may rashly imagine that this latter manner of operation might have been more useful to us and it would have been no distraction to omnipotence: but then the great beauty had been lost, and there had been no more pleasure in the contemplation of this scene, which is now so delightful. One would rather choose to run the hazard of its casual evils, than part with that harmonious form, which has been an unexhausted source of delight to the successive spectators in all ages.

XXII. Hence we see, 'that however miracles may prove the superintendency of a voluntary agent, and that the universe is not guided by necessity or fate, yet that mind must be weak and inadvertent, which needs them to confirm the belief of a wise and good deity; since the deviation from general laws, unless upon very extraordinary occasions, must be a presumption of inconstancy and weakness, rather than of steady wisdom and power, and must weaken the best arguments we can have for the sagacity and power of the universal mind.'

Sect. VI.
Of the universality of the sense of beauty among men

...IV. But as to the universal agreement of mankind in their sense of beauty from uniformity amidst variety, we must consult experience: and as we allow all men reason, since all men are capable of understanding simple arguments, though few are capable of complex demonstrations; so in this case it must be sufficient to prove this sense of beauty universal, 'if all men are better pleased with uniformity in the simpler instances than the contrary, even when there is no advantage observed attending it; and likewise if all men, according as their capacity enlarges, so as to receive and compare more complex ideas, have a greater delight in uniformity, and are pleased with its more complex kinds, both original and relative.'

Now let us consider if ever any person was void of this sense in the ampler instances. Few trials have been made in the simplest instances of harmony, because, as soon as we find an ear incapable of relishing complex compositions, such as our tunes are, no farther pains are employed about such. But in figures, did ever any man make choice of a trapezium, or any irregular curve, for the ichnography or plan of his house, without necessity, or some great motive of convenience? Or to make the opposite walls not parallel, or unequal in height? Were ever trapeziums, irregular polygons or curves chosen for the forms of doors or windows, though these figures might have answered the uses as well, and would have often saved a great part of the time, labour and expense to workmen, which is now employed in suiting the stones and timber to the regular forms? Among all the fantastic modes of dress, none was ever quite void of uniformity, if it were only in the resemblance of the two sides of the same robe, and in some general aptitude to the human form. The pictish painting had always relative beauty, by resemblance to other objects, and often those objects were originally beautiful; however justly we might here apply Horace's censure of impertinent poetry, 'For such things, there is a place, but not just now.'[4] But never, were any so extravagant as to affect such figures as are made by the casual spilling of liquid colours. Who was ever pleased with an inequality of heights in windows of the same range, or dissimilar shapes of them? With unequal legs or arms, eyes or cheeks in a mistress? It must however be acknowledged, 'that interest may often counterbalance our, sense of beauty, in this affair as well as in others, and superior good qualities may make us overlook such imperfections.'

V. Nay farther, it may perhaps appear, 'that regularity and uniformity are so copiously diffused through the universe, and we are so readily determined to pursue this as the foundation of beauty in works of art, that there is scarcely anything ever fancied as beautiful, where there is not really something of this uniformity and regularity.' We are indeed often mistaken in imagining that there is the greatest possible beauty, where it is but very imperfect; but still it is some degree of beauty which pleases, although there may be higher degrees which we do not observe; and our sense acts with full regularity when we are pleased, although we are kept by a false prejudice from pursuing objects which would please us more.

A Goth, for instance, is mistaken, when from education he imagines the architecture of his country to be the most perfect: and a conjunction of some hostile ideas, may make him have an aversion to Roman buildings, and study to demolish them, as some of our reformers did the popish buildings, not being able to separate the ideas of the superstitious worship from the forms of the buildings where it was practiced: and yet it is still real beauty which pleases the Goth, founded upon uniformity amidst variety. For the Gothic pillars are uniform to each other, not only in their sections, which are lozenge-formed but also in their heights and ornaments: their arches are not one uniform curve, but yet they are segments of similar curves, and generally equal in the same ranges. The very Indian buildings have some

---

4 [Hutcheson partially quotes line 19 of the *Art of Poetry*. Translation of full line from Fairclough.]

kind of uniformity, and many of the eastern nations, though they differ much from us, yet have great regularity in [their] manner, as well as the Romans in [theirs]. Our Indian screens, which wonderfully supply our imaginations with ideas of deformity, in which nature is very churlish and sparing, do want indeed all the beauty arising from proportion of parts, and conformity to nature; and yet they cannot divert themselves of all beauty and uniformity in the separate parts: and this diversifying the human body into various contortions, may give some wild pleasure from variety, since some uniformity to the human shape is still retained. The faint light in Gothic buildings has had the same association of a very foreign idea, which our poet shows in his epithet, 'A dim religious light.'[5]

VII. What has been said will probably be assented to, if we always remember in our inquiries into the universality of the sense of beauty, 'that there may be real beauty, where there is not the greatest; and that there are an infinity of different forms which may all have some unity, and yet differ from each other.' So that men may have different fancies of beauty, and yet uniformity be the universal foundation of our approbation of any form whatsoever as beautiful. And we shall find that it is so in the architecture, gardening, dress, equipage, and furniture of houses, even among the most uncultivated nations; where uniformity still pleases, without any other advantage than the pleasure of the contemplation of it.

VIII. It will deserve our consideration on this subject, how, in like cases, we form very different judgments concerning the internal and external senses. Nothing is more ordinary among those, who after Mr. Locke have rejected innate ideas,[6] than to allege, 'that all our relish for beauty and order, is either from prospect of advantage, custom, or education,'

---

5 [Line 159 of John Milton's (1608–1674) poem, *Il Penseroso*.]

6 [According to the doctrine of innate ideas, the human mind enters the world with some knowledge already built into it. Locke attacks this doctrine in the first book of *An Essay Concerning Human Understanding*.]

for no other reason but the variety of fancies in the world: and from this they conclude, 'that our fancies do not arise from any natural power of perception, or sense.' And yet all allow our external senses to be natural, and that the pleasures or pains of their sensations, however they may be increased or diminished by custom or education, and counterbalanced by interest, yet are really antecedent to custom, habit, education, or prospect of interest. Now it is certain, 'that there is at least as great a variety of fancies about their objects, as the objects of beauty': nay, it is much more difficult, and perhaps impossible, to bring the fancies or relishes of the external senses to any general foundation at all, or to find any rule for the agreeable or disagreeable: and yet we all allow, 'that these are natural powers of perception.'

IX. The reason of this different judgment can be no other than this, that we have got distinct names for the external senses, and none, or very few, for the internal; and by this are led, as in many other cases, to look upon the former as some way more fixed, and real, and natural, than the latter. The sense of harmony has got its name, *viz.* a good ear; and we are generally brought to acknowledge this a natural power of perception, or a sense some way distinct from hearing: now it is certain, 'that there is as necessary a perception of beauty upon the presence of regular objects, as of harmony upon hearing certain sounds.'

X. But let it be observed here once for all, 'that an internal sense no more presupposes an innate idea, or principle of knowledge, than the external.' Both are natural powers of perception, or determinations of the mind to receive necessarily certain ideas from the presence of objects. The internal sense is a passive power of receiving ideas of beauty from all objects in which there is uniformity amidst variety. Nor does there seem anything more difficult in this matter, than that the mind should be always determined to receive the idea of sweet, when particles of such a form enter the pores of the tongue; or to have the idea of sound upon any quick undulation of the air. The one seems to have as little connection with its idea, as the other: and the same power could with equal ease constitute the former the occasion of ideas, as the latter.

XI. The association of ideas above hinted at [see T1.VI.v; also see T1.VI.iii, not included here], is one great cause of the apparent diversity of fancies in the sense of beauty, as well as in the external senses; and often makes men have an aversion to objects of beauty, and a liking to others void of it, but under different conceptions than those of beauty or deformity. And here it may not be improper to give some instances of some of these affectations. The beauty of trees, their cool shades, and their aptness to conceal from observation, have made groves and woods the usual retreat to those who love solitude, especially to the religious, the pensive, the melancholy, and the amorous. And do not we find that we have so joined the ideas of these dispositions of mind with those external objects, that they always recur to us along with them? The cunning of the heathen priests might make such obscure places the scene of the fictitious appearances of their deities; and hence we join ideas of something divine to them. We know the like effect in the ideas of our churches, from the perpetual use of them only in religious exercises…

In like manner it is known, that often all the circumstances of actions, or places, or dresses of persons, or voice, or song, which have occurred at any time together, when we were strongly affected by any passion, will be so connected that any one of these will make all the rest recur. And this is often the occasion both of great pleasure and pain, delight and aversion to many objects, which of themselves might have been perfectly indifferent to us: but these approbations, or distastes, are remote from the ideas of beauty, being plainly different ideas.

XII. There is also another charm in music to various persons, which is distinct differently, from the harmony, and is occasioned by its raising agreeable passions. The human voice is obviously varied by all the stronger passions; now, when our ear discerns any resemblance between the air of a tune, whether sang or played upon an instrument, either in its time, or modulation, or any other circumstance, to the sound of the human voice, in any passion, we shall be touched by it in a very sensible manner, and have melancholy, joy, gravity, thoughtfulness, excited in us by a sort of sympathy or contagion. The same connection is observable between the very air of a tune, and the words expressing any passion which we have heard it fitted to, so that they shall both recur to us together, though but one of them affects our senses.

Now in such a diversity of pleasing or displeasing ideas, which may be joined with forms of bodies, or tunes, when men are of such different dispositions, and prone to such a variety of passions, it is no wonder, 'that they should often disagree in their fancies of objects, even although their sense of beauty and harmony were perfectly uniform'; because many other ideas may either please or displease, according to persons tempers, and past circumstances. We know how agreeable a very wild country may be to any person who has spent the cheerful days of his youth in it, and how disagreeable very beautiful places may be, if they were the scenes of his misery. And this may help us in many cases to account for the diversities of fancy, without denying the uniformity of our internal sense of beauty.

XIII. Grandeur and novelty are two ideas different from beauty, which often recommend objects to us. The reason of this is foreign to the present subject...[7]

Sect. VII.
Of the power of custom, education, and example, as to our internal senses

I. Custom, education, and example are so often alleged in this affair, as the occasion of our relish for beautiful objects, and for our approbation of, or delight in, a certain conduct in life in a moral species, that it is necessary to examine these three particularly, to make it appear, 'that there is a natural power of perception, or sense of beauty in objects, antecedent to all custom, education, or example.'

---

7 [Hutcheson directs us here to the writer Joseph Addison's (1672–1719) essay number 412 in the *Spectator*, a magazine Addison co-founded in 1711.]

II. ...As to our approbation of, or delight in external objects; when the blood or spirits, of which anatomists talk, are roused, quickened, or fermented as they call it, in any agreeable manner, by medicine or nutriment; or any glands frequently stimulated to secretion; it is certain, that to preserve the body easy, we shall delight in objects of taste, which of themselves are not immediately pleasant to it, if they promote that agreeable state, which the body had been accustomed to. Farther, custom will so alter the state of the body, that what at first raised uneasy sensations, will cease to do so, or perhaps raise another agreeable idea of the same sense; but custom can never give us any idea of a sense different from those we had antecedent to it: it will never make the blind approve objects as coloured, or those who have no taste approve meats as delicious, however they might approve them as strengthening or exhilarating. Were our glands and the parts about them, void of feeling, did we perceive no pleasure from certain brisker motions in the blood, custom could never make simulating or intoxicating fluids or medicines agreeable, when they were not so to the taste: so, by like reasoning, had we no natural sense of beauty from uniformity, custom could never have made us imagine any beauty in objects; if we had had no ear, custom could never have given us the pleasures of harmony. When we have these natural senses antecedently, custom may make us capable of extending our views farther, and of receiving more complex ideas of beauty in bodies, or harmony in sounds, by increasing our attention, and quickness of perception. But however custom may increase our power of receiving or comparing complex ideas, yet it seems rather to weaken than strengthen the ideas of beauty, or the impressions of pleasure from regular objects; else how is it possible that any person could go into the open air on a sunny day, or clear evening, without the most extravagant raptures, such as Milton represents our ancestor in, upon his first creation?[8] For such any person would certainly fall into, upon the first representation of such a scene.

---

8 [Hutcheson cites Book 8 of Milton's poem, *Paradise Lost*.]

Custom in like manner may make it easier for any person to discern the use of a complex machine, and approve it as advantageous; but he would never have imagined it beautiful, had he no natural sense of beauty. Custom may make us quicker in apprehending the truth of complex theorems, but we all find the pleasure or beauty of theorems as strong at first as ever. Custom makes us more capable of retaining and comparing complex ideas, so as to discern more complicated uniformity, which escapes the observation of novices in any art; but all this presupposes a natural sense of beauty in uniformity: for, had there been nothing in forms, which was constituted the necessary occasion of pleasure to our senses, no repetition of indifferent ideas as to pleasure or pain, beauty or deformity, could ever have made them grow pleasing or displeasing.

III. The effect of education is this, that thereby we receive many speculative opinions, which are sometimes true, and sometimes false; and are often led to believe, that objects may be naturally apt to give pleasure or pain to our external senses, which in reality have no such qualities. And farther, by education there are some strong associations of ideas without any reason, by mere accident sometimes, as well as by design, which it is very hard for us ever after to break asunder. Thus aversions are raised to darkness, and to many kinds of meat, and to certain innocent actions: approbations without ground are raised in like manner. But in all these instances, education never makes us apprehend any qualities in objects, which we have not naturally senses capable of perceiving...

Thus education and custom may influence our internal senses, where they are antecedently, by enlarging the capacity of our minds to retain and compare the parts of complex compositions: and then, if the finest objects are presented to us, we grow conscious of a pleasure far superior to what common performances excite. But all this presupposes our sense of beauty to be natural. Instruction in anatomy, observation of nature, and of those airs of the countenance, and attitudes of body, which accompany any sentiment, action, or passion, may enable us to know where there is a just imitation: but why should an exact imitation please upon observation, if we had not naturally a sense of beauty in it, more than the observing the situation of fifty or a hundred pebbles thrown at random? And should we observe them ever so often, we should never dream of their growing beautiful.

IV. There is something worth our observation as to the manner of rooting out the prejudices of education, not quite foreign to the present purpose. When the prejudice arises from affectations of ideas without any natural connection, we must frequently force ourselves to bear representations of those objects, or the use of them when separated from the disagreeable idea; and this may at last disjoin the unreasonable association, especially if we can join new agreeable ideas to them: thus, opinions of superstition are best removed by pleasant conversation of persons we esteem for their virtue, or by observing that they despise such opinions. But when the prejudice arises from an apprehension or opinion of natural evil, as the attendant, or consequent of any object or action; if the evil be apprehended to be the constant and immediate attendant, a few trials, without receiving any damage, will remove the prejudice, as in that against meats: but where the evil is not represented as the perpetual concomitant, but as what may possibly or probably at some time or other accompany the use of the object, there must be frequent reasoning with ourselves, or a long series of trials without any detriment, to remove the prejudice; such is the case of our fear of spirits in the dark, and in church-yards. And when the evil is represented as the consequence perhaps a long time after, or in a future state, it is then hardest of all to remove the prejudice; and this is only to be effected by slow processes of reason, because in this case there can be no trials made: and this is the case of superstitious prejudices against actions apprehended as offensive to the deity; and hence it is that they are so hard to be rooted out.

V. Example seems to operate in this manner. We are conscious that we act very much for pleasure, or private good and are thereby led to imagine that others do so too: hence we conclude there must be some perfection in the objects which we see others pursue, and evil in those which we observe them constantly shunning. Or, the example of others may serve to us as so many trials to remove the apprehension of evil in objects to which we had an aversion. But all this is done upon an apprehension of qualities perceivable by the senses which we have; for no example will induce the blind or deaf to pursue objects as coloured or sonorous; nor could example any more engage us to pursue objects as beautiful or harmonious, had we no natural sense of beauty or harmony.

Example may make us conclude without examination, that our countrymen have obtained the perfection of beauty in their works, or that there is less beauty in the orders of architecture or painting, used in other nations, and so content ourselves with very imperfect forms. And fear of contempt as void of taste or genius, often makes us join in approving the performances of the reputed masters in our country, and restrains those who have naturally a fine genius, or the internal senses very acute, from studying to obtain the greatest perfection; it makes also those of a bad taste pretend to a livelier perception of beauty than in reality they have: but all this presupposes some natural power of receiving ideas of beauty and harmony. Nor can example affect anything farther, unless it be to lead men to pursue objects by implicit faith, for some perfection which the pursuer is conscious he does not know, or which perhaps is some very different quality from the idea perceived by those of a good taste in such affairs.

Sect. VIII.
Of the importance of the internal senses in life, and the final causes of them

I. The busy part of mankind may look upon these things as airy dreams of an inflamed imagination, which a wise man should despise, who rationally pursues more solid possessions independent on fancy: but a little reflection will convince us, 'that the gratifications of our internal senses are as natural, real, and satisfying enjoyments as any sensible pleasure whatsoever; and that they are the chief ends for which we commonly pursue wealth and power.' For how is wealth or power advantageous? How do they make us happy, or prove good to us? No otherwise than as they supply gratifications to our senses, or faculties of perceiving pleasure. Now, are these senses or faculties only the external ones? No: everybody sees, that a small portion of wealth or power will supply more pleasures of the external senses than we can enjoy; we know that scarcity often heightens these perceptions more than abundance, which cloys that appetite which is necessary to all pleasure in enjoyment: and hence the poet's advice is perfectly just; 'So earn your sauce with hard exercise.'[9] In short, the only use of a great fortune above a very small one (except in good offices, and moral pleasures) must be to supply us with the pleasures of beauty, order, and harmony.

It is true indeed, that the noblest pleasures of the internal senses, in the contemplation of the works of nature, are exposed to everyone without expense; the poor and the low, may have as free use of these objects, in this way, as the wealthy or powerful. And even in objects which may be appropriated, the property is of little consequence to the enjoyment of their beauty, which is often enjoyed by others beside the proprietor. But then there are other objects of these internal senses, which require wealth or power to procure the use of them as frequently as we desire; as appears in architecture, music, gardening, painting, dress, equipage, furniture; of which we cannot have the full enjoyment without property. And there are some confused imaginations, which often lead us to pursue property, even in objects where it is not necessary to the true enjoyment of them. These are the ultimate motives of our pursuing the greater degrees of wealth, where there are no generous intentions of virtuous actions.

This is confirmed by the constant practice of the very enemies to these senses. As soon as they think they are got above the world, or extricated from the hurries of avarice and ambition; banished nature will return upon them, and set them upon pursuits of beauty and order in their houses, gardens, dress, table, equipage. They are never easy without some degree of this; and were their hearts open to our view, we should see regularity, decency, beauty, as what their wishes terminate upon, either to themselves or to their pos-

---

9 [Book II of the *Satires*, Satire II, line 20. Fairclough's translation.]

terity; and what their imagination is always presenting to them as the possible effects of their labours. Nor without this could they ever justify their pursuits to themselves.

There may perhaps be some instances of human nature perverted into a thorough miser, who loves nothing but money, and whose fancy arises no higher than the cold dull thought of possession; but such an instance in an age, must not be made the standard of mankind against the whole body.

If we examine the pursuits of the luxurious, who is imagined wholly devoted to his belly; we shall generally find that the far greater part of his expense is employed to procure other sensations than those of taste; such as fine attendants, regular apartments, services of plate, and the like. Besides, a large share of the preparation must be supposed designed for some sort of generous friendly purposes, to please acquaintance, strangers, parasites. How few would be contented to enjoy the same sensations alone, in a cottage, or out of earthen pitchers? To conclude this point, however these internal sensations may be overlooked in our philosophical inquiries about the human faculties, we shall find in fact, 'that they employ us more, and are more efficacious in life, either to our pleasure or uneasiness, than all our external senses taken together.'

II. As to the final causes of this internal sense, we need not inquire, 'whether, to an almighty, and all-knowing being, there be any real excellence in regular forms, in acting by general laws, in knowing by theorems?' We seem scarce capable of answering such questions any way; nor need we inquire, 'whether other animals may not discern uniformity and regularity in objects which escape our observations, and may not perhaps have their senses constituted so as to perceive beauty from the same foundation which we do, in objects which our senses are not fit to examine or compare?' We shall confine ourselves to a subject where we have some certain foundation to go upon, and only inquire, 'if we can find any reasons worthy of the great author of nature, for making such a connection between regular objects, and the pleasure which accompanies our perceptions of them; or, what reasons might possibly influence him to create the world, as it at present is, as far as we can observe, everywhere full of regularity and uniformity?'

Let it be here observed, that as far as we know concerning any of the great bodies of the universe, we see forms and motions really beautiful to our senses; and if we were placed in any planet, the apparent courses would still be regular and uniform, and consequently beautiful to us. Now this gives us no small ground to imagine, that if the senses of their inhabitants are in the same manner adapted to their habitations, and the objects occurring to their view, as ours are here, their senses must be upon the same general foundation with ours.

But to return to the questions: what occurs to resolve them, may be contained in the following propositions.

1. The manner of knowledge by universal theorems, and of operation by universal causes, as far as we can attain it, must be most convenient for beings of limited understanding and power; since this prevents distraction in their understandings through the multiplicity of propositions, and toil and weariness to their powers of action; and consequently their reason, without any sense of beauty, must approve of such methods when they reflect upon their apparent advantage.

2. Those objects of contemplation in which there is uniformity amidst variety, are more distinctly and easily comprehended and retained, than irregular objects; because the accurate observation of one or two parts often leads to the knowledge of the whole: thus we can from a pillar or two, with an intermediate arch, and cornice, form a distinct idea of a whole regular building, if we know of what species it is, and have its length and breadth: from a side and solid angle, we have the whole regular solid; the measuring one side, gives the whole square; one radius, the whole circle; two diameters, an oval; one ordinate and abscissa, the parabola; thus also other figures, if they have any regularity, are in every point determined from a few data: whereas it must be a long attention to a vast multiplicity of parts, which can ascertain or fix the idea of any irregular form, or give any distinct idea of it, or make us capable of retaining it; as

appears in the forms of rude rocks, and pebbles, and confused heaps, even when the multitude of sensible parts is not so great as in the regular forms: for such irregular objects distract the mind with variety, since for every sensible part we must have a quite different idea.

3. From these two propositions it follows, 'that beings of limited understanding and power, if they act rationally for their own interest, must choose to operate by the simplest means, to invent general theorems, and to study regular objects, if they be as useful as irregular ones; that they may avoid the endless toil of producing each effect by a separate operation, of searching out each different truth by a different inquiry, and of imprinting the endless variety of dissimilar ideas in irregular objects.'

4. But then, beside this consideration of interest, there does not appear to be any necessary connection, antecedent to the constitution of the author of nature, between regular forms, actions, theorems, and that sudden sensible pleasure excited in us upon observation of them, even when we do not reflect upon the advantage mentioned in the former proposition. And possibly, the deity could have formed us so as to have received no immediate pleasure from such object, or connected pleasure to those of a quite contrary nature. We have a tolerable presumption of this in the beauties of various animals; they give some small pleasure indeed to everyone who views them; but then everyone seems far more delighted with the peculiar beauties of its own species, than with those of a different one, which seldom raise any desire. This makes it probable, that the pleasure is not the necessary result of the form itself, otherwise it would equally affect all apprehensions in what species soever; but depends upon a voluntary constitution, adapted to preserve the regularity of the universe, and is probably not the effect of necessity, but choice, in the supreme agent, who constituted our senses.

5. Now from the whole we may conclude 'that supposing the deity so kind as to connect sensible pleasure with certain actions or contemplations, beside the rational advantage perceivable in them; there is a great moral

necessity, from his goodness, that the internal sense of men should be constituted as it is at present, so as to make uniformity amidst variety the occasion of pleasure.' For were it not so, but on the contrary, if irregular objects, particular truths and operations pleased us, beside the endless toil this would involve us in, there must arise a perpetual dissatisfaction in all rational agents with themselves; since reason and interest would lead us to simple general causes, while a contrary sense of beauty would make us disapprove them: universal theorems would appear to our understanding the best means of increasing our knowledge of what might be useful; while a contrary sense would set us on the search after particular truths: thought and reflection would recommend objects with uniformity amidst variety, and yet this perverse instinct would involve us in labyrinths of confusion and dissimilitude. And hence we see 'how suitable it is to the sagacious bounty which we suppose in the deity, to constitute our internal senses in the manner in which they are; by which pleasure is joined to the contemplation those objects which a finite mind can best imprint and retain the ideas of with the least distraction; to those actions which are most efficacious, and fruitful in useful effects; and to those theorems which most enlarge our minds.'

III. As to the other question, 'what reason might influence the deity, whom no diversity of operation could distract or weary, to choose to operate by simplest means, and general laws, and to diffuse uniformity, proportion, and similitude through all the parts of nature which we can observe?' Perhaps there may be some real excellence in this manner of operation, and in these forms, which we know not: but this we may probably say, that since the divine goodness, for the reasons above-mentioned, has constituted our sense of beauty as it is at present, the same goodness might have determined the great architect to adorn this stupendous theatre in a manner agreeable to the spectators, and that part which is exposed to the observation of men, so as to be pleasant to them; especially if we suppose, that he designed to discover himself to them as wise and good, as well as powerful: for thus he has given them greater evidences, through the whole earth, of his art, wisdom, design, and bounty, than they can possibly have for the reason, counsel, and good-will of their fellow-creatures, with whom they converse, with full persuasion of these qualities in them, about their common affairs.

As to the operations of the deity by general laws, there is still a farther reason from a sense superior to these already considered, even that of virtue, or the beauty of action, which is the foundation of our greatest happiness. For were there no general laws fixed in the course of nature, there could be no prudence or design in men, no rational expectation of effects from causes, no schemes of action projected, or any regular execution. If then, according to the frame of our nature, our greatest happiness must depend upon our actions, as it may perhaps be made appear it does, 'the universe must be governed, not by particular wills, but by general laws, upon which we can found our expectations, and project our schemes of action.' Nay farther, though general laws did ordinarily obtain, yet if the deity usually stopped their effects whenever it was necessary to prevent any particular evils; this would effectually, and justly supersede all human prudence and care about actions; since a superior mind did thus relieve men from their charge.

Two

The Nature of Laughter

From writings from the *Dublin Journal*

'Reflections upon Laughter' [from No. 10, June 5, 1725]

> 'When you drag him into court he will laugh at your expense.'[1]

There is scarce anything that concerns human nature which does not deserve to be inquired into: I send you some thoughts upon a very common subject, laughter; which you may publish, if you think they can be of any use, to help us to understand what so often happens in our own minds, and to know the use for which it is designed in the constitution of our nature.

Aristotle, in his art of poetry,[2] has very justly explained the nature of one species of laughter, *viz.* the ridiculing of persons... [for] some mistake, or some turpitude, without grievous pain, and not very pernicious or destructive. But this he never intended as a general account of all sorts of laughter.

But Mr. Hobbes,[3] who very much owes his character of a philosopher to his assuming positive solemn airs, which he

1 [Horace's *Satires*, Book II, Satire III, line 72. Fairclough's translation.]

2 [Hutcheson is referring here to the text *Poetics* by the philosopher Aristotle (384–322 B.C.E.).]

3 [Thomas Hobbes (1588–1679), political philosopher and egoist.]

uses most when he is going to assert some palpable absurdity, or some ill-natured nonsense, assures us, that laughter is nothing else but sudden 'glory, arising from some sudden conception of some eminency in ourselves, by comparison with the infirmity of others, or with our own formerly: for men laugh at the follies of themselves past, when they come suddenly to remembrance, except they bring with them any present dishonor.'...

If Mr. Hobbes' notion be just, then first, there can be no laughter on any occasion where we make no comparison of ourselves to others, or of our present state to a worse state, or where we do not observe some superiority of ourselves above some other thing: and again, it must follow, that every hidden appearance of superiority over another must excite laughter, when we attend to it. If both these conclusions be false, the notion from whence they are drawn must be so too.

First, then, that laughter often arises without any imagined superiority of ourselves, may appear from one great fund of pleasantry, the parody, and burlesque allusion; which move laughter in those who may have the highest veneration for the writing alluded to, and also admire the wit of the person who makes the allusion...

It is said, 'that when men of wit make us laugh, it is by representing some oddness or infirmity in themselves, or others.'[4] Thus allusions made on trifling occasions, to the most solemn figured speeches of great writers, contain such an obvious impropriety, that we imagine ourselves incapable of such mistakes as the alluder seemingly falls into; so that in this case too, there is an imagined superiority. But in answer to this, we may observe, that we often laugh at such allusions when we are conscious that the person who raises the laugh knows abundantly the justest propriety of speaking, and knows, at present, the oddness and impropriety of his own allusion as well as any in company; nay, laughs at it himself: we often admire his wit in such allusions, and study to imitate him in it, as far as we can. Now, what hidden sense of glory, or joy in our superiority, can arise from observing a

---

4 [Here Hutcheson cites issue 47 of the *Spectator*.]

quality in another, which we study to imitate, I cannot imagine. I doubt, if men compared themselves with the alluder, whom they study to imitate, they would rather often grow grave or sorrowful.

Nay, farther, this is so far from truth, that imagined superiority moves our laughter, that one would imagine from some instances the very contrary: for if laughter arose from our imagined superiority, then, the more that any object appeared inferior to us, the greater would be the jest; and the nearer anyone came to an equality with us, or resemblance of our actions, the less we should be moved with laughter. But we see, on the contrary, that some ingenuity in dogs and monkeys, which comes near to some of our own arts, very often makes us merry; whereas their duller actions, in which they are much below us, are no matter of jest at all. Whence the author in the *Spectator* drew his observation, that the actions of beasts which move our laughter, bear a resemblance to a human blunder, I confess I cannot guess; I fear the very contrary is true, that their imitation of our grave wise actions would be fitter to raise mirth in the observer.

The second part of the argument, that opinion of superiority suddenly incited in us does not move laughter, seems the most obvious thing imaginable: if we observe an object in pain while we are at ease, we are in greater danger of weeping than laughing: and yet here is occasion for Hobbes' sudden joy. It must be a very merry state in which a fine gentleman is, when well dressed, in his coach, he passes our streets, where he will see so many ragged beggars, and porters and chairmen sweating at their labour, on every side of him. It is a great pity that we had not an infirmary or lazar-house[5] to retire to in cloudy weather, to get an afternoon of laughter at these inferior objects: strange, that none of our Hobbists banish all canary birds and squirrels, and lap-dogs, and pugs, and cats out of their houses, and substitute in their places asses, and owls, and snails, and oysters to be merry upon. From these they might have higher joys of

---

5 [A place where lepers are quarantined.]

superiority, than from those with who we now please ourselves. Pride, or a high opinion of ourselves, must be entirely inconsistent with gravity; emptiness must always make men solemn in their behaviour; and conscious virtue and great abilities must always be upon the sneer. An orthodox believer who is very sure that he is in the true way to salvation must always be merry upon heretics, to whom he is so much superior in his own opinion; and no other passion but mirth should arise upon hearing of their heterodoxy. In general, all men of true sense and reflection and integrity of great capacity for business and penetration into the tempers and interests of men, must be the merriest little grigs imaginable; Democritus must be the sole leader of all the philosophers; and perpetual laughter must succeed into the place of the long beard, 'To be the grace / Both of our wisdom and our face.'[6]

It is pretty strange, that the authors whom we mentioned above, have never distinguished between the words laughter and ridicule: this last is but one particular species of the former, when we are laughing at the follies of others; and in this species there may be some pretense to allege that some imagined superiority may occasion it; but then there are innumerable instances of laughter where no person is ridiculed; nor does he who laughs compare himself to anything whatsoever…

And then farther, even in ridicule itself there must be something else than bare opinion to raise it, as may appear from this, that if anyone would relate in the simplest manner these very weaknesses of others, their extravagant passions, their absurd opinions, upon which the man of wit would rally, should we hear the best vouchers of all the facts alleged, we shall not be disposed to laughter by bare narration; or should one do a real important injury to another, by taking advantage of his weakness, or by some pernicious fraud let us see another's simplicity, this is no matter of laughter: and yet these important cheats do really discover

---

6 [Democritus (460–370 B.C.E.), Greek thinker known as 'the laughing philosopher'. Hutcheson does not provide any reference for the quotation.]

our superiority over the person cheated, more than the trifling impostures of our humourists. The opinion of our superiority may raise a sedate joy in our minds, very different from laughter; but such a thought seldom arises in our minds in the hurry of a cheerful conversation among friends, where there is often a high mutual esteem. But we go to our closest often to spin out some fine conjectures about the principles of our actions, which no mortal is conscious of in himself during the action; thus the same authors above-mentioned tell us, that the desire which we have to see tragical representations is because of the secret pleasure we find in thinking ourselves secure from such evils; we know from what sect this notion was derived. ''Tis sweet to mark what evils we ourselves be spared.'[7]

This pleasure must indeed be a secret one, so very secret, that many a kind, compassionate heart was never conscious of it, but felt itself in a continual state of horror and sorrow; our desiring such sights flows from a kind instinct of nature, a secret bond between us and our fellow-creatures. 'It is at nature's behest that we weep when we meet the bier of a full-grown maiden, or when the earth closes over a babe... for what good man... believes that any human woes concern him not?'[8]

[from No. 11, June 12, 1725]

> 'If a painter chose to join a human head to the neck of a horse, and to spread feathers of many a hue over limbs picked up now here, now there, so that what at top is a lovely woman ends below in a black and ugly fish, would you, my friend, if favored with a private view, refrain from laughing?'[9]

---

7 [Book II, line 4 of *On the Nature of Things*, by Lucretius (99–55 B.C.E.), Roman poet and egoist. Translation from William E. Leonard's edition (London: Dent, 1916).]

8 [Hutcheson quotes selectively from lines 138–42 of Satire XV from the *Satires*, by Juvenal (ca. 100), Roman poet. Translation from G.G. Ramsay's *Juvenal and Persius* (London: Heinemann, 1920).]

9 [Horace's *Art of Poetry*, lines 1–5. Fairclough's translation.]

In my former letter, I attempted to show that Mr. Hobbes' account of laughter was not just. I shall now endeavour to discover some other ground of that sensation, action, passion, or affection, I know not which of them a philosopher would call it...

That then which seems generally the cause of laughter, is 'the bringing together of images which have contrary additional ideas, as well as some resemblance in the principal idea: this contrast between ideas of grandeur, dignity, sanctity, perfection, and ideas of meanness, baseness, profanity, seems to be the very spirit of burlesque; and the greatest part of our raillery and jest are founded upon it.'

We also find ourselves moved to laughter by an overstraining of wit, by bringing resemblances from subjects of a quite different kind from the subject to which they are compared. 'When we see, instead of the easiness, and natural resemblance which constitutes true wit, a forced straining of a likeness, our laughter is apt to arise; as also, when the only resemblance is not in the idea, but in the sound of the words.' And this is the matter of laughter in the pun.

Let us see if this thought may not be confirmed in many instances. If any writing has obtained a high character for grandeur, sanctity, inspiration, or sublimity of thoughts, and boldness of images; the application of any known sentence of such writings to low, vulgar, or base subjects, never fails to divert the audience, and set them a laughing. This fund of laughter the ancients had by allusions to Homer:[10] of this the lives of some of the philosophers in Diogenes Laertius[11] supply abundance of instances. Our late burlesque writers derive a great part of their pleasantry from their introducing, on the most trifling occasions, allusions to some of the bold schemes, or figures, or sentences of the great poets, upon the most solemn subjects. *Hudibras*[12] and *Don Quixote*[13] will

---

10 [Homer, 8th century B.C.E., author of the *Iliad* and the *Odyssey*.]

11 [Diogenes Laertius, third-century author of the *Lives of Eminent Philosophers*.]

12 [Satirical poem written in the 17th century by Samuel Butler (1613–1680).]

supply one with instances of this in almost every page. It were to be wished that the boldness of our age had never carried their ludicrous allusions to yet more venerable writings. We know that allusions to the phrases of holy writ have obtained to some gentlemen a character of wit, and often furnished laughter to their hearers, when their imaginations have been too barren to give any other entertainment. But I appeal to the religious themselves, if these allusions are not apt to move laughter, unless a more strong affection of the mind, a religious horror at the profanity of such allusions, prevents their allowing themselves the liberty of laughing at them. Now in this affair I fancy anyone will acknowledge that an opinion of superiority is not at all the occasion of the laughter.

Again, any little accident to which we have joined the idea of meanness, befalling a person of great gravity, ability, dignity, is a matter of laughter, for the very same reason; thus the strange contortions of the body in a fall, the dirtying of a decent dress, the natural functions which we study to conceal from sight, are matter of laughter, when they occur to observation in persons of whom we have high ideas: nay, the very human form has the ideas of dignity so generally joined with it, that even in ordinary persons such mean accidents are matter of jest; but still the jest is increased by the dignity, gravity, or modesty of the person; which shows that it is this contrast, or opposition of ideas of dignity and meanness, which is the occasion of laughter.

We generally imagine in mankind some degree of wisdom above other animals, and have high ideas of them on this account. If then along with our notion of wisdom in our fellows, there occurs any instance of gross inadvertence, or great mistake; this is a great cause of laughter. Our countrymen are very subject to little trips of this kind, and furnish often some diversion to their neighbours, not only by mistakes in their speech, but in actions. Yet even this kind of laughter cannot well be said to arise from our sense of superiority. This alone may give sedate joy, but not be a

---

13 [Comic novel written in early 17th century by Miguel de Cervantes (1547–1616).]

matter of laughter; since we shall find the same kind of laughter arising in us, where this opinion of superiority does not attend it: for if the most ingenious person in the world, whom the whole company esteems, should through inadvertent hearing, or any other mistake, answer quite from the purpose, the whole audience may laugh heartily, without the least abatement of their good opinion. Thus we know some very ingenious men have not in the least suffered in their characters by an extemporary pun, which raises the laugh very readily; whereas a premeditated pun, which diminishes our opinion of a writer, will seldom raise any laughter.

Again, the more violent passions, as fear, anger, sorrow, compassion, are generally looked upon as something great and solemn; the beholding of these passions in another strikes a man with gravity: now if these passions are artfully, or accidentally raised upon a small or a fictitious occasion, they move the laughter of those who imagine the occasions to be final and contemptible, or who are conscious of the fraud: this is the occasion of the laugh in biting, as they call such deceptions.

According to this scheme, there must necessarily arise a great diversity in men's sentiments of the ridiculous in actions or characters, according as their ideas of dignity and wisdom are various. A truly wise man who places the dignity of human nature in good affections and suitable actions may be apt to laugh at those who employ their most solemn and strong affections about what, to the wise man, appears perhaps very useless or mean. The same solemnity of behaviour and keenness of passion, about a place or ceremony, which ordinary people only employ about the absolute necessaries of life, may make them laugh at their betters. When a gentleman of pleasure, who thinks that good fellowship and gallantry are the only valuable enjoyments of life observes men with great solemnity and earnestness, heaping up money, without using it, or encumbering themselves with purchases and mortgages, which the gay gentleman with his paternal revenues, thinks very silly affairs, he may make himself very merry upon them: and the frugal man, in his turn, makes the same jest of the man of pleasure. The successful gamester, whom no disaster forces to lay aside the trifling ideas of an annulment in his play, may laugh to see the serious looks and passions of the gravest business, arising in the loser, amidst the ideas of a recreation. There is indeed in these last cases an opinion of superiority in the laughter; but this is not the proper occasion of his laughter; otherwise I see not how we should ever meet with a composed countenance anywhere: men have their different relishes of life, most people prefer their own talk to that of others; but this moves no laughter, unless in representing the pursuits of others, they do join together some whimsical image of opposite ideas.

In the more polite nations there are certain modes of dress, behaviour, ceremony, generally received by all the better sort, as they are commonly called: to these modes, ideas of decency, grandeur, and dignity are generally joined; hence men are fond of imitating the mode: and if any polite assembly, a contrary dress, behaviour, or ceremony appear, to which we have joined in our country the contrary ideas of meanness, rusticity, sullenness, a laugh does ordinarily arise, or a disposition to it, in those who have not the thorough good breeding, or reflection, to restrain themselves, or break through these customary associations.

And hence we may see, that what is counted ridiculous in one age or nation, may not be so in another. We are apt to laugh at Homer, when he compares Ajax unwillingly retreating to an ass driven out of a cornfield; or when he compares him to a boar: or Ulysses tossing all night without sleep through anxiety to a pudding frying on the coals.[14] Those three similes, have got low mean ideas joined to them with us, which it is very probable they had not in Greece in Homer's days; nay, as to one of them, the boar, it is well known, that in some countries of Europe, where they have wild boars for hunting, even in our times, they have not these low sordid ideas joined to the animal, which we have in these kingdoms, who never see them but in their dirty sties, or on dunghills. This may teach us how impertinent a great many jests are, which are made upon the style of some other ancient writings, in ages when manners were very

---

14 [Legendary Greek heroes portrayed in the *Iliad* and the *Odyssey*, respectively.]

different from ours, though perhaps fully as rational, and every way as human and just.

[from No. 12, June 19, 1725]

'Jesting oft cuts hard knots more forcefully and effectively than gravity.'[15]

To treat this subject of laughter gravely may subject the author to a censure, like to that which Longinus[16] makes upon a prior treatise of the sublime, because wrote in a manner very unsuitable to the subject. But yet it may be worth our pains to consider the effects of laughter, and the ends for which it was implanted in our nature, that thence we may know the proper use of it: which may be done in the following observations.

First, we may observe, that laughter, like many other dispositions of our mind, is necessarily pleasant to us, when it begins in the natural manner, from some perception in the mind of something ludicrous, and does not take its rise unnaturally from external motions in the body. Everyone is conscious that a state of laughter is an easy and agreeable state, that the recurring or suggestion of ludicrous images tends to dispel fretfulness, anxiety, or sorrow, and to reduce the mind to an easy, happy state; as on the other hand, an easy and happy state is that in which we are most lively and acute in perceiving the ludicrous in objects: anything that gives us pleasure, puts us also in a fitness for laughter, when something ridiculous occurs; and ridiculous objects occurring to a soured temper, will be apt to recover it to easiness. The implanting then a sense of the ridiculous, in our nature, was giving us an avenue to pleasure, and an easy remedy for discontent and sorrow.

Again, laughter, like other affections, is very contagious; our whole frame is so sociable, that one merry countenance may diffuse cheerfulness to many; nor are they all fools who

---

15 [Horace's *Satires*, Book I, Satire X, lines 14–15. Fairclough's translation.]

16 [Longinus, author of *On the Sublime*, written somewhere between the first and third centuries.]

are apt to laugh before they know the jest, however curiosity in wise men may restrain it, that their attention may be kept awake.

We are disposed by laughter to a good opinion of the person who raises it, if neither ourselves nor our friends are made the butt. Laughter is none of the smallest bonds of common friendships, though it be of less consequence in great heroic friendships.

If an object, action or event be truly great in every respect, it will have no natural relation or resemblance to anything mean or base; and consequently no mean idea can be joined to it with any natural resemblance. If we make some forced remote jests upon such subjects, they can never be pleasing to a man of sense and reflection, but raise contempt of the ridiculous, as void of just sense of those things which are truly great. As to any great and truly sublime sentiments, we may perhaps find that, by a playing upon words, they may be applied to a trifling or mean action, or object but this application will not diminish our high idea of the great sentiment...

Let any of our wits try their mettle in ridiculing the opinion of a good and wise mind governing the whole universe; let them try to ridicule integrity and honesty, gratitude, generosity, or the love of one's country, accompanied with wisdom. All their art will never diminish the admiration which we must have for such dispositions, wherever we observe them pure and unmixed with any low views, or any folly in the exercise of them.

When in any object there is a mixture of what is truly great along with something weak or mean, ridicule may, with a weak mind which cannot separate the great from the mean, bring the whole into disesteem, or make the whole appear weak or contemptible: but with a person of just discernment and reflection it will have no other effect, but to separate what is great from what is not so.

When any object either good or evil is aggravated and increased by the violence of our passions, or an enthusiastic admiration, or fear, the application of ridicule is the readiest way to bring down our high imaginations to a conformity to the real moment or importance of the affair. Ridicule gives our minds as it were a bend to the contrary side; so that upon reflection they may be more capable of settling in a just conformity to nature...

This engine of ridicule, no doubt, may be abused, and have a bad effect upon a weak mind; but with men of any reflection, there is little fear that it will ever be very pernicious. An attempt of ridicule before such men, upon a subject every way great, is sure to return upon the author of it. One might dare the boldest wit in company with men of sense, to make a jest upon a completely great action, or character. Let him try the story of Scipio and his fair captive, upon the taking of Cartagena;[17] or the old story of Pylades and Orestes;[18] I fancy he would sooner appear in a fool's coat himself, than he could put either of these characters in such a dress. The only danger is in objects of a mixed nature before people of little judgment, who by jests upon the weak side, are sometimes led into neglect, or contempt, of that which is truly valuable in any character, institution, or office. And this may show us the impertinence, and pernicious tendency of general undistinguished jests upon any character, or office, which has been too much over-rated. But, that ridicule may be abused, does not prove it useless, or unnecessary, more than a like possibility of abuse would prove all our senses, and passions, impertinent, or hurtful. Ridicule, like other edged tools, may do good in a wise man's hands, though fools may cut their fingers with it, or be injurious to an unwary bystander.

The rules to avoid abuse of this kind of ridicule, are, first, either never to attempt ridicule upon what is every way great, whether it be any great being, character, sentiments: or, if our wit must sometimes run into allusions, on low occasions, to the expressions of great sentiments, let it not be in weak company, who have not a just discernment of true grandeur. And, secondly, concerning objects of a mixed nature, partly great, and partly mean, let us never turn meanness into ridicule, without acknowledging what is truly

---

17 [Scipio Africanus, 236–183 B.C.E, Roman general who orchestrated defeat of Carthage at the Battle of Cartagena. Hutcheson has in mind a story about Scipio's respectful treatment of a female captive.]

18 [Pylades and Orestes, famous friends in Greek mythology.]

great, and paying a just veneration to it. In this sort of jesting we ought to be cautious of our company. 'For men more quickly learn and more gladly recall what they deride than what they approve and esteem.'[19]

Another valuable purpose of ridicule is with relation to smaller vices which are often more effectually corrected by ridicule, than by grave admonition. Men have been laughed out of faults which a sermon could not reform; nay, there are many little indecencies which are improper to be mentioned in such solemn discourses. Now ridicule with contempt or ill-nature, is indeed always irritating and offensive; but we may, by testifying a just esteem for the good qualities of the person ridiculed, and our concern for his interests, let him see that our ridicule of his weakness flows from love to him, and then we may hope for a good effect. This then is another necessary rule, that along with our ridicule of smaller faults we should always join evidences of good nature and esteem.

As to jests upon imperfections, which one cannot amend, I cannot see of what use they can be: men of sense cannot relish such jests; foolish trifling minds may by them be led to despise the truest merit, which is not exempted from the casual misfortunes of our mortal state. If these imperfections occur along with a vicious character, against which people should be alarmed and cautioned, it is below a wise man to raise aversions to bad men from their necessary infirmities, when they have a juster handle from their vicious dispositions...

'Remarks upon the *Fable of the Bees*' [from No. 46, February 12, 1726]

> 'When a man's fortune will not fit him, 'tis as oftentimes with a shoe—if too big for the foot, it will trip him; if too small, it will chafe.'[20]

---

19 [Horace's *Epistles*, Book II, Epistle I, lines 262–3. Fairclough's translation.]

20 [Horace's *Epistles*, Book I, Epistle X, lines 42–3. Fairclough's translation.]

The only arguments brought to prove that vice tends to the public happiness of society in this world, are these; 'That the power and grandeur of any nation depends much upon the numbers of people and their industry, which cannot be procured unless there be consumption of manufactures: now the intemperance, luxury, and pride, of men consume manufactures, and promote industry.' In like manner it is asserted, 'that in fact all wealthy and powerful lives abound with these vices, and that their industry is owing to them.'

But if it can be made appear that there may be an equal consumption of manufactures without these vices, and the evils which flow from them; that wealth and power do not naturally tend to vice, or necessarily produce it; then, though we allow that these vices do consume manufactures and encourage industry in the present corruption of manners, and that these vices often attend wealth and power, yet it will be unjust to conclude, either that 'vices naturally tend to public prosperity, or are necessary to it; or that public happiness does necessarily occasion them.'

Intemperance is that use of meat and drink which is pernicious to the health and vigour of any person in the discharge of the offices of life. Luxury is the using more curious and expensive habitation, dress, table, equipage, than the person's wealth will bear, so as to discharge his duty to his family, his friends, his country, or the indigent. Pride is having an opinion of our own virtues, abilities, or perfection of any kind, in comparison of others, as greater than what they really are; arrogating to ourselves either obedience, service, or external marks of honour, to which we have no right; and with this view desiring to equal those of higher nations in our whole manner of living. There is no sort of food, architecture, dress, or furniture, the use of which can be called evil of itself. Intemperance and luxury are plainly terms relative to the bodily constitution, and wealth of the person. Pride, as it affects our expenses, is also relative to the person; so that it is impossible to fix one invariable quantity of food, one fixed sum in expenses, the surpassing of which should be called intemperance, luxury, or pride. Everyone's own knowledge, and experience of his constitution and fortune, will suggest to him what is suitable to his own circumstances. It is ridiculous to say, 'that using anything above the bare necessaries of life is intemperance, pride, or luxury; and that no other universal boundaries can be fixed; because what in one station or fortune is bare study of decency, or conveniency, would be extravagance in another.' As if temperance, frugality, or moderation, denoted fixed weights or measures or sums, which all were to observe, and not a proportion to men's circumstances. Great and little are relative to a species or kind. Those dimensions are great in a deer which are small in a horse; what is great in a house would be small in a mountain. Will anyone thence argue, that there can be no adapting one form to another, so that it shall neither be too big nor little? Can not a coat suit a middle stature, because the same dimensions would be too great for a dwarf, and too little for a giant? If then in each constitution, station, or degree of wealth, a man of good sense may know how far he may go in eating and drinking, or any other expenses, without impairing his health or fortune, or hindering any offices of religion or humanity, he has found the bounds of temperance, frugality, and moderation for himself; and any other, who keeps the same proportion, is equally temperate, though he eats and drinks, or spends more than the other.

That these are the ideas of temperance, frugality, and moderation, given by all moralists, ancient and modern, except a few Cynics[21] of old, and some popish hermits, is plain to all who read them. All sects, as well as the Stoics,[22] recommended the correction of our opinions and imaginations about the pleasures above necessity; and yet the use of them they all allow when it is not inconsistent with the offices of life: in such circumstances they were always looked upon as preferable to their contraries. The Christian law suggests nothing contrary to this; it has set before us, beside the present pleasures of virtue, which it represents as superior to all others, the hopes of eternal happiness; yet it

---

21 [Cynics, ancient philosophical sect founded around 400 B.C.E. that emphasized the replacement of conventional values with more natural ones. The result tended to be asceticism.]

22 [Stoics, ancient philosophical sect founded around 300 B.C.E. that also emphasized living in accordance with nature. The result also tended to be asceticism.]

frequently recommends diligence and industry in providing for ourselves and families, and for a fund of good offices toward others: it nowhere condemns the rich or powerful for being so, or for desiring high stations, unless when these desires are so violent as to counteract our duty. The requiring some to part with their possessions was only a candid forewarning of the first disciples, what their possession of Christianity would probably cost them in those days of persecution. A community of goods is nowhere commanded; though men who knew the approaching persecution did wisely sell their possessions, to turn them to the only valuable purpose then in their power, and conveyed them to persons who could possess them.

Since then intemperance, or pride, were scarce ever understood to denote all use of anything above bare necessaries, all conveniency of life above Hottentots;[23] why anyone should affect to change their meaning, is not easily guessed, unless it be with this view. Luxury, intemperance, and pride, in their common meaning, are vices; but in this new meaning are often innocent, nay virtuous; and without them, in this new sense, there can be no consumption of manufactures. Common readers however will still imagine that these sounds denote vices; and finding that what they confusedly imagine as vicious is necessary to public good, they will lose their aversion to moral evil in general, and imagine it well compensated by some of its advantages.

But let us retain the common meaning of these words. It is certain, luxury, intemperance, and pride, tend to consume manufactures; but the luxurious, intemperate, or proud, are not a whit the less odious, or free from inhumanity and barbarity, in the neglect of families, friends, the indigent, or their country, since their whole intention is a poor selfish pleasure. The good arising to the public is no way owing to them, but to the industrious, who must supply all customers, and cannot examine whether their expenses are proportioned to their fortunes or not...

---

23 ['Hottentots', then-used word by Europeans for natives of South Africa.]

But let us in the next place examine if an equal consumption of manufactures, and encouragement of trade, may be without these vices. Any given number, in a small time, will certainly consume more wine by being drunkards, than by being sober men; will consume more manufactures by being luxurious or proud, if their pride turn upon expenses, than by being frugal and moderate. But it may be justly questioned, whether that same number would not have consumed more in their whole lives, by being temperate and frugal: since all allow that they would probably live longer, and with better health and digestion; and temperance makes a country populous, were it only by prolonging life.

Again, would there not be the same consumption of the same products, if inferior people contracted their drinking and dress within the bounds of temperance and frugality, and allowed poor wives and children what might be necessary to exhilarate and strengthen them for labour, and to defend them from the cold, or make their lives easier? Would there be a less consumption, if those of greater wealth kept themselves within the bounds of temperance, and reserved the money thus saved to supply the interest of money lent *gratis* to a friend, who may be thereby enabled, consistently with temperance, to drink as much wine, as, had it been added to the quantity drunk by the lender, would have taken away his senses? Or, if all men drink too much, and families too; what if they retrenched? The money saved might improve their dress, habitation, or studies; or might enable a poorer friend to consume the same, or other manufactures, with equal advantage to the public; or might preserve the same persons longer in life, and health and good circumstances, so as in their whole lives to consume more. In general, if the single luxury of the master of a family consumes manufactures, might not an equal quantity be consumed by retrenching his own expenses, and allowing conveniences to his family? If a whole family be luxurious in dress, furniture, equipage; suppose this retrenched, the increase of wealth to the family may soon enable younger children in their families to consume among them frugally, as much as would have been consumed luxuriously by the ancestor; or the frugal consumption of fifty years, in the condition of a wise gentleman, may be as great, as the luxurious consumption of twenty years, succeeded by thirty years of pinching, remorse or beggary. If a man of wealth has no children, his own moderate enjoyment, with what he may enable worthy friends to consume in their own houses, or what he may spend temperately at a hospitable table, and genteel equipage, may amount to as much as the squandering of a luxurious Epicure,[24] or vain fool, upon his own person, in the short time his life or fortune will last.

Unless therefore all mankind are fully provided not only with all necessaries, but all innocent conveniences and pleasures of life, it is still possible without any vice, by an honest care of families, relations, or some worthy persons in distress, to make the greatest consumption. Two or three plain suits becoming gentlemen, worn by younger brothers or friends, will employ as many hands as a foppish one worn by a vain heir. The same may be said of furniture of houses, equipage, or table. If there be sufficient wealth to furnish the most sumptuous dress, habitation, equipage, and table, to the proprietor, and discharge all offices of humanity, after a proportionable rate, why should this be called vice? It plainly tends to public good, and injures no man. It is indeed the business of a wise man to look before him, and to be armed against those hazards or accidents which may reduce the highest fortunes: all men should correct their imaginations, and avoid any habit of body or mind, which might be pernicious upon a change of fortune, or unfit them for any duty of life: but this may be done without reducing men to a Cynical tub,[25] or frize coats. Wherein then the virtue of this retrenchment should consist, or the vice of a more pleasant cheerful way of life, is not easy to tell; unless it lies in the confused use of ambiguous words, temperance, and frugality, and humility...

As to the question of fact in this matter: perhaps, whoever looks into all the ranks of men, will find it is but a small part of our consumptions which owing to our vices. If we find too

---

24 [Follower of Epicurus (341–270 B.C.E.), Greek philosopher who espoused egoism, hedonism, and materialism.]

25 [The Greek Cynic philosopher Diogenes of Sinope (ca. 412–323 B.C.E.) was said to have lived in a tub.]

splendid dress at court, or at Lucas',[26] or at public meetings for diversion; we shall find plain dresses at the exchange, at the custom-house, at churches. The expensive gaiety continues but a few years of most people's lives, during their amours, or expectation of preferment: nor would a good-natured man call this gaiety always vicious. Our gentlemen in the country seldom suffer in their fortunes by their dress. The consumption in tables would not be much diminished, though men would never run into surfeiting and drunkenness: it is not one in a hundred who is frequently guilty of these vices; and yet all are every day consuming. The extraordinary consumption of revels occasions generally abstinence for some time following; so that in a sober week as much may be confirmed as in the week one has had a debauch. Did we examine our own manufactures, either linen or woollen, we should find that coarse cloths and the wearing of which none count extravagant, employ ten times as many hands as the fine. And of the fine cloths which are bought, not one of the buyers in ten can be called extravagant. Were even this extravagance removed, the consumption of the same persons during their lives might be as great, as by the vanity of a few years with the poverty of the remainder.

Thus we may see with how little reason vices are either counted necessary, or actually subservient to the public happiness even in our present corruption.

---

26 [Hutcheson signals this as, 'The gayest coffee-house in Dublin.']

Three

The Moral Sense

From *An Inquiry Concerning Moral Good and Evil*

Introduction

The word moral goodness, in this treatise, denotes our idea of some quality apprehended in actions, which procures approbation, attended with desire of the agent's happiness. Moral evil denotes our idea of a contrary quality, which excites condemnation or dislike. Approbation and condemnation are probably simple ideas, which cannot be farther explained. We must be contented with these imperfect descriptions, until we discover whether we really have such ideas, and what general foundation there is in nature for this difference of actions, as morally good or evil.

These descriptions seem to contain a universally acknowledged difference of moral good and evil, from natural. All men who speak of moral good, acknowledge that it procures approbation and good-will toward those we apprehend possessed of it; whereas natural good does not. In this matter men must consult their own breasts. How differently are they affected toward those they suppose possessed of honesty, faith, generosity, kindness; and those who are possessed of the natural goods, such as houses, lands, gardens, vineyards, health, strength, sagacity? We shall find that we necessarily love and approve the possessors of the former but the possession of the latter procures no approbation or good-will at all toward the possessor, but often contrary affections of envy and hatred. In the same manner, whatever quality we apprehend to be morally evil, raises our dislike toward the person in whom we observe it, such as treachery, cruelty, ingratitude; whereas we heartily love, esteem, and pity many who are exposed to natural evils, such as pain, poverty, hunger, sickness, death.

Now the first question on this subject is, 'whence arise these different ideas of actions?'

Because we shall afterwards frequently use the words interest, advantage, natural good, it is necessary here to fix their ideas. The pleasure in our sensible perceptions of any kind, gives us our first idea of natural good or happiness; and then all objects which are apt to excite this pleasure are called immediately good. Those objects which may procure others immediately pleasant, are called advantageous: and we pursue both kinds from a view of interest, or from self-love.

Our sense of pleasure is antecedent to advantage or interest, and is the foundation of it. We do not perceive pleasure in objects, because it is our interest to do so; but objects or actions are advantageous, and are pursued or undertaken from interest, because we receive pleasure from them. Our perception of pleasure is necessary, and nothing is advantageous or naturally good to us, but what is apt to raise pleasure mediately, or immediately. Such objects as we know either from experience of sense, or reason, to be immediately or mediately advantageous, or apt to minister pleasure, we are said to pursue from self-interest, when our intention is only to enjoy this pleasure, which they have the power of exciting. Thus meats, drink, harmony, fine prospects, painting, statues, are perceived by our senses to be immediately good; and our reason shows riches and power to be mediately so, that is, apt to furnish us with objects of immediate pleasure: and both kinds of these natural goods are pursued from interest, or self-love.

Now the greatest part of our latter moralists establish it as undeniable, 'that all moral qualities have necessarily some relation to the law of a superior, of sufficient power to make us happy or miserable'; and since all laws operate only by sanctions of rewards or punishments, which determine us to obedience by motives of self-interest, they suppose, 'that it is thus that laws do constitute some actions mediately good, or advantageous, and others the same way disadvantageous.' They say indeed, 'that a benevolent legislator constitutes no actions advantageous to the agent by law, but such as in their own nature tend to the natural good of the whole, or, at least, are not inconsistent with it; and that therefore we approve the virtue of others, because it has some small tendency to our happiness, either from its own nature, or from this general consideration, that obedience to a benevolent legislator is in general advantageous to the whole, and to us in particular; and that for the contrary reasons alone, we disapprove the vice of others, that is, the prohibited action, as tending to our particular detriment in some degree.' And then they maintain, 'that we are determined to obedience to laws, or deterred from disobedience, merely by motives of self-interest, to obtain either the natural good arising from the commanded action, or the rewards promised by the sanction; or to avoid the natural evil consequences of disobedience, or at least the penalties of the law.'

Some other moralists suppose 'an immediate natural good in the actions called virtuous; that is, that we are determined to perceive some beauty in the actions of others, and to love the agent, even without reflecting upon any advantage which can any way redound to us from the action; that we have also a secret sense of pleasure arising from reflection upon such of our own actions as we call virtuous, even when we expect no other advantage from them.' But they allege at the same time, 'that we are excited to perform these actions, even as we pursue, or purchase pictures, statues, landscapes, from self-interest, to obtain this pleasure which arises from reflection upon the action, or some other future advantage.' The design of the following sections is to inquire into this matter; and perhaps the reasons to be offered may prove,

> I. 'That some actions have to men an immediate goodness; or, that by a superior sense, which I call a moral one we approve the actions of others, and perceive them to be their perfection and dignity, and are determined to love the agent; a like perception we have in reflecting on such actions of our own, without any view of natural advantage from them.'
>
> II. It may perhaps also appear, 'that the affection, desire, or intention, which gains approbation to the actions flowing from it, is not an intention to obtain even this sensible pleasure; much less the future rewards from

sanctions of laws, or any other natural good, which may be the consequence of the virtuous action; but an entirely different principle of action from self love, or desire of private good.'

Sect. I.
Of the moral sense by which we perceive virtue and vice, and approve or disapprove them in others

I. That the perceptions of moral good and evil, are perfectly different from those of natural good or advantage, everyone must convince himself, by reflecting upon the different manner in which he finds himself affected when these objects occur to him. Had we no sense of good distinct from the advantage or interest arising from the external senses, and the perceptions of beauty and harmony; the sensations and affections toward a fruitful, field, or commodious habitation, would be, much the same with what we have toward a generous friend, or any noble character; for both are or may be advantageous to us: and we should no more admire any action, or love any person in a distant country, or age, whose influence could not extend to us, than we love the mountains of Peru, while we are unconcerned in the Spanish trade. We should have the same sentiments and affections toward inanimate brings, which we have toward rational agents, which yet everyone knows to be false. Upon comparison, we say, 'why should we approve or love inanimate beings? They have no intention of good to us, or to any other person; their nature makes them fit for our uses, which they neither know nor study to serve. But it is not so with rational agents: they study the interest, and desire the happiness of other beings with whom they converse.'

We are all then conscious of the difference between that approbation or perception of moral excellence, which benevolence excites toward the person in whom we observe it, and that opinion of natural goodness, which only raises desire of possession toward the good object. Now 'what should make this difference, if all approbation, or sense of good be from prospect of advantage? Do not inanimate objects promote our advantage as well as benevolent persons, who do us offices of kindness and friendship? Should we not then have the same endearing approbation of both?

Or only the same cold opinion of advantage in both?' The reason why it is not so, must be this, 'that we have a distinct perception of beauty or excellence in the kind affections of rational agents; whence we are determined to admire and love such characters and persons.'

Suppose we reap the same advantage from two men, one of whom serves us from an ultimate desire of our happiness, or good-will toward us; the other from views of self-interest, or by constraint: both are in this case equally beneficial or advantageous to us, and yet we shall have quite different sentiments of them. We must then certainly have other perceptions of moral actions, than those of advantage; and that power of receiving these perceptions may be called a moral sense, since the definition agrees to it, *viz.* a determination of the mind, to receive any idea from the presence of an object which occurs to us, independent on our will.

This perhaps will be equally evident from our ideas of evil, done to us designedly by a rational agent. Our senses of natural good and evil would make us receive, with equal serenity and composure, an assault, a buffet, an affront from a neighbour, a cheat from a partner, or trustee, as we would an equal damage from the fall of a beam, a tile, or a tempest; and we should have the same affections and sentiments on both occasions. Villainy, treachery, cruelty, would be as meekly resented as a blast, or mildew, or an overflowing stream. But I fancy everyone is very differently affected on these occasions, though there may be equal natural evil in both. Nay, actions no way detrimental may occasion the strongest anger and indignation, if they evidence only impotent hatred or contempt. And, on the other hand, the intervention of moral ideas may prevent our condemnation of the agent, or bad moral apprehension of that action, which causes to us the greatest natural evil. Thus the opinion of justice in any sentence, will prevent all ideas of moral evil in the execution, or hatred toward the magistrate, who is the immediate cause of our greatest sufferings.

II. In our sentiments of actions which affect ourselves, there is indeed a mixture of the ideas of natural and moral good, which require some attention to separate them. But when we reflect upon the actions which affect other persons only, we may observe the moral ideas unmixed with those of natural good or evil. For let it be here observed, that those senses by which we perceive pleasure in natural objects, whence they are constituted advantageous, could never raise in us any desire of public good, but only of what was good to ourselves in particular. Nor could they ever make us approve an action merely because of its promoting the happiness of others. And yet, as soon as any action is represented to us as flowing from love, humanity, gratitude, compassion, a study of the good of others, and an ultimate desire of their happiness, although it were in the most distant part of the world, or in some past age, we feel joy within us, admire the lovely action, and praise its author. And on the contrary, every action represented as flowing from ill-will, desire of the misery of others without view to any prevalent good to the public, or ingratitude, raises abhorrence and aversion.

It is true indeed, that the actions we approve in others, are generally imagined to tend to the natural good of mankind, or of some parts of it. But whence this secret chain between each person and mankind? How is my interest connected with the most distant parts of it? And yet I must admire actions which show good-will toward them, and love the author. Whence this love, compassion, indignation and hatred toward even feigned characters, in the most distant ages, and nations, according as they appear kind, faithful, compassionate, or of the opposite dispositions, toward their imaginary contemporaries? If there is no moral sense, which makes benevolent actions appear beautiful; if all approbation be from the interest of the approver, 'What's Hecuba to us, or we to Hecuba?'[1]

III. Some refined explainers of self-love may tell us, 'that we approve or condemn characters, according as we apprehend we should have been supported, or injured by them, had we lived in their days.' But how obvious is the answer, if we only observe, that had we no sense of moral good in humanity, mercy, faithfulness, why should not self-love, and our sense of natural good engage us always to the victorious

---

1 [Act 2, Scene 2, Verse 562 of *Hamlet* by playwright William Shakespeare (1564–1616).]

side, and make us admire and love the successful tyrant, or traitor? Why do not we love Sinon or Pyrrhus, in the *Aeneid*? For, had we been Greeks, these two would have been very advantageous characters. Why are we affected with the fortunes of Priamus, Polites, Choroebus or Aeneas?[2] Would not the parsimony of a miser be as advantageous to his heir, as the generosity of a worthy man is to his friend? And cannot we as easily imagine ourselves heirs to misers, as the favourites of heroes? Why don't we then approve both alike? It is plain we have some secret sense which determines our approbation without regard to self-interest; otherwise we should always favour the fortunate side without regard to virtue, and suppose ourselves engaged with that party…

IV. Some moralists, who will rather twist self-love into a thousand shapes, than allow any other principle of approbation than interest, may tell us, 'that whatever profits one part without detriment to another, profits the whole, and then some small share will redound to each individual, that those actions which tend to the good of the whole, if universally performed, would most effectually secure to each individual his own happiness; and that consequently, we may approve such actions, from the opinion of their tending ultimately to our own advantage.'

We need not trouble these gentlemen to show by their nice train of consequences, and influences of actions by way of precedent in particular instances, that we in this age reap any advantage from Oreste's killing the treacherous Aegysthus, or from the actions of Codrus or Decius.[3] Allow their reasonings to be perfectly good, they only prove, that after long reflection and reasoning, we may find out some ground to judge certain actions advantageous to us, which every man admires as soon as he bears of them; and that too under a quite different conception.

Should any of our travellers find some old Grecian treasure, the miser who hid it, certainly performed an action

---

2 [These are classical figures featured in the *Aeneid*, an epic poem composed by Virgil (70–19 B.C.E.).]

3 [Ibid.]

more to the traveller's advantage, than Codrus or Orestes; for he must have but a small share of benefit from their actions, whose influence is so dispersed, and lost in various ages and nations: surely then this miser must appear to the traveller a prodigious hero in virtue! For self-interest will recommend men to us only according to the good they do to ourselves, and not give us high ideas of public good, but in proportion to our share of it. But must a man have the reflection of Cumberland or Pufendorf,[4] to admire generosity, faith, humanity, gratitude? Or reason so nicely to apprehend the evil in cruelty, treachery, ingratitude? Do not the former excite our admiration, and love, and study of imitation, wherever we see them, almost at first view, without any such reflection, and the latter, our contempt, and abhorrence? Unhappy would it be for mankind, if a sense of virtue was of as narrow an extent, as a capacity for such metaphysics.

V. This moral sense, either of our own actions, or of those of others, has this in common with our other senses, that however our desire of virtue may be counterbalanced by interest, our sentiment or perception of its beauty cannot; as it certainly might be, if the only ground of our approbation were views of advantage. Let us consider this both as to our own actions, and those of others.

A covetous man shall dislike any branch of trade, how useful soever it may be to the public, if there is no gain for himself in it; here is an aversion from interest. Propose a sufficient premium, and he shall be the first who sets about it, with full satisfaction in his own conduct. Now is it the same way with our sense of moral actions? Should anyone advise us to wrong a minor, or orphan, or to do an ungrateful action, toward a benefactor; we at first view abhor it: allure us that it will be very advantageous to us, propose even a reward; our sense of the action is not altered. It is true, these motives may make us undertake it; but they have no more influence upon us to make us approve it, than a physician's advice has to make a nauseous potion pleasant to

---

4 [Richard Cumberland (1631–1718) and Samuel von Pufendorf (1632–94), both important philosophers in the natural law tradition.]

the taste, when we perhaps force ourselves to take it for the recovery of health.

Had we no notion of actions, beside our opinion of their advantage or disadvantage, could we ever choose an action as advantageous, which we are conscious is still evil? As it too often happens in human affairs. Where would be the need of such high bribes to prevail with men to abandon the interests of a ruined party, or of tortures to force out the secrets of their friends? Is it so hard to convince men's understandings, if that be the only faculty we have to do with, that it is probably more advantageous to secure present gain, and avoid present evils, by joining with the prevalent party, than to wait for the remote possibility of future good, upon a revolution often improbable, and sometimes unexpected? And when men are over-persuaded by advantage, do they always approve their own conduct? Nay, how often is their remaining life odious, and shameful, in their own sense of it, as well as in that of others, to whom the base action was profitable?

If anyone becomes satisfied with his own conduct in such a case, upon what ground is it? How does he please himself, or vindicate his actions to others? Never by reflecting upon his private advantage, or alleging this to others as a vindication; but by gradually warping into the moral principles of his new party; for no party is without them. And thus men become pleased with their actions under some appearance of moral good, distinct from advantage.

It may perhaps be alleged, 'that in those actions of our own which we call good, there is this constant advantage, superior to all others, which is the ground of our approbation, and the motive to them from self-love, *viz.* that we suppose the deity will reward them.' This will be more fully considered hereafter [see T2.II.vii]: at present it is enough to observe, that many have high notions of honour, faith, generosity, justice, who have scarce any opinions about the deity, or any thoughts of future rewards, and abhor anything which is treacherous, cruel, or unjust, without any regard to future punishments.

But farther, though these rewards and punishments, may make my own actions appear advantageous to me, yet they would never make me approve, and love another person for the like actions, whose merit would not be imputed to me. Those actions are advantageous indeed to the agent; but his advantage is not my advantage: and self-love could never recommend to me actions as advantageous to others, or make me like the authors of them on that account.

This is the second thing to be considered, 'whether our sense of the moral good or evil in the actions of others, can be overbalanced, or bribed by views of interest.' Now I may indeed easily be capable of wishing, that another would do an action I abhor as morally evil, if it were very advantageous to me: interest in that case may overbalance my desire of virtue in another: but no interest to myself will make me approve an action as morally good, which without that interest to myself would have appeared morally evil; if upon computing its whole effects, it appears to produce as great a moment of good in the whole, when it is not beneficial to me, as it did before, when it was. In our sense of moral good or evil, our own private advantage or loss is of no more moment, than the advantage or loss of a third person to make an action appear good or evil. This sense therefore cannot be overbalanced by interest. How ridiculous an attempt would it be, to engage a man by rewards or threatenings into a good opinion of an action, which was contrary to his moral notions? We may procure dissimulation by such means, and that is all.

VI. A late witty author[5] says, 'that the leaders mankind do not really admire such actions as those of Regulus, or Decius,[6] but only observe, that men of such dispositions are very useful for the defence of any state; and therefore by panegyrics, and statues, they encourage such tempers in others, as the most tractable and useful.' Here first let us consider, if a traitor, who would sell his own country to us, may not often be as advantageous to us, as a hero who defends

---

5 [Bernard Mandeville (1670–1733), philosopher, satirist, and frequent target of Hutcheson's arguments. See Mandeville's *Fable of the Bees*, 2 vols., ed. F.B. Kaye (Indianapolis: Liberty Fund, 1988, vol. 2, pp. 47–51).]

6 [Regulus (ca. 307–250 B.C.E.), Roman statesman. Trajan Decius (ca. 201–251), emperor of Rome.]

us: and yet we can love the treason, and hate the traitor. We can at the same time praise a gallant enemy, who is very pernicious to us. Is there nothing in all this but an opinion of advantage?

Again, upon this scheme what could a statue or panegyric effect? Men love praise—they will do the actions which they observe to be praised—praise, with men who have no other idea of good but self-interest, is the opinion which a nation or party have of a man as useful to them—Regulus, or Cato,[7] or Decius, had no advantage by the actions which profited their country, and therefore they themselves could not admire them, however the persons who reaped the advantage might praise such actions.—Regulus or Cato could not possibly praise or love another hero for a virtuous action; for this would not gain them the advantage of honour; and their own actions they must have looked upon as the hard terms on which honour was to be purchased, without anything amiable in them, which they could contemplate or reflect upon with pleasure. Nay, what should excite a Cato or a Decius to desire praise, if it is only the cold opinion of others that they were useful to the state, without any perception of excellence in such conduct? Now how unlike is this to what the least observation would teach a man concerning such characters?

But says [Mandeville, in the *Fable*], 'these wondrous cunning governors made men believe, by their statues and panegyrics, that there was public spirit, and that this was in itself excellent; and hence men are led to admire it in others, and to imitate it in themselves, forgetting the pursuit of their own advantage.' So easy a matter it seems to him, to quit judging of others by what we feel in ourselves!—for a person who is wholly selfish, to imagine others to be public-spirited—for one who has no ideas of good but in his own advantage, to be led by the persuasions of others, into a conception of goodness in what is avowedly detrimental to himself, and profitable to others; nay, so entirely, as not to approve the action thoroughly, but so far as he was conscious that it

---

7 [Cato (95–46 B.C.E.), Roman statesman.]

proceeded from a disinterested study of the good of others! Yet this it seems statues and panegyrics can accomplish! 'The olive has no hardness within, the nut has none without.'[8]

It is an easy matter for men to assert anything in words; but our own hearts must decide the matter, 'whether some moral actions do not at first view appear amiable even to those who are unconcerned in their influence? Whether we do not sincerely approve and love a generous kind friend, or patriot, whose actions procure honour to him only, without any advantage to ourselves?' It is true, that the actions which we approve, are useful to mankind; but not always to the approver. It would perhaps be useful to the whole, that all men agreed in performing such actions; and then everyone would have his share of the advantage: but this only proves, that reason and calm reflection may recommend to us, from self-interest, those actions, which at first view our moral sense determines us to admire, without considering this interest. Nay, our sense shall operate even where the advantage to ourselves does not hold. We can approve the justice of a sentence against ourselves: a condemned traitor may approve the vigilance of a Cicero[9] in discovering conspiracies, though it had been for the traitor's advantage, that there never had been in the world any men of such sagacity. To say that he may still approve such conduct as tending to the public good, is a jest from one whose only idea of good is self-interest. Such a person has no approbation of public spirit, nor desire of public good, farther than it tends to his own advantage, which it does not at all in the present case.

VII. If what is said makes it appear, that we have some other amiable idea of actions than that of advantageous to ourselves, we may conclude, 'that this perception of moral good is not derived from custom, education, example, or study.' These give us no new ideas: they might make us see private advantage in actions whose usefulness did not at first

---

8 [Book II of Horace's *Epistles*, Epistle II, line 31. Fairclough's translation.]

9 [Marcus Tullius Cicero (106–43 B.C.E.), Roman philosopher and statesman.]

appear; or give us opinions of some tendency of actions to our detriment, by some nice deductions of reason, or by a rash prejudice, when upon the first view of the action we should have observed no such thing: but they never could have made us apprehend actions as amiable or odious, without any consideration of our own advantage.

VIII. It remains then, 'that as the author of nature has determined us to receive, by our external senses, pleasant or disagreeable ideas of objects, according as they are useful or hurtful to our bodies; and to receive from uniform objects the pleasures of beauty and harmony, to excite us to the pursuit of knowledge, and to reward us for it; or to be an argument to us of his goodness, as the uniformity itself proves his existence, whether we had a sense of beauty in uniformity or not; in the same manner he has given us a moral sense, to direct our actions, and to give us still nobler pleasures: so that while we are only intending the good of others, we undesignedly promote our own greatest private good.'

We are not to imagine, that this moral sense, more than the other senses, supposes any innate ideas, knowledge, or practical proposition: we mean by it only a determination of our minds to receive the simple ideas of approbation or condemnation, from actions observed, antecedent to any opinions of advantage or loss to redound to ourselves from them; even as we are pleased with a regular form, or a harmonious composition, without having any knowledge of mathematics, or seeing any advantage in that form or composition, different from the immediate pleasure.

That we may discern more distinctly the difference between moral perceptions and others, let us consider, when we taste a pleasant fruit, we are conscious of pleasure; when another tastes it, we only conclude or form an opinion that he enjoys pleasure; and, abstracting from some previous good-will or anger, his enjoying this pleasure is to us a matter wholly indifferent, raising no new sentiment or affection. But, when we are under the influence of a virtuous temper, and thereby engaged in virtuous actions, we are not always conscious of any pleasure, nor are we only pursuing private pleasures, as will appear hereafter: 'tis only by reflex acts upon our temper and conduct that we enjoy the delights of virtue. When also we judge the temper of another to be virtuous, we do not necessarily imagine him then to enjoy pleasure, though we know reflection will give it to him: and farther, our apprehension of his virtuous temper raises sentiments of approbation, esteem or admiration, and the affection of good-will toward him. The quality approved by our moral sense is conceived to reside in the person approved, and to be a perfection and dignity in him: approbation of another's virtue is not conceived as making the approver happy, or virtuous, or worthy, though 'tis attended with some small pleasure. Virtue is then called amiable or lovely, from its raising good-will or love in spectators toward the agent; and not from the agent's perceiving the virtuous temper to be advantageous to him, or desiring to obtain it under that view. A virtuous temper is called good or beatific, not that it is always attended with pleasure in the agent much less that some small pleasure attends the contemplation of it in the approver: but from this, that every spectator is persuaded that the reflex acts of the virtuous agent upon his own temper will give him the highest pleasures. The admired quality is conceived as the perfection of the agent, and such a one as is distinct from the pleasure either in the agent or the approver; though 'tis a sure source of pleasure to the agent. The perception of the approver, though attended with pleasure, plainly represents something quite distinct from this pleasure; even as the perception of external forms is attended with pleasure, and yet represents something distinct from this pleasure. This may prevent many cavils upon this subject.

Sect. II.
Concerning the immediate motive to virtuous actions

The motives of human actions, or their immediate causes, would be best understood after considering the passions and affections [see T3]; but here we shall only consider the springs of the actions which we call virtuous, as far as it is necessary to settle the general foundation of the moral sense.

I. Every action, which we apprehend either morally good or evil, is always supposed to flow from some affection toward sensitive natures; and whatever we call virtue or vice, is either some such affection, or some action consequent upon it. Or it may perhaps be enough to make an action or omission, appear vicious, if it argues the want of such affection toward rational agents, as we expect in characters counted morally good. All the actions counted religious in any country, are supposed, by those who count them so, to flow from some affections toward the deity; and whatever we call social virtue, we still suppose to flow from affections toward our fellow-creatures: for in this all seem to agree, 'that external motions, when accompanied with no affections toward God or man, or evidencing no want of the expected affections toward either, can have no moral good or evil in them.'

Ask, for instance, the most abstemious hermit, if temperance of itself would be morally good, supposing it showed no obedience toward the deity, made us no fitter for devotion, or the service of mankind, or the search after truth, than luxury; and he will easily grant, that it would be no moral good, though still it might be naturally good or advantageous to health: and mere courage, or contempt of danger, if we conceive it to have no regard to the defence of the innocent, or repairing of wrongs or self-interest, would only entitle its possessor to bedlam. When such sort of courage is sometimes admired, it is upon some secret apprehension of a good intention in the use of it, or as a natural ability capable of a useful application. Prudence, if it was only employed in promoting private interest, is never imagined to be a virtue: and justice, or observing a strict equality, if it has no regard to the good of mankind, the preservation of rights, and securing peace, is a quality properer for its ordinary gestamen, a beam and scales, than for a rational agent. So that these four qualities, commonly called cardinal virtues, obtain that name, because they are dispositions universally necessary to promote public good, and denote affections toward rational agents; otherwise there would appear no virtue in them.

II. Now, if it can be made appear, that none of these affections which we approve as virtuous, are either self-love, or desire of private interest; since all virtue is either some such affections, or actions consequent upon them; it must, necessarily follow, 'that virtue springs from some other affection than self-love, or desire of private advantage. And where self-interest excites to the same action, the approbation is given only to the disinterested principle.'

The affections which are of most importance in morals, are commonly included under the names love and hatred. Now in discoursing of love, we need not be cautioned not to include that love between the sexes, which, when no other affections accompany it, is only desire of pleasure, and is never counted a virtue. Love toward rational agents, is subdivided into love of complacence or esteem, and love of benevolence: and hatred is subdivided into hatred of displicence or contempt, and hatred of malice. Complacence denotes approbation of any person by our moral sense; and is rather a perception than an affection; though the affection of good-will is ordinarily subsequent to it. Benevolence is the desire of the happiness of another. Their opposites are called dislike and malice. Concerning each of these separately we shall consider, 'whether they can be influenced by motives of self- interest.'

Complacence, esteem, or good-liking, at first view appears to be disinterested, and so displicence or dislike; and are entirely excited by some moral qualities, good or evil, apprehended to be in the objects; which qualities the very frame of our nature determines us to approve or disapprove, according to the moral sense above explained [see T1.I]. Propose to a man all the rewards in the world, or threaten all the punishments, to engage him to esteem and complacence toward a person entirely unknown, or if known, apprehended to be cruel, treacherous, ungrateful; you may procure external obsequiousness, or good offices, or dissimulation; but real esteem no price can purchase. And the same is obvious as to contempt, which no motive of advantage can prevent. On the contrary, represent a character as generous, kind, faithful, humane, though in the most distant parts of the world, and we cannot avoid esteem and complacence. A bribe may possibly make us attempt to ruin such a man, or some strong motive of advantage may excite us to oppose his interest; but it can never make us disapprove him, while we retain the same opinion of his temper and intentions. Nay, when we consult our own hearts, we shall find, that we can scarce ever persuade ourselves to attempt any mischief against such persons, from any motive of advantage; nor execute it without the strongest reluctance and remorse, until we have blinded ourselves into a false opinion about his temper.

III. As to the love of benevolence, the very name excludes self-interest. We never call that man benevolent, who is in fact useful to others, but at the same time only intends his own interest, without any ultimate desire of the good of others. If there be any benevolence at all, it must be disinterested; for the most useful action imaginable loses all appearance of benevolence, as soon as we discern that it only flowed from self-love, or interest. Thus, never were any human actions more advantageous, than the inventions of fire, and iron; but if these were casual, or if the inventor only intended his own interest in them, there is nothing which can be called benevolent in them. Wherever then benevolence is supposed, there it is imagined disinterested, and designed for the good of others. To raise benevolence, no more is required than calmly to consider any sensitive nature not pernicious to others. Gratitude arises from benefits conferred from good-will on ourselves, or those we love; complacence is a perception of the moral sense. Gratitude includes some complacence, and complacence still raises a stronger good-will than that we have toward indifferent characters, where there is no opposition of interests.

But it must be here observed, that as all men have self-love, as well as benevolence, these two principles may jointly excite a man to the same action; and then they are to be considered as two forces impelling the same body to motion; sometimes they conspire, sometimes are indifferent to each other, and sometimes are in some degree opposite. Thus, if a man have such strong benevolence, as would have product an action without any views of self-interest; that such a man has also in view private advantage, along with public good, as the effect of his action, does no way diminish the benevolence of the action. When he would not have produced so much public good, had it not been for prospect of self-interest, then the effect of self-love is to be deducted, and his benevolence is proportioned to the remainder of good, which pure benevolence would have produced. When a man's benevolence is hurtful to himself, then self-love is opposite to benevolence, and the benevolence is proportioned to the sum of the good produced, added to the resistance of self-love surmounted by it. In most cases it is impossible for men to know how far their fellows are influenced by the one or other of these principles; but yet the general truth is sufficiently certain, that this is the way in which the benevolence of actions is to be computed.

IV. There are two ways in which some may deduce benevolence from self-love, the one supposing that 'we voluntarily bring this affection upon ourselves, whenever we have an opinion that it will be for our interest to have this affection, either as it may be immediately pleasant, or may afford pleasant reflection afterwards by our moral sense, or as it may tend to procure some external reward from God or man.' The other scheme alleges no such power in us of raising desire or affection of any kind by our choice or volition; but 'supposes our minds determined by the frame of their nature to desire whatever is apprehended as the means of any private happiness; and that the observation of the happiness of other persons, in many cases is made, the necessary occasion of pleasure to the observer, as their misery is the occasion of his uneasiness: and in consequence of this connection, as soon as we have observed it, we begin to desire the happiness of others as the means of obtaining this happiness to ourselves, which we expect from the contemplation of others in a happy state. They allege it to be impossible to desire either the happiness of another, or any event whatsoever, without conceiving it as the means of some happiness or pleasure to ourselves; but own at the same time, that desire is not raised in us directly by any volition, but arises necessarily upon our apprehending any object or event to be conducive to our happiness.'

That the former scheme is not just, may appear from this general consideration, that 'neither benevolence nor any other affection or desire can be directly raised by volition.' If they could, then we could be bribed into any affection whatsoever toward any object, even the most improper: we might raise jealousy, fear, anger, love, toward any sort of persons indifferently by hire, even as we engage men to external actions, or to the dissimulation of passions; but this every person will by his own reflection find to be impossible. The prospect of any advantage to arise to us from having any affection, may indeed turn our attention to those qualities in the object, which are naturally constituted the necessary causes or occasions of the advantageous affection; and if we find such qualities in the object, the affection will certainly arise. Thus indirectly the prospect of advantage may tend to raise any affection; but if these qualities be not found or apprehended in the object, no volition of ours, nor desire, will ever raise any affection in us.

But more particularly, that desire of the good of others, which we approve as virtuous, cannot be alleged to be voluntarily raised from prospect of any pleasure accompanying the affection itself: for 'tis plain that our benevolence is not always accompanied with pleasure; nay, 'tis often attended with pain, when the object is in distress. Desire in general is rather uneasy then pleasant. 'Tis true, indeed, all the passions and affections justify themselves; while they continue (as Malebranche[10] expresses it), we generally approve our being thus affected on this occasion, as an innocent disposition, or a just one, and condemn a person who would be otherwise affected on the like occasion. So the sorrowful, the angry, the jealous, the compassionate, approve their several passions on the apprehended occasion; but we should not therefore conclude, that sorrow, anger, jealousy or pity are pleasant, or chosen for their concomitant pleasure. The case is plainly thus: the frame of our nature on the occasions which move these passions, determines us to be thus affected, and to approve our affection at least as innocent. Uneasiness generally attends our desires of any kind; and this sensation tends to fix our attention, and to continue the desire. But the desire does not terminate upon the removal of the pain accompanying the desire, but upon some other event: the concomitant pain is what we seldom reflect upon, unless when it is very violent. Nor does any desire or affection terminate upon the pleasure which may accompany the affection; much less is it raised by an act of our will, with a view to obtain this pleasure.

---

10 [Nicolas Malebranche (1638–1715), philosopher in the Cartesian tradition.]

The same reflection will show, that we do not by an act of our will raise in ourselves that benevolence which we approve as virtuous, with a view to obtain future pleasures of self-approbation by our moral sense. Could we raise affections in this manner, we should be engaged to any affection by the prospect of an interest equivalent to this of self-approbation, such as wealth or sensual pleasure, which with many tempers are more powerful; and yet we universally own, that disposition to do good offices to others, which is raised by these motives, is not virtuous: how can we then imagine, that the virtuous benevolence is brought upon us by a motive equally selfish?

But what will most effectually convince us of the truth on this point, is reflection upon our own hearts, whether we have not a desire of the good of others, generally without any consideration or intention of obtaining these pleasant reflections on our own virtue: nay, often this desire is strongest where we least imagine virtue, in natural affection toward offspring, and in gratitude to a great benefactor; the absence of which is indeed the greatest vice, but the affections themselves are not esteemed in any considerable degree virtuous. The same reflection will also convince us, that these desires or affections are not produced by choice, with a view to obtain this private good.

In like manner, if no volition of ours can directly raise affections from the former prospects of interest, no more can any volition raise them from prospects of eternal rewards, or to avoid eternal punishments, the former motives differ from these only as smaller from greater, shorter from more durable. If affections could be directly raised by volition, the same consideration would make us angry at the most innocent or virtuous character, and jealous of the most faithful and affectionate, or sorrowful for the prosperity of a friend, which we all find to be impossible. The prospect of a future state, may, no doubt, have a greater indirect influence, by turning our attention to the qualities in the objects naturally apt to raise the required affection, than any other consideration...

'Tis indeed probably true in fact, that those who are engaged by prospect of future rewards to do good offices to mankind, have generally the virtuous benevolence jointly exciting them to action; because, as it may appear hereafter, benevolence is natural to mankind, and still operates where there is no opposition of apparent interest, or where any contrary apparent interest is overbalanced by a greater interest. Men, conscious of this, do generally approve good offices, to which motives of a future state partly excited the agent. But that the approbation is founded upon the apprehension of a disinterested desire partly exciting the agent, is plain from this, that not only obedience to an evil deity in doing mischief, or even in performing trifling ceremonies, only from hope of reward, or prospect of avoiding punishment, but even obedience to a good deity only from the same motives, without any love or gratitude towards him, and with a perfect indifference about the happiness or misery of mankind, abstracting from this private interest, would meet with no approbation. We plainly see that a change of external circumstances of interest under an evil deity, without any change in the disposition of the agent, would lead him into every cruelty and inhumanity.

Gratitude toward the deity is indeed disinterested, as it will appear hereafter. This affection therefore may obtain our approbation, where it excites to action, though there were no other benevolence exciting the agent. But this case scarce occurs among men. But where the sanction of the law is the only motive of action, we could expect no more benevolence, nor no other affection, than those in one forced by the law to be curator to a person for whom he has not the least regard. The agent would so manage as to save himself harmless if he could, but would be under no concern about the success of his attempts, or the happiness of the person whom he served, provided he performed the task required by law; nor would any spectator approve this conduct.

V. The other scheme is more plausible: that benevolence is not raised by any volition upon prospect of advantage; but that we desire the happiness of others, as conceiving it necessary to procure some pleasant sensations which we expect to feel upon seeing others happy; and that for like reason we have aversion to their misery. This connection between the happiness of others and our pleasure, say they, is chiefly felt among friends, parents and children, and eminently virtuous characters. But this benevolence flows as directly from self-love as any other desire.

To show that this scheme is not true in fact, let us consider, that if in our benevolence we only desired the happiness of others as the means of this pleasure to ourselves, whence is it that no man approves the desire of the happiness of others as a means of procuring wealth or sensual pleasure to ourselves? If a person had wagered concerning the future happiness of a man of such veracity, that he would sincerely confess whether he were happy or not; would this wagerer's desire of the happiness of another, in order to win the wager, be approved as virtuous? If not, wherein does this desire differ from the former? Except that in one case there is one pleasant sensation expected, and in the other case other sensations: for by increasing or diminishing the sum wagered, the interest in this case may be made either greater or less than that in the other.

Reflecting on our own minds again will best discover the truth. Many have never thought upon this connection: nor do we ordinarily intend the obtaining of any such pleasure when we do generous offices. We all often feel delight upon seeing others happy, but during our pursuit of their happiness we have no intention of obtaining this delight. We often feel the pain of compassion; but were our sole ultimate intention or desire the freeing ourselves from this pain, would the deity offer to us either wholly to blot out all memory of the person in distress, to take away this connection, so that we should be easy during the misery of our friend on the one hand, or on the other would relieve him from his misery, we should be as ready to choose the former way as the latter; since either of them would free us from our pain, which upon this scheme is the sole end proposed by the compassionate person. Don't we find in ourselves that our desire does not terminate upon the removal of our own pain? Were this our sole intention, we would run away, shut our eyes, or divert our thoughts from the miserable object, as the readiest way of removing our pain: this we seldom do, nay, we crowd about such objects, and voluntarily expose ourselves to this pain, unless calm reflection upon our inability to relieve the miserable, countermand our inclination, or some selfish affection, as fear of danger, overpower it.

To make this yet clearer, suppose that the deity should declare to a good man that he should be suddenly annihilated, but at the instant of his exit it should be left to his choice whether his friend, his children, or his country should be made happy or miserable for the future, when he himself could have no sense of either pleasure or pain from their state. Pray would he be any more indifferent about their state now, that he neither hoped nor feared anything to himself from it, than he was in any prior period of his life? Nay, is it not a pretty common opinion among us, that after our decease we know nothing of what befalls those who survive us? How comes it then that we do not lose, at the approach of death, all concern for our families, friends, or country? Can there be any instance given of our desiring anything only as the means of private good as violently when we know that we shall not enjoy this good many minutes, as if we expected the possession of this good for many years? Is this the way we compute the value of annuities?

How the disinterested desire of the good of others should seem inconceivable, 'tis hard to account: perhaps 'tis owing to the attempts of some great men to give definitions of simple ideas. Desire, say they, is uneasiness, or uneasy sensation upon the absence of any good. Whereas desire is as distinct from uneasiness, as volition is from sensation. Don't they themselves often speak of our desiring to remove uneasiness? Desire then is different from uneasiness, however a sense of uneasiness accompanies it, as extension does the idea of colour, which yet is a very distinct idea. Now wherein lies the impossibility of desiring the happiness of another without conceiving it as the means of obtaining anything farther, even as we desire our own happiness without farther view? If any allege, that we desire our own happiness as the means of removing the uneasiness we feel in the absence of happiness, then at least the desire of removing our own uneasiness is an ultimate desire: and why may we not have other ultimate desires?

'But can any being be concerned about the absence of an event which gives it no uneasiness?' Perhaps superior natures desire without uneasy sensation. But what if we cannot? We may be uneasy while a desired event is in suspense and yet not desire this event only as the means of removing this uneasiness: nay, if we did not desire the event without view to this uneasiness, we should never have brought the uneasiness upon ourselves by desiring it. So likewise we may feel delight upon the existence of a desired event, when yet we did not desire the event only as the means of obtaining this delight; even as we often receive delight from events which we had an aversion to.

VI. If anyone should ask, since none of these motives of self-interest excite our benevolence, but we are in virtuous actions intending solely the good of others, to what purpose serves our moral sense, our sense of pleasure from the happiness of others? To what purpose serves the wise order of nature, by which virtue is even made generally advantageous in this life? To what end are eternal rewards appointed and revealed? The answer to these questions was given partly already: all these motives may make us desire to have benevolent affections, and consequently turn our attention to those qualities in objects which excite them; they may overbalance all apparent contrary motives, and all temptations to vice. But farther, I hope it will be still thought an end worthy of the deity, to make the virtuous happy, by a wise constitution of nature, whether the virtues were in every action intending to obtain this happiness or not. Beneficent actions tend to the public good; it is therefore good and kind to give all possible additional motives to them; and to excite men, who have some weak degrees of good affection, to promote the public good more vigorously by motives of self-interest or even to excite those who have no virtue at all to external acts of beneficence, and to restrain them from vice…

From the whole it may appear, that there is in human nature a disinterested ultimate desire of the happiness of others; and that our moral sense determines us only to approve actions as virtuous, which are apprehended to proceed partly at least from such desire.

VII. As to malice, human nature seems scarce capable of malicious disinterested hatred, or a sedate ultimate desire of the misery of others, when we imagine them no way pernicious to us, or opposite to our interest: and for that hatred which makes us oppose those whose interests are opposite to ours, it is only the effect of self-love, and not of disinterested malice. A sudden passion may give us wrong representations of our fellow-creatures, and for a little time represent them as absolutely evil; and during this imagination perhaps we may give some evidences of disinterested malice: but as soon as we reflect upon human nature, and form just conceptions, this unnatural passion is allayed, and only self-love remains, which may make us, from self-interest, oppose our adversaries.

Everyone at present rejoices in the destruction of our pirates; and yet let us suppose a band of such villains cast in upon some desolate island, and that we were assured some fate would confine them there perpetually, so that they should disturb mankind no more: now let us calmly reflect, that these persons are capable of knowledge and counsel, may be happy and joyful, or may be involved in misery, sorrow, and pain; that they may return to a state of love, humanity, kindness, and become friends, citizens, husbands, parents, with all the sweet sentiments which accompany these relations: then let us ask ourselves, when self-love, or regard to the safety of better men, no longer makes us desire their destruction, and when we cease to look upon them under the ideas suggested by fresh resentment of injuries done to us or our friends, as utterly incapable of any good moral quality; whether we would wish them the fate of Cadmus's[11] army, by plunging their swords in each other's breast, or a worse fate by the most exquisite tortures; or rather, that they should recover the ordinary affections of men, become kind, compassionate, and friendly; contrive laws, constitutions, governments, properties; and form an honest happy society with marriages, and 'Relations dear, and all the charities / Of father, son, and brother'?[12]

I fancy the latter would be the wish of every mortal, notwithstanding our present just abhorrence of them from self-interest, or public love, and desire of promoting the interest of our friends who are exposed to their fury. Now this plainly evidences, that we scarce ever have any sedate malice against any person, or ultimate desire of his misery. Our

---

11 [Legendary Greek hero.]

12 [Book IV, lines 756–7 of Milton's poem, *Paradise Lost.*]

calm ill-will is only from opposition of interest; or if we can entertain sedate malice, it must be toward a character apprehended necessarily and unalterably evil in a moral sense; such as a sudden passion sometimes represents our enemies to us: yet perhaps no such being occurs to us among the works of a good deity.

VIII. Having offered what may perhaps prove, that neither our [esteem] or benevolence is founded on self-love, or views of interest; let us see 'if some other affections, in which virtue may be placed, arise from self-love'; such as fear, or reverence, arising from an apprehension of goodness, power, and justice. For nobody apprehends any virtue in base dread and servitude toward a powerful evil being: this is indeed the meanest selfishness. Now the same arguments which prove esteem to be disinterested, will prove this honourable reverence to be so too; for it plainly arises from an apprehension of amiable qualities in the person, and love toward him, which raises an abhorrence of offending him. Could we reverence a being because it was our interest to do so, a third person might bribe us into reverence toward a being neither good, nor powerful, which everyone sees to be a jest. And this we might show to be common to all other passions, which have been reputed virtuous.

IX. There is one objection against disinterested good-will, which occurs from considering, 'that nothing so effectually excites our love toward rational agents, as their beneficence, and especially toward ourselves; whence we are led to imagine, that our love of persons, as well as irrational objects, flows entirely from self-interest.' But let us here examine ourselves more narrowly. Do we only wish well to the beneficent, because it is our interest to do so? Or do we choose to love them, because our love is the means of procuring their bounty? If it be so, then we could indifferently love any character, even to obtain the bounty of a third person; or we could be bribed by a third person to love the greatest villain heartily, as we may be bribed to external offices: now this is plainly impossible. Nay, farther, is not our good-will the consequent of bounty, and not the means of procuring it? External show, obsequiousness, and dissimulation may precede an opinion of beneficence; but real love always presupposes it, and will necessarily arise even when we expect no more, from consideration of past benefits.

Or can anyone say he only loves the beneficent, as he does a field or garden because of its advantage? His love then must cease toward one who has ruined himself in kind offices to him, when he can do him no more; as we cease to love an inanimate object, which ceases to be useful, unless a poetical prosopopoeia animate it, and raise an imaginary gratitude, which is indeed pretty common. Beneficence then must increase our good-will, as it raises complacence, which is still attended with stronger degrees of benevolence: and hence we love even those who are beneficent to others.

In the benefits which we receive ourselves, we are more fully sensible of their value, and of the circumstances of the action, which are evidences of a generous temper in the donor; and from the good opinion we have of ourselves, we are apt to look upon the kindness as better employed, than when it is bestowed on others, of whom perhaps we have less favourable sentiments. It is however sufficient to remove the objection, that bounty from a donor apprehended as morally evil, or extorted by force, or conferred with some view of self-interest, will not procure real good-will; nay, it may raise indignation, if we suspect dissimulation of love, or a design to allure us into anything dishonourable; whereas wisely employed bounty is always approved, and gains love to the author from all who hear of it.

If then no good-will toward persons arises from self-love, or views of interest, and all virtue flows from good-will, or some other affection equally disinterested; it remains, 'that there must be some other affection than self-love, or interest, which excites us to the actions we call virtuous.'

Had we no other ultimate desire but that of private advantage, we must imagine that every rational being acts only for its own advantage; and however we may call a beneficent being a good being, because it acts for our advantage, yet upon this scheme we should not be apt to think there is any beneficent being in nature, or a being who acts for the good of others. Particularly, if there is no sense of excellence in public love, and promoting the happiness of others, whence should this persuasion arise, 'that the deity will make the virtuous happy?' Can we prove that it is for the advantage of the deity to do so? This I fancy will be looked upon as very absurd, by many who yet expect mercy and beneficence in the deity. And if there be such dispositions in the deity, where is the impossibility of some small degree of this public love in his creatures? And why must they be supposed incapable of acting but from self-love?

In short, without acknowledging some other principle of action in rational agents than self-love, I see no foundation to expect beneficence, or rewards from God or man, farther than it is the interest of the benefactor; and all expectation of benefits from a being whose interests are independent on us, must be perfectly ridiculous. What should engage the deity to reward virtue? Virtue is commonly supposed, upon this scheme, to be only a consulting our own happiness in the most artful way, consistently with the good of the whole; and in vice the same thing is foolishly pursued, in a manner which will not so probably succeed, and which is contrary to the good of the whole. But how is the deity concerned in this whole, if every agent always acts from self-love? And what ground have we, from the idea of infinite power and art, to believe the deity is good in the Christian sense, that is, studious of the good of his creatures? Perhaps the misery of his creatures may give him as much pleasure, as their happiness: and who can find fault, or blame such a being to study their misery? For what else should we expect? A Manichean evil god,[13] is a notion which men would as readily run into, as that of a good one, if there is no excellence in disinterested love, and no being acts but for its own advantage; unless we proved, that the happiness of creatures was advantageous to the deity.

X. Having removed these false springs of virtuous actions, let us next establish the true one, *viz.* some determination of our nature to study the good of others; or some instinct, antecedent to all reason from interest, which influences us to the love of others; even as the moral sense, above explained [see

---

[13] [Manichaeism was a religion founded by the Persian prophet Mani (ca. 216–274) that held that the world is governed by two divine forces, one good and one evil.]

T1.I], determines us to approve the actions which flow from this love in ourselves or others. This disinterested affection, may appear strange to men impressed with notions of self-love, as the sole spring of action, from the pulpit, the schools, the systems, and conversations regulated by them: but let us consider it in its strongest and simplest kinds; and when we see the possibility of it in these instances, we may easily discover its universal extent.

An honest farmer will tell you, that he studies the preservation and happiness of his children, and loves them without any design of good to himself. But say some of our philosophers, 'the happiness of their children gives parents pleasure, and their misery gives them pain; and therefore to obtain the former, and avoid the latter, they study, from self-love, the good of their children.' Suppose several merchants joined in partnership of their whole effects; one of them is employed abroad in managing the stock of the company; his prosperity occasions gain to all, and his losses give them pain for their share in the loss: is this then the same kind of affection with that of parents to their children? Is there the same tender, personal regard? I fancy no parent will say so. In this case of merchants there is a plain conjunction of interest; but whence the conjunction of interest between the parent and child? Do the child's sensations give pleasure or pain to the parent? Is the parent hungry, thirsty, sick, when his children are so? No; but his naturally implanted desire of their good, and aversion to their misery, makes him be affected with joy or sorrow from their pleasures or pains. This desire then is antecedent to the conjunction of interest, and the cause of it, not the effect: it then must be disinterested. 'No, says another sophist, children are parts of ourselves, and in loving them we but love ourselves in them.' A very good answer! Let us carry it as far as it will go. How are they parts of ourselves? Not as a leg or an arm: we are not conscious of their sensations. 'But their bodies were formed from parts of ours.' So is a fly, or a maggot, which may breed in any discharged blood or humour: very dear insects surely! There must be something else then which makes children parts of ourselves; and what is this but that affection, which nature determines us to have toward them? This love makes them parts of ourselves, and therefore does not flow from their being so before. This is indeed a good metaphor; and wherever we find a determination among several rational agents to mutual love, let each individual be looked upon as a part of a great whole, or system, and concern himself in the public good of it.

But [Mandeville, on p. 67 of the *Fable*, Vol. I] observes, 'that natural affection in parents is weak, till the children begin to give evidences of knowledge and affections.' Mothers say they feel it strong from the very first: and yet I could wish, for the destruction of his hypothesis, that what he alleges was true; as I fancy it is in some measure, though we may find in some parents an affection toward idiots. The observing of understanding and affections in children, which make them appear moral agents, can increase love toward them without prospect of interest; for I hope, this increase of love is not from prospect of advantage from the knowledge or affections of children, for whom parents are still toiling, and never intend to be refunded their expenses, or recompensed for their labour, but in cases of extreme necessity. If then the observing a moral capacity can be the occasion of increasing love without self-interest, even from the frame of our nature; pray, may not this be a foundation of weaker degrees of love, where there is no preceding tie of parentage, and extend it to all mankind?

XI. And that this is so in fact, will appear by considering some more distant attachments. If we observe any neighbours, from whom perhaps we have received no good offices, formed into friendships, families, partnerships, and with honesty and kindness assisting each other; pray ask any mortal, if he would not more desire their prosperity when their interests are no way inconsistent with his own, than their misery and ruin? And you shall find a bond of benevolence farther extended than a family and children, although the ties are not so strong. Again, suppose a person, for trade, had left his native country, and with all his kindred had settled his fortunes abroad, without any view of returning; and only imagine he had received no injuries from his country: ask such a man, would he not rather desire the prosperity of his country? Or could he now that his interests are separated from that of his nation, as readily wish that it was laid waste by tyranny, or a foreign power? I fancy his answer would show us a benevolence extended beyond neighbourhoods or acquaintances. Let a man of a composed temper, out of the hurry of his private affairs, only read of the constitution of a foreign country, even in the most distant parts of the earth, and observe art, design, and a study of public good in the laws of this affection; and he shall find his mind moved in their favour; he shall be contriving rectifications and amendments in their constitution, and regret any unlucky part of it, which may be pernicious to their interest; he shall bewail any disaster which befalls them, and accompany all their fortunes with the affections of a friend. Now this proves benevolence to be in some degree extended to all mankind, where there is no interfering interest, which from self-love may obstruct it. And had we any notions of rational agents, capable of moral affections, in the most distant planets, our good wishes would still attend them, and we should desire their happiness. And that all these affections, whether more or less extensive, are properly disinterested, not even founded on any desire of that happiness we may expect in seeing their prosperous condition; may appear from this, that they would continue even at the instant of our death, or entire destruction, as was already observed [see T2.II.iv].

XII. Here we may transiently remark the foundation of what we call national love, or love of one's native country. Whatever place we have lived in for any considerable time, there we have most distinctly remarked the various affections of human nature; we have known many lovely characters; we remember the associations, friendships, families, natural affections, and other human sentiments: our moral sense determines us to approve these lovely dispositions, where we have most distinctly observed them; and our benevolence concerns us in the interests of those persons possessed of them. When we come to observe the like as distinctly in another country, we begin to acquire a national love toward it also; nor has our own country any other preference in our idea, unless it be by an association of the pleasant ideas of our youth, with the buildings, fields, and woods where we received them. This may let us see how tyranny, faction, a neglect of justice, a corruption of manners, and anything which occasions the misery of the subjects, destroys this national love, and the dear idea of a country.

We ought here to observe, that the only reason of that apparent want of natural affection, among collateral relations, is, that these natural inclinations, in many cases, are overpowered by self-love, where there happens any opposition of interests; but where this does not happen, we shall find all mankind under its influence, though with different degrees of strength, according to the nearer or more remote relations they stand in to each other; and according as the natural affection of benevolence is joined with and strengthened by esteem, gratitude, compassion, or other kind affections; or on the contrary, weakened by displicence, anger, or envy.

Sect. III.
The sense of virtue, and the various opinions about it, reducible to one general foundation. The manner of computing the morality of actions

I. If we examine all the actions which are counted amiable anywhere, and inquire into the grounds upon which they are approved, we shall find that in the opinion of the person who approves them, they always appear as benevolent, or flowing from good-will to others, and a study of their happiness, whether the approver be one of the persons beloved, or profited, or not; so that all those kind affections which incline us to make others happy, and all actions supposed to flow from such affections, appear morally good, if, while they are benevolent towards some persons, they be not pernicious to others. Nor shall we find anything amiable in any action whatsoever, where there is no benevolence imagined; nor in any disposition, or capacity, which is not supposed applicable to, and designed for, benevolent purposes. Nay, as was before observed [see T1.II.iii.1 and T1.II.ix.2], the actions which in fact are exceedingly useful, shall appear void of moral beauty, if we know they proceeded from no kind intentions towards others; and yet an unsuccessful attempt of kindness, or of promoting public good, shall appear as amiable as the most successful, if it flowed from as strong benevolence.

II. Hence those affections, which would lead us to do good to our benefactor, shall appear amiable, and the contrary affections odious, even when our actions cannot possibly be of any advantage or hurt to him. Thus a sincere love and gratitude toward our benefactor, a cheerful readiness to do whatever he shall require, how burdensome soever, a hearty inclination to comply with his intentions, and contentment with the state he has placed us in, are the strongest evidences of benevolence we can show to such a person; and therefore they must appear exceedingly amiable. And under these is included all the rational devotion, or religion toward a deity apprehended as good, which we can possibly perform.

We may here transiently observe one circumstance in the frame of our nature, which is wonderfully adapted to promote benevolence, *viz.* that as a benefit conferred necessarily raises gratitude in the person who receives it, so the expressions of this gratitude, even from the meanest of mankind, are wonderfully, delightful to the benefactor. Never were there any mortals so poor, so inconsiderable, whose grateful praise would not be some way delightful and by whom we would not rather choose to be beloved than hated, if their love no way evidenced us to be partners in their vices, or concerned in their meanness. And thus the most abject person obliged is capable, and inclined to make no small addition to our happiness by his love and gratitude, when he is utterly incapable of any other return, and when we expect none from him: Thus, 'a grateful mind / By owing owes not, but still pays, at once / Indebted and discharged.'[14]

As to external performances of religion, they are no doubt very various in different nations and ages; and education may give men opinions, that certain actions are pleasing, and others displeasing to the deity: but then, wherever any external rite of worship is approved, there also it is looked upon to proceed from love toward the deity, or some other affection necessarily joined with love, as reverence, repentance, or sorrow to have offended. So that the general principle of love is the foundation of all the apparent moral

---

14 [Book IV, lines 55–7 of Milton's *Paradise Lost.*]

excellence, even in the most fantastic rites of worship which were ever approved. For as to rites designed only to appease a furious being, no mortal, I fancy, apprehends there is any virtue, or excellence in them; but that they are chosen only as the dishonourable means of avoiding a greater evil. Now as there are various speculative opinions about what is, acceptable to the deity, it necessarily follows, 'that, accordingly, practices, and approbation, must be various; though all the moral goodness of actions is still presumed to flow from love.'

III. Again, that we may see how benevolence is the foundation of all apprehended excellence in social virtues, let us only observe, that amidst the diversity of sentiments on this head among various sects, this is still allowed to be the way of deciding the controversy about any disputed practice, *viz.* to inquire whether this conduct, or the contrary, will most effectually promote the public good. The morality is immediately adjusted, when the natural tendency, or influence of the action upon the universal natural good of mankind, is agreed upon. That which produces more good than evil in the whole, is acknowledge good; and what does not, is counted evil. In this case, we no other way regard the good of the actor, or that of those who are thus inquiring, than as they make a part of the great system…

But let us quit the disputes of the learned, on whom, it may be alleged, custom and education have a powerful influence; and consider upon what grounds, in common life, actions are approved or condemned, vindicated or excused. We are universally ashamed to say an action is just, because it tends to my advantage, or to the advantage of the actor: and we as seldom condemn a beneficent kind action, because it is not advantageous to us, or to the actor. Blame and censure are founded on a tendency to public evil, or a principle of private malice in the agent, or neglect at least of the good of others; on inhumanity of temper, or at least such strong selfishness as makes the agent careless of the sufferings of others: and thus we blame and censure when the action no way affects ourselves. All the moving and persuasive vindications of actions, which may, from some partial evil tendency, appear evil, are taken from this, that they were necessary to some greater good, which counterbalance the evil: 'severity toward a few, is compassion toward multitudes. Transitory punishments are necessary for avoiding more durable evils. Did not some suffer on such occasions, there would be no living for honest men.' And such like. And even when an action cannot be entirely justified, yet how greatly is the guilt extenuated, if we can allege, 'that it was only the effect of inadvertence without malice, or of partial good nature, friendship, compassion, natural affection, or love of a party?' All these considerations show, what is the universal foundation of our sense of moral good, or evil, *viz.* benevolence toward others on the one hand, and malice, or even indolence, and unconcernedness about the apparent public evil on the other. And let it be here observed, that we are so far from imagining all men to act only from self-love, that we universally expect in others a regard for the public; and do not look upon the want of this, as barely the absence of moral good, or virtue, but even as positively evil and hateful.

IV. Contraries may illustrate each other; let us therefore observe the general foundation of our sense of moral evil more particularly. Disinterested malice, or ultimate desire of the misery of others, is the highest pitch of what we count vicious; and every action appears evil, which is imagined to flow from any degree of this affection. Perhaps a violent passion may hurry men into it for a few moments, and our rash angry sentiments of our enemies, may represent them as having such odious dispositions; but it is very probable, from the reasons offered above [see T2.II.iv], that there is no such degree of wickedness in human nature, as, in cold blood, to desire the misery of others, when it is conceived no way useful to our interests.

The frequent, and seemingly unprovoked cruelties of the Nero's and Domitian's,[15] are often alleged in opposition to all this; but perhaps unjustly. Such tyrants are conscious that they are hated by all those whom the world repute virtuous, and they apprehend danger from them: a tyrant looks upon such men as designing, artful, or ambitious, under a false

---

15 [Nero (37–68) and Domitian (51–96), Roman emperors.]

show of virtue. He imagines the surest means of his own safety is to appear terrible, and to deprive his enemies of all hopes of escaping by his compassion. The same of virtue in eminent subjects is matter of envy, and is a reproach upon the tyrant: it weakens his power, and makes them dangerous to him. Power becomes the object of delight to the tyrant; and in ostentation of it, he may break through all regards to justice and humanity. Habits of cruelty can be acquired in such a course. Any of these apparent interests seem better to account for the cruelties of tyrants, than the supposing in them a principle of calm malice without interest, of which the rest of mankind seem entirely incapable.

The temper of a tyrant seems a continued state of anger, hatred, and fear. To form our judgment then of his motives of action, and those of men of like tempers in lower stations, let us reflect upon the apprehensions we form of mankind, when we are under any of those passions which to the tyrant are habitual. When we are under the fresh impressions of an injury, we find, that our minds are wholly filled with apprehensions of the person who injured us, as if he were absolutely evil, and delighted in doing mischief: we overlook the virtues, which, when calm, we could have observed in him: we forget that perhaps he acted from self-love, and not malice, or, it may be, some generous or kind intention toward others. These, probably, are the opinions which a tyrant constantly forms concerning mankind; and having very much weakened all kind affections in himself, however he may pretend to them, he judges of the tempers of others by his own. And were men really such as he apprehends them, his treatment of them would not be very unreasonable. We shall generally find our passions arising suitably to the apprehensions we form of others: if they are rashly formed upon some sudden slight views, it is no wonder if we find dispositions following upon them, very little suited to the real state of human nature.

The ordinary spring of vice then among ordinary men, must be mistaken self-love, made so violent, as to overcome benevolence; or such strong appetites, or passions either selfish, or toward some narrow systems, as overcome our regard to public good; or affections arising from false, and rashly formed opinions of mankind; which we run into through the weakness of our benevolence. When men, who had good opinions of each other, happen to have contrary interests, they are apt to have their good opinions of each other abated, by imagining a designed opposition from malice; without this, they can scarcely hate one another. Thus two candidates for the same office wish each other dead, because that is an ordinary way by which men make room for each other; but if there remains any reflection on each other's virtue, as there sometimes may in benevolent tempers, then their opposition may be without hatred; and if another better post, where there is no competition, were bestowed on one of them, the other shall rejoice at it.

V. Actions which flow solely from self-love, and yet evidence no want of benevolence, having no hurtful effects upon others, seem of a middle nature, neither virtuous nor vicious, and neither raise the love or hatred of the observer. Our reason can indeed discover certain bounds, within which we may not only act from self-love, confidently with the good of the whole; but every mortal's acting thus within these bounds for his own good, is absolutely necessary for the good of the whole; and the want of such self-love would be universally pernicious. Hence, he who pursues his own private good, with an intention also to concur with that constitution which tends to the good of the whole; and much more he who promotes his own good, with a direct view of making himself more capable of serving God, or doing good to mankind; acts not only innocently, but also honourably, and virtuously: for in both these cases, benevolence concurs with self-love to excite him to the action. And thus a neglect of our own good may be morally evil, and argue a want of benevolence toward the whole. But when self-love breaks over the bounds above-mentioned, and leads us into actions detrimental to others, and to the whole; or makes us insensible of the generous kind affections; then it appears vicious, and is disapproved. So also when upon any small injuries, or sudden resentment, or any weak superstitious suggestions, our benevolence becomes so faint, as to let us entertain odious conceptions of men, or any part of them, without just ground, as if they were wholly evil, or malicious, or as if they were a worse sort of beings than they really are; these conceptions must lead us into malevolent affections, or at least weaken our good ones, and make us really vicious.

VI. Benevolence is a word fit enough in general, to denote the internal spring of virtue, as Bishop Cumberland always uses it. But to understand this more distinctly, 'tis highly necessary to observe, that under this name are included very different dispositions of the soul. Sometimes, [1.] it denotes a calm, extensive affection, or good-will toward all beings capable of happiness or misery: sometimes, 2. a calm deliberate affection of the soul toward the happiness of certain smaller systems or individuals; such as patriotism, or love of a country, friendship, parental affection, as it is in persons of wisdom and self-government: or, 3. the several kind particular passions of love, pity, sympathy, congratulation. This distinction between the calm motions of the will, affections, dispositions, or instincts of the soul, and the several turbulent passions, is elsewhere more fully considered [see T4.VI.iv and T3.II.iii].

Now though all these different dispositions come under the general character of benevolent, yet as they are in nature different, so they have very different degrees of moral beauty. The first sort is above all amiable and excellent: 'tis perhaps the sole moral perfection of some superior natures; and the more this prevails and rules in any human mind, the more amiable the person appears, even when it not only checks and limits our lower appetites, but when it controuls our kind particular passions, or counteracts them. The second sort of benevolence is more amiable than the third, when it is sufficiently strong to influence our conduct: and the third sort, though of a lesser moral dignity, is also beautiful, when it is no way opposite to these more noble principles. And when it is opposite, though it does not justify such actions as are really detrimental to greater systems, yet it is a strong extenuating circumstance, and much alleviates the moral deformity. We are all sensible of this, when any person from friendship, parental affection, or pity, has done something hurtful to larger societies.

VII. Here we must also observe, that every moral agent justly considers himself as a part of this rational system, which may be useful to the whole; so that he may be, in part, an object of his own universal benevolence. Nay farther, as was hinted above, he may see, that the preservation of the system requires everyone to be innocently solicitous about himself. Hence he may conclude, that an action which brings greater evil to the agent, than good to others, however it may evidence the strength of some particular kind attachment, or of a virtuous disposition in the agent, yet it must be founded upon a mistaken opinion of its tendency to public good; so that a man who reasoned justly, and considered the whole, would not be led into it, by the calm extensive benevolence, how strong soever it were; nor would he recommend it to the practice of others; however he might acknowledge, that the detriment arising to the agent from a kind action, did evidence a strong virtuous disposition. Nay farther, if any good was proposed to the pursuit of an agent, and he had a competitor in every respect only equal to himself; the highest universal benevolence possible would not lead a wise man to prefer another to himself, were there no ties of gratitude, or some other external circumstance, to move him to yield to his competitor. A man surely of the strongest benevolence, may just treat himself as he would do a third person, who was a competitor of equal merit with the other; and as his preferring one to another, in such a case, would argue no weakness of benevolence; so no more would he evidence it by preferring himself to a man of only equal abilities.

Wherever a regard to myself tends as much to the good of the whole, as regard to another; or where the evil to myself is equal to the good obtained for another; though by acting, in such cases, for the good of another, I really show a very amiable disposition; yet by acting in the contrary manner, from regard to myself, I evidence no evil disposition, nor any want of the most extensive benevolence; since the moment of good to the whole is, in both cases, exactly equal. And let it be here observed, that this does not supersede the necessity of liberality, or gratuitous gifts, although in such actions the giver loses what the other receives; since the moment of good to any person, in any given case, is in a compound proportion of the quantity of the good itself, and the indigence of the person. Hence it appears, that a gift may make a much greater addition to the happiness of the receiver, than the diminution it occasions in the happiness of the giver: and that the most useful and important gifts are those from the wealthy to the indigent. Yet gifts from equals are not useless, since they often increase the happiness or moral importance of persons, may compensate numbers and in equal numbers, the virtue is as the quantity of the happiness, or natural good; or that the virtue is in a compound ratio of the quantity of good, and number of enjoyers. In the same manner, the moral evil, or vice, is as the degree of misery, and number of sufferers; so that that action is best, which procures the greatest happiness for the greatest numbers; and that worst, which, in like manner, occasions misery.

Again, when the consequences of actions are of a mixed nature, partly advantageous, and partly pernicious; that action is good, whose good effects preponderate the evil by being useful to many, and pernicious to few; and that evil, which is otherwise. Here also the moral importance of characters, or dignity of persons may compensate numbers; as may also the degrees of happiness or misery: for to procure an inconsiderable good to many, but an immense evil to few, may be evil; and an immense good to few, may preponderate a small evil to many.

But the consequences which affect the morality of actions, are not only the direct and natural effects of the actions themselves; but also all those events which otherwise would not have happened. For many actions which have no immediate of natural evil effects, nay, which actually produce good effects, may be evil; if a man foresees, that the evil consequences, which will probably flow from the folly of others, upon his doing of such actions, are so great as to overbalance all the good produced by those actions, or all the evils which would flow from the omission of them: and in such cases the probability is to be computed on both sides. Thus, if an action of mine will probably, through the mistake or corruption of others, be made a precedent in unlike cases, to very evil actions; or when my action, though good in itself, will probably provoke men to very evil actions, upon some mistaken notion of their right; any of these considerations foreseen by me, may make such an action of mine evil, whenever the evils which will probably be occasioned by the action, are greater than the evils occasioned by the omission.

And this is the reason, that many laws prohibit actions in general, even when some particular instances of those actions would be very useful; because a universal allowance of them, considering the mistakes men would probably fall into, would be more pernicious than a universal prohibition; nor could there be any more special boundaries fixed between the right and wrong cases. In such cases, it is the duty of persons to comply with the generally useful constitution; or if in some very important instances, the violation of the law would be of less evil consequence, than obedience to it, they must patiently resolve to undergo those penalties, which the state has, for valuable ends to the whole, appointed: and this disobedience will have nothing criminal in it.

IX [sic.]. 'Tis here to be observed, that though every kind affection abstractly considered, is approved by our moral sense, yet all sorts of affections or passions which pursue the good of others are not equally approved, or do not seem in the same degree virtuous. Our calm affections, either private or public, are plainly distinct from our particular passions; calm self-love quite distinct from hunger, thirst, ambition, lust, or anger; so calm good-will toward others is different from pity, passionate love, the parental affection, or the passion of particular friends. Now every kind passion, which is not pernicious to others, is indeed approved as virtuous and lovely: and yet a calm good-will toward the same persons appears more lovely. So calm good-will toward a small system is lovely and preferable to more passionate attachments; and yet a more extensive calm benevolence is still more beautiful and virtuous; and the highest perfection of virtue is a universal calm good-will toward all sensitive natures. Hence it is, that we condemn particular attachments, when inconsistent with the interest of great societies, because they argue some defect in that more noble principle, which is the perfection of virtue [see T4.VI.iv and T3.II.ii].

X. From these observations, we may see what actions our moral sense would most recommend to our election, as the most perfectly virtuous: *viz.* such as appear to have the most universal unlimited tendency to the greatest and most extensive happiness of all the rational agents, to whom our influence can reach. All beneficence, even toward a part, is amiable, when not inconsistent with the good of the whole: but this is a smaller degree of virtue, unless our beneficence be restrained by want of power, and not want of love to the whole. All strict attachments to parties, sects, factions, have but an imperfect species of beauty, even when the good of the whole requires a stricter attachment to a part, as in natural affection, or virtuous friendships; except when some parts are so eminently useful to the whole, that even universal benevolence does determine us with special care and affection to study their interests. Thus universal benevolence would incline us to a more strong concern for the interests of great and generous characters in a high station, or make us more earnestly study the interests of any generous society, whose whole constitution was contrived to promote universal good. Thus a good fancy in architecture would lead a man, who was not able to bear the expense of a completely regular building, to choose such a degree of ornament as he could keep uniformly through the whole, and not move him to make a vain unfinished attempt in one part, of what he foresaw he could not succeed in as to the whole. And he would condemn a great profusion of ornament on one part, above the proportion of the whole, unless that part be some eminent place of the edifice, such as the chief front, or public entrance; the adorning of which would beautify the whole more than an equal expense of ornament on any other part.

This constitution of our sense, whereby the moral beauty of actions, or dispositions, increases according to the number of persons to whom the good effects of them extend; whence also actions which flow from the nearer attachments of nature, such as that between the sexes, and the love of our offspring, do not appear so virtuous as actions of equal moment of good towards persons less attached to us; has been chosen by the author of nature for this good reason, 'that the more limited instincts tend to produce a smaller moment of good, because confined to small numbers. Whereas the more extensive calm instinct of good-will, attended with power, would have no bounds in its good effects, and would never lead into any evil, as the particular passions may: and hence it is made more lovely to our sense, that we might be induced to cultivate and strengthen it; and make it check even kind passions, when they are opposite to a greater good.'

X [sic.]. From this primary idea of moral good in actions, may arise a notion of moral good in those dispositions, whether natural or acquired, which enable us to do good to others; or which are presumed to be designed, and acquired or cultivated for that purpose; or are natural indications of a good temper, and usually accompany it. And hence those abilities, while nothing appears contrary to our presumption, may increase our approbation of the possessor of them; but when they are imagined to be intended for public mischief they make us hate him the more: such are a penetrating judgment, a tenacious memory, a quick invention; patience of labour, pain, hunger, watching; a contempt of wealth, rumour, death. These may be rather called natural abilities, than moral qualities: and we seem to have a natural relish for them distinct from moral approbation. But if we plainly see them maliciously employed, they make the agent more detestable.

XI. To find a universal rule to compute the morality of any actions, with all their circumstances, when we judge of the actions by ourselves, or by others, we must observe the following propositions or axioms.

1. The moral importance of any agent, or the quantity of public good he produces, is in a compound proportion of his benevolence and abilities. For 'tis plain that his good offices depend upon these two jointly. In like manner, the quantity of private good which any agent obtains for himself, is in a like compound proportion of his selfish principles, and his abilities. We speak here only of the external goods of this world, which one pursues from some selfish principles. For as to internal goods of the mind, these are most effectually obtained by the exercise of other affections than those called selfish, even those which carry the agent beyond himself toward the good of others.

2. In comparing the virtues of different agents, when the abilities are equal, the moments of public good are proportioned to the goodness of the temper, or the benevo-

lence; and when the tempers are equal, the quantities of good are as the abilities.

3. The virtue then or goodness of temper is directly as the moment of good, when other circumstances are equal, and inversly as the abilities. That is to say, where the abilities are greatest, there is less virtue evidenced in any given moment of good produced.

4. But as the natural consequences of our actions are various, some good to ourselves, and evil to the public; and others evil to ourselves, and good to the public; or either useful both to ourselves and others, or pernicious to both; the entire spring of good actions is not always benevolence alone; or of evil, malice alone (nay, sedate malice is rarely found); but in most actions we must look upon self-love as another force, sometimes conspiring with benevolence, and assisting it, when we are excited by views of private interest, as well as public good; and sometimes opposing benevolence, when the good action, is any way difficult or painful in the performance, or detrimental in its consequences to the agent.

These selfish motives shall be hereafter more fully explained [see T2.V, not included here]; here we may in general denote them by the word interest: which when it concurs with benevolence, in any action capable of increase or diminution, must produce a greater quantity of good, than benevolence alone in the same abilities; and therefore when the moment of good, in an action partly intended for the good of the agent, is but equal to the moment of good in the action of another agent, influenced only by benevolence, the former is less virtuous; and in this case the interest must be deducted to find the true effect of the benevolence or virtue. In the same manner, when interest is opposite to benevolence, and yet is surmounted by it; this interest must be added to the moment, to increase the virtue of the action, or the strength of the benevolence. By interest, in this last case, is understood all the advantage which the agent might have obtained by omitting the action, which is a negative motive to it; and this, when subtracted, becomes positive.

But here we must observe, that no advantage, not intended, although casually, or naturally, redounding to us from the action, does at all affect its morality to make it less amiable: nor does any difficulty or evil unforeseen, or not resolved upon, make a kind action more virtuous; since in such cases self-love neither assists nor opposes benevolence. Nay, self-interest then only diminishes the benevolence, when without this view of interest the action would not have been undertaken, or so much good would not have been produced by the agent; and it extenuates the vice of an evil action, only when without this interest the action would not have been done by the agent, or so much evil have been produced by him.

The sixth axiom[16] only explains the external marks by which men must judge, who do not see into each other's hearts; for it may really happen in many cases, that men may have benevolence sufficient to surmount any difficulty, and yet they may meet with none at all: and in that case, it is certain there is as much virtue in the agent, though he does not give such proof of it to his fellow-creatures, as if he had surmounted difficulties in his kind actions. And this too must be the case with the deity, to whom nothing is difficult.

Since then, in judging of the goodness of temper in any agent, the abilities must come into computation, as is above-mentioned, and none can act beyond their natural abilities; that must be the perfection of virtue, where the moment of good produced equals the ability, or when the being acts to the utmost of his power for the public good; and hence the perfection of virtue, in this case, is as unity. And this may show us the only foundation for the boasting of the Stoics, 'that a creature supposed innocent, by pursuing virtue with his utmost power, may in virtue equal the gods.' For in their case, if the ability be infinite, unless the good to be produced in the whole, be so too, the virtue is not absolutely perfect; and the quotient can never surmount unity.

XII. In the same manner we may compute the degree of depravity of any temper, directly as the moment of evil

---

16 [Earlier editions of the text listed six axioms here (along with corresponding mathematical formulas). Clearly, in making his revisions, Hutcheson overlooked this particular phrasing.]

effected, and inversely as the abilities. The springs of vicious actions however are seldom any real ultimate intention of mischief, and never ultimate deliberate malice; but only sudden anger, self-love, some selfish passion or appetite, some kind attachments to parties, or particular kind passions.

The motives of interest may sometimes strongly cooperate with a depraved temper, or may oppose it, in the same manner that they cooperate with or oppose a good temper. When they cooperate, they diminish the moral evil; when they oppose, they may argue the depravity of temper to be greater, which is able to surmount such motives of interest.

But we must observe, that not only innocence is expected from all mortals, but they are presumed, from their nature, in some measure inclined to public good [see T4.VI] ; so that a bare absence of this desire is enough to make an agent be reputed evil: nor is a direct intention of public evil necessary to make an action evil; it is enough that it flows from self-love, with a plain neglect of the good of others, or an insensibility of their misery, which we either actually foresee, or have a probable presumption of.

It is true indeed, that that public evil which I neither certainly foresee, nor have actual presumptions of, as the consequence of my action, does not make my present action criminal or odious; even although I might have foreseen this evil by a serious examination of my own actions; because such actions do not, at present, evidence either malice, or want of benevolence. But then it is also certain, that my prior negligence, in not examining the tendency of my actions, is a plain evidence of the want of that degree of good affections which is necessary to a virtuous character; and consequently the guilt properly lies in this neglect, rather than in an action which really flows from a good intention. Human laws however, which cannot examine the intentions, or secret knowledge of the agent, must judge in gross of the action itself; presupposing all that knowledge as actually attained, which we are obliged to attain.

In like manner, no good effect, which I did not actually foresee and intend, makes my action morally good; however human laws or governors, who cannot search into men's intentions, or know their secret designs, justly reward actions which tend to the public good, although the agent was engaged to those actions only by selfish views; and consequently had no virtuous disposition influencing him to them.

The difference in degree of guilt between crimes of ignorance, when the ignorance is vincible, and faulty, as to the natural tendency of the action; and crimes of malice, or direct evil intention; consists in this, that the former, by a prior neglect, argues a want of the due degree of benevolence, or right affection; the latter evidences direct evil affections, which are vastly more odious.

XIII. From the former reasonings we may form almost a demonstrative conclusion, 'that we have a sense of goodness and moral beauty in actions, distinct from advantage'; for had we no other foundation of approbation of actions, but the advantage which might arise to us from them, if they were done toward ourselves, we should make no account of the abilities of the agent, but would barely esteem them according to their moment. The abilities come in only to show the degree of benevolence, which supposes benevolence necessarily amiable. Who was ever the better pleased with a barren rocky farm, or an inconvenient house, by being told that the poor farm gave as great increase as it could; or that the house accommodated its possessor as well as it could? And yet in our sentiments of actions, whose moment is very inconsiderable, it shall wonderfully increase the beauty to allege, 'that it was all the poor agent could do for the public, or his friend.'

XIV. The moral beauty of characters arises from their actions, or sincere intentions of the public good, according to their power. We form our judgment of them according to what appears to be their fixed disposition, and not according to any particular sallies of unkind passions; although these abate the beauty of good characters, as the motions of the kind affections diminish the deformity of the bad ones. What then properly constitutes a virtuous character, is not some few accidental motions of compassion, natural affection, or gratitude; but such a fixed humanity, or desire of the public good of all, to whom our influence can extend, as uniformly excites us to all acts of beneficence; and makes us careful of informing ourselves right, concerning the truest methods of serving their interests. Every motion indeed of the kind affections appears in some degree amiable; but we denominate the character from the prevailing principle.

XV. Some will not allow that virtue can spring from passions, instincts, or affections of any kind. 'Tis true, kind particular passions are but a lower kind of goodness, even when they are not opposite to the general good. Those calmer determinations of the will, whether of greater or less extent, or sedate strong affections, or desires of the good of others, are more amiable. These may be as much rooted in the frame of the soul, or there may be as natural a disposition to them as to particular passions. They tell us, that 'virtue should wholly spring from reason'; as if reason or knowledge of any true proposition could ever move to action where there is no end proposed, and no affection or desire toward that end… [see T4.I; also see T4.II, not included here.]

The ultimate end, according to many of our moralists, is to each one his own happiness; and yet this he seeks by instinct; now may not another instinct toward the public, or the good of others, be as proper a principle of virtue, as the instinct toward private happiness? This is certain, that whereas we behold the selfish actions of others, with indifference at best, we see something amiable in every action which flows from kind affections or passions toward others; if they be conducted by prudence, so as any way to attain their end, confidently with the general good. If it be said, 'that actions from instinct are not the effect of prudence and choice'; this objection holds full as strongly against the actions which flow from self-love; since the use of our reason is as requisite to find the proper means of promoting public good, as private good. And as it must be an instinct, or a determination previous to reason, which makes us pursue private good, as well as public good as our end; there is the same occasion for prudence and choice, in the election of proper means for promoting of either. I see no harm in supposing, 'that men are naturally disposed to virtue, and not left merely indifferent, until some prospect of interest allures them to it.' Surely, the supposition of a benevolent universal instinct would recommend human nature, and its author, more to the love of a good man, and leave room enough for the exercise of our reason, in contriving and settling rights, laws, constitutions in inventing arts, and practicing them so as to gratify, in the most effectual manner, that generous inclination. And if we must bring in self-love to make virtue rational, a little reflection will discover, as shall appear hereafter, that this benevolence is our greatest happiness; and thence we may resolve to cultivate, as much as possible, this sweet disposition, and to despise every opposite interest. Not that we can be truly virtuous, if we intend only to obtain the pleasure which arises from beneficence, without the love of others: nay, this very pleasure is founded on our being conscious of disinterested love to others, as the spring of our actions. But self-interest may be our motive in studying to raise these kind affections, and to continue in this agreeable state; though it cannot be the sole or principal motive of any action, which to our moral sense appears virtuous...

From the preceding reasonings we shall only draw this one inference, which seems the most joyful imaginable, even to the lowest rank of mankind, *viz.* 'that no external circumstances of fortune, no involuntary disadvantages, can exclude any mortal from the most heroic virtue.' For how small soever the moment of public good be, which anyone can accomplish, yet if his abilities are proportionably small, the virtue may be as great as any whatsoever. Thus, not only the prince, the statesman, the general, are capable of true heroism, though these are the chief characters, whose fame is diffused through various nations and ages: but when we find in an honest trader, the kind friend, the faithful prudent adviser, the charitable and hospitable neighbour, the tender husband, and affectionate parent, the sedate yet cheerful companion, the generous assistant of merit, the cautious allayer of contention and debate, the promoter of love and good understanding among acquaintances; if we consider, that these were all the good offices which his station in the world gave him an opportunity of performing to mankind, we must judge this character really as amiable, as those, whose external splendor dazzles an injudicious world into an opinion, 'that they are the only heroes in virtue.'

From *Illustrations on the Moral Sense*

How far a regard to the deity is necessary to make an action virtuous. 'What degrees of affection necessary to innocence'

...IV. But previously to these inquiries we must consider 'what degrees or kinds of affection are necessary to obtain the simple approbation of innocence?' 'Tis plain, the bare absence of malice is not enough. We may have the general benevolence toward a mere sensitive nature, which had no other desire but self-love; but we can apprehend no moral goodness in such a being: nay, 'tis not every small degree of kind affections which we approve. There must be some proportion of kind affections to the other faculties in any nature, particularly to its understanding and active powers to obtain approbation. Some brutes evidence small degrees of good-will, which make them be approved in their kind; but the same degrees would not be approved in a man. There is a higher degree expected in mankind, to which, if they do not come up, we do not account them innocent. It is not easy to fix precisely that degree which we approve as innocent by our moral sense. Every kind affection, if it be considered only with relation to its own object, is indeed approved; such as natural affection, gratitude, pity, friendship: and yet when we take a more extensive view of the tendency of some actions proceeding even from these affections, we may often condemn these actions when they are apprehended as pernicious to larger systems of mankind. In the same manner we often condemn actions done from love to a particular country, when they appear to be pernicious to mankind in general. In like manner, self-preservation and pursuing private advantage, abstractly considered, is innocent: but when it is apprehended as very pernicious in any case to the safety of others, it is condemned.

Mankind are capable of large extensive ideas of great societies. And it is expected of them, that their general benevolence should continually direct and limit, not only their selfish affections, but even their nearer attachments to others: that their desire of public good, and aversion to public misery, should overcome at least their desire of positive private advantages, either to themselves, or their particular favourites so as to make them abstain from any action which would be positively pernicious or hurtful to mankind, however beneficial it might be to themselves, or their favourites. To undergo positive evil for the sake of positive good to others, seems some degree of virtue above innocence, which we do not universally expect: but to reject positive attainable good, either for ourselves or our particular favourites, rather than occasion any considerable misery to others, is requisite to obtain the approbation of innocence. The want of this degree we condemn as positive evil; and an agent must rise above it by positive services to mankind, with some trouble and expense to himself, before we approve him as virtuous. We seem indeed universally to expect, from all men those good offices which give the agent no trouble or expense: whoever refuses them is below innocence. But we do not positively condemn those as evil, who will not sacrifice their private interest to the advancement of the positive good of others, unless the private interest be very small, and the public good very great.

But as the desire of positive private good is weaker than aversion to private evil, or pain; so our desire of the positive good of others, is weaker than our aversion to their misery: it seems at least requisite to innocence, that the stronger public affection, *viz.* our aversion to the misery of others, should surmount the weaker private affection, the desire of positive private good; so that no prospect of good to ourselves, should engage us to that which would occasion prepollent misery to others. It is in like manner requisite to innocence, that our aversion to the misery of greater or equal systems, should surmount our desire of the positive good of these to which we are more particularly attached.

How far it may be necessary to the character of innocence to submit to smaller private pains to prevent the greater sufferings of others, or to promote some great positive advantages; or how far the happiness of private systems should be neglected for the happiness of the greater, in order to obtain the approbation of innocence, it is perhaps impossible precisely to determine, or to fix any general rules; nor indeed is it necessary. Our business is not to find out 'at how cheap a rate we can purchase innocence, but to know what is most noble, generous and virtuous in life.' This we know consists in sacrificing all positive interests, and bearing all private evils for the public good: and in submitting also the interests of all smaller systems to the interests of the whole: without any other exception or reserve than this, that every man may look upon himself as a part of this system, and consequently not sacrifice an important private interest to a less important interest of others. We may find the same sort of difficulty about all our other senses, in determining precisely what objects are indifferent, or where pleasure ends, and disgust begins, though the higher degrees of the grateful and ungrateful are easily distinguished.

It is also very difficult to fix any precise degree of affection toward the deity, which should be barely requisite to innocence. Only in general we must disapprove that temper, which, upon apprehension of the perfect goodness of the deity, and of his innumerable benefits to mankind, has not stronger affections of love and gratitude toward him, than those toward any other being. Such affections would necessarily raise frequent attention and consideration of our actions; and would engage us, if we apprehended any of them to be offensive to him, or contrary to that scheme of events in which we apprehended the deity to delight, to avoid them with a more firm resolution than what we had in any other affairs. Positive virtue toward the deity must go farther than a resolute abstaining from offence, by engaging us with the greatest vigour, to do whatever we apprehend as positively pleasing, or conducive to those ends in which we apprehended the deity delights. It is scarce conceivable that any good temper can want such affections toward the deity, when once he is known, as were above supposed necessary to innocence. Nor can we imagine positive degrees of goodness of temper above innocence, where affections toward the deity do not arise proportionably.

What is here said relates only to the apprehensions of our moral sense, and not to those degrees of virtue which the deity may require by revelation: and everyone's heart may inform him whether or no he does not approve, at least as innocent, those who omit many good offices which they might possibly have done, provided they do a great deal of good; those who carefully abstain from every apprehended offence toward the deity, though they might possibly be more frequent in acts of devotion. 'Tis true indeed, the omission of what we know to be required is positively evil: so that by a revelation we may be obliged to farther services than were requisite previously to it, which we could not innocently omit, after this revelation is known: but we are here only considering our moral sense...

From *An Inquiry Concerning Moral Good and Evil*

Sect. IV.
All mankind agree in this general foundation of their approbation of moral actions.
The grounds of the different opinions about morals

...II. ...But to prove that men are void of a moral sense, we should find some instances of cruel, malicious actions, done without any motive of interest, real or apparent; and approved without any opinion of tendency to public good, or flowing from good-will: we must find a country where murder in cold blood, tortures, and everything malicious, without any advantage, is, if not approved at least looked upon with indifference, and raises no aversion toward the actors in the unconcerned spectators: we must find men with whom the treacherous, ungrateful, cruel, are in the same account with the generous, friendly, faithful, and humane; and who approve the latter, no more than the former, in all cases where they are not affected by the influence of these dispositions, or when the natural good or evil befalls other persons. And it may be questioned, whether the universe, though large enough, and stored with no inconsiderable variety of characters, will yield us any instance, not only of a nation, but even of a club, or a single person, who will think all actions indifferent, but those which regard his own concerns.

III. From what has been said, we may easily account for the vast diversity of moral principles, in various nations and ages; and the grounds of this diversity are principally these:

1st. Different opinions of happiness, or natural good, and of the most effectual means to advance it. Thus in one country, where there prevails a courageous disposition, where liberty is counted a great good, and war an inconsiderable evil, all insurrections in defence of privileges will have the appearance of moral good to our sense, because of their appearing benevolent; and yet the same sense of moral good in benevolence shall in another country, where the spirits of men are more abject and timorous, where civil war appears the greatest natural evil, and liberty no great purchase, make the same actions appear odious. So in Sparta, where through contempt of wealth the security of possessions was not much regarded, but the thing chiefly desired, as naturally good to the state, was to abound in a hardy shifting youth; theft, if dexterously performed, was so little odious, that it received the countenance of a law to give it impunity.

But in these, and all other instances of the like nature, the approbation is founded on benevolence, because of some real, or apparent tendency to the public good. For we are not to imagine, that this sense should give us, without observation, ideas of complex actions, or of their natural tendencies to good or evil: it only determines us to approve benevolence, whenever it appears in any action, and to hate the contrary. So our sense of beauty does not, without reflection, instruction or observation, give us ideas of the regular solids, temples, cirques, and theatres; but determines us to approve and delight in uniformity amidst variety, wherever we observe it. Let us read the preambles of any laws we count unjust, or the vindications of any disputed practice by the moralists, and we shall find, no doubt, that men are often mistaken in computing the excess of the natural good or evil consequences of certain actions; but the ground on which any action is approved, is still some tendency to the greater natural good of others, apprehended by those who approve it.

The same reason may remove also the objections against the universality of this sense, from some stories of travellers, concerning strange cruelties practiced toward the aged, or children, in certain countries. If such actions be done in such angry passions, they only prove, that other motives, or springs of action, may overpower benevolence in its strongest ties: and if they really be universally allowed, looked upon as innocent, and vindicated; it is certainly under some appearance of benevolence; such as to secure them from insults of enemies, to avoid the infirmities of age, which perhaps appear greater evils than death, or to free the vigorous and useful citizens from the charge of maintaining them, or the troubles of attendance upon them. A love of pleasure and ease, may in the immediate agents be stronger in some instances, than gratitude toward parents, or natural affection to children. But that such nations are continued, notwithstanding all the toil in educating their young, is still a sufficient proof of natural affection: for I fancy we are not to imagine any nice laws in such places, compelling parents to a proper education of some certain number of their offspring. We know very well that an appearance of public good was the ground of laws equally barbarous, enacted by Lycurgus and Solon,[17] of killing the deformed, or weak, to prevent a burdensome crowd of useless citizens.

A late ingenious author[18] has justly observed the absurdity of the monstrous taste, which has possessed both the readers and writers of travels. They are sparing enough in accounts of the natural affections, the families, associations, friendships, clans, of the Indians; and as transiently do they mention their abhorrence of treachery among themselves; their proneness, to mutual aid, and to the defence of their several states; their contempt of death in defence of their country, or upon points of honour. 'These are but common stories. No need to travel to the Indies for what we see in Europe every day.' The entertainment therefore in these ingenious studies consists chiefly in exciting horror, and making men stare. The ordinary employment of the bulk of the Indians in support of their wives and offspring, or relations, has nothing of the prodigious: but a human sacrifice, a feast upon enemies carcasses, can raise a horror and admiration of the wondrous barbarity of Indians, in nations no strangers to the massacre at Paris, the Irish rebellion, or the journals of the inquisition. These they behold with religious veneration; but the Indian sacrifices, flowing from a like per-

---

17 [Lycurgus (ca. 800–730 B.C.E.) and Solon (ca. 638–558 B.C.E.), statesmen of Sparta and Athens, respectively.]

18 [Anthony Ashley Cooper, 3rd Earl of Shaftesbury (1671–1713), philosopher, politician. See Shaftesbury's *Characteristics of Men, Manners, Opinions, Times* (Cambridge: Cambridge UP, 1999, pp. 154–6).]

version of humanity by superstition, raise the highest abhorrence and amazement. What is most surprising in these studies, is the wondrous credulity of some gentlemen of great pretensions in other matters to caution of assent, for these marvellous memoirs of monks, friars, sea-captains, pirates; and for the histories, annals, chronologies, received by oral tradition, or hieroglyphics.

Men have reason given them, to judge of the tendencies of their actions, that they may not stupidly follow the first appearance of public good; but it is still some appearance of good which they pursue. And it is strange, that reason is universally allowed to men, notwithstanding all the stupid ridiculous opinions received in many places; and yet absurd practices, founded upon those very opinions, shall seem an argument against any moral sense, although the bad conduct is not owing to any irregularity in the moral sense, but to a wrong judgment or opinion. If putting the aged to death, with all its consequences, really tends to the public good, and the lesser misery of the aged, it is, no doubt, justifiable; nay, perhaps the aged choose it, in hopes of a future state. If a deformed or weak race could never, by ingenuity and art, make themselves useful to mankind, but should grow an absolutely unsupportable burden, so as to involve a whole state in misery, it is just to put them to death. This all allow to be just, in the case of an over-loaded boat in a storm. And as for killing of their children, when parents are sufficiently stocked, it is perhaps practiced, and allowed from self-love; but I can scarce think it passes for a good action anywhere. If wood or stone, or metal be deities, have government, and power, and have been the authors of benefits to us; it is morally amiable to praise and worship them. Or if the true deity be pleased with worship before statues, or any other symbol of some more immediate presence or influence; image-worship is virtuous. If he delights in sacrifices, penances, ceremonies, cringings; they are all laudable. Our sense of virtue generally leads us exactly enough according to our opinions; and therefore the absurd practices which prevail in the world, are much better arguments that men have no reason, than that they have no moral sense of beauty in actions.

IV. The next ground of diversity in sentiments, is the diversity of systems, to which men, from foolish opinions, confine their benevolence. We intimated above [see T2.III.x.1], that it is regular and beautiful, to have stronger benevolence toward the morally good parts of mankind, who are useful to the whole, than toward the useless or pernicious. Now, if men receive a low or base opinion of any body, or sect of men; if they imagine them bent upon the destruction of the more valuable parts, or but useless burdens of the earth; benevolence itself will lead them to neglect the interests of such, and to suppress them. This is the reason why, among nations who have high notions of virtue, every action toward an enemy may pass for just; why Romans and Greeks could approve of making those they called barbarians, slaves.

A late ingenious author [Shaftesbury, pp. 51–3 of the *Characteristics*] justly observes, 'that the various sects, parties, factions, cabals of mankind in larger societies, are all influenced by a public spirit: that some generous notions of public good, some strong friendly dispositions, raise them at first, and excite men of the same faction or cabal to the most disinterested mutual succour and aid: that all the contentions of the different factions, and even the fiercest wars against each other, are influenced by a sociable public spirit in a limited system.' But certain it is, that men are little obliged to those, who often artfully raise and foment this party spirit; or cantonize them into several sects for the defence of very trifling causes. Associations for innocent commerce, or manufactures; cabals for defence of liberty, against a tyrant; or even lower clubs for pleasantry, or improvement by conversation, are very amiable and good. But when men's heads are filled with some trifling opinions; when designing men raise in their minds some unaccountable notion of sanctity and religion, in tenets or practices, which neither increase our love to God, or our own species; when the several factions are taught to look upon each other as odious, contemptible, profane, because of their different tenets or opinions; even when these tenets, whether true or false, are perhaps perfectly useless to the public good; when the keenest passions are raised about such trifles, and men begin to hate each other for what, of itself, has no evil in it; and to love the zealots of their own sect for what is no way valuable; nay, even for their fury, rage, and malice against opposite sects (which is what all parties commonly call zeal); 'tis then no wonder, if our moral sense be much impaired, and our natural notions of good and evil almost lost, when our admiration, and love or contempt, and hatred, are thus perverted from their natural objects.

If any mortals are so happy as never to have heard of the party-tenets of most of our sects; or, if they have heard of them, have either never espoused any sect, or all equally; they bid fairest for a truly natural and good disposition, because their tempers have never been soured about vain trifles; nor have they contracted any sullenness or rancour against any part of their own kind. If any opinions deserve to be contended for, they are those which give us lovely ideas of the deity, and of our fellow-creatures: if any opinions deserve opposition, they are such as raise scruples in our minds about the goodness of providence, or represent our fellow-creatures as base and selfish, by instilling into us some ill-natured, cunning, shrewd insinuations, 'that our most generous actions proceed wholly from selfish views.' This wise philosophy of some moderns, after Epicurus, must be fruitful of nothing but discontent, suspicion, and jealousy; a state infinitely worse than any little transitory injuries, to which we might be exposed by a good-natured credulity. But thanks be to the kind author of our nature, that in spite of such opinions, our nature itself leads us into friendship, trust, and mutual confidence.

Were we freely conversant with robbers, who show a moral sense in the equal or proportionable division of their prey, and in faith to each other, we should find they have their own sublime moral ideas of their party, as generous, courageous, trusty, nay honest too; and that those we call honest and industrious, are imagined by them to be mean-spirited, selfish, churlish, or luxurious, on whom that wealth is ill bestowed, which therefore they would apply to better uses, to maintain gallanter men, who have a right to a living as well as their neighbours, who are their professed enemies. Nay, if we observe the discourse of our professed debauchees, our most dissolute rakes, we shall find their vices clothed, in their imaginations, with some amiable dress of liberty, generosity, just resentment against the contrivers of artful rules to enslave men, and rob them of their pleasures.

Perhaps never any men pursued vice long with peace of mind, without some such deluding imagination of moral good [see T2.VI.ii.1, not included here], while they may be still inadvertent to the barbarous and inhuman consequences of their actions. The idea of an ill-natured villain is too frightful ever to become familiar to any mortal. Hence we shall find that the basest actions are dressed in some tolerable mask. What others call avarice, appears to the agent a prudent care of a family, or friends; fraud, artful conduct; malice and revenge, a just sense of honour, and a vindication of our right in possessions, or fame; fire and sword, and deflation, among enemies, a just thorough defence of our country; persecution, a zeal for the truth, and for the eternal happiness of men, which heretics oppose. In all these instances, men generally act from a sense of virtue upon false opinions, and mistaken benevolence; upon wrong or partial views of public good, and the means to promote it; or upon very narrow systems formed by like foolish opinions. It is not a delight in the misery of others, or malice, which occasions the horrid crimes which fill our histories; but generally an injudicious, unreasonable enthusiasm for some kind of limited virtue. 'Let the wise bear the name of madman, the just of unjust, should he pursue virtue herself beyond due bonds.'[19]

V. The last ground of diversity which occurs are the false opinions of the will or laws of the deity. To obey these we are determined from gratitude, and a sense of right imagined in the deity, to dispose at pleasure the fortunes of his creatures. This is so abundantly known to have produced follies, superstitions, murders, devastations of kingdoms, from a sense of virtue and duty, that it is needless to mention particular instances. Only we may observe, 'that all those follies, or barbarities, rather confirm than destroy the opinion of a moral

---

19 [Book I of Horace's *Epistles*, Epistle VI, lines 15–16. Fairclough's translation.]

sense'; since the deity is believed to have a right to dispose of his creatures; and gratitude to him, if he be conceived good, must move us to obedience to his will: if he be not conceived good, self-love may overcome our moral sense of the action which we undertake to avoid his fury.

As for the vices which commonly proceed from love of pleasure, or any violent passion, since generally the agent is soon sensible of their evil, and that sometimes amidst the heat of the action, they only prove, 'that this moral sense and benevolence may be overcome by the more importunate solicitations of other desires.'

VI. Before we leave this subject, it is necessary to remove one of the strongest objections against what has been said so often, *viz.* 'that this sense is natural, and independent on custom and education.' The objection is this, 'that we shall find some actions always attended with the strongest abhorrence, even at first view, in some whole nations, in which there appears nothing contrary to benevolence; and that the same actions shall in another nation be counted innocent, or honourable. Thus incest, among Christians, is abhorred at first appearance as much as murder; even by those who do not know or reflect upon any necessary tendency of it to the detriment of mankind. Now we generally allow, that what is from nature in one nation, would be so in all. This abhorrence therefore cannot be from nature, since in Greece, the marrying half-sisters was counted honourable; and among the Persian Magi, the marrying of mothers. Say they then, may not all our approbation or dislike of actions arise the same way from custom and education?'

The answer to this may be easily found from what is already said. Had we no moral sense natural to us, we should only look upon incest as hurtful to ourselves, and shun it, and never disapprove other incestuous persons, more than we do a broken merchant; so that still this abhorrence supposes a sense of moral good. And farther, it is true, that many who abhor incest do not know, or reflect upon the natural tendency of some sorts of incest to the public detriment: but wherever it is hated, it is apprehended as offensive to the deity, and that it exposes the person concerned to his just vengeance. Now it is universally acknowledged to be the grossest ingratitude and baseness, in any creature, to counteract the will of the deity, to whom it is under such obligations. This then is plainly a moral evil quality apprehended in incest, and reducible to the general foundation of malice, or rather want of benevolence. Nay farther, where this opinion, 'that incest is offensive to the deity,' prevails, incest must have another direct contrariety to benevolence; since we must apprehend the incestuous, as exposing an associate, who should be dear to him by the ties of nature, to the lowest state of misery and baseness, infamy and punishment. But in those countries where no such opinion prevails of the deity's abhorring or prohibiting incest; if no obvious natural evils attend it, it may be looked upon as innocent. And farther, as men who have the sense of tasting, may, by company and education, have prejudices against meats they never tasted, as unsavoury, so may men who have a moral sense, acquire an opinion by implicit faith, of the moral evil of actions, although they do not themselves discern in them any tendency to natural evil; imagining that others do: or, by education, they may have some ideas associated, which raise an abhorrence without reason. But without a moral sense we could receive no prejudice against actions, under any other view than as naturally disadvantageous to ourselves.

VII. The universality of this moral sense, and that it is antecedent to instruction, may appear from observing the sentiments of children, upon hearing the stories with which they are commonly entertained as soon as they understand language. They always passionately interest themselves on that side where kindness and humanity are found; and detest the cruel, the covetous, the selfish, or the treacherous. How strongly do we see their passions of joy, sorrow, love, and indignation, moved by these moral representations, even though there have been no pains taken to give them ideas of a deity, of laws, of a future state, or of the more intricate tendency of the universal good to that of each individual!

Sect. V.
A farther confirmation, that we have practical dispositions to virtue implanted in our nature; with a farther explication of our benevolent instincts of various kinds, with the additional motives of interest, *viz.* honour, shame, and pity.

'Love of honour' and 'moral sense, not from love of honour'

...III. From considering that natural gratitude, and love toward our benefactors, which was already shown to be disinterested [see T2.II.vi]; we are easily led to consider another determination of our minds, equally natural with the former, which is to desire and delight in the good opinion and love of others; even when we expect no other advantage from them, except what flows from this constitution, whereby honour is made an immediate good. This desire of honour I would call ambition, had not custom joined some evil ideas to that word, making it denote such a violent desire of honour, and of power also, as will make us stop at no base means to obtain them. On the other hand, we are by nature subjected to a grievous sensation of misery, from the unfavourable opinions of others concerning us, even when we dread no other evil from them. This we call shame; which in the same manner is constituted an immediate evil, as we said honour was an immediate good.

Now, were there no moral sense, or had we no other idea of actions but as advantageous or hurtful, I see no reason why we should be delighted with honour, or subjected to the uneasiness of shame; or how it could ever happen, that a man, who is secure from punishment for any action, should ever be uneasy at its being known to all the world. The world may have an opinion of him as pernicious to his neighbours; but what subjects his ease to this opinion of the world? Why, perhaps, he shall not be so much trusted henceforward in business, and so suffer loss. If this be the only reason of shame, and it has no immediate evil or pain in it, distinct from fear of loss, then, wherever we expose ourselves to loss, we should be ashamed, and endeavour to conceal the action: and yet it is quite otherwise.

A merchant, for instance, lest it should impair his credit, conceals a shipwreck, or a very bad market, which he has sent his goods to. But is this the same with the passion of shame? Has he that anguish, that dejection of mind, and self-condemnation, which one shall have whose treachery is detected? Nay, how will men sometimes glory in their losses, when in a cause imagined morally good, though they really weaken their credit in the merchant's sense; that is, the opinion of their wealth, or fitness for business? Was any man ever ashamed of impoverishing himself to serve his country, or his friend?...

VI. To explain what has been said of the power of honour: suppose a state or prince, observing the money which is drawn out of England by Italian musicians, should decree honours, statues, titles, for great musicians: this would certainly excite all who had hopes of success, to the study of music; and all men would look upon the good performers as useful subjects, as well as very entertaining. But would this give all men a good ear, or make them delight in harmony? Or could it ever make us really love a musician, who studyed nothing but his own gain, in the same manner we do a patriot, or a generous friend? I doubt, not. And yet friendship, without the assistance of statues, or honours, can make persons appear exceedingly amiable.

Let us take another instance: suppose statues and triumphal arches were decreed, as well as a large sum of money, to the discoverer of the longitude, or any other useful invention in mathematics: this would raise a universal desire of such knowledge from self-love; but would men therefore love a mathematician, as they do a virtuous man? Would a mathematician love every person who had attained perfection in that knowledge, wherever he observed it, although he knew that it was not accompanied with any love to mankind, or study of their good, but with ill-nature, pride, covetousness? In short, let us honour other qualities by external show as much as we please; if we do not discern a benevolent intention in the application, or presume upon it, we may look upon these qualities as useful, enriching, or otherwise advantageous to anyone who is possessed of them; but they shall never meet with those endearing sentiments of esteem and love, which our nature determines us to appropriate to benevolence or virtue.

Love of honour, and aversion to shame, may often move us to do actions, for which others profess to honour us, even though we see no good in them ourselves: and compliance with the inclinations of others, as it evidences humanity, may procure some love to the agent, from spectators who see no moral good in the action itself. But without some sense of good in the actions, men shall never be fond of such actions in solitude, nor ever love anyone for perfection in them, or for practising them in solitude; and much less shall they be dissatisfied with themselves, when they act otherwise in solitude. Now this is the case with us, as to virtue; and therefore we must have, by nature, a moral sense of it antecedent to honour…

Four

The Passions & the Moral Life

From *An Essay on the Nature and Conduct of the Passions and Affections*

Sect. I.
A general account of our several senses and desires, selfish or public

The nature of human actions cannot be sufficiently understood without considering the affections and passions; or those modifications, or actions of the mind consequent upon the apprehension of certain objects or events, in which the mind generally conceives good or evil. In this inquiry we need little reasoning, or argument, since certainty is only attainable by distinct attention to what we are conscious happens in our minds.

I. 'Objects, actions, or events obtain the name of good, or evil, according as they are the causes, or occasions, mediately, or immediately, of a grateful, or ungrateful perception to some sensitive nature.' To understand therefore the several kinds of good, or evil, we must apprehend the several powers of perception or senses natural to us.

It is by some power of perception, or sense, that we first receive the ideas of these objects we are conversant with, or by some reasoning upon these perceived objects of sense. By sensation we not only receive the image or representation, but some feelings of pleasure or pain; nay sometimes the sole perception is that of pleasure or pain, as in smells, and the feelings of hunger and thirst. The pleasures or pains perceived, are sometimes simple, without any other previous idea, or any image, or other concomitant ideas, save those of duration or time, which accompanies every perception, whether of sense, or inward consciousness. Other pleasures arise only upon some previous idea, or image, or assemblage, or comparison of ideas. These pleasures presupposing previous ideas, were called perceptions of an internal sense, in a former treatise [see T1]. Thus regularity and uniformity in figures, are no less grateful than tastes, or smells; the harmony of notes, is more grateful than simple sounds… In like manner affections, tempers, sentiments, or actions, reflected upon in ourselves, or observed in others, are the constant occasions of agreeable or disagreeable perceptions, which we call approbation, or dislike. These moral perceptions arise in us as necessarily as any other sensations; nor can we alter, or stop them, while our previous opinion or apprehension of the affection, temper, or intention of the agent continues the same; any more than we can make the taste of wormwood sweet, or that of honey bitter.

If we may call 'every determination of our minds to receive ideas independently on our will, and to have perceptions of pleasure and pain, a sense,' we shall find many other senses beside those commonly explained. Though it is not easy to assign accurate divisions on such subjects, yet we may reduce them to the following classes, leaving it to others to arrange them as they think convenient. A little reflection will show that there are such natural powers in the human mind, in whatever order we place them. In the 1st class are the external senses, universally known. In the 2nd, the pleasant perceptions arising from regular, harmonious, uniform objects; as also from grandeur and novelty. These we may call, after Mr. Addison, the pleasures of the imagination; or we may call the power of receiving them, an internal sense. Whoever dislikes this name may substitute another. 3. The next class of perceptions we may call a public sense, *viz.* 'our determination to be pleased with the happiness of others, and to be uneasy at their misery.' This is found in some degree in all men, and was sometimes called… *sensus communis*[1] by some of the ancients. This inward pain of compassion cannot be called a sensation of sight. It solely arises from an opinion of misery felt by another, and not immediately from a visible form. The same form presented to the eye by the exactest painting, or the action of a player, gives no pain to those who remember that there is no misery felt. When men by imagination conceive real pain felt by an actor, without recollecting that it is merely feigned, or when they think of the real story represented, then, as there is a confused opinion of real misery, there is also pain in compassion. 4. The fourth class we may call the moral sense, by which 'we perceive virtue or vice, in ourselves, or others.' This is plainly distinct from the former class of perceptions, since many are strongly affected with the fortunes of others, who seldom reflect upon virtue or vice, in themselves, or others, as an object: as we may find in natural affection, compassion, friendship, or even general benevolence to mankind, which connect our happiness or pleasure with that of others, even when we are not reflecting upon our own temper, nor delighted with the perception of our own virtue. 5. The fifth class is a sense of honour, which makes the approbation, or gratitude, of others, for any good actions we have done, the necessary occasion of pleasure; and their dislike, condemnation, or resentment of injuries done by us, the occasion of that uneasy sensation called shame, even when we fear no further evil from them.

There are perhaps other perceptions distinct from all these classes, such as some ideas 'of decency, dignity, suitableness to human nature in certain actions and circumstances; and of an indecency, meanness, and unworthiness, in the contrary actions or circumstances, even without any conception of moral good, or evil.' Thus the pleasures of sight, and hearing, are more esteemed than those of taste or touch: the pursuits of the pleasures of the imagination are more approved than those of simple external sensations. Plato makes one of his dialogists[2] [see T2.V.vii, not included

---

1 [Common sense.]

2 [Hutcheson refers here to *Hippias Major*, a dialogue by the philosopher Plato (427–347 B.C.E.).]

here] account for this difference from a constant opinion of innocence in this sort of pleasures, which would reduce this perception to the moral sense. Others may imagine that the difference is not owing to any such reflection upon their innocence, but that there is a different sort of perceptions in these cases, to be reckoned another class of sensations.

II. Desires arise in our mind, from the frame of our nature, upon apprehension of good or evil in objects, actions, or events, to obtain for ourselves or others the agreeable sensation, when the object or event is good; or to prevent the uneasy sensation, when it is evil. Our original desires and aversions may therefore be divided into five classes, answering to the classes of our senses. 1. The desire of sensual pleasure (by which we mean that of the external senses, of taste and touch chiefly); and aversion to the opposite pains. 2. The desires of the pleasures of imagination or internal sense [see T1], and aversion to what is disagreeable to it. 3. Desires of the pleasures arising from public happiness, and aversion to the pains arising from the misery of others. 4. Desires of virtue, and aversion to vice, according to the notions we have of the tendency of actions to the public advantage or detriment. 5. Desires of honour, and aversion to shame [see T2.V.iii–viii, partly included here].

And since we are capable of reflection, memory, observation, and reasoning about the distant tendencies of objects and actions, and not confined to things present, there must arise, in consequence of our original desires, 'secondary desires of everything imagined useful to gratify any of the primary desires, and that with strength proportioned to the several original desires, and the imagined usefulness, or necessity, of the advantageous object.' Thus as soon as we come to apprehend the use of wealth or power to gratify any of our original desires, we must also desire them. Hence arises the universality of these desires of wealth and power since they are the means of gratifying all other desires. 'How foolish then is the inference, some would make, from the universal prevalence of these desires, that human nature is wholly selfish, or that each one is only studious of his own advantage; since wealth or power are as naturally fit to gratify our public desires, or to serve virtuous purposes, as the selfish ones?'

'How weak also are the reasonings of some recluse moralists, who condemn in general all pursuits of wealth or power, as below a perfectly virtuous character': since wealth and power are the most effectual means, and the most powerful instruments, even of the greatest virtues, and most generous actions? The pursuit of them is laudable, when the intention is virtuous; and the neglect of them, when honourable opportunities offer, is really a weakness. This justifies the poet's sentiments: 'One dreads the burden as too big for his small soul and small body: another lifts it and carries it to the end. Either manhood is an empty name, or the man who makes the attempt justly aims at honor and reward.'[3]

Further, the laws or customs of a country, the humour of our company may have made strange associations of ideas, so that some objects, which of themselves are indifferent to any sense, yet by reason of some additional grateful idea, may become very desirable; or by like addition of an ungrateful idea may raise the strongest aversion. Thus many a trifle, when once it is made a badge of honour, an evidence of some generous disposition, a monument of some great action, may be impatiently pursued, from our desire of honour. When any circumstance, dress, state, posture, is constituted as a mark of infamy, it may become in like manner the object of aversion, though in itself most inoffensive to our senses. If a certain way of living, of receiving company, of showing courtesy, is once received among those who are honoured; they who cannot bear the expense of all this, may be made uneasy at their condition, though much freer from trouble than that of higher stations. Thus dress, retinue, equipage, furniture, behaviour, and diversions are made matters of considerable importance by additional ideas [see T1.I.vii; also see T2.VI.vi, not included here]. Nor is it in vain that the wisest and greatest men regard these things; for however it may concern them to break such associations in their own minds, yet, since the bulk of mankind will retain them, they must comply with their sentiments and humours

---

3 [Book I of Horace's *Epistles*, Epistle XVII, lines 39–42. Fairclough's translation.]

in things innocent, as they expect the public esteem, which is generally necessary to enable men to serve the public.

Should anyone be surprised at this disposition in our nature to associate any ideas together for the future, which once presented themselves jointly, considering what great evils, and how much corruption of affections is owing to it, it may help to account for this part of our constitution, to consider, 'that all our language and much of our memory depends upon it': so that were there no such associations made, we must lose the use of words, and a great part of our power of recollecting past events; beside many other valuable powers and arts which depend upon them. Let it also be considered that it is much in our power by a vigorous attention either to prevent these affectations, or by abstraction to separate ideas when it may be useful for us to do so.

Concerning our pursuit of honour, it is to be observed, that 'since our minds are incapable of retaining a great diversity of objects, the novelty, or singularity of any object is enough to raise a particular attention to it among many of equal merit': and therefore were virtue universal among men, yet, it is probable, the attention of observers would be turned chiefly toward those who distinguished themselves by some singular ability, or by some circumstance, which, however trifling in its own nature, yet had some honourable ideas commonly joined to it, such as those of magnificence, generosity, or the like. We should perhaps, when we considered sedately the common virtues of others, equally love and esteem them [see T2.III.xv.2]: and yet probably our attention would be generally fixed to those who thus were distinguished from the multitude. Hence our natural love of honour, raises in us an emulation or desire of eminence, either by higher degrees of virtue; or, if we cannot easily or probably obtain it this way, we attempt it in an easier manner, by any circumstance, which, through a confusion of ideas, is reputed honourable.

This desire of distinction has great influence on the pleasures and pains of mankind, and makes them choose things for their very rarity, difficulty, or expense; by a confused imagination that they evidence generosity, ability, or a finer taste than ordinary; nay, often the merest trifles are by these means ardently pursued. A form of dress, a foreign dish, a title, a place, a jewel; a useless problem, a criticism on an obsolete word, the origin of a poetic fable, the situation of a razed town, may employ many an hour in tedious labour: 'So light, so small is what casts down or upbuilds a soul that craves for praise.'[4]

III. There is another division of our desires taken from the persons for whose advantage we pursue or shun any object. 'The desires in which one intends or pursues what he apprehends advantageous to himself, we may call selfish; and those in which we pursue what we apprehend advantageous to others, and do not apprehend advantageous to ourselves, or do not pursue with this view, we may call public or benevolent desires.' If there be a just foundation for this division, it is more extensive than the former division, since each of the former classes may come under either member of this division, according as we are desiring any of the five sorts of pleasures for ourselves, or desiring them for others. The former division may therefore be conceived as a subdivision of the latter.

This division has been disputed since Epicurus who with his old followers, and some of late, who detest other parts of his scheme, maintain, 'that all our desires are selfish or, that what everyone intends or designs ultimately, in each action, is the obtaining pleasure to himself, or the avoiding his own private pain' [see Cicero, *On the Ends of Good and Evil*, Book I].

It requires a good deal of subtlety to defend this scheme, so seemingly opposite to natural affection, friendship, love of a country, or community, which many find very strong in their breasts. The defences and schemes commonly offered, can scarce free the sustainers of this cause from manifest absurdity and affectation. But some [see John Clarke of Hull's remarks on T2 in his *Foundation of Morality in Theory*

---

4 [Book II of Horace's *Epistles*, Epistle I, lines 179–80. Fairclough's translation.]

and Practice[5]] do acknowledge a public sense in many instances; especially in natural affection, and compassion, by which 'the observation of the happiness of others is made the necessary occasion of pleasure, and their misery the occasion of pain to the observer.' That this sympathy with others is the effect of the constitution of our nature, and not brought upon ourselves by any choice, with view to any selfish advantage, they must own: whatever advantage there may be in sympathy with the fortunate, none can be alleged in sympathy with the distressed: and everyone feels that this public sense will not leave his heart, upon a change of the fortunes of his child or friend; nor does it depend upon a man's choice, whether he will be affected with their fortunes or not. But supposing this public sense, they insist, 'that by means of it there is a conjunction of interest: the happiness of others becomes the means of private pleasure to the observer; and for this reason, or with a view to this private pleasure, he desires the happiness of another.' Others deduce our desire of the happiness of others from self-love, in a less specious manner.

If a public sense be acknowledged in men, by which the happiness of one is made to depend upon that of others, independently of his choice, this is indeed a strong evidence of the goodness of the author of our nature. But whether this scheme does truly account for our love of others, or for generous offices, may be determined from the following considerations; which being matters of internal consciousness, everyone can best satisfy himself by attention, concerning their truth and certainty.

Let it be premised, that there is a certain pain or uneasiness accompanying most of our violent desires. Though the object pursued be good, or the means of pleasure, yet the desire of it generally is attended with an uneasy sensation. When an object or event appears evil, we desire to shun or prevent it. This desire is also attended with uneasy sensation of impatience: now this sensation immediately connected

5 [It appears that little is known about this John Clarke's life, including his exact birth and death dates.]

with the desire, is a distinct sensation from those which we dread, and endeavour to shun. It is plain then,

1. 'That no desire of any event is excited by any view of removing the uneasy sensation attending this desire itself.' Uneasy sensations previously felt, will raise a desire of whatever will remove them; and this desire may have its concomitant uneasiness. Pleasant sensations expected from any object may raise our desire of it; this desire too may have its concomitant uneasy sensations: but the uneasy sensation, accompanying and connected with the desire itself, cannot be a motive to that desire which it presupposes. The sensation accompanying desire is generally uneasy, and consequently our desire is never raised with a view to obtain or continue it; nor is the desire raised with a view to remove this uneasy sensation, for the desire is raised previously to it. This holds concerning all desire public or private.

There is also a peculiar pleasant sensation of joy, attending the gratification of any desire, beside the sensation received from the object itself which we directly intended. 'But desire does never arise from a view of obtaining that sensation of joy, connected with the success or gratification of desire; otherwise the strongest desires might arise toward any trifle, or an event in all respects indifferent: since, if desire arose from this view, the stronger the desire were, the higher would be the pleasure of gratification and therefore we might desire the turning of a straw as violently as we do wealth or power.' This expectation of that pleasure which merely arises from gratifying of desire, would equally excite us to desire the misery of others as their happiness; since this pleasure of gratification might be obtained from both events alike.

2. It is certain that 'that desire of the happiness of others which we account virtuous, is not directly excited by prospects of any secular advantage, wealth, power, pleasure of the external senses, reward from the deity, or future pleasures of self-approbation.' To prove this let us consider, 'that no desire of any event can arise immediately or directly from an opinion in the agent, that his

having such a desire will be the means of private good.' This opinion would make us wish or desire to have that advantageous desire or affection; and would incline us to use any means in our power to raise that affection: but no affection or desire is raised in us, directly by our volition or desiring it. That alone which raises in us from self-love the desire of any event, is an opinion that that event is the means of private good. As soon as we form this opinion, a desire of the event immediately arises: but if having the desire, or the mere affection, be imagined the means of private good, and not the existence, of the event desired, then from self-love we should only desire or wish to have the desire of that event, and should not desire the event itself, since the event is not conceived as the means of good.

For instance, suppose God revealed to us that he would confer happiness on us, if our country were happy; then from self-love we should have immediately the subordinate desire of our country's happiness, as the means of our own. But were we assured that, whether our country were happy or not, it should not affect our future happiness; but that we should be rewarded, provided we desired the happiness of our country, our self-love could never make us now desire the happiness of our country, since it is not now conceived as the means of our future happiness, but is perfectly indifferent to it. The means of our happiness is the having a desire of our country's happiness; we should therefore from self-love only wish to have this desire.

It is true indeed in fact, that, because benevolence is natural to us, a little attention to other natures will raise in us good-will towards them, whenever by any opinions we are persuaded that there is no real opposition of interest. But had we no affection distinct from self-love, nothing could raise our desire of the happiness of others, but conceiving their happiness as the means of ours. An opinion that our having kind affections would be the means of our private happiness, would only make us desire to have those affections. Now that affections do not arise upon our wishing to have them, or our volition of raising them, as conceiving the affections themselves to be the means of private good; is plain from this, that if they did thus arise, then a bribe might raise any desire toward any event, or any affection toward the most improper object. We might be hired to love or hate any sort of persons, to be angry, jealous, or compassionate, as we can be engaged into external actions which we all see to be absurd. Now those who allege, that our benevolence may arise from prospect of secular advantage, honour, self-approbation, or future rewards; must own, that the two former are motives only to external actions; and the other two only show that having the desire of the happiness of others, would be the means of private good; while the event desired, *viz.* the happiness of others, is not supposed the means of any private good. But the best defenders of this part of the scheme of Epicurus, acknowledge that 'desires are not raised by volition.'

3. 'There are in men desires of the happiness of others, when they do not conceive this happiness as the means of obtaining any sort of happiness to themselves.' Self-approbation, or rewards from the deity, might be the ends, for obtaining which we might possibly desire or will from self-love, to raise in ourselves kind affections but we could not from self-love desire the happiness of others, except we imagined their happiness to be the means of our own. Now it is certain that sometimes we may have this subordinate desire of the happiness of others, conceived as the means of our own; as suppose one had laid a wager upon the happiness of a person of such veracity, that he would own sincerely whether he were happy or not; when men are partners in stock, and share in profit or loss; when one hopes to succeed to, or some way to share in the prosperity of another; or if the deity had given such threatenings, as they tell us Telamon[6] gave his sons when they went to war, that he would reward or punish one according as others were happy or miserable: in such cases one might have this subordinate desire of another's happiness from self-love.

---

6 [Telamon, king and father of Ajax in Greek mythology.]

But as we are sure the deity has not given such comminations, so we often are conscious of the desire of the happiness of others, without any such conception of it as the means of our own; and are sensible that this subordinate desire is not that virtuous affection which we approve. The virtuous benevolence must be an ultimate desire, which would subsist without view to private good. Such ultimate public desires we often feel, without any subordinate desire of the same event, as the means of private good. The subordinate may sometimes, nay often does concur with the ultimate and then indeed the whole moment of these conspiring desires may be greater than that of either alone: but the subordinate alone is not that affection which we approve as virtuous.

IV. This will clear our way to answer the chief difficulty: 'may not our benevolence be at least a desire of the happiness of others, as the means of obtaining the pleasure of the public sense, from the contemplation of their happiness?' If it were so, it is very unaccountable, that we should approve this subordinate desire as virtuous, and yet not approve the like desire upon a wager, or other considerations of interest. Both desires proceed from self-love in the same manner: in the latter case the desires might be extended to multitudes, if anyone would wager so capriciously; and, by increasing the sum wagered, the motive of interest might, with many tempers, be made stronger than that from the pleasures of the public sense.

Do not we find that we often desire the happiness of others without any such selfish intention? How few have thought upon this part of our constitution which we call a public sense? Were it our only view, in compassion to free ourselves from the pain of the public sense; should the deity propose it to our choice, either to obliterate all ideas of the person, in distress, or to harden our hearts against, all feelings of compassion, on the one hand, while yet the object continued in misery; or on the other hand to relieve him from it; should we not upon this scheme be perfectly indifferent, and choose the former as soon as the latter? Should the deity assure us that we should be immediately annihilated, so that we should be incapable of either pleasure or pain, but that it should depend upon our choice at our very exit, whether our children, our friends, or our country should be happy or miserable; should we not upon this scheme be entirely indifferent? Or, if we should even desire the pleasant thought of their happiness, in our last moment, would not this desire be the faintest imaginable?

It is true, our public sense might be as acute at our exit as ever; as a man's taste of meat or drink and his sensations of hunger and thirst might be as lively the instant before his dissolution as in any part of his life. But would any man have as strong desires of the means of obtaining these pleasures, only with a view to himself, when he was to perish the next moment? It is supposable that any desire of the means of private pleasure can be as strong when we only expect to enjoy it a minute, as when we expect the continuance of it for many years? And yet, it is certain, any good man would as strongly desire at his exit the happiness of others, as in any part of his life, which must be the case with those who voluntarily hazard their lives, or resolve on death for their country or friends. We do not therefore desire it as the means of private pleasure.

Should any allege, that this desire of the happiness of others, after our exit, is from some confused association of ideas; as a miser, who loves nobody, might desire an increase of wealth at his death; or as anyone may have an aversion to have his body dissected, or made a prey to dogs after death: let any honest heart try if the deepest reflection will break this association (if there be any) which is supposed to raise the desire. The closest reflection would be found rather to strengthen it. How would any spectator like the temper of one thus rendered indifferent to all others at his own exit, so that he would not even open his mouth to procure happiness to posterity? Would we esteem it refined wisdom, or a perfection of mind, and not rather the vilest perverseness? It is plain then we feel this ultimate desire of the happiness of others to be a most natural instinct, which we also expect in others, and not the effect of any confused ideas.

The occasion of the imagined difficulty in conceiving disinterested desires, has probably been from the attempting to define this simple idea, desire. It is called an uneasy sensation in the absence of good [see Book II, Chapter 20 of Locke's *Essay Concerning Human Understanding*]. Whereas desire is as distinct from any sensation, as the will is from the understanding or senses. This everyone must acknowledge, who speaks of desiring to remove uneasiness or pain.

We may perhaps find, that our desires are so far from tending always towards private good, that they are oftener employed about the state of others. Nay further, we may have a propensity toward an event, which we neither apprehend as the means of private good, or public. Thus an Epicurean who denies a future state; or, one to whom God revealed that he should be annihilated, might at his very exit desire a future fame, from which he expected no pleasure to himself, nor intended any to others. Such desires indeed no selfish being, who had the modelling of his own nature, would choose to implant in itself. But since we have not this power, we must be content to be thus 'outwitted by nature into a public interest against our will'; as an ingenious author expresses it.[7]

The prospect of any interest may be a motive to us, to desire whatever we apprehend as the means of obtaining it. Particularly, 'if rewards of any kind are proposed to those who have virtuous affections, this would raise in us the desire of having these affections, and would incline us to use all means to raise them in ourselves; particularly to turn our attention to all those qualities in the deity, or our fellows, which are naturally apt to raise the virtuous affections.' Thus it is, that interest of any kind may influence us indirectly to virtue, and rewards particularly may overbalance all motives to vice.

This may let us see, that 'the sanctions of rewards and punishments, as proposed in the gospel, are not rendered useless or unnecessary, by supposing the virtuous affections to be disinterested'; since such motives of interest, proposed and attended to, must incline every person to desire to have virtuous affections, and to turn his attention to everything which is naturally apt to raise them; and must overbalance every other motive of interest, opposite to these affections, which could incline men to suppress or counteract them.

---

7 [Hutcheson provides no citation here but likely has Mandeville in mind.]

Sect. II.
Of the affections and passions: the natural laws of pure affection: the confused sensations of the passions, with their final causes

I. After the general account of sensations, we may consider other modifications of our minds, consequent upon these perceptions, whether grateful, or uneasy. The first which occur to anyone are desire of the grateful perceptions, and aversion to the uneasy, either for ourselves or others. If we would confine the word affection to these two, which are entirely distinct from all sensation, and directly incline the mind to action or volition of motion, we should have less debate about the number or division of affections. But since, by universal custom, this name is applied to other modifications of the mind, such as joy, sorrow, despair, we may consider what universal distinction can be assigned between these modifications, and the several sensations abovementioned; and we shall scarce find any other than this, that we call 'the direct immediate perception of pleasure or pain from the present object or event, the sensation': but we denote by the affection or passion some other 'perceptions of pleasure or pain, not directly raised by the presence or operation the event or object, but by our reflection upon, or apprehension of their present or future existence; so that we expect or judge that the object or event will raise the direct sensations in us.' In beholding a regular building we have the sensation of beauty; but upon our apprehending ourselves possessed of it, or that we can procure this pleasant sensation when we please, we feel the affection of joy. When a man has a fit of the gout, he has the painful sensation; when he is not at present pained, yet apprehends a sudden return of it, he has the affection of sorrow, which might be called a sort of sensation: as the physicians call many of our passions internal senses.

When the word passion is imagined to denote anything different from the affections, it includes a strong brutal impulse of the will, sometimes without any distinct notions of good, public or private, attended with 'a confused sensation either of pleasure or pain, occasioned or attended by some violent bodily motions, which keeps the mind much employed upon the present affair, to the exclusion of everything else, and prolongs or strengthens the affection sometimes to such a degree, as to prevent all deliberate reasoning about our conduct' […see Malebranche's *Search after Truth*, Book V, Chapter 3; also see T3.III.ii, not included here].

II. We have little reason to imagine, that all other agents have such confused sensations accompanying their desires as we often have. Let us abstract from them, and consider in what manner we should act upon the several occasions which now excite our passions, if we had none of these sensations whence our desires become passionate.

There is a distinction to be observed on this subject, between 'the calm desire of good, and aversion to evil, either selfish or public, as they appear to our reason or reflection; and the particular passions towards objects immediately presented to some sense.' Thus nothing can be more distinct than the general calm desire of private good of any kind, which alone would incline us to pursue whatever objects were apprehended as the means of good, and the particular selfish passions, such as ambition, covetousness, hunger, lust, revenge, anger, as they arise upon particular occasions. In like manner our public desires may be distinguished into the general calm desire for the happiness of others, or aversion to their misery upon reflection; and the particular affections or passions of love, congratulation, compassion, natural affection. These particular affections are found in many tempers, where, through want of reflection, the general calm desires are not found: nay, the former may be opposite to the latter, where they are found in the same temper. Sometimes the calm motion of the will conquers the passion, and sometimes is conquered by it. Thus lust or revenge may conquer the calm affection toward private good, and sometimes are conquered by it. Compassion will prevent the necessary correction of a child, or the use of a severe cure, while the calm parental affection is exciting to it. Sometimes the latter prevails over the former. All this is beautifully represented in the 9th book of Plato's *Republic*. We obtain command over the particular passions, principally by strengthening the general desires through frequent reflection, and making them habitual, so as to obtain strength superior to the particular passions…

Again, the calm public desires may be considered as 'they either regard the good of particular persons or societies presented to our senses; or that of some more abstracted or general community, such as a species or system.' This latter sort we may call universal calm benevolence. Now it is plain, that not only particular kind passions, but even calm particular benevolence do not always arise from, or necessarily presuppose, the universal benevolence; both the former may be found in persons of little reflection, where the latter is wanting: and the former two may be opposite to the other, where they meet together in one temper. So the universal benevolence might be where there was neither of the former; as in any superior nature or angel, who had no particular intercourse with any part of mankind.

Our moral sense, though it approves all particular kind affection or passion, as well as calm particular benevolence abstractedly considered; yet it also approves the restraint or limitation of all particular affections or passions, by the calm universal benevolence. To make this desire prevalent above all particular affections, is the only sure way to obtain constant self-approbation.

The calm selfish desires would determine any agent to pursue every object or event, known either by reason or prior experience to be good to itself. We need not imagine any innate idea of good in general, of infinite good, or of the greatest aggregate: much less need we suppose any actual inclination toward any of these, as the cause or spring of all particular desires. It is enough to allow, 'that we are capable by enlarging, or by abstraction, of coming to these ideas: that we must, by the constitution of our nature, desire any apprehended good which occurs apart from any evil: that of two objects inconsistent with each other, we shall desire that which seems to contain the greatest moment of good.' So that it cannot be pronounced concerning any finite good, that it shall necessarily engage our pursuit; since the agent may possibly have the idea of a greater, or see this to be inconsistent with some more valuable object, or that it may bring upon him some prepollent evil. The certain knowledge of any of these things, of probable presumption of them, may stop the pursuit of any finite good. If this be any sort of liberty, it must be allowed to be in men, even by those who maintain 'the desire or will to be necessarily determined by the prepollent motive'; since this very presumption may be a prepollent motive, especially to those, who by frequent attention make the idea of the greatest good always present to themselves on all important occasions. The same may easily be applied to our aversion to finite evils.

There seems to be this degree of liberty even in the acts of the understanding, or in judging, that though the highest certainty or demonstration does necessarily engage our assent, yet we can suspend any absolute conclusion from probable arguments, until we examine whether this apparent probability be not opposite to demonstration, or superior probability on the other side.

This may let us see, that though it were acknowledged that 'men are necessarily determined to pursue their own happiness, and to be influenced by whatever motive appears to be prepollent'; yet they might be proper subjects of a law; since the very sanctions of the law, if they attend to them, may suggest a motive prepollent to all others. In like manner, 'errors may be criminal, where there are sufficient data or object evidence for the truth'; since no demonstration can lead to error, and we can suspend our assent to probable arguments, till we have examined both sides [see T2.VI.vi.4, not included here]. Yet human penalties concerning opinions must be of little consequence, since no penalty can supply the place of argument, or probability to engage our assent, however they may as motives determine our election.

In the calm public desires, in like manner, where there are no opposite desires, the greater good of another is always preferred to the less: and in the calm universal benevolence, the choice is determined by the importance or moment of the good, and the number of those who shall enjoy it.

When the public desires are opposite to the private, or seem to be so, that kind prevails which is stronger or more intense…

V. If it be granted, that we have implanted in our nature the several desires above-mentioned, let us next inquire 'into what state we would incline to bring ourselves, upon the several accidents which now raise our passions supposing that we had the choice of our own state entirely, and were not, by the frame of our nature, subjected to certain sensations independently of our volition.'

If it seems too rash to assert a distinction between affections and passions, or that desire may subsist without any uneasiness, since perhaps we are never conscious of any desire absolutely free from all uneasiness; 'let it be considered, that the simple idea of desire is different from that of pain of any kind, or from any sensation whatsoever: nor is there any other argument for their identity than this, that they occur to us at once: but this argument is inconclusive, otherwise it would prove colour and figure to be the same, or incision and pain.'

There is a middle state of our minds, when we are not in the pursuit of any important good, nor know of any great indigence of those we love. In this state, when any smaller positive good to ourselves or our friend is apprehended to be in our power, we may resolutely desire and pursue it, without any considerable sensation of pain or uneasiness. Some tempers seem to have as strong desires as any, by the constancy and vigour of their pursuits, either of public or private good; and yet give small evidence of any uneasy sensation. This is observable in some sedate men, who seem no way inferior in strength of desire to others: nay, if we consult our hearts, we shall perhaps find, that 'the noblest desire in our nature, that of universal happiness, is generally calm, and wholly free from any confused uneasy sensation': except in some warm tempers, who, by a lively imagination, and frequent attention to general ideas, raise something of passion even toward universal nature.[8] Yea, further, desire may be as strong as possible toward a certainly future event, the fixed time of its existence being also known, and yet we are not conscious of any pain attending such desires. But though this should not be granted to be fact with men, yet the difference of the ideas of desire and pain, may give sufficient ground for abstracting them; and for our making the supposition of their being separated.

---

8 [Here Hutcheson directs us to 'many places' in the writings of Roman emperor and Stoic philosopher, Marcus Aurelius (121–180).]

Upon this supposition then, when any object was desired, if we found it difficult or uncertain to be obtained, but worthy of all the labour it would cost; we would set about it with diligence, but would never choose to bring upon ourselves any painful sensation accompanying our desire, nor to increase our toil by anxiety. Whatever satisfaction we had in our state before the prospect of this additional good, we should continue to enjoy it while this good was in suspense; and if we found it unattainable, we should be just as we were before: we should never choose to bring upon ourselves those frettings which now commonly arise from disappointments. Upon opinion of any impending evil, we should desire and use all means to prevent it, but should never voluntarily bring upon ourselves the uneasy sensation of fear, which now naturally anticipates our misery, and gives us a foretaste of it, more ungrateful sometimes than the suffering itself. If the evil did befall us, we should never choose to increase it, by the sensations of sorrow or despair we should consider what was the sum of good remaining in our state, after subtracting this evil; and should enjoy ourselves as well as a being, who had never known greater good, nor enjoyed greater pleasure, than the absolute good yet remaining with us; or perhaps we should pursue some other attainable good. In the like manner, did our state and the modifications of our mind depend upon our choice, should we be affected upon the apprehended approach of good or evil, to those whom we love; we should have desires of obtaining the one for them, and of defending them from the other, accompanied with no uneasy sensations. We indeed find in fact, that our stronger desires, whether private or public, are accompanied with uneasy sensations but these sensations seem not the necessary result of the desire itself: they depend upon the present constitution of our nature, which might possibly have been otherwise ordered. And in fact we find a considerable diversity of tempers in this matter; some sedate tempers equally desiring either public or private good with the more passionate tempers; but without that degree of ferment, confusion, and pain, which attend the same desires in the passionate.

According to the present constitution of our nature, we find that the modifications or passions of our mind, are very different from those which we would choose to bring upon ourselves, upon their several occasions. The prospect of any considerable good for ourselves, or those we love, raises desire; and this desire is accompanied with uneasy confused sensations, which often occasion fretfulness, anxiety, and impatience. We find violent motions in our bodies; and are often made unfit for serious deliberation about the means of obtaining the good desired. When it is first obtained, we find violent confined sensations of joy, beyond the proportion of the good itself, or its moment to our happiness. If we are disappointed, we feel a sensation of sorrow and dejection, which is often entirely useless to our present state. Foreseen evils are antedated by painful sensations of fear; and reflection, attended with sensations of sorrow, gives a tedious existence to transitory misfortunes. Our public desires are in the same manner accompanied with painful sensations. The presence or suspense of good or evil to others, is made the occasion of the like confused sensations. A little reflection will show, that none of these sensations depend upon our choice, but arise from the very frame of our nature, however we may regulate or moderate them.

VI. Let us then examine 'for what purpose our nature was so constituted, that sensations do thus necessarily arise in us.' Would not those first sort of sensations, by which we apprehend good and evil in the objects themselves, have been sufficient, along with our reason and pure desires, without those sensations attending the very desires themselves, for which they are called passions, or those sensations which attend our reflection upon the presence, absence, or approach of good or evil?

The common answer, that 'they are given to us as useful incitements or spurs to action, by which we are roused more effectually to promote our private good, or that of the public,' is too general and undetermined. What need is there for rousing us to action, more than a calm pure desire of good, and aversion to evil would do, without these confused sensations? Say they, 'we are averse to labour; we are apt to be hurried away by avocations of curiosity or mirth; we are often so indolent and averse to the vigorous use of our powers, that we should neglect our true interest without these soliciting sensations.' But may it not be answered, that if labour and vigorous use of our powers be attended with uneasiness or pain, why should not this be brought into the account? The pursuit of a small good by great toil is really foolish; violent labour may be as pernicious as anything else: why should we be excited to any uneasy labour, except for prepollent good? And, when the good is prepollent, what need of any further incitement than the calm desire of it? The same may be said of the avocations of curiosity or mirth; if their absolute pleasures be greater than that of the good from which they divert us, why should we not be diverted from it? If not, then the real moment of the good proposed is sufficient to engage our pursuit of it, in opposition to our curiosity or mirth.

If, indeed, our aversion to labour, or our propensity to mirth be accompanied with these sensations, then it was necessary that other desires should be attended with like sensations, that so a balance might be preserved. So if we have confused sensation strengthening and fixing our private desires; the like sensation joined to public affections is necessary, lest the former desires should wholly engross our minds: if weight be cast into one scale, as much must be put into the other to preserve an equilibrium. But the first question is, 'whence arose the necessity of such additional incitements on either side?'

It must be very difficult for beings of such imperfect knowledge as we are, to answer such questions: we know very little of the constitution of nature, or what may be necessary for the perfection of the whole. The author of nature has probably formed many active beings, whose desires are not attended with confused sensations, raising them into passions like to ours. There are perhaps orders of rational beings also without these particular limited attachments, to which our natures are subjected; who may perhaps have no parental affection, friendships, or love to a country, or to any special smaller systems; but have universal goodwill to all, and this solely proportioned to the moral excellencies of the several objects, without any other bonds of affection. There is probably an infinite variety of beings, of all possible degrees, in which the sum of happiness exceeds that of misery. We know that our state is absolutely good, notwithstanding a considerable mixture of evil. The goodness of the great author of nature appears even in producing the inferior natures, provided their state in the whole be absolutely good: since we may probably conclude that there are in the universe as many species of superior natures, as was consistent with the most perfect state of the whole...[9] We know not if this globe be a fit place for the habitation of natures superior to ours: if not, it must certainly be in the whole better that it should have its imperfect inhabitants, whose state is absolutely good, than that it should be desolate.

All then which we can expect to do in this matter, is only to show, that 'these confused sensations are necessary to such natures as we are in other respects: particularly that beings of such degrees of understanding, and such avenues to knowledge as we have, must need these additional forces, which we call passions, beside the first sensations by which objects are constituted good or evil, and the pure desire or aversion arising from opinion or apprehension of good or evil.'

Now our reason, or knowledge of the relations of external things to our bodies, is so inconsiderable, that it is generally some pleasant sensation which teaches us what tends to their preservation; and some painful sensation which shows what is pernicious. Nor is this instruction sufficient; we need also to be directed when our bodies want supplies of nourishment; to this our reason could not extend: here then appears the first necessity of uneasy sensation, preceding desire, and continuing to accompany it when it is raised.

Again, our bodies could not be preserved without a sense of pain, connected with incisions, bruises, or violent labour, or whatever else tends to destroy any part of their mechanism since our knowledge does not extend so far, as to judge in time what would be pernicious to it: and yet, without a great deal of human labour, and many dangers, this earth could not support the tenth part of its inhabitants. Our

---

9 [Here Hutcheson references the 6th-century commentator Simplicius' discussion of chapter 34 of the 1st century Stoic Epictetus' *Handbook*. Hutcheson also directs us, 'above all others,' to Archbishop William King's (1650–1729) *The Origin of Evil*.]

nature therefore required a sensation, accompanying its desires of the means of preservation, capable to surmount the uneasiness of labour: this we have in the pains or uneasiness accompanying the desires of food.

In like manner, the propagation of animals is a mystery to their reason, but easy to their instinct. An offspring of such creatures as men are, could not be preserved without perpetual labour and care; which we find could not be expected from the more general ties of benevolence. Here then again appears the necessity of strengthening the... natural affection, with strong sensations, or pains of desire, sufficient to counterbalance the pains of labour, and the sensations of the selfish appetites; since parents must often check and disappoint their own appetites, to gratify those of their children.

'When a necessity of joining strong sensations to one class of desires appears, there must appear a like necessity of strengthening the rest by like sensations, to keep a just balance.' We know, for instance, that the pleasures of the imagination tend much to the happiness of mankind: the desires of them therefore must have the like sensations assisting them, to prevent our indulging a nasty, solitary luxury. The happiness of human life cannot be promoted without society and mutual aid, even beyond a family; our public affections must therefore be strengthened as well as the private, to keep a balance; so must also our desires of virtue and honour. Anger, which some have thought a useless passion, is really as necessary as the rest; since men's interests often seem to interfere with each other; and they are thereby led from self-love to do the worst injuries to their fellows, there could not therefore be a wiser contrivance to restrain injuries, than to make every mortal some way formidable to an unjust invader, by such a violent passion. We need not have recourse to a Prometheus in this matter, with the old poets: they might have ascribed it to their Optimus Maximus.[10]

---

10 [Hutcheson partially quotes from lines 13–16 of Ode 16 from Book I of Horace's *Odes*. Taken fully, the lines read: 'Prometheus, forced to take from every creature / Some element to add to the first clay / From which he made man, grafted, so they say / The ravening lion's

VII. With this balance of public passions against the private, with our passions toward honour and virtue, we find that human nature may be as really amiable in its low sphere, as superior natures endowed with higher reason, and influenced only by pure desires; provided we vigorously exercise the powers we have in keeping this balance of affections, and checking any passion which grows so violent, as to be inconsistent with the public good. If we have selfish passions for our own preservation, we have also public passions, which may engage us into vigorous and laborious services to offspring, friends, communities, countries. Compassion will engage us to succour the distressed, even with our private loss or danger. An abhorrence of the injurious, and love toward the injured, with a sense of virtue and honour, can make us despise labour, expense, wounds, and death.

The sensations of joy or sorrow, upon the success or disappointment of any pursuit, either public or private, have directly the effect of rewards or punishments, to excite us to act with the utmost vigour, either for our own advantage, or that of others, for the future, and to punish past negligence. The moment of every event is thereby increased: as much as the sensations of sorrow add to our misery, so much those of joy add to our happiness. Nay, since we have some considerable power over our desires, as shall be explained hereafter, we may probably, by good conduct, obtain more frequent pleasures of joy upon our success, than pains of sorrow upon disappointment.

'Tis true indeed, that there are few tempers to be found, wherein these sensations of the several passions are in such a balance, as in all cases to leave the mind in a proper state, for considering the importance of every action or event. The sensations of anger in some tempers are violent above their proportion; those of ambition, avarice, desire of sensual pleasure, and even of natural affection, in several disposi-

---

violence to our nature.' Translation from James Michie's edition (New York: Random House, 2007). In Greek mythology, Prometheus was the deity who created human beings from clay. Optimus Maximus, also known as Jupiter, was the ruling deity in Roman mythology.]

tions, possess the mind too much, and make it incapable of attending to anything else. Scarce any one temper is always constant and uniform in its passions. The best state of human nature possible, might require a diversity of passions and inclinations, for the different occupations necessary for the whole: but the disorder seems to be much greater than is requisite for this end. Custom, education, habits, and company, may often contribute much to this disorder, however its original may be ascribed to some more universal cause. But it is not so great, but that human life is still a desirable state, having a superiority of goodness and happiness. Nor, if we apply ourselves to it, does it hinder us from discerning that just balance and economy, which would constitute the most happy state of each person, and promote the greatest good in the whole.

Let physicians or anatomists explain the motions in the fluids or solids of the body, which accompany any passion; or the temperaments of body which either make men prone to any passion, or are brought upon us by the long continuance, or frequent returns of it. It is only to our purpose in general to observe, 'that probably certain motions in the body accompany every passion by a fixed law of nature; and alternately, that temperament which is apt to receive or prolong these motions in the body, does influence our passions to heighten or prolong them.' Thus a certain temperament may be brought upon the body, by its being frequently put into motion by the passions of anger, joy, love, or sorrow; and the continuance of this temperament shall make men prone to the several passions for the future. We find ourselves after a long fit of anger or sorrow, in an uneasy state, even when we are not reflecting on the particular occasion of our passion. During this state, every trifle shall be apt to provoke or deject us. On the contrary, after good success, after strong friendly passions, or a state of mirth, some considerable injuries or losses, which at other times would have affected us very much, shall be overlooked, or meekly received, or at most but slightly resented; perhaps because our bodies are not fit easily to receive these motions which are constituted the occasion of the uneasy sensations of anger. This diversity of temper everyone has felt, who reflects on himself at different times. In some tempers it will appear like madness. Whether the only seat of these habits, or the occasion rather of these dispositions, be in the body; or whether the soul itself does not, by frequent returns of any passion, acquire some greater disposition to receive and retain it again, let those determine, who sufficiently understand the nature of either the one or the other.

Sect. IV.
How far our several affections and passions are in our power, either to govern them when raised, or to prevent their arising: with some general observations about their objects

I. From what was said above it appears, that our passions are not so much in our power, as some seem to imagine, from the topics used either to raise or allay them. We are so constituted by nature, that, as soon as we form the idea of certain objects or events, our desire or aversion will arise toward them; and consequently our affections, must very much depend upon the opinions we form, concerning anything which occurs to our mind, its qualities, tendencies, or effects. Thus the happiness of every sensitive nature is desired, as soon as we remove all opinion or apprehension of supposition of interest between this being and others. The apprehension of morally good qualities, is the necessary cause of approbation, by our moral sense, and of stronger love. The cause of hatred, is the apprehension of the opposite qualities. Fear, in like manner, must arise from opinion of power, and inclination to hurt us: pity from the opinion of another's undeserved misery: shame only arises from apprehension of contempt from others, or consciousness of moral evil: joy, in any event, must arise from an opinion of its goodness. Our selfish passions in this, do not differ from our public ones.

This may show us some inconsistency in topics of argument, often used to inculcate piety and virtue. Whatever motives of interest we suggest, either from a present or future reward, must be ineffectual, until we have first laboured to form amiable conceptions of the deity, and of our fellow-creatures. And yet in many writers, even in this cause, 'mankind are represented as absolutely evil, or at best as entirely selfish; nor are there any nobler ideas of the deity suggested. It is grown a fashionable topic, to put some sly selfish construction upon the most generous human actions; and he passes for the shrewdest writer, or orator, who is most artful in these insinuations.'

II. The government of our passions must then depend upon our opinions: but we must here observe an obvious difference among our desires, *viz.* that 'some of them have a previous, painful, or uneasy sensation, antecedently to any opinion of good in the object; nay, the object is often chiefly esteemed good, only for its allaying this pain or uneasiness; or if the object gives also positive pleasure, yet the uneasy sensation is previous to, and independent of this opinion of good in the object.' These desires we may call appetites. 'Other desires and aversions necessarily presuppose an opinion of good and evil in their objects; and the desires or aversions, with their concomitant uneasy sensations, are produced or occasioned by this opinion or apprehension.' Of the former kind are hunger and thirst, and the desires between the sexes; to which desires there is an uneasy sensation previous, even in those, who have little other notion of good in the objects, than allaying this pain or uneasiness. There is something like to this in the desire of society, or the company of our fellow-creatures. Our nature is so much formed for this, that although the absence of company is not immediately painful, yet if it be long, and the person be not employed in something which tends to society at last, or which is designed to fit him for society, an uneasy fretfulness, sullenness, and discontent, will grow upon him by degrees, which company alone can remove. He shall not perhaps be sensible always, that it is the absence of company which occasions his uneasiness: a painful sensation dictates nothing of itself: it must be therefore some reflection or instinct, distinct from the pain, which suggests the remedy. Our benevolence and compassion presuppose indeed some knowledge of other sensitive beings, and of what is good or evil to them: but they do not arise from any previous opinion, that 'the good of others tends to the good of the agent.' They are determinations of our nature, previous to our choice from interest, which excite us to action, as soon as we know other sensitive or rational beings, and have any apprehension of their happiness or misery.

In other desires the case is different. No man is distressed for want of fine smells, harmonious sounds, beautiful objects, wealth, power, or grandeur, previously to some opinion formed of these things as good, or some prior sensation of their pleasures. In like manner, virtue and honour as necessarily give us pleasure, when they occur to us, as vice and contempt give us pain; but, antecedently to some experience or opinion of this pleasure, there is no previous uneasy sensation in their absence, as there is in the absence of the objects of appetite. The necessity of these sensations previous to our appetites, has been considered already [see T3.II.vi]. The sensations accompanying or subsequent to our other desires, by which they are denominated passions, keep them in a just balance with our appetites, as was before observed.

But this holds in general, concerning all our desires or aversions, that according to the opinion or apprehension of good or evil, the desire or aversion is increased or diminished: every gratification of any desire gives at first, pleasure; and disappointment, pain; generally proportioned to the violence of the desire. In like manner, the escaping any object of aversion, though it makes no permanent addition to our happiness, gives at first a pleasant sensation, and relieves us from misery, proportioned to the degree of aversion or fear. So when any event, to which we had an aversion, befalls us, we have at first misery proportioned to the degree of aversion. So that some pain is subsequent upon all frustration of desire or aversion, but it is previous to those desires only, which are called appetites.

III. Hence we see how impossible it is for one to judge of the degrees of happiness or misery in others, unless he knows their opinions, their associations of ideas, and the degrees of their desires and aversions. We see also of how much consequence our associations of ideas and opinions are to our happiness or misery, and to the command of our passions.

For though in our appetites there are uneasy sensations, previous to any opinion, yet our very appetites may be strengthened or weakened, and variously altered by opinion, or associations of ideas. Before their intervention, the bodily appetites are easily satisfied; nature has put it in almost everyone's power, so far to gratify them, as to support the body, and remove pain. But when opinion, and confused ideas, or fancy comes in, and represents some particular kinds of gratifications, or great variety of them, as of great importance; when ideas of dignity, grandeur, magnificence, generosity, or any other moral species, are joined to the objects of appetites, they may furnish us with endless labour, vexation, and misery of every kind.

As to the other desires which presuppose some opinion or apprehension of good, previous to any sensation of uneasiness; they must still be more directly influenced by opinion, and associations of ideas. The higher the opinion or apprehension of good or evil is, the stronger must the desire or aversion be; the greater is the pleasure of success at first, and the greater the pain of disappointment. Our public desires are influenced in the same manner with the private: what we conceive as good, we shall desire for those we love, as well as for ourselves; and that in proportion to the degree of good apprehended in it: whatever we apprehend as evil in any degree to those we love, to that we shall have proportionable aversion.

The common effect of these associations of ideas is this, 'that they raise the passions into an extravagant degree, beyond the proportion of real good in the object: and commonly beget some secret opinions to justify the passions. But then the confutation of these false opinions is not sufficient to break the association, so that the desire or passion shall continue, even when our understanding has suggested to us, that the object is not good, or not proportioned to the strength of the desire.' Thus we often may observe, that persons, who by reasoning have laid aside all opinion of spirits being in the dark more than in the light, are still uneasy to be alone in the dark [Book II, lines 55–8 of Lucretius' *On the Nature of Things*]. Thus the luxurious, the extravagant lover, the miser, can scarce be supposed to have opinions of the several objects of their pursuit, proportioned to the vehemence of their desires; but the constant indulgence of any desire, the frequent repetition of it, the diverting our minds from all other pursuits, the strain of conversation among men of the same temper, who often haunt together, the contagion in the very air and countenance of the passionate, beget such wild associations of ideas, that a sudden conviction of reason will not stop the desire or aversion, any more than an argument will surmount the loathings or aversions, acquired against certain meats or drinks, by surfeits or emetic preparations.

The luxurious are often convinced, when any accident has revived a natural appetite, of the superior pleasures in a plain dinner, with a sharp stomach [see Book II, Satire II, lines 8–18 of Horace's *Satires*]: but this does not reform them; they have got all the ideas of dignity, grandeur, excellence, and enjoyment of life joined to their table. Explain to a miser the folly of his conduct, so that he can allege nothing in his defence; yet he will go on, 'to live in want that you may be wealthy when you die.'[11] He has likewise all ideas of good, worth, and importance in life confounded with his coffers.

A romantic lover has in like manner no notion of life without his mistress, all virtue and merit are summed up in his inviolable fidelity. The connoisseur has all ideas of valuable knowledge, gentleman-like worth and ability associated with his beloved arts. The idea of property comes along with the taste, and makes his happiness impossible, without possession of what he admires. A plain question might confute the opinion, but will not break the association: 'what pleasure has the possessor more than others, to whose eyes they are exposed as well as his?'

Our public desires are affected by confused ideas, in the same manner with our private desires. What is apprehended as good, through an association of foreign ideas, shall be pursued for those we love, as well as what is really good for them. Our benevolent passions in the nearer ties, are as apt to be too violent as any whatsoever: this we may often experience in the love of offspring, relations, parties, cabals. The violence of our passion makes us sometimes incapable of pursuing effectually their good, and sinks us into a useless state of sorrow upon their misfortunes. Compassion often makes the evil greater to the spectator than to the sufferer; and sometimes subjects the happiness of a person of great worth, to every accident befalling one entirely void of it.

---

11 [Satire XIV, line 137 of Juvenal's *Satires*. Ramsay's translation.]

The desire of virtue, upon extensive impartial schemes of public happiness, can scarce be too strong; but, upon mistaken or partial views of public good, this desire of virtue may often lead men into very pernicious actions. One may conceive a sort of extravagancy, and effeminate weakness even of this desire; as when men are dissatisfied with themselves for disappointments in good attempts, which it was not in their power to accomplish; when some heroic tempers show no regard to private good; when the pursuit of the lovely form is so passionate, that the agent does not relish his past conduct by agreeable reflection, but like the ambitious, 'thinking nothing done, if anything remains to be done.'[12]

But the most pernicious perversions of this desire are 'some partial admirations of certain moral species, such as fortitude, propagation of true religion, zeal for a party; while other virtues are overlooked, and the very end to which the admired qualities are subservient is forgotten. Thus some phantoms of virtue are raised, wholly opposite to its true nature, and to the sole end of it, the public good.'

Honour, in like manner, has had its foolish associations, and the true nature of it has been overlooked, so that the desire of it has run into enthusiasm, and pernicious madness. Thus, 'however our desires, when our opinions are true, and the desire is proportioned to the true opinion, are all calculated for good, either public or private; yet false opinions, and confused ideas, or too great a violence in any of them, above a due proportion to the rest, may turn the best of them into destructive follies.'

This is probably the case in those affections which some suppose natural, or at least incident to our natures, and yet absolutely evil: such as rancour, or disinterested malice, revenge, misanthropy. We indeed find our nature determined to disapprove an agent apprehended as evil, or malicious, through direct intention; we must desire the destruction of such a being, not only from self-love, but from our benevolence to others. Now when we rashly form

---

12 [See Book II, line 657 of Lucan's *Pharsalia*. Translation from H.T. Riley's *The Pharsalia of Lucan* (London: Bohn, 1853). Lucan (39–65), Roman poet.]

opinions of sects, or nations, as absolutely evil; or get associated ideas of impiety, cruelty, profaneness, recurring upon every mention of them: when, by repeated reflection upon injuries received, we strengthen our dislike into an obdurate aversion, and conceive that the injurious are directly malicious; we may be led to act in such a manner, that spectators, who are unacquainted with our secret opinions, or confused apprehensions of others, may think we have pure disinterested malice in our nature; a very instinct toward the misery of others, when it is really only the overgrowth of a just natural affection, upon false opinions, or confused ideas; even as our appetites, upon which our natural life depends, may acquire accidental loathings at the most wholesome food. Our ideas and opinions of mankind are often very rashly formed, but our affections are generally suited to our opinions. When our ideas and opinions of the moral qualities of others are just, our affections are generally regular and good: but when we give loose reins to our imagination and opinion, our affections must follow them into all extravagance and folly; and inadvertent spectators will imagine some dispositions in us wholly useless, and absolutely and directly evil.

Now the gratification of these destructive desires, like those of all the rest, gives at first some pleasure, proportioned to their violence; and the disappointment gives proportioned pain. But as to the continuance of these pleasures or pains, we shall find hereafter great diversity.

From this view of our desires, we may see 'the great variety of objects, circumstances, events, which must be of importance to the happiness of a creature, furnished with such a variety of senses of good and evil, with equally various desires corresponding to them: especially considering the strange combinations of ideas, giving importance to many objects, in their own nature indifferent.'

IV. We must in the next place enquire 'how far these several desires must necessarily arise, or may be prevented by our conduct.'

The pleasures and pains of the external senses must certainly be perceived by everyone who comes into the world; the one raising some degree of desire, and the other aversion: the pains of appetites arise yet more certainly than others, and are previous to any opinion. But then it is very much in our power to keep these sensations pure and unmixed with any foreign ideas: so that the plainest food and raiment, if sufficiently nourishing and healthful, may keep us easy, as well as the rarest or most expensive. Nay the body, when accustomed to the simpler sorts, is easiest in the use of them: and we are raised to a higher degree of cheerfulness, by a small improvement in our table, than it is possible to bring a pampered body into, by any of the productions of nature. Whatever the body is once accustomed to, produces no considerable change in it.

The pleasures of the imagination, or of the internal sense of beauty, and decency, and harmony, must also be perceived by us. The regularity, proportion and order in external forms, will as necessarily strike the mind, as any perceptions of the external senses. But then, as we have no uneasiness of appetite, previous to the reception of those grateful ideas, we are not necessarily made miserable in their absence; unless by some fantastic habit we have raised very violent desires, or by a long pursuit of them, have made ourselves incapable of other enjoyments.

Again, the sense and desire of beauty of several kinds is entirely abstracted from possession or property; so that the finest relish of this kind, and the strongest subsequent desires, if we admit no foolish conjunctions of ideas, may almost everywhere be gratified with the prospects of nature, and with the contemplation of the more curious works of art, which the proprietors generally allow to others without restraint. But if this sense or desire of beauty itself be accompanied with the desire of possession or property; if we let it be guided by custom, and receive associations of foreign ideas in our fancy of dress, equipage, furniture, retinue; if we relish only the modes of the great, or the marks of distinction as beautiful; if we let such desires grow strong, we must be very great indeed, before we can secure constant pleasure by this sense: and every disappointment or change of fortune, must make us miserable. The like fate may attend the pursuit of speculative sciences, poetry, music, or painting; to excel in these things is granted but to few. A violent desire of distinction and eminence may bring on vexation and sorrow for the longest life.

The pleasures and pains of the public sense will also necessarily arise in us. Men cannot live without the society of others, and their good offices; they must observe both the happiness and misery, the pleasures and pains of their fellows: desire and aversion must arise in the observer. Nay farther, as we cannot avoid more near attachments of love, either from the instinct between the sexes, or that toward offspring, or from observation of the benevolent tempers of others, or their particular virtues and good offices, we must feel the sensations of joy and sorrow, from the state of others even in the stronger degrees, and have the public desires in a greater height. All we can do to prevent the pains of general benevolence, will equally lessen the pleasures of it. If we restrain our public affection from growing strong, we abate our pleasures from the good success of others, as much as we lessen our compassion for their misfortunes: if we confine our desires to a small circle of acquaintance, or to a cabal or faction, we contract our pleasures as much as we do our pains. The distinction of pleasures and pains into real and imaginary, or rather into necessary and voluntary, would be of some use, if we could correct the imaginations of others, as well as our own; but if we cannot, we are sure, whoever thinks himself miserable, is really so; however he might possibly, by a better conduct of his imagination, have prevented this misery. All we can do in this affair, is to obtain a great share of the pleasures of the stronger ties, with fewer pains of them, by confining the stronger degrees of love, or our friendships, to persons of corrected imaginations, to whom as few of the uncertain objects of desire are necessary to happiness as is possible. Our friendship with such persons may probably be to us a much greater source of happiness than of misery, since the happiness of such persons is more probable than the contrary.

Since there is nothing in our nature determining us to disinterested hatred toward any person; we may be secure against all the pains of malice, by preventing false opinions of our fellows as absolutely evil, or by guarding against habitual anger, and rash aversions.

The moral ideas do arise also necessarily in our minds. We cannot avoid observing the affections of those we converse with; their actions, their words, their looks betray them. We are conscious of our own affections, and cannot avoid reflection upon them sometimes: the kind and generous affections will appear amiable, and all cruelty, malice, or even very selfish affections, will be disapproved, and appear odious. Our own temper, as well as that of others, will appear to our moral sense either lovely or deformed, and will be the occasion either of pleasure or uneasiness. We have not any proper appetite toward virtue, so as to be uneasy, even antecedently to the appearance of the lovely form; but as soon as it appears to any person, as it certainly must very early in life, it never fails to raise desire, as vice does raise aversion. This is so rooted in our nature, that no education, false principles, depraved habits, or even affectation itself can entirely root it out. Lucretius and Hobbes show themselves in innumerable instances struck with some moral species; they are full of expressions of admiration, gratitude, praise, desire of doing good; and of censure, disapprobation, aversion to some forms of vice.

Since then there is no avoiding these desires and perceptions of morality, all we can do to secure ourselves in the possession of pleasures of this kind, without pain, consists in 'a vigorous use of our reason, to discern what actions really tend to the public good in the whole, that we may not do that upon a partial view of good, which afterwards, upon a fuller examination, we shall condemn and abhor ourselves for; and withal, to fix our friendships with persons of like dispositions, and just discernment.' Men of partial views of public good, if they never obtain any better, may be easy in a very pernicious conduct, since the moral evil or deformity does not appear to them. But this is seldom to be hoped for in any partial conduct. Those who are injured by us fail not to complain; the spectators, who are disengaged from our partial attachments, will often take the freedom to express their sentiments, and set our conduct in a full light: this must very probably occasion to us shame and remorse. It cannot therefore be an indifferent matter, to an agent with a moral sense, what opinions he forms of the tendency of actions; what partial attachments of love he has toward parties or factions. If he has true opinions of the tendencies of actions; if he carefully examines the real dignity of persons and causes, he may be sure that the conduct which he now approves he shall always approve, and have delight in reflection upon it, however it be censured by others. But if he takes up at hazard opinions of actions; if he has a foolish admiration of particular sects, and as foolish aversions and dislike to others, not according to any real importance or dignity, he shall often find occasion for inconstancy and change of his affections, with shame and remorse for his past conduct, and an inward dislike and self-condemnation.

What most deeply affects our happiness or misery, are the dispositions of those persons with whom we voluntarily contract some nearer intimacies of friendship: if we act wisely in this point, we may secure to ourselves the greatest pleasures with the fewest pains, by attaching ourselves to persons of real goodness, good offices toward whom are useful to the world. The ties of blood are generally very strong, especially toward offspring; they need rather the bridle than the spur, in all cases wherein the object is not recommended to a singular love by his good qualities. We may, in a considerable measure, restrain our natural affection toward a worthless offspring, by setting our public affections and our moral sense against it, in frequent contemplation of their vices, and of the mischief which may arise to persons of more worth from them, if we give them any countenance in their vices.

The regulating our apprehensions of the actions of others, is of very great importance, that we may not imagine mankind worse than they really are, and thereby bring upon ourselves a temper full of suspicion, hatred, anger and contempt toward others which is a constant state of misery, much worse than all the evils to be feared from credulity. If we examine the true springs of human action, we shall seldom find their motives worse than self-love. Men are often subject to anger, and upon sudden provocations do injuries to each other, and that only from self-love, without malice; but the greatest part of their lives is employed in offices of natural affection, friendship, innocent self-love, or love of a country. The little party-prejudices are generally founded upon ignorance, or false opinions, rather apt to move pity than hatred. Such considerations are the best preservative against anger, malice, and discontent of mind with the order of nature. 'When you would make yourself cheerful and easy (says the

Emperor) [Marcus Aurelius, *Meditations*, Book VI, Chapter 48] consider the virtues of your several acquaintances, the industry and diligence of one, the modesty of another, the generosity or liberality of a third, and in some persons some other virtue. There is nothing so delightful, as the resemblances of the virtues appearing in the conduct of your contemporaries as frequently as possible. Such thoughts we should still retain with us.'

When the moral sense is thus assisted by a sound understanding and application, our own actions may be a constant source of solid pleasure, along with the pleasures of benevolence, in the highest degree which our nature will admit, and with as few of its pains as possible.

As to the desires of honour, since we cannot avoid observing or hearing of the sentiments of others concerning our conduct, we must feel the desire of the good opinions of others, and aversion to their censures or condemnation: since the one necessarily gives us pleasure, and the other pain. Now it is impossible to bring all men into the same opinions of particular actions, because of their different opinions of public good, and of the means of promoting it; and because of opposite interests; so that it is often impossible to be secure against all censure or dishonour from some of our fellows. No one is so much master of external things, as to make his honourable intentions successful; and yet success is a mark by which many judge of the goodness of attempts. Whoever therefore suffers his desire of honour or applause to grow violent, without distinction of the persons to whose judgment he submits, runs a great hazard of misery. But our natural desire of praise, is in a compounded proportion of the numbers of applauders, and their dignity. 'He therefore who makes distinction of persons justly, and acts wisely for the public good, may secure himself from much uneasiness upon injudicious censure, and may obtain the approbation, of those whose esteem alone is valuable, or at least far overbalances the censure of others.'

The desire of wealth must be as necessary as any other desires of our nature, as soon as we apprehend the usefulness of wealth to gratify all other desires. While it is desired as the means of something farther, the desire tends to our happiness, proportionably to the good economy of the principal desires to which it is made subservient. It is in every man's power, by a little reflection, to prevent the madness and enthusiasm with which wealth is insatiably pursued even for itself, without any direct intention of using it. The consideration of the small addition often made by wealth to the happiness of the possessor, may check this desire, and prevent that insatiability which sometimes attends it.

Power in like manner is desired as the means of gratifying other original desires; nor can the desire be avoided by those who apprehend its usefulness. It is easy to prevent the extravagance of this desire, and many of its consequent pains, by considering 'the danger of affecting it by injurious means, supporting it by force, without consent of the subject, and employing it to private interest, in opposition to public good.' No mortal is easy under such subjection; every slave to such a power is an enemy: the possessor must be in a continual state of fear, suspicion and hatred.

There is nothing in our nature leading us necessarily into the fantastic desires; they wholly arise through our ignorance and negligence; when, through want of thought, we suffer foolish associations of ideas to be made, and imagine certain trifling circumstances to contain something honourable and excellent in them from their being used by persons of distinction. We know how the inadvertencies, negligences, infirmities, and even vices, either of great or ingenious men, have been affected, and imitated by those who were incapable of imitating their excellencies. This happens often to young gentlemen of plentiful fortunes which set them above the employments necessary to others, when they have not cultivated any relish for the pleasures of the imagination, such as architecture, music, painting, poetry, natural philosophy, history: when they have no further knowledge of these things, than stupidly to praise what they hear others praise: when they have neglected to cultivate their public affections, are bantered a long time from marriage and offspring; and have neither themselves minds fit for friendships, nor any intimate acquaintance with such as are fit to make friends of: when their moral sense is weakened, or, if it be strong in any points, these are fixed at random, without any regular scheme: when through ignorance of public affairs, or want of eloquence to speak what they know, they despair of the esteem or honour of the wise: when their hearts are too gay to be entertained with the dull thoughts of increasing their wealth, and they have not ability enough to hope for power; such poor empty minds have nothing but trifles to pursue; anything becomes agreeable, which can supply the void of thought, or prevent the sullen discontent which must grow upon a mind conscious of no merit, and expecting the contempt of its fellows as a pack of dogs, a horse, a jewel, an equipage, a pack of cards, a tavern; anything which has got any confused ideas of honour, dignity, liberality, or genteel enjoyment of life joined to it. These fantastic desires any man might have banished at first, or entirely prevented. But if we have lost the time of substituting better in their stead, we shall only change from one sort to another, with a perpetual succession of inconstancy and dissatisfaction. 'But if a morbid whim has given him the omen—can the same persons persist for one hour in liking the same things?'[13]

V. The end of all these considerations, is to find out the most effectual way of advancing the happiness of mankind; in order to which, they may perhaps appear of considerable consequence, since happiness consists in 'the highest and most durable gratifications of, either all our desires, or, if all cannot be gratified at once, of those which tend to the greatest and most durable pleasures, with exemption either from all pains and objects of aversion, or at least from those which are the most grievous.' The following general observations may be premised concerning their objects…

---

13 [Hutcheson quotes selectively from lines 82–6 of Book I, Epistle I of Horace's *Epistles*. Fairclough's translation.]

From *A System of Moral Philosophy*

Book I, Part II, Chapter VII. A comparison of the several sorts of enjoyment, and the opposite sorts of uneasiness, to find their importance to happiness

[I.] To discover wherein our true happiness consists we must compare the several enjoyments of life, and the several kinds of misery, that we may discern what enjoyments are to be parted with, or what uneasiness to be endured, in order to obtain the highest and most beatific satisfactions, and to avoid the most distressing sufferings.

As to pleasures of the same kind, 'tis manifest their values are in a joint proportion of their intenseness and duration. In estimating the duration, we not only regard the constancy of the object, or its remaining in our power, and the duration of the sensations it affords, but the constancy of our fancy or relish: for when this changes it puts an end to the enjoyment.

In comparing pleasures of different kinds, the value is as the duration and dignity of the kind jointly. We have an immediate sense of a dignity, a perfection, or beatific quality in some kinds, which no intenseness of the lower kinds can equal, were they also as lasting as we could wish [see *System* Book I, Chapter IV, Paragraph 10, not included here]. No intenseness or duration of any external sensation gives it a dignity or worth equal to that of the improvement of the soul by knowledge, or the ingenious arts; and much less is it equal to that of virtuous affections and actions. We never hesitate in judging thus about the happiness or perfection of others, where the impetuous cravings of appetites and passions do not corrupt our judgments, as they do often in our own case. By this intimate feeling of dignity, enjoyments and exercises of some kinds, though not of the highest degree of those kinds, are incomparably more excellent and beatific than the most intense and lasting enjoyments of the lower kinds. Nor is duration of such importance to some higher kinds, as it is to the lower. The exercise of virtue for a short period, provided it be not succeeded by something vicious, is of incomparably greater value than the most lasting sensual pleasures. Nothing destroys the excellence and perfection of the state but a contrary quality of the same kind defacing the former character. The peculiar happiness of the virtuous man is not so much abated by pain, or an early death, as that of the sensualist; though his complex state which is made up of all his enjoyments and sufferings of every kind is in some degree affected by them [...see Cicero, *On the Ends*, Book 3, Chapter 10]. Nor is it a view of private sublime pleasures in frequent future reflections which recommends virtue to the soul. We feel an impulse, an ardour toward perfection, toward affections and actions of dignity, and feel their immediate excellence, abstracting from such views of future pleasures of long duration. Though no doubt these pleasures, which are as sure as our existence, are to be regarded in our estimation of the importance of virtue to our happiness.

Now if we denote by intenseness, in a more general meaning, the degree in which any perceptions or enjoyments are beatific, then their comparative values are in a compound proportion of their intenseness and duration. But to retain always in view the grand differences of the kinds, and to prevent any imaginations, that the intenser sensations of the lower kinds with sufficient duration may complete our happiness; it may be more convenient to estimate enjoyments by their dignity and duration: dignity denoting, the excellence of the kind, when those of different kinds are compared; and the intenseness of the sensations, when we compare those of the same kind.

II. Though the several original powers above-mentioned are natural to all men, yet through habit, associated ideas, education, or opinion, some generally pursue enjoyments of one kind; and show a disregard of others, which are highly valued by men of a different turn. Some are much given to sensuality; others to more ingenious pleasures; others pursue wealth and power; others moral and social enjoyments, and honour. Wealth and power have some few faithful votaries adoring them for themselves: but the more numerous worshipers adore them only as ministring spirits, or mediators with some superior divinities, as pleasure, honour, beneficence.

Thus different men have different tastes. What one admires as the supreme enjoyments, another may despise.

Must we not examine these tastes? Are all persons, all orders of beings equally happy if each obtains the enjoyments reflectively most relished? At this rate the meanest brute or insect may be as happy as the wisest hero, patriot, or friend can be. What may make a brute as happy as that low order is capable of being, may be but despicable to an order endued with finer perceptive powers, and a nobler sort of desires. Beings of these higher orders are immediately conscious of the superior dignity and importance to happiness in their peculiar enjoyments, of which lower orders are incapable. Nature has thus distinguished the different orders by different perceptive powers, so that the same objects will not be sufficient for happiness to all; nor have all equal happiness when each can gratify all the desires and senses he has.

The superior orders in this world probably experience all the sensations of the lower orders, and can judge of them. But the inferior do not experience the enjoyments of the superior. Nay in the several stages of life each one finds different tastes and desires. We are conscious in our state of mature years that the happiness of our friends, our families, or our country are incomparably nobler objects of our pursuit, and administer proportionably a nobler pleasure than the toys which once abundantly entertained us when we had experienced nothing better. God has assigned to each order, and to the several stages of life in the same person, their peculiar powers and tastes. Each one is as happy when its taste is gratified as it can then be. But we are immediately conscious that one gratification is more excellent than another, when we have experienced both. And then our reason and observation enables us to compare the effects, and consequences, and duration. One may be transitory, and the occasion of great subsequent misery, though for the present the enjoyment be intense: another may be lasting, safe, and succeeded by no satiety, shame, disgust, or remorse.

Superior beings by diviner faculties and fuller knowledge may, without experience of all sorts, immediately discern what are the noblest. They may have some intuitive knowledge of perfection, and some standard of it, which may make the experience of some lower sorts useless to them. But of mankind these certainly are the best judges who have full experience, with their tastes or senses and appetites in a natural vigorous state. Now it never was alleged that social affections, the admiration of moral excellence, the desire of esteem, with their attendant and guardian temperance, the pursuits of knowledge, or a natural activity, impaired any sense or appetite. This is often charged with great justice upon luxury, and forfeiting, and indolence. The highest sensual enjoyments may be experienced by those who employ both mind and body vigorously in social virtuous offices, and allow all the natural appetites to recur in their due seasons. Such certainly are the best judges of all enjoyments. Thus according to the maxim often inculcated by Aristotle, 'The good man is the true judge and standard of everything.'[14]

But it may justly be questioned, whether men much devoted to sensual pleasures, to those of the imagination, or to wealth and power, are sufficiently prepared to judge in this question. Such pursuits indeed are seldom continued long without some notion of their innocence, nay of some duty or moral obligation. Habits sometimes deface natural characters and powers. Men of vicious habits have small experience of the generous affections, social joys, and the delights of true impartial uniform goodness. Bad habits weaken social feelings, and the relish of virtue. And yet even such men on some occasions give a strong testimony to the cause of virtue.

III. Having premised these things we may first compare the several sorts of enjoyment in point of dignity and duration; and in like manner their opposites, sufferings. And then compare a little the several tempers or characters in point of inward satisfaction.

The pleasures of the external senses, are of two classes; those of the palate, and those between the sexes. Both these we call sensual.

The pleasures of the palate how grateful soever they may be to children, must appear the meanest and most despicable

---

14 [Hutcheson does not cite a particular text here, but he likely has line 1166a13 of the *Nicomachean Ethics* in mind.]

enjoyments to all men of reflection who have experienced any others. The uneasiness felt when the body needs support may be pretty intense; as 'tis wisely contrived, to engage us to take necessary care of the body. The allaying this pain may give a strong sensation of pleasure at first. But the proper pleasure of taste, the positive enjoyment, must be despicable to all who are above the order of brutes. The differences in point of pleasure among the several kinds of food is so small, that the keenness of appetite is allowed to make a much greater. The most exquisite cookery can scarce give such high sensation of this kind to a satisfied appetite, though it be not surfeited; as the plainest fare will give to a brisk appetite after abstinence and exercise; even although there was no pain, inconsistent with mirth and gaiety, to be allayed. When therefore the allaying so gentle an uneasiness causes more pleasure than any exquisite savours without it, the positive pleasure must be very inconsiderable. The preventing of appetite, or the increasing or prolonging it by incentives of any kind, are vain efforts for pleasure; so are all arts, except exercise and abstinence, till the natural appetite returns. The greatest Epicures have acknowledged this when business or diversions have casually led them to make the experiment.

Men would universally agree in this point, were not these pleasures generally blended with others of very different natures. Not only nice economy, art, and elegance in fine services and grandeur of apartments, but even moral qualities, liberality, communication of pleasure, friendship, and meriting well from others, are joined in our imaginations. Strip sensuality of all these borrowed charms, and view it naked and alone as mere pleasing the palate in solitude, and it is shameful and despicable to all.

Imagine a life spent in this enjoyment without interruption, and that, contrary to the present order of nature, the appetite still remained; but that there was no social enjoyment or affection, no finer perceptions, of exercise of the intellectual powers; this state is below that of many brutes. Their appetites allow intervals for some pleasures of a social nature, and for action; and when thus employed, they show a higher joy than in feeding.

The duration too of these sensations is inconsiderable. Such indeed is the bounty of God, that the means or allaying the cravings or appetite may be easily procured; and thus by good management we may all frequently enjoy almost the highest pleasures of this kind. But the appetite is soon satisfied, and recurs not till after long intervals. Artificial incentives may raise an unnatural craving, but the allaying of this gives little pleasure. 'Tis a real depravation and sickness; and, when long continued, turns to such bodily indisposition as must stop all enjoyments. Where grandeur and variety are affected, the fancy grows capricious and inconstant, and the objects uncertain. The humour may grow too expensive for our fortunes, and increase, while the means of gratification are diminished.

Many of the same considerations depreciate the other species of sensual pleasure, which much depends upon the allaying the uneasy craving of a brutal impulse, as the positive good is of itself mean and inconsiderable. Conceive the sensation alone, without love or esteem of any moral qualities, or the thought of communicating pleasure, and of being beloved; it would not equal the delights which some of the finer brute beasts seem plainly conscious of. And then this enjoyment is the most transitory of all. Indulgence, and variety, and incentives, bring upon the mind a miserable craving; an impatient ardour; an incapacity of self-government, and of all valuable improvement; a wretched slavery, which strips the mind of all candour, integrity, and sense of honour. Add to this the capriciousness of fancy, the torments of disappointment, which such wandering dissolute desires must be exposed to; and that after the transient sensation, there can scarce remain anything agreeable, to one who has not lost all manly sense of good. The reflection on any past sensual enjoyments gives no sense of any merit or worth, no ground of self-esteem, or scarce any sort of joy except from the low hopes of repeating the same, which may a little revive the appetite after intervals. The remembrance is no support under any calamity, chagrin, pain, provocation or sorrow, or any inward disturbance of mind, or outward misfortune. The very nature of these sensations we call sensual, and the inward sentiments of our hearts about them, abundantly declare that the supreme happiness of human nature must consist in very different enjoyments of a more noble and durable nature.

IV. 'Tis often occurring, on the other hand, that we see multitudes who prefer such pleasures to all others, and make the pursuits of sensuality the business of their lives; and that therefore the bent of the mind is naturally toward them; and their power superior to our moral sense, and to the generous affections.

To remove this cause of suspicion; let us recollect that the constant pursuits of sensuality are seldom ever observed without an opinion of their innocence. Our moral faculty, our sympathetic sense, and our kind affections are seldom set in opposition to them, or combat with them, in the minds of men much devoted to sensuality. Where without this notion of innocence men are hurried into sensual enjoyments by impetuous appetites, the state is miserable and full of abject remorse after the transient gratifications. The professedly dissolute have some specious reasons by which they are deluded into a persuasion of the innocence of their pursuits.

Nay some moral notions, such as communication of pleasure, love, friendship, meriting well, and being beloved, make the main charm even in sensual enjoyments. This is manifest in the luxury and intemperance of such as are not sunk below the beasts, and universally despised. It holds too in the unchaste passions: and hence some notions of moral excellencies, good nature, friendliness, sweetness of temper, wit, and obligingness recommend their objects. But on the other hand; such as by generous affections, and love of moral excellence and honour, are led into a virtuous course, avowedly despise sensual enjoyments; nor does any confused imaginations of them, or hopes even of immunity from labour and pain recommend it to their choice. The external evils, toil, expense, and hardships are known and despised as well as the allurements of ease and pleasure: the moral forms by their own proper power are superior to them. In the voluptuous, the moral sense is seldom conquered; the enjoyments seem innocent, or at least the guilt is so diminished by the sophistry of the passions, that 'tis only the smallest moral evil which seems to be incurred for the highest sensual good; and the weakest efforts of the moral kind overcome by the strongest of sensuality; and often, even by the assistance of some mistaken moral species.

It is here likewise proper to observe that all sensual gratifications are not opposite to moral enjoyments. There is a moderate indulgence perfectly innocent, sufficient to allay the uneasiness of appetite; which too by wise economy may frequently be as high as any sort of sensual enjoyments, and even subservient to the moral. The temperate, and such as, after proper self-government in celibacy, have made a wise choice in marriage, may have as high sensual enjoyments as any. In recommending of virtue we need not suppose it opposite to all gratifications of sense; though its power in our hearts should be maintained so high that it may be able to control all the appetites which by accident may oppose it. Its gentle sway generally allows such gratifications, as may be the highest of the kind; or where it does not, it makes abundant compensation for the loss, by the joyful approbation of such abstinence and self-government. What rich compensation is made by the joyful approbation one must feel of fidelity; friendship, and meriting well, and by the returns of a constant affection from a worthy heart, for the want of the irregular, shameful, perplexing, joyless passions and indulgences, with persons of no moral worth or steadfastness of affection.

V. We come next to consider the pleasures of the imagination in the grandeur and elegance of living, and the perceptions of beauty and harmony, to which we may add those of the ingenious arts, and knowledge. Here there is no brutal uneasy previous appetite, the sating of which might enhance the pleasure; and yet one may immediately find that these are enjoyments superior to the sensual, and more recommended by the constitution of our nature. When the cravings of appetite are grown painful, one will readily quit these pleasures till the pain is removed; especially when there are no apprehensions of our not being at liberty of speedily returning to them. But the beholding beautiful forms, the curious works of art, or the more exquisite works of nature; the entertainments of harmony, of imitation in the ingenious arts; the discovering of the immutable relations and proportions of the objects of the pure intellect and reason, give enjoyments in dignity far superior to anything sensual, where the sensual are considered alone without borrowed charms of a higher nature. These more manly pleasures are more suited to our nature; and are always more esteemed and approved when we are judging of the pursuits of others.

These pleasures too far surpass the sensual likewise in duration. They can employ a great part of life without satiety or cloying, as their pleasure is so much positive enjoyment independent upon the allaying of any previous uneasy sensations. They are the proper exercises of the soul, where none of the higher social offices, or those of rational piety claim its activity. They partake of its lasting nature, and are not transitory, as all enjoyments are which are merely subservient to the perishing body. Thus, as often as the more important offices of virtue allow any intervals, our time is agreeably and honourably employed in history natural or civil, in geometry, astronomy, poetry, painting, and music, or such entertainments as ingenious arts afford. And some of the sweetest enjoyments of this sort require no property, nor need we ever want the objects. If familiarity abates the pleasure of the more obvious beauties of nature, their more exquisite inward structures may give new delights, and the stores of nature are inexhaustible.

Such objects of these tastes as require property are more uncertain, and the pursuit of them more solicitous and anxious, and the fancy more inconstant, as long possession abates the relish. The imagination here needs strict reins, that it may not run out into excessive admiration by associated notions of moral dignity, and liberality; and thus involve us in innumerable vexatious pursuits of what is not essential to happiness.

VI. Pleasures of the sympathetic kind arising from the fortunes of others are proportioned to the strength of the kind affections we have for them. Our nature is exceedingly susceptible of these affections; especially the stronger sorts of them toward offspring, parents, kinsmen, benefactors, or eminently worthy characters; toward sects, parties, countries. They furnish the far greater part of the business, and of the happiness or misery of life.

Compare these with others: consider the joy of heart upon any considerable prosperity, or any eminent virtue of one whom we heartily love, of a child, a brother, a friend: upon any glory or advantage to our party, or country; to any honourable cause we have espoused, or any admired character; or upon their escaping any imminent danger. Where there is a hearty affection these joys are incomparably superior to any of the former. What pleasure of sense or imagination would we not forego to obtain these events? Some ecstasies of joy upon the escaping of great imminent personal dangers have been too violent for nature, and have proved fatal: we have more instances of sympathetic joys which proved also unsupportable and fatal [see Livy,[15] *History* of Rome, Book XXII, Chapter 7; also see Cicero, *On the Ends*, Book V, Chapter 24]. And if some tempers cannot bear life after some misfortunes befallen themselves; more instances are found of such as throw it away upon the misfortunes of others. The enjoyments must be very high which can sweeten all the toil and labour about offspring and friends, even in common characters. Having affluence of all things desired for one's self, abates very little of the diligence of mankind.

These pleasures endure as long as the person continues to be beloved and to be prosperous. New successes of our own, or of our friend, raise greater commotions at first than advantages long possessed. But while the affection continues, the sense remains; and the sympathetic pleasure never cloys. Where indeed affections are founded upon wrong sentiments of the merit of persons, or causes, they can have no stability, and the sympathetic joy may be lost, and succeeded by disgust and indignation. But the chief cause of instability in this branch of happiness is the uncertainty of the fortunes of those we love; for their misery must occasion the most severe distress. In this we wholly depend on providence.

All that we can do to secure any fund of joys of this kind is to examine well the merit or persons, and causes, and by these means to turn our stronger affections toward the superior merit of men of true goodness and correct imaginations, whose happiness is less inconstant than that of others; to have a firm persuasion of the wisdom and goodness of providence, and to cultivate the most extensive affections.

---

15 [Livy (59 B.C.E.–19), Roman historian.]

The stronger our universal good-will is, if our joys be so much the higher upon the general prosperity, the greater also shall our regret be upon apprehended general misery. But what makes this affection ever safe in all events, and a fund of superior joy, is a firm persuasion of a good Providence governing the universe for the best, amidst all the apparent evils and disorders. Of this more hereafter.[16]

VII. The fourth class of enjoyments are the moral, arising from the consciousness of good affections and actions. These joys are different from the sympathetic, which may arise from that happiness of others to which our affections and actions contributed nothing. But our affections and actions themselves, abstracting from the state of others, cannot be indifferent to us when we attend to them. When we find our whole soul kind and benign, we must have a joyful approbation; and a further and higher joy arises from exerting these affections in wise beneficent offices. These joys we find the highest and most important both in respect of dignity and duration.

How much inferior are the highest sensual pleasures, or even those of the imagination, or speculative knowledge, to the stable joy of conscious goodness of heart; and to that high approbation one feels of himself in any important offices for the good of his country, or his friend; and to the joyful thought of meriting well of mankind, and deserving their applauses? The kind affections alone fit easy in the heart; there is an inward complacence in them, and we joyfully entertain them for life [as observed by Aristotle and Cicero]. But our nature is fitted for more than inactive affection. A high happiness arises from the exerting our powers; and the nobler the power is, the more beatific is its exercise: when the virtuous efforts are successful, there is such an assemblage of pure joys from conscious goodness, sympathy with others, and the expected love and approbation of all, especially the complacency of our Maker, as far surpasses all other enjoyments. If we should fail of success, we may want the sympathetic joy, and may be touched with compassion; but the

---

16 [See Part 5 of this anthology.]

other sources of joy remain: the moral enjoyments can sweeten these distresses from the misfortunes of the person or cause espoused; which without the consciousness of our having acted our part well, must have been much more intolerable.

The fancy here is not inconsistent. Our taste for virtue increases by exercise; and habits make it still more pleasant. The remembrance is ever delightful, and makes the enjoyment lasting, where there have been just notions of virtue, and of the merit of persons and causes. One end proposed in the creating different orders of beings, and ordaining the different states of those of the same species, some more, some less perfect, is probably this, that the nobler minds should never want opportunities for the joyful exercise of their good dispositions toward the inferior either in perfection or in fortune. These joys too are seated above the power of fortune while men retain soundness of mind. A low station, and a hard condition of life, or external disadvantages may prevent our doing the most important services to others in external things; but can neither hinder the sound inward affections of heart, nor a course of action suited to our abilities; and this is the highest virtue.

Unexamined admirations of some partial moral forms, and some narrow affections, without true notions of merit in persons and causes, may lead us into such conduct as upon better information may be matter of shame and remorse. But where by close reflection we have attained just notions of virtue and merit, and of the effectual means of doing good, virtuous action, as it is the natural purpose of a rational and social species, so it is their highest happiness, and always in their power.

Among these moral enjoyments, the joys of religion and devotion toward God well deserve to be particularly remarked, which in the class of moral enjoyments are the highest of all. But as these enjoyments are of a pretty different nature from the rest of the moral ones, they shall be considered apart hereafter, for reasons above-mentioned; and we shall show their high importance to a stable and sublime happiness above all others.[17]

IX [sic.]. The pleasures of honour from the approbation, esteem, and gratitude of others as they naturally ensue upon virtue, so when they are founded on it, are among the most grateful feelings of the soul. These joys of honour and virtue and the sympathetic joys are naturally connected, nor need we minutely compare them; as the same conduct is naturally subservient to them all: and where they concur, no words can express the happiness enjoyed. The sympathetic feelings may be more intense in some tender affectionate hearts: active spirits in public stations may be more affected with conscious virtue and merited glory. But where the three are united, with a firm persuasion of a good God approving our temper, and ensuring the universal order and happiness, our state must come nearest to that joy unspeakable and full of glory, which we hope for as the perfect consummation of the rational nature.

True glory is also durable, not like the sensual enjoyments, which pass like the shadow of a cloud leaving no trace behind them. The approbation and esteem of others, when founded on virtue, may probably continue during life, and survive us: and the approbation of God shall be everlasting. The pursuits of extensive fame for eminent abilities and virtues may indeed be subject to disappointment, and be full of labour and liable to excess. Ordinary virtues, or even the highest virtues in the low stations will not obtain the extensive applauses of nations. But a wise and virtuous man may generally obtain such honour either in a narrower or larger sphere as may give great joy. And a good heart, persuaded of a good providence observing all things, is sure of the approbation of the best judge, and that to eternity.

X [sic.]. Among such solemn subjects the pleasures of mirth and gaiety must be of small account. And yet even children despise sensuality in comparison of them: and sensual enjoyments borrow from them many of their charms, without

---

17 [See Part 5 of this anthology.]

which they would be despicable and shameful. They are an agreeable seasoning to other enjoyments, and some relief from the fatigues of serious business. The nobler joys are grave, severe, and solemn. But human life must have relaxations. Now whatever value we put upon mirth and gaiety it must be cast into the side of virtue: since that mind is always best disposed for the reception of all cheerfulness and pleasantry where all is kind and easy; free from anger, ill-will, envy, or remorse. These pleasures, are always social, and fly solitude. They are best cherished amidst love, good-nature, and mutual esteem.

As wealth and power are not immediately pleasant, but the means of obtaining pleasures; their importance to happiness must be in proportion to that of the enjoyments to which they are referred by the possessor. The virtuous man therefore who refers them to generous and virtuous purposes, has a much nobler enjoyment of them than those who refer them to the pleasures of the imagination, or the elegance of life; and yet this is a finer reference than that to sensuality. Where through confused imaginations they are not directly referred to their natural purposes, but pursued for themselves, avarice and ambition become wretched insatiable cravings, hateful to all mankind; and the possessions become joyless to the person who obtains them.

XI [sic.]. As to some other pretended enjoyments in gratifying the passions of anger, malice, envy, revenge: 'tis certain there is no small sense of joy in these gratifications, where the passions were intense. But then 'tis obvious, that as good-will, love, esteem, gratitude, and every kind affection are natural and original pleasures sitting easy in the mind; so the happiness of any innocent person observed is the occasion of pure unmixed joy, not arising from the allaying any previous pain. If the person has been in misery, and thus has raised our compassion: his being relieved adds also another joy from stopping our sympathetic pain. But the misery of another is naturally uneasy to the observer: it must then be by some accident that it ever becomes grateful: by some previous anger, or envy; some injury apprehended, or some opposition to the interests of some person beloved.

These passions of the unkind sort are not useless parts in our constitution. Upon apprehension of injury or damage done to us, or to those we love, anger naturally arises to rouse us for defence. When persons we do not esteem are preferred to those of higher merit, an honest concern and indignation arises. A like indignation arises against all such as appear grossly immoral. Indulgence may make these passions strong and habitual. The feelings attending them are original uneasiness and torment; to which however it was reasonable for the general good that we should be in some degree subjected on certain occasions, as we are to bodily pain. The sweetest tempers have experienced some short fits of them, and have felt how uneasy these moments pass. Where such passions are high and lasting, degenerating into rancour and stated malice and envy, the misery must be very great: no wonder then that the removal of it should give at first a considerable pleasure. The misery is removed by the sufferings of the person hated or envied. But this turbulent joy, even while it lasts, is not to be compared with the sweet sympathetic joys, the sense of merited love and esteem, or the self-approbation of forgiving, where no public interest requires punishing. And then this ill-natured joy soon ceases after the passion is fated, as the misery of the most hated object cannot please us long; nor is it ever the object of approbation, either in ourselves or others, upon reflection; nay 'tis generally succeeded by remorse, regret, and sorrow. The calm mind can have no pleasure in the misery of another, though it may acquiesce in such sufferings as a public interest requires. We cannot wish to prolong vengeance but upon some notion of repeated acts of unrelenting wickedness; or from some remains of the preceding fear with which we were tormented. And this shows one reason why 'the brave are not cruel.' The pleasures then of this ill-natured kind are to the calm joys of humanity, as the slaking the burning thirst of a fever, or the sating a gnawing diseased stomach, to the enjoyment of grateful food with a healthy and vigorous appetite.

XII [sic.]. We may observe concerning these several enjoyments, that with the most benign counsel our minds are so constituted that we value them upon calm reflection in proportion to their importance to the happiness of the whole system. These which only regard the safety and animal gratifications of the individual are felt to be the meanest; such as may be of more extensive use, and incite men to be serviceable to others, are naturally more esteemed, and that in different degrees according to their extent. Thus we value more the pleasures of the ingenious arts, and such exercises of body or mind as may naturally be useful to many. The partial narrow affections are lovely and joyful; but still the more stable and calm and extensive, as they are more useful, are also more joyful both in the exercise, and in the remembrance, where there has been any tolerable attention and reflection. We see then that the moral faculty most approves and recommends such dispositions as tend most to the general good, and at the same time such as may give the noblest enjoyments to the agent upon reflection. And thus the two grand determinations of our nature, by a thorough consideration of our constitution, may appear perfectly consistent, and be generally gratified by the same means…

From *An Essay on the Nature and Conduct of the Passions and Affections*

Sect. VI.
Some general conclusions concerning the best management of our desires. With some principles necessary to happiness

Thus, upon comparing the several kinds of pleasures and pains, both as to intention and duration, we see that 'the whole sum of interest lies upon the side of virtue, public-spirit, and honour: to forfeit these pleasures in whole, or in part, for any other enjoyment, is the most foolish bargain; and, on the contrary, to secure them with the sacrifice of all others, is the truest gain.'

There is one general observation to be premised, which appears of the greatest necessity for the just management of all our desires; *viz.* that we should, as much as possible, in all affairs of importance to ourselves or others, prevent the violence of their confused sensation, and stop their propensities from breaking out into action, till we have fully examined the real moment of the object, either of our desires or aversions. The only way to effect this is, 'a constant attention of mind, a habitual discipline over ourselves, and a fixed resolution to stop all action, before a calm examination of every circumstance attending it; more particularly, the real values of external objects, and the moral qualities or tempers of rational agents, about whom our affections may be employed.' This power we may obtain over ourselves, by a frequent consideration of the great calamities, and pernicious actions, to which even the best of our passions may lead us, by the confused sensations, and fantastic associations of ideas which attend them: thus we may raise a habitual suspicion and dread of every violent passion, which, recurring along with them, continually, may in some measure counterbalance their propensities and confused sensations. This discipline of our passions is in general necessary: the unkind or destructive affections, our anger, hatred, or aversion to rational agents, seem to need it most; but there is also a great necessity for it, even about the tender and benign affections, lest we should be hurried into universal and absolute evil, by the appearance of particular good: and consequently it must be of the highest importance to all, to strengthen as much as possible, by frequent meditation and reflection, the calm desires either private or public, rather than the particular passions, and to make the calm universal benevolence superior to them...

From *A System of Moral Philosophy*

Book I, Part I, Chapter 3.
Concerning the ultimate determinations of the will, and benevolent affections.
[The problem of conflict between calm self-love and calm benevolence]

...VI. As we observed formerly that the particular motions of the will toward private good are, either the calm stable affections, or turbulent passions; so are the particular motions of the generous kind: some of them are calm, sedate, and steady; aiming at the happiness of their object, whether an individual or a society, attended with no turbulent sensations, and only causing uneasiness when they are defeated in their intention; others are turbulent, and attended with uneasy sensations. We may proceed further in this comparison.

As there is found in the human mind, when it recollects itself, a calm general determination toward personal happiness of the highest kind it has any notion of; so we may find a like principle of a generous kind. When upon recollection we present to our minds the notion of the greatest possible system of sensitive beings, and the highest happiness it can enjoy, there is also a calm determination to desire it, abstracting from any connection with or subserviency to our private enjoyment. We shall find these two grand determinations, one toward our own greatest happiness, the other toward the greatest general good, each independent on the other, each capable of such strength as to restrain all the particular affections of its kind, and keep them subordinate to itself.

But here arises a new perplexity in this complex structure, where these two principles seem to draw different ways. Must the generous determination, and all its particular affections, yield to the selfish one, and be under its control? Must we indulge their kind motions so far as private interest admits and no further? Or must the selfish yield to the generous? Or can we suppose that in this complex system there are two ultimate principles which may often oppose each other, without any umpire to reconcile their differences? Or shall we deny any original calm determination toward a public interest; allowing only a variety of particular ultimate kind affections; not indeed arising from self-love, or directly aiming at private good as their natural termination, and yet in all our deliberate counsels about the general tenor of our conduct, subjected, in common with all the particular appetites and passions of the selfish kind, to the original impulse in each one toward his own perfection and happiness? This last seems to be the scheme of some excellent authors both ancient and modern.

To allege here that, by our reason and reflection, we may see what was the intention of God the author of our nature in this whole fabric of our affections; that he plainly intended the universal happiness, and that of each individual, as far as it is consistent with it; and that this intention should be our rule: that we should therefore restrain and control, not only all selfish affections, but even all generous particular affections, within such bounds as the universal interest requires: this is true in fact, but does not remove the difficulty, unless we are first told from what determination of soul, from what motive, are we to comply with the divine intentions? If from a desire of reward, then the selfish calm determination is the sole ultimate principle of all deliberate counsels in life: if from a perception of his moral excellence, a desire of imitating him, and from love and gratitude, then the desire of moral excellence must be the supreme original determination. But this desire of moral excellence, however an original principle, must presuppose some antecedent determinations of the will as its object. And among these there must be someone in which the supreme moral excellence consists, otherwise our very sense and desire of moral excellence, since it may recommend many particular affections, which may interfere with each other, will again lead us into a new labyrinth of perplexity. The solution of these difficulties must be found by considering fully that moral faculty above-mentioned, to which, in the next place, we proceed; briefly touching at those reasons which show this moral faculty to be an original determination or sense in our nature, not capable of being referred to other powers of perception.

Book I, Part I, Chapter 4.
Concerning the moral sense, or faculty of perceiving moral excellence, and its objects.
[The authority of the moral sense]

...VI. This moral sense from its very nature appears to be designed for regulating and controlling all our powers. This dignity and commanding nature we are immediately conscious of, as we are conscious of the power itself. Nor can such matters of immediate feeling be otherwise proved but by appeals to our hearts [...see Cicero, *On the Ends*, Book 3, Chapter 10]. It does not estimate the good it recommends as merely differing in degree, though of the same kind with other advantages recommended by other senses, so as to allow us to practice smaller moral evils acknowledged to remain such, in order to obtain some great advantages of other sorts; or to omit what we judge in the present case to be our duty or morally good, that we may decline great evils of another sort. But as we immediately perceive the difference in kind, and that the dignity of enjoyment from fine poetry, painting, or from knowledge is superior to the pleasures of the palate, were they never so delicate; so we immediately discern moral good to be superior in kind and dignity to all others which are perceived by the other perceptive powers.

In all other grateful perceptions, the less we shall relish our state, the greater sacrifice we have made of inferior enjoyments to the superior; and our sense of the superior, after the first flutter of joy in our success is over, is not a whit increased by any sacrifice we have made to it: nay in the judgment of spectators, the superior enjoyment, or our state at least, is generally counted the worse on this account, and our conduct the less relished. Thus in sacrificing ease, or health, or pleasure, to wealth, power, or even to the ingenious arts; their pleasures gain no dignity by that means; and the conduct is not more alluring to others. But in moral good, the greater the necessary sacrifice was which was made to it, the moral excellence increases the more, and is the more approved by the agent, more admired by spectators, and the more they are roused to imitation. By this sense the heart can not only approve itself in sacrificing every other gratification to moral goodness, but have the highest self-enjoyment, and approbation of its own disposition in doing so: which plainly shows this moral sense to be naturally destined to command all the other powers…

XII. Without a distinct consideration of this moral faculty, a species endued with such a variety of senses, and of desires frequently interfering, must appear a complex confused fabric, without any order or regular consistent design. By means of it, all is capable of harmony, and all its powers may conspire in one direction, and be consistent with each other. 'Tis already proved that we are capable of many generous affections ultimately terminating on the good of others, neither arising from any selfish view, nor terminating on private good. This moral faculty plainly shows that we are also capable of a calm settled universal benevolence, and that this is destined, as the supreme determination of the generous kind, to govern and control our particular generous as well as selfish affections; as the heart must entirely approve its doing thus in its calmest reflections: even as in the order of selfish affections, our self-love, or our calm regard to the greatest private interest controls our particular selfish passions; and the heart is satisfied in its doing so.

To acknowledge the several generous ultimate affections of a limited kind to be natural, and yet maintain that we have no general controlling principle but self-love, which indulges or checks the generous affections as they conduce to, or oppose, our own noblest interest; sometimes allowing these kind affections their full exercise, because of that high enjoyment we expect to ourselves in gratifying them; at other times checking them, when their gratification does not overbalance the loss we may sustain by it; is a scheme which brings indeed all the powers of the mind into one direction by means of the reference made of them all to the calm desire of our own happiness, in our previous deliberations about our conduct: and it may be justly alleged that the author of nature has made a connection in the event at last between our gratifying our generous affections, and our own highest interest. But the feelings of our heart, reason, and history, revolt against this account: which seems however to have been maintained by excellent authors and strenuous defenders of the cause of virtue.

This connection of our own highest interests with the gratifying our generous affections, in many cases is imperceptible to the mind; and the kind heart acts from its generous impulse, not thinking of its own interest. Nay all its own interests have sometimes appeared to it as opposite to, and inconsistent with the generous part, in which it persisted. Now were there no other calm original determination of soul but that toward one's own interest, that man must be approved entirely who steadily pursues his own happiness, in opposition to all kind affections and all public interest. That which is the sole calm determination, must justify every action in consequence of it, however opposite to particular kind affections. If it be said 'that 'tis a mistake to imagine our interest opposite to them while there is a good providence': grant it to be a mistake; this is only a defect of reasoning: but that disposition of mind must upon this scheme be approved which coolly sacrifices the interest of the universe to its own interest. This is plainly contrary to the feelings of our hearts.

Can that be deemed the sole ultimate determination, the sole ultimate end, which the mind in the exercise of its noblest powers can calmly resolve, with inward approbation, deliberately to counteract? Are there not instances of men who have voluntarily sacrificed their lives, without thinking of any other state of existence, for the sake of their friends or their country? Does not every heart approve this temper and conduct, and admire it the more, the less presumption there is of the love of glory and posthumous fame, or of any sublimer private interest mixing itself with the generous affection? Does not the admiration rise higher, the more deliberately such resolutions are formed and executed? All this is unquestionably true, and yet would be absurd and impossible if self-interest of any kind is the sole ultimate termination of all calm desire. There is therefore another ultimate determination which our souls are capable of, destined to be also an original spring of the calmest and most deliberate purposes of action; a desire of communicating happiness, an ultimate good-will, not referred to any private interest, and often operating without such reference.

In those cases where some inconsistency appears between these two determinations, the moral faculty at once points out and recommends the glorious [and] the amiable part; not by suggesting prospects of future interests of a sublime sort by pleasures of self-approbation, or of praise. It recommends the generous part by an immediate undefinable perception; it approves the kind ardour of the heart in the sacrificing even life itself, and that even in those who have no hopes of surviving, or no attention to a future life in another world. And thus, where the moral sense is in its full vigor, it makes the generous determination to public happiness the supreme one in the soul, with that commanding power which it is naturally destined to exercise.

It must be obvious we are not speaking here of the ordinary condition of mankind, as if these calm determinations were generally exercised, and habitually controlled the particular passions; but of the condition our nature can be raised to by due culture; and of the principles which may and ought to operate, when by attention we present to our minds the objects or representations fit to excite them. Doubtless some good men have exercised in life only the particular kind affections, and found a constant approbation of them, without either the most extensive views of the whole system, or the most universal benevolence. Scarce any of the vicious have ever considered wherein it is that their highest private happiness consists, and in consequence of it exerted the calm rational self-love; but merely follow inconsiderately the selfish appetites and affections. Much less have all good men made actual references of all private or generous affections to the extensive benevolence, though the mind can make them; or bad men made references of all their affections to calm self-love.

XIII. But as the selfish principles are very strong, and by custom, by early and frequent indulgences, and other causes, are raised in the greatest part of men above their due proportion, while the generous principles are little cultivated, and the moral sense often asleep; our powers of reasoning and comparing the several enjoyments which our nature is capable of, that we may discover which of them are of greatest consequence to our happiness; our capacity, by reasoning, of arriving to the knowledge of a governing mind presiding in this world, and of a moral administration, are of the highest consequence and necessity to preserve our affections in a just order, and to corroborate our moral faculty: as by such reasoning and reflection we may discover a perfect consistency of all the generous motions of the soul with private interest; and find out a certain tenor of life and action the most effectually subservient to both these determinations...

Five

The Moral Life & God

From *An Essay on the Nature and Conduct of the Passions and Affections*

From Sect. VI.
Some general conclusions concerning the best management of our desires. With some principles necessary to happiness. 'Ideas of divinity arise from the internal senses'

...III. Under this head of our internal sense, we must observe one natural effect of it, that it leads us into apprehensions of a deity. Grandeur, beauty, order, harmony, wherever they occur, raise an opinion of a mind, of design, and wisdom. Everything great, regular, or proportioned, excites veneration, either toward itself, if we imagine it animated, if not animated, toward some apprehended cause. No determination of our mind is more natural than this, no effect more universal. One has better reason to deny the inclination between the sexes to be natural, than a disposition in mankind to religion.

We cannot open our eyes, without discerning grandeur and beauty everywhere. Whoever receives these ideas feels an inward veneration arise. We may fall into a thousand vain reasonings: foolish limited notions of divinity may be formed, as attached to the particular places or objects, which strike us in the most lively manner. Custom, prejudice of sense or education, may confirm some foolish opinion about the nature or cause of these appearances: but wherever a superior mind, a governing intention or design is imagined, there religion begins in its most simple form, and an inward devotion arises. Our nature is as much determined to this, as to any other perception or affection. How we manage these ideas and affections, is indeed of the greatest importance to our happiness or misery.

When we have the apprehension of a universal mind with power and knowledge, we must also conceive something correspondent to our affections in the divinity, with some moral apprehensions of the actions and tempers of his creatures. The order of nature will suggest many confirmations of this. We must conclude some worship acceptable, and some expressions of gratitude as our duty. Conceptions of the deity must be various, according to the different degrees of attention and reasoning in the observers, and their own tempers and affections. Imagining the divine mind as cruel, wrathful, or capricious, must be a perpetual source of dread and horror; and will be apt to raise a resemblance of temper in the worshiper, with its attendant misery. A contrary idea of the divinity, as good, and kind, delighting in universal happiness, and ordering all events of the universe to this end, as it is the most delightful contemplation, so it fills the good mind with a constant security and hope, amidst either public disorders, or private calamities.

To find out which of these two representations of the deity is the true one, we must consult the universe, the effect of his power, and the scene of his actions. After what has been observed by so many ingenious authors, both ancient and modern, one cannot be at a loss which opinion to choose. We may only on this occasion consider the evidences of divine goodness appearing in the structure of our own nature, and in the order of our passions and senses.

It was observed above, how admirably our affections are contrived for good in the whole. Many of them indeed do not pursue the private good of the agent; nay, many of them, in various cases, seem to tend to his detriment, by concerning him violently in the fortunes of others, in their adversity, as well as their prosperity. But they all aim at good, either private or public: and by them each particular agent is made, in a great measure, subservient to the good of the whole. Mankind are thus insensibly linked together, and make one great system, by an invisible union. He who voluntarily continues in this union, and delights in employing his power for his kind, makes himself happy: he who does not continue this union freely, but affects to break it, makes himself wretched; nor yet can he break the bonds of nature. His public sense, his love of honour, and the very necessities of his nature, will continue to make him depend upon his system and engage him to serve it, whether he inclines to it or not. Thus we are formed with a view to a general good end; and may in our own nature discern a universal mind watchful for the whole.

The same is observable in the order of our external senses. The simple productions of nature, which are useful to any species of animals, are also grateful to them; and the pernicious, or useless objects are made disagreeable. Our external sensations are no doubt often painful, when our bodies are in a dangerous state; when they want supplies of nourishment; when anything external would be injurious to them. But if it appears, 'that the general laws are wisely constituted, and that it is necessary to the good of a system of such agents, to be under the influence of general laws, upon which there is occasion for prudence and activity'; the particular pains occasioned by a necessary law of sensation, can be no objection against the goodness of the author [see T1.VII].

Now that there is no room for complaint, that 'our external sense of pain is made too acute,' must appear from the multitudes we daily see so careless of preserving the blessing of health, of which many are so prodigal as to lavish it away, and expose themselves to the most severe external pain for very trifling reasons. Can we then repine at the friendly admonitions of nature, joined with some austerity, when we see that they are scarce sufficient to restrain us from ruin[?] The same may be said of pain of other kinds, shame and remorse are never to be called too severe, while so many are not sufficiently restrained by them. Our compassion and friendly sense of sorrow, what are they else but the alarms and exhortations of a kind impartial father, to engage his children to relieve a distressed brother? Our anger itself is a necessary piece of management, by which every pernicious attempt is made dangerous to its author.

Would we allow room to our invention, to conceive what sort of mechanism, what constitutions of senses or affections a malicious powerful being might have formed, we should soon see how few evidences there are for any such apprehension concerning the author of this world. Our mechanism, as far as we have ever yet discovered, is wholly contrived for good. No cruel device, no art or contrivance to produce evil: no such mark or scope seems ever to be aimed at. How easy had it been to have contrived some necessary engines of misery without any use; some member of no other service but to be matter of torment; senses incapable of bearing the surrounding objects without pain; eyes pained with the light; a palate offended with the fruits of the earth; a skin as tender as the coats of the eye, and yet some more furious pain forcing us to bear these torments? Human society might have been made as uneasy as the company of enemies, and yet a perpetual more violent motive of fear might have forced us to bear it. Malice, rancour, distrust, might have been our natural temper. Our honour and self-approbation might have depended upon injuries; and the torments of others been made our delight, which yet we could not have enjoyed through perpetual fear. Many such contrivances we may easily conceive, whereby an evil mind could have gratified his malice by our misery. But how unlike are they all to the intention or design of the mechanism of this world?

Our passions no doubt are often [a] matter of uneasiness to ourselves, and sometimes occasion misery to others, when any one is indulged into a degree of strength beyond its proportion. But which of them could we have wanted, without greater misery in the whole? They are by nature balanced against each other, like the antagonist muscles of the body; either of which separately would have occasioned distortion and irregular motion, yet jointly, they form a machine, most accurately subservient to the necessities, convenience, and happiness of a rational system. We have a power of reason and reflection, by which we may see what course of action will naturally tend to procure us the most valuable gratifications of all our desires, and prevent any intolerable or unnecessary pains, or provide some support under them. We have wisdom sufficient to form ideas of rights, laws, constitutions; so as to preserve large societies in peace and prosperity, and promote a general good amidst all the private interests.

If from the present order of nature, in which good appears far superior to evil, we have just ground to conclude the deity to be benevolent, it is not conceivable 'that any being, who desires the happiness of others, should not desire a greater degree of happiness to them rather than a less; and that consequently the whole series of events is the best possible, and contains in the whole the greatest possible absolute good': especially since we have no presumption of any private interest, which a universal mind can have in view, in opposition to the greatest good of the whole. Nor are the particular evils occurring to our observation, any just objection against the perfect goodness of the universal providence to us, who cannot know how far these evils may be necessarily connected with the means of the greatest possible absolute good...

These thoughts plainly show a prevalence of good in the world. But still our public sense finds much matter of compassionate sorrow among men. The many are in a tolerable good state; but who can be unconcerned for the distressed few? They are few in comparison of the whole, and yet a great multitude.

What parent would be much concerned at the pains of breeding of teeth, were they sure they would be short, and end well? Or at the pain of a medicine, or an incision, which was necessary for the cure, and would certainly accomplish it? Is there then no parent in nature, no physician who sees what is necessary for the whole, and for the good of each individual in the whole of his existence, as far as is consistent with the general good? Can we expect, in this our childhood of existence, to understand all the contrivance and art of this parent and physician of nature? May not some harsh discipline be necessary to good? May not many natural evils be necessary to prevent future moral evils, and to correct the tempers of the agents, nay to introduce moral good? Is not suffering and distress requisite, before there can be room for generous compassion, succour, and liberality? Can there be forgiveness, returns of good for evil, unless there be some moral evil? Must the whole want the eternally delightful consciousness of such actions and dispositions, to prevent a few transient sensations of pain, or natural evil? May there not be some unseen necessity for the greatest universal good, that [see William King's *Essay on the Origin of Evil*] there should be an order of beings no more perfect than we are, subject to error and wrong affections sometimes? May not all the present disorders which attend this state of prevalent order, be rectified by the directing providence in a future part of our existence? This belief of a deity, a providence, and a future state, are the only sure supports to a good mind. Let us then acquire and strengthen our love and concern for this whole, and acquiesce in what the governing mind, who presides in it, is ordering in the wisest manner, though not yet fully known to us, for its most universal good...

VII. To conclude: let us consider that common character, which when ascribed to any state, quality, disposition, or action, engages our favour and approbation of it, *viz.* its being natural. We have many suspicions about tempers or dispositions formed by art, but are some way prepossessed in favour of what is natural: we imagine it must be advantageous and delightful to be in a natural state, and to live according to nature. This very presumption in favour of what is natural, is a plain indication that the order of nature is good, and that men are some way convinced of it. Let us enquire then what is meant by it.

If by natural we mean 'that which we enjoy or do when we first begin to exist, or to think,' it is impossible to know what state, temper, or actions, are natural. Our natural state in this sense differs little from that of a plant, except in some accidental sensations of hunger, or of ease, when we are well nourished.

Some elaborate treatises of great philosophers about innate ideas, or principles, practical or speculative, amount to no more than this, 'that in the beginning of our existence we have no ideas or judgments'; they might have added too, no sight, taste, smell, hearing, desire, volition. Such dissertations are just as useful for understanding human nature, as it would be in explaining the animal economy, to prove that the foetus is animated before it has teeth, nails, hair, or before it can eat, drink, digest, or breathe: or in a natural history of vegetables, to prove that trees begin to grow before they have branches, leaves, flowers, fruit, or seed: and consequently that all these things were adventitious, or the effect of art.

But if we call 'that state, those dispositions and actions, natural, to which we are inclined by some part of our constitution, antecedently to any volition of our own; or which flow from some principles in our nature, not brought upon us by our own art, or that of others'; then it may appear, from what was said above, that 'a state of good-will, humanity, compassion, mutual aid, propagating and supporting offspring, love of a community or country, devotion, or love and gratitude to some governing mind, is our natural state,' to which we are naturally inclined, and do actually arrive, as universally, and with as much uniformity, as we do to a certain stature and shape.

If by natural we understand 'the highest perfection of the kind, to which any species may be improved by cultivating its natural dispositions or powers'; as few arrive at this in the growth of their bodies, so few obtain it in their minds. But we may see what this perfection is, to which our natural dispositions tend, when we improve them to the utmost, as far as they are consistent with each other, making the weaker or meaner yield to the more excellent and stronger. Our several senses and affections, public and private, with our powers of reason and reflection, show this to be the perfection of our kind, *viz.* 'to know, love, and reverence the great author of all things; to form the most extensive ideas of our own true interests, and those of all other natures, rational or sensitive; to abstain from all injury, to pursue regularly and impartially the most universal absolute good, as far as we can; to enjoy constant self-approbation, and honour from wise men; with trust in divine providence, hope of everlasting happiness, and a full satisfaction and assurance of mind, that the whole series of events is directed by an unerring wisdom, for the greatest universal happiness of the whole.'

To assert that 'men have generally arrived to the perfection of their kind in this life,' is contrary to experience. But on the other hand, to suppose 'no order at all in the constitution of our nature, or no prevalent evidences of good order,' is yet more contrary to experience, and would lead to a denial of providence in the most important affair which can occur to our observation. We actually see such degrees of good order, of social affection, of virtue and honour, as make the generality of mankind continue in a tolerable, nay, an agreeable state. However, in some tempers we see the selfish passions by habits grown too strong; in others we may observe humanity, compassion, and good-nature sometimes raised by habits, as we say, to an excess.

Were we to strike a medium of the several passions and affections, as they appear in the whole species of mankind, to conclude thence what has been the natural balance previously to any change made by custom or habit, which we see calls the balance to either side, we should perhaps find the medium of the public affections not very far from a sufficient counterbalance to the medium of the selfish; and consequently the overbalance on either side, in particular characters, is not to be looked upon as the original constitution, but as the accidental effect of custom, habits, or associations of ideas, or other preternatural causes: so that a universal increasing of the strength of either, might in the whole be of little advantage. The raising universally the public affections, the desires of virtue and honour, would make the hero of Cervantes, pining with hunger and poverty, no rare character.[1] The universal increasing of selfishness, unless we had more accurate understandings to discern our nicest interests, would fill the world with universal rapine and war, the consequences of either universally abating, or increasing the desires between the sexes, the love of offspring, or the several tastes and fancies in other pleasures, would perhaps be found more pernicious to the whole, than the present constitution. What seems most truly wanting in our nature, is greater knowledge, attention, and consideration: had we a greater perfection this way, and were evil habits, and foolish associations of ideas prevented, our passions would appear in better order.

But while we feel in ourselves so much public affection in the various relations of life, and observe the like in others; while we find everyone desiring indeed his own happiness, but capable of discerning, by a little attention, that not only

---

1 [Reference to Cervantes' *Don Quixote*.]

his external conveniency, or worldly interest, but even the most immediate and lively sensations of delight, of which his nature is susceptible, immediately flow from a public spirit, a generous, human, compassionate temper, and a suitable deportment; while we observe so many thousands enjoying a tolerable state of ease and safety, for each one whose condition is made intolerable, even during our present corruption: how can anyone look upon this world as under the direction of an evil nature, or even question a perfectly good providence? How clearly does the order of our nature point out to us our true happiness and perfection, and lead us to it as naturally as the several powers of the earth, the sun, and air, bring plants to their growth, and the perfection of their kinds? We indeed are directed to it by our understanding and affections, as it becomes rational and active natures; and they by mechanic laws. We may see, that 'attention to the most universal interest of all sensitive natures, is the perfection of each individual of mankind': that they should thus be like well-tuned instruments, affected with every stroke or touch upon anyone. Nay, how much of this do we actually see in the world? What generous sympathy, compassion, and congratulation with each other? Does not even the flourishing state of the inanimate parts of nature, fill us with joy? Is not thus our nature admonished, exhorted and commanded to cultivate universal goodness and love, by a voice heard through all the earth, and words sounding to the ends of the world?

From *Illustrations on the Moral Sense*

From Sect. VI.
How far a regard to the deity is necessary to make an action virtuous

I. Some imagine, that 'to make an action virtuous, it is necessary that the agent should have previously known his action to be acceptable to the deity, and have undertaken it chiefly with design to please or obey him. We have not, say they, reason to imagine a malicious intention in many of the worst actions: the very want of good affections in their full degree, must constitute moral evil. If so, then the moral evil in the want of love or gratitude, must increase in proportion to the causes of love or gratitude in the object: by the causes of love, they mean those qualities in the object upon observation of which love or gratitude arise in every good temper. Now the causes of love toward the deity are infinite; therefore the want of the highest possible degree of love to him, must be infinitely evil.—To be excited more by smaller motives or causes than by greater; to love those who are less lovely, while we neglect him in whom are infinite causes of love, must argue real perverseness of affections. But the causes of love in the deity, his infinite goodness toward all, and even toward ourselves, from whence springs all the happiness of our lives, are infinitely above any causes of love to be found in creatures: therefore to act from love to them without intention to please God, must be infinitely evil.'

If this reasoning be just, the best of men are infinitely evil. The distinction between habitual and actual intention will not remove the difficulty, since these arguments require actual intention. A habitual intention is not a present act of love to the deity, influencing our actions more than actual love to creatures, which this argument requires; but a prior general resolution not at present repeated...

III. ...Here it must be remembered, that in arguing concerning the goodness of temper from the degree of love directly, and the causes of love inversely, actual attention to the causes of love is supposed in the person. For 'tis plain, that in the best temper no one affection or idea can always continue present, and there can be no affection present to the mind, toward any object, while the idea of it is not present. The bare absence therefore of affection, while the mind is employed upon a different object, can argue no evil in the temper, farther than want of attention may argue want of affection. In like manner, in the best temper, there can be no love toward an object unknown: the want therefore of love to an object unknown, can argue no evil in the temper further than ignorance may argue want of affection. It is certain indeed, that he who knows that there is a good deity, and actually thinks of him, and of all his benefits, yet has not the strongest love and gratitude toward him, must have a temper void of all goodness; but it will not follow, that the mind is void of goodness which is not always thinking of the deity, or actually loving him, or even does not know him.

How far the want of attention to the deity, and ignorance of him, may argue an evil temper, must be shown from different topics; to be considered hereafter...

V. Now let us inquire how far ignorance of a deity, or unaffected atheism evidences an evil disposition, or defect of good affections below innocence.

1. Affections arising upon apparent causes, or present opinions, though false, if they be such as would arise in the best temper, were these opinions true, cannot argue any present want of goodness in any temper, of themselves the opinions indeed may often argue a want of goodness at the time they were formed: but to a benevolent temper there is no cause of malice, or of the ultimate desire of the misery or non-existence of any being for itself. There may be causes of dislike and desire of misery or non-existence, as the means of greater good, or of lessening evil.

2. No object which is entirely unknown, or of which we have no idea, can raise affection in the best temper; consequently want of affections to an unknown object evidences no evil. This would be the case of those who never heard even the report of a deity, if ever there were any such: or who never heard of any fellow-creatures, if one may make a supposition like to that made by Cicero [see Book 2, Chapter 37 of *On the Nature of the Gods*[2]]. And this is perhaps the case, as to the deity, of any unfortunate children, who may have some little use of reason, before they are instructed in any religion.

If there really were an innate idea of a deity so imprinted, that no person could be without it; or if we are so disposed, as necessarily to receive this idea, as soon as we can be called moral agents: then no ignorance of a deity can be innocent; all atheism must be affected, or an opinion formed, either through evil affection, or want of good affection below innocence. But if the idea of a deity be neither imprinted, nor offer itself previously to any

2 [Hutcheson also remarks here, 'ex. Aristotle.']

reflection, nor be universally excited by tradition, the bare want of it, where there has been no tradition or reflection, cannot be called criminal upon any scheme. Those who make virtue and vice relative to a law, may say, 'men are required to reflect, and thence to know a deity.' But they must allow promulgation necessary, before disobedience to a law can be criminal. Now previously to reflection it is supposed impossible for the agent to know the legislator, or to know the law requiring him to reflect, therefore this law requiring him to reflect, was not antecedently to his reflection published to him.

The case of human laws, the ignorance of which does not excuse, is not parallel to this. No person under any civil government can be supposed ignorant that there are laws made for the whole state. But in the present supposition, men antecedently to reflection may be ignorant of the deity, or that there are laws of nature. If any subject could thus be unapprised, that he lived under civil government, he should not be accounted *compos mentis*.[3] The supposition indeed in both cases is perhaps wholly imaginary; at least as to persons above childhood. One can scarce imagine that ever any person was wholly unapprised of a governing mind, and of a right and wrong in morals. Whether this is to be ascribed to innate ideas, to universal tradition, or to some necessary determination in our nature, to imagine a designing cause of the beautiful objects which occur to us, with a moral sense, let the curious inquire.

3. Suppose an idea formed in a benevolent mind, of other sensitive natures, desire of their existence and happiness would arise.

4. A good temper would incline anyone to wish, that other natures were benevolent, or morally good, since this is the chief happiness.

5. A good temper would desire that the administration of nature were by a benevolent or good mind.

---

3 [Of sound mind.]

> 6. All desire of any event or circumstance inclines any mind to search into the truth of that event or circumstance, by all the evidence within its power to obtain.
>
> 7. Where there is such desire, and sufficiently obvious evidence given in proportion to the sagacity of the desiring mind, it will come to the knowledge of the truth, if its desire be strong.

Now from these propositions we may deduce the following conclusions.

> 1. Supposing the idea of a good deity once apprehended, or excited either by report, or the slightest reflection; if there be objective evidence in nature proportioned to the capacity of the inquirer, for the existence of a good deity, atheism directly argues want of good affection below innocence.
>
> 2. If there be only the simple tradition or presumption of a governing mind once raised; and if there be evidence as before for his goodness, to conclude the deity evil or malicious, must argue want of good affection as before.
>
> 3. Suppose the idea of an evil deity once excited, and some presumptions for his malice from tradition, or slight reflection upon particular evils in nature; to rest in this opinion without inquiry, would argue want of good affection; to desire to reject this opinion, or confute it by contrary evidence, would argue good affection: suppose such contrary evidences obvious enough in nature to one who inquired as diligently about it as about his own interest; to continue in the false opinion cannot be innocent.

VI. In like manner concerning our fellow-creatures, who are actually known to us.

> 4. To imagine fellow-creatures morally good, either according to evidence upon inquiry, or even by a rash opinion, evidences good affection.
>
> 5. Imagining them evil contrary to obvious evidence, argues want of good affection below innocence.

6. Retaining and inculcating an opinion either of the causes of love in others, or of the causes of aversion, induces a habit; and makes the temper prone to the affection often raised. Opinion of goodness in the deity and our fellows increases good affection, and improves the temper: contrary opinion of either, by raising frequent aversions, weakens good affections, and impairs the temper.

This may show how cautious men ought to be in passing sentence upon the impiety of their fellows, or representing them as wicked and profane, or hateful to the deity, and justly given over to eternal misery: we may see also what a wise mark it is to know the true church by, that 'it pronounces damnation on all others.' Which is one of the characters of the Romish Church, by which it is often recommended as the safest for Christians to live in.

The same propositions may be applied to our opinions concerning the natural tendencies of actions. Where the evidence is obvious as before, good affection will produce true opinions, and false opinions often argue want of good affection below innocence. Thus, though in assent or dissent of themselves, there can neither be virtue nor vice, yet there may be evidences of either in the agent, as well as his external motions. It is not possible indeed for men to determine precisely in many cases the quantity of evidence, and its proportion to the sagacity of the observer, which will argue guilt in him, who contrary to it, forms a false opinion. But men are no better judges of the degrees, of virtue and vice in external actions. This therefore will not prove that false opinions or errors are innocent, more than external actions: the searcher of hearts can judge exactly of both. Human punishments are only methods of self-defence; in which proper measure, but the necessity of restraining actions for the safety of the public.

VII. It is next to be considered, how far want of attention to the deity can argue want of good affections, in any agent, to whom he is known.

Every good temper will have strong affections to a good deity, and where there is strong affection there will be frequent reflection upon the object beloved, desire of pleasing, and caution of offence. In like manner every person of good temper, who has had the knowledge of a country, a system, a species, will consider how far these great societies may be affected by his actions, with such attention as he uses in his own affairs; and will abstain from what is injurious to them.

Attention to a deity apprehended as good, and governing the universe, will increase the disposition to beneficence in any good agent various ways; by prospects of reward, either present or future; by improving his temper through observation of so amiable a pattern; or by raising sentiments of gratitude toward the deity, to whom we may imagine the public happiness to be acceptable. In like manner, the considering a species or system may increase our good offices, since their interests are advanced by good offices to individuals.

But then from a like reasoning to that in Art. II [not included here] it is plain, that in equal moments of good produced by two agents, the goodness of the temper is rather inversely as the several additional helps, or motives to it. So that where no more good is done, in equal abilities, by one agent who had prevented to him the joint motives of piety toward God and humanity toward men, than is done by another from mere humanity, the latter gives a better evidence of a good temper. And where higher motives of gratitude to God are presented to one than to another, unless the good done from these stronger motives is greater, the temper must be so much the worse [see Luke, X.12–14].

But an injurious action which appeared to the agent not only pernicious to his fellows, or to particular persons, but offensive to the deity, and pernicious to a system, is much more vicious than when the agent did not reflect upon the deity, or a community.

VIII. We must not hence imagine, that in order to produce greater virtue in ourselves, we should regard the deity no further, than merely to abstain from offences. Were it our sole intention in beneficent actions, only to obtain the private pleasure of self-approbation for the degree of our virtue, this might seem the proper means of having great virtue with the least expense. But if the real intention, which constitutes an action virtuous, be the promoting public good; then voluntarily to reject the confederation of any motive which would increase the moment of public good, or would make us more vigorous and steadfast in virtue, must argue want of good affection. Good offices done from mere humanity, while the motives of piety were not present to the mind, provided they were not excluded by direct design, or blamable inadvertence, may in this particular case be a better indication of a good temper, than offices only of equal importance done by another of equal abilities, from the joint motives of piety and humanity; yet the retaining designedly and frequently recalling all these motives with a view to increase the moment of public good in our actions, if they really do so, argues virtue equal to, or greater than that in the former case: and the affected neglect of these motives, that so we may acquit ourselves virtuously with the least expense to ourselves, or with the least moment of public good, must evidence want of good affections, and base trick and artifice to impose upon observers, or our own hearts. Therefore:

> Since gratitude to the deity, and even consideration of private interest, tend to increase the moment of our beneficence, and to strengthen good affections, the voluntary retaining them with this view evidences virtue, and affecting to neglect them evidences vice.[4] And yet,
>
> If the moment produced by the conjunction of these motives, be not greater than that produced with unaffected neglect of these motives, from particular good

---

[4] This may sufficiently justify the writers of morality in their proving, 'that virtue is the surest means of happiness to the agent.' 'Tis also plain from universal experience that a regard to the deity, frequent reflection on his goodness, and consequent acts of love are the strongest and most universally prevailing means of obtaining a good temper. Whatever institution therefore does most effectually tend to raise men's attention, to recall their minds from the hurry of their common affairs, to instruct them in the ways of promoting public good farther than the busy part of the world without assistance would probably apprehend, must be so wise and good, that every honest mind should rejoice in it, even though it had no other authority than human to recommend it. Everyone will understand that by this is meant a public worship on set days, in which a stop is put to commerce, and the busy part of mankind instructed in the duties of piety and humanity.

affection, there is less virtue in the former than in the latter.

Men may use names as they please, and may choose to call nothing virtue but 'what is intended chiefly to evidence affection of one kind or other toward the deity.' Writers on this scheme are not well agreed about what this virtuous intention is; whether only to evidence submission, or submission and love, or to express gratitude by compliance with the divine will, or to express a disinterested esteem, or to obtain our own happiness by means of the divine favour. This last intention may influence a very corrupt mind in some things. And the former more generous intentions must really increase the goodness of every action, and are the highest virtues of themselves. But let them not assert, against universal experience, that we approve no actions which are not thus intended toward the deity. 'Tis plain, a generous compassionate heart, which, at first view of the distress of another, flies impatiently to his relief, or spares no expense to accomplish it, meets with strong approbation from every observer, who has not perverted his sense of life by school-divinity, or philosophy. Joining frequently and habitually the acts of piety with those of humanity is, no doubt, the perfection of goodness and virtue. But we must not deny the reality of virtue in these actions, which are not of the most perfect sort.

To be led by a weaker motive, where a stronger is alike present to the mind, to love a creature more than God, or to have stronger desires of doing what is grateful to creatures than to God, when we equally attend to both, would certainly argue great perversion of our affections; or to study the particular good of one, more than that of a system, when we reflected on both: but as no finite mind can retain at once a multiplicity of objects, so it cannot always retain any one object. When a person therefore not thinking at present of the deity, or of a community, or system, does a beneficent action from particular love, he evidences goodness of temper. The bare absence of the idea of a deity, or of affections, to him, can evidence no evil; otherwise it would be a crime to fall asleep, or to think of anything else: if the bare absence of this idea be no evil, the presence of kind affections to fellow-creatures cannot be evil. If indeed our love to the deity excited to any action, and at the same time love to a creature excited to the omission of it, or to a contrary action, we must be very criminal if the former do not prevail; yet this will not argue all actions to be evil in which pleasing the deity, is not directly and chiefly intended. Nay, that temper must really be very deficient in goodness, whichever needs to recall the thoughts of a divine command and its sanctions, or even the thoughts of the interests of greater societies or systems, before it can be engaged into any particular acts of kindness. Accordingly we find in nature that the particular kind passions generally move the mind first. And upon reflection, more extensive motives begin to occur, and regards to the great head of the rational system. The frequent recalling these thoughts, indeed, does strengthen all good affections, and increases the moment of beneficence to be expressed from any temper; and with this view frequently to recall such thoughts, must be one of the best helps to virtue, and evidence high degrees of it. Nay, one cannot call that temper entire and complete, which has not the strongest affection toward the greatest benefactor, and the most worthy object.

Beings of such degrees of knowledge, and such extent of thought, as mankind are not only capable of, but generally obtain, when nothing interrupts their inquiries, must naturally arise to the knowledge of the deity, if their temper be good. They must form general conceptions of the whole, and see the order, wisdom, and goodness in the administration of nature in some degree. The knowledge and love of the deity, the universal mind, is as natural a perfection to such a being as man, as any accomplishment to which we arrive by cultivating our natural dispositions; nor is that mind come to the proper state and vigour of its kind, where religion is not the main exercise and delight.

IX. There is one very subtle argument on this subject. Some allege, 'That since the deity is really the cause of all the good in the universe, even of all the virtue, or good affection in creatures, which are the seeming causes of love toward them, it must argue strange perversion of temper to love those in whom there is no cause of love, or who are (as they affect to speak) nothing, or emptiness of all goodness. The deity alone is amiable, in whom there is infinite fullness of every amiable quality. The deity, say they, not without some reason, is the cause of every pleasant sensation, which he immediately excites according to a general law, upon the occasion of motions arising in our bodies; that likewise he gave us that general inclination, which we modify into all our different affections; God therefore, say they, is alone lovely. Other things are not to be beloved, but only the goodness of God appearing in them; nay some make the loving of them, without considering God as displaying his goodness in them, to be infinitely evil.'

In answer to this it must be owned, that 'God's being the cause of all the good in the universe, will no doubt raise the highest love to him in a good temper, when it reflects upon it.'

> But first, had all men this apprehension that 'there was no good in any creature,' they really would not love them at all. But men generally imagine with very good ground, that there are good beings distinct from God, though produced by him: and whether this opinion be true or false, it evidences no evil.
>
> 2. As upon this scheme God is the cause of all pleasant sensation, so is he the cause of all pain: he is, according to them, the cause of that inclination which we modify into evil affection, as well as into good. If then we are to love God only, for what we call good affection in creatures, and not the creatures themselves, we must also only love God upon observing evil affections in creatures, and have no aversion to the basest temper, since God gave the general inclination alike in both cases.
>
> 3. If we may suppose real beings distinct from God, that their affections are not God's affections, if God is not the only lover and hater, if our moral sense is determined to approve kind affections, and our love or benevolence must arise toward what we approve; or if we find an instinct to desire the happiness of every sensitive nature, we cannot avoid loving creatures, and we must approve any kind affections observed in others toward their fellows. 'Tis true, we must approve the highest affections toward the deity, and condemn, as a deficiency of just affections toward God any degree which is not superior

to our other affections. But still, affections towards creatures, if they be distinct natures, must be approved.

4. If to make a mind virtuous, or even innocent, it be necessary that it should have such sublime speculations of God… then God has placed the bulk of mankind in an absolute incapacity of virtue, and inclined them perpetually to infinite evil, by their very instincts and natural affections. Does the parental affection direct a man to love the deity, or his children? Is it the divinity, to which our pity or compassion is directed? Is God the object of humanity? Is it a design to support the divinity, which we call generosity or liberality? Upon receipt of a benefit, does our nature suggest only gratitude toward God? Affections toward the deity may indeed often accompany affections toward creatures, and do so in a virtuous temper: but these are distinct affections. This notion of making all virtuous affections to be only directed toward God, is not suggested to men by anything in their nature, but arises from the long subtle reasonings of men at leisure, and unemployed in the natural affairs of life.

5. If there be no virtue or cause of love in creatures, it is vain for them to debate wherein their virtue consists, whether in regard toward the deity, or in anything else, since they are supposed to have none at all.

To conclude this subject. It seems probable, that however we must look upon that temper as exceedingly imperfect, inconstant, and partial, in which gratitude toward the universal benefactor, admiration and love of the supreme original beauty, perfection and goodness, are not the strongest and most prevalent affections; yet particular actions may be innocent, nay, virtuous, where there is no actual intention of pleasing the deity, influencing the agent.

Six

Reason's Role in Morality

From *Illustrations on the Moral Sense*

Introduction

The differences of actions from which some are constituted morally good, and others morally evil, have always been accounted a very important subject of inquiry: and therefore, every attempt to free this subject from the usual causes of error and dispute, the confusion of ambiguous words, must be excusable...

There have been many ways of speaking introduced, which seem to signify something different from both the former opinions [*i.e.* egoistic and non-egoistic but both affect-based accounts of moral action and evaluation]. Such as these, that 'morality of actions consists in conformity to reason, or disformity from it': that 'virtue is acting according to the absolute fitness and unfitness of things, or agreeably to the natures or relations of things,' and many others in different authors. To examine these is the design of the following sections; and to explain more fully how the moral sense alleged to be in mankind, must be presupposed even in these schemes.

Sect. I.
Concerning the character of virtue, agreeable to truth or reason

Since reason is understood to denote our power of finding out true propositions, 'reasonableness' must denote the same thing, with conformity to true propositions, or to truth.

'Reasonableness' in an action is a very common expression, but yet upon inquiry, it will appear very confused, whether we suppose it the motive to election, or the quality determining approbation.

There is one sort of conformity to truth which neither determines to the one or the other; *viz.* that conformity which is between every true proposition and its object. This sort of conformity can never make us choose or approve one action more than its contrary, for it is found in all actions alike: whatever attribute can be ascribed to a generous kind action, the contrary attribute may as truly be ascribed to a selfish cruel action: both propositions are equally true, and the two contrary actions, the objects of the two truths are equally conformable to several truths, with that sort of conformity which is between a truth and its object. This conformity then cannot make a difference among actions, or recommend one more than another either to election or approbation, since any man may make as many truths about villainy, as about heroism, by ascribing to it contrary attributes.

For instance, these are truths concerning the preservation of property. 'It tends to the happiness of human society: it encourages industry: it shall be rewarded by God.' These are also truths concerning robbery. 'It disturbs society: it discourages industry: it shall be punished by God.' The former three truths have the preservation of property for their object: the latter three have robbery. And each class of truth has that sort of conformity to its objects, which is common to all truths with their objects. The moral difference cannot therefore depend upon this conformity, which is common to both.

The number of truths in both cases may be plainly the same; so that a good action cannot be supposed to agree to more truths than an evil one, nor can an evil action be disagreeable to any truth or compages of truths made about it; for whatever propositions do not agree with their objects are not truths.

If 'reasonableness', the character of virtue, denote some other sort of conformity to truth, it were to be wished that these gentlemen, who make it the original idea of moral good, antecedent to any sense or affections, would explain it, and show how it determines us antecedently to a sense, either to election or approbation.

They tell us, 'we must have some standard antecedently to all sense or affections, since we judge even of our senses and affections themselves, and approve or disapprove them: this standard must be our reason, conformity to which must be the original idea of moral good.'

But what is this 'conformity of actions to reason'? When we ask the reason of an action, we sometimes mean, 'What truth shows a quality in the action, exciting the agent to do it?' Thus, why does a luxurious man pursue wealth? The reason is given by this truth, 'wealth is useful to purchase pleasures.' Sometimes for a reason of actions we show the truth expressing a quality, engaging our approbation. Thus the reason of hazarding life in just war, is, that 'it tends to preserve our honest countrymen, or evidences public spirit': the reason for temperance, and against luxury is given thus, 'luxury evidences a selfish base temper.' The former sort of reasons we will call 'exciting', and the latter 'justifying'.[1] Now we shall find that all exciting reasons presuppose instincts and affections; and the justifying presuppose a moral sense.

As to exciting reasons, in every calm rational action some end is desired or intended; no end can be intended or desired previously to some one of these classes of affections, self-love, self-hatred, or desire of private misery (if this be possible), benevolence toward others, or malice: all affections are included under these: no end can be previous to them all; there can therefore be no exciting reason previous to affection.

We have indeed many confused harangues on this subject, telling us, 'We have two principles of action, reason and affection or passion: the former in common with angels, the latter with brutes: no action is wise, or good, or reasonable, to which we are not excited by reason, as distinct from all affections; or, if any such actions as flow from affections be good, it is only by chance, or materially and not formally.' As

---

1 [See Book II, Chapter I of *On the Law of War and Peace* by Hugo Grotius (1583–1645), philosopher of law.]

if indeed reason, or the knowledge of relations of things, could excite to action when we proposed no end, or as if ends could be intended without desire or affection…

But are there not also exciting reasons, even previous to any end, moving us to propose one end rather than another? To this Aristotle long ago answered, 'that there are ultimate ends desired without a view to anything else, and subordinate ends, or objects, desired with a view to something else.'[2] To subordinate ends those reasons or truths excite, which show them to be conducive to the ultimate end, and show one object to be more effectual than another: thus subordinate ends may be called 'reasonable.' But as to the ultimate ends, to suppose exciting reasons for them, would infer, that there is no ultimate end, but that we desire one thing for another in an infinite series.

Thus ask a being who desires private happiness, or has self-love[:] 'what reason excites him to desire wealth?' He will give this reason, that 'wealth tends to procure pleasure and ease.' Ask his reason for desiring pleasure or happiness: one cannot imagine what proposition he could assign as his exciting reason. This proposition is indeed true, 'there is an instinct or desire fixed in his nature, determining him to pursue his happiness'; but it is not this reflection on his own nature, or this proposition which excites or determines him, but the instinct itself. This is a truth, 'rhubarb strengthens the stomach': but it is not a proposition which strengthens the stomach, but the quality in that medicine. The effect is not produced by propositions showing the cause, but by the cause itself.

In like manner, what reason can a benevolent being give, as exciting him to hazard his life in just war? This, perhaps, 'such conduct tends to the happiness of his country.' Ask him, 'why he serves his country?' He will say, 'his country is a very valuable part of mankind.' Why does he study the happiness of mankind? If his affections be really disinterested, he can give no exciting reasons for it: the happiness of

---

2 [Hutcheson does not cite a particular text here, but he likely has lines 1094a–b of *Nicomachean Ethics* in mind.]

mankind in general, or of any valuable part of it, is an ultimate end to that series of desires.

We may transiently observe a mistake some fall into; they suppose, because they have formed some conception of an infinite good, or greatest possible aggregate, or sum of happiness, under which all particular pleasures may be included; that there is also some one great ultimate end, with a view to which every particular object is desired; whereas, in truth, each particular pleasure is desired without further view, as an ultimate end in the selfish desires. It is true, the prospect of a greater inconsistent pleasure may surmount or stop this desire; so may the fear of a prepollent evil. But this does not prove 'that all men have formed ideas of infinite good, or greatest possible aggregate, or that they have any instinct or desire, actually operating without an idea of its object.' Just so in the benevolent affections, the happiness of any one person is an ultimate end, desired with no further view: and yet the observing its inconsistency with the happiness of another more beloved, or with the happiness of many, though each one of them were but equally beloved, may overcome the former desire. Yet this will not prove, that in each kind action men form the abstract conception of all mankind, or the system of rationals. Such conceptions are indeed useful, that so we may gratify either our self-love or kind affections in the fullest manner, as far as our power extends; and may not content ourselves with smaller degrees either of private or public good, while greater are in our power: but when we have formed these conceptions, we do not serve the individual only from love to species, no more than we desire grapes with an intention of the greatest aggregate of happiness, or from an apprehension that they make a part of the general sum of our happiness. These conceptions only serve to suggest greater ends than would occur to us without reflection; and by the prepollency of one desire toward the greater good, to either private or public, to stop the desire toward the smaller good, when it appear inconsistent with the greater.

Let us examine the truths assigned as exciting to the pursuit of public good, even by those, who, though they allow disinterested affections, and a moral sense, yet suppose something reasonable in it antecedently. They assign such as these, 'public good is the end proposed by the deity.' Then what reason excites men to concur with the deity? It is this, 'concurring with the deity will make the agent happy.' This is an exciting reason indeed, but plainly supposes self-love: and let anyone assign the exciting reason to the desire of happiness. Is the reason exciting to concur with the deity this, 'the deity is our benefactor?' Then what reason excites to concur with benefactors? Here we must recur to an instinct. Is it this truth, 'the divine ends are reasonable ends?' Then what means the word 'reasonable'? Does it mean, that 'the deity has reasons exciting him to promote the public good?' What are these reasons? Why, perhaps 'we do not know them particularly, but in general are sure that the deity has reasons for them.' Then the question recurs, what reason excites us to implicit concurrence with the ends of the deity? The reasons which excite one nature may not excite another: the tendency of an action to the happiness of one agent may excite him, but will not excite another agent to concur, unless there appears a like tendency to the happiness of that other. They may say, 'they are sure the divine ends are good.' What means 'goodness'? Is it moral or natural? If the divine ends be natural good, *i.e.* pleasant, or the cause of pleasure, to whom is this pleasure? If to the deity, then why do we study the happiness or the pleasing of the deity? What reason excites us? All the possible reasons must either presuppose some affection, if they are exciting; or some moral sense, if they are justifying.—Is the divine end naturally good to us? This is an exciting reason, but supposes self-love. If we say the divine ends are 'morally good', we are just where we began. What is 'moral goodness'? Conformity to reason. What are the reasons exciting or justifying[?]

If any allege as the reason exciting us to pursue public good, this truth, that 'the happiness of a system, a thousand, or a million, is a greater quantity of happiness than that of one person: and consequently, if men desire happiness they must have stronger desires toward the greater sum, than toward the less.' This reason still supposes an instinct toward happiness as previous to it: and again, to whom is the happiness of a system a greater happiness? To one individual, or to the system? If to the individual, then his reason exciting his desire of a happy system supposes self-love: if to the system, then what reason can excite to desire the greater happiness of a system, or any happiness to be in the possession of others? None surely which does not presuppose public affections. Without such affections this truth, 'that a hundred felicities is a greater sum than one felicity,' will no more excite to study the happiness of the hundred, than this truth, 'a hundred stones are greater than one,' will excite a man, who has no desire of heaps, to cast them together.

The same may be observed concerning that proposition, assigned by some as the ultimate reason both exciting to, and justifying the pursuit of public good, *viz.* 'it is best that all should be happy.' Best is most good: good to whom? To the whole, or to each individual? If to the former, when this truth excites to action, it must presuppose a kind affection; if it is good to each individual, it must suppose self-love.

Let us once suppose affections, instincts or desires, previously implanted in our nature: and we shall easily understand the exciting reasons for actions, *viz.* 'these truths which show them to be conducive towards some ultimate end, or toward the greatest end of that kind in our power.' He acts reasonably, who considers the various actions in his power, and forms true opinions of their tendencies; and then chooses to do that which will obtain the highest degree of that, to which the instincts of his nature incline him, with the smallest degree of those things from which the affections in his nature make him averse.

More particularly, the exciting reasons to a nature which had only selfish affections, are those truths which showed 'what object or event would occasion to it the greatest quantity of pleasure': these would excite to the prosecution of it. The exciting truths about means, would be only those which pointed out some means as more certainly effectual than any other, or with less pain or trouble to the agent. Public usefulness of ends or means, or public hurtfulness would neither excite nor dissuade, farther than the public state might affect that of the agent.

If there is any nature with public affections: the truths exciting to any end in this order, are such as show, 'that any event would promote the happiness of others.' That end is called most 'reasonable', which our reason discovers to contain a greater quantity of public good, than any other in our power.

When any event may affect both the agent and others, if the agent have both self-love and public affections, he acts according to that affection which is strongest, when there is any opposition of interests; if there be no opposition, he follows both. If he discovers this truth, that 'his constant pursuit of public good is the most probable way of promoting his own happiness,' then his pursuit is truly reasonable and constant; thus both affections are at once gratified, and he is consistent with himself. Without knowledge of that truth he does not act reasonably for his own happiness, but follows it by means not tending effectually to this end: and must frequently from the power of self-love, neglect or counteract his other end, the public good. If there be also a moral sense in such an agent, while yet he is inadvertent to the connection of private happiness with the study of the public; he must be perpetually yet more uneasy, either through the apprehended neglect of private interest when he serves in public; or when he pursues only private interest, he will have perpetual remorse and dissatisfaction with his own temper, through his moral sense. So that the knowledge of this connection of private interest, with the study of public good, seems absolutely necessary to preserve a constant satisfaction of mind, and to prevent an alternate prevalence of seemingly contrary desires.

Should any one ask even concerning these two ultimate ends, private good and public, is not the latter more reasonable than the former?—What means the word 'reasonable' in this question? If we are allowed to presuppose instincts and affections, then the truth just now supposed to be discoverable concerning our state, is an exciting reason to serve the public interest, since this conduct is the most effectual means to obtain both ends. But I doubt if any truth can be assigned which excites in us either the desire of private happiness or public. For the former none ever alleged any exciting reason: and a benevolent temper finds as little reason exciting him to the latter; which he desire without any view to private good. If the meaning of the question be this, 'does not every spectator approve the pursuit of public good more than private?' The answer is obvious, that he does: but not for any reason or truth, but from a moral sense in the constitution of the soul.

This leads [us] to consider approbation of actions, whether it be for conformity to any truth, or reasonableness, that actions are ultimately approved, independently of any moral sense? Or if all justifying reasons do not presuppose it[?]

If 'conformity to truth,' or 'reasonable,' denote nothing else but that 'an action is the object of a true proposition,' it is plain, that all actions should be approved equally, since as many truths may be made about the worst, as can be made about the best. See what was said above about exciting reasons.

But let the truths commonly assigned as justifying be examined. Here it is plain, 'a truth showing an action to be fit to attain an end,' does not justify it; nor do we approve a subordinate end for any truth, which only shows it to be fit to promote the ultimate end; for the worst actions may be conducive to their ends, and reasonable in that sense. The justifying reasons then must be about the ends themselves, especially the ultimate ends. The question then is, 'does a conformity to any truth make us approve an ultimate end, previously to any moral sense?' For example, we approve pursuing the public good. For what reason? Or what is the truth for conformity to which we call it a 'reasonable' end? I fancy we can find none in these cases, more than we could give for our liking any pleasant fruit…

The reasons assigned are such as these; 'It is the end proposed by the deity.' But why do we approve concurring with the divine ends? This reason is given, 'He is our benefactor'; but then, for what reason do we approve concurrence with a benefactor? Here we must recur to a sense. Is this the reason moving to approbation, 'study of public good tends to the advantage of the approver?' Then the quality moving us to approve an action, is its being advantageous to us, and not conformity to a truth. This scheme is intelligible but not true in fact. Men approve without perception of private advantage; and often do not condemn or disapprove what is plainly pernicious; as in the execution of a just sentence, which even the sufferer may approve.

If any allege, that this is the justifying reason of the pursuit of public good, 'that it is best all be happy,' then we approve actions for their tendency to what state which is best, and not for conformity to reason. But here again, what means 'best'? Morally best, or naturally best? If the former, they explain the same word by itself in a circle: if they mean the latter, that 'it is the most happy state where all are happy'; then, most happy, for whom? The system, or the individual? If for the former, what reason makes us approve the happiness of a system? Here we must recur to a sense or kind affections. Is it most happy for the individual? Then the quality moving approbation is again tendency to private happiness, not reasonableness.

There are some other reasons assigned in words differing from the former, but more confused, such as these: 'It is our duty to study public good. We are obliged to do it. We owe obedience to the deity. The whole is to be preferred to a part.' But let these words, 'duty,' 'obligation,' 'owing,' and the meaning of that gerund or participle, 'is to be preferred,' be explained; and we shall find ourselves still at a loss for exciting reasons previously to affections, or justifying reasons without recourse to a moral sense.

When we say one is 'obliged' to an action, we either mean, 1. That the action is necessary to obtain happiness to the agent, or to avoid misery: or, 2. That every spectator, or he himself upon reflection, must approve his action, and disapprove his omitting it, if he considers fully all its circumstances. The former meaning of the word 'obligation' presupposes selfish affections, and the senses of private happiness: the latter meaning includes the moral sense…

Many other confused definitions have been given of 'obligation,' by no obscure names in the learned world. But let anyone give a distinct meaning, different from the two above-mentioned. To pursue them all would be endless; only let the definitions be substituted in place of the word 'obligation,' in other parts of each writer, and let it be observed whether it makes good sense or not…

Before we quit this character 'reasonableness,' let us consider the arguments brought to prove that there must be some standard of moral good antecedent to any sense. Say they, 'Perceptions of sense are deceitful, we must have some perception or idea of virtue more stable and certain; this must be conformity to reason: truth discovered by our reason, is certain and invariable: that then alone is the original idea of virtue, agreement with reason.' But in like manner our sight and sense of beauty is deceitful, and does not always represent the true forms of objects. We must not call that 'beautiful' or 'regular,' which pleases the sight, or an internal sense; but beauty in external forms too, consists in conformity to reason. So our taste may be vitiated: we must not say that savour is perceived by taste, but must place the original idea of grateful savours in conformity to reason, and of ungrateful in contrariety to reason. We may mistake the real extent of bodies, or their proportions, by making a conclusion upon the first sensible appearance: therefore ideas of extension are not originally acquired by a sense, but consist in conformity to reason.

If what is intended in this 'conformity to reason' be this, 'that we should call no action virtuous, unless we have some reason to conclude it to be virtuous, or some truth showing it to be so.' This is very true; but then in like manner we should count no action vicious, unless we have some reason for counting it so, or when it is truth 'that it is vicious.' If this be intended by 'conformity to truth,' then at the same rate we may make conformity to truth the original idea of vice as well as virtue; nay, of every attribute whatsoever. That taste alone is sweet, which there is reason to count sweet; that taste alone is bitter, concerning which it is true that it is bitter; that form alone is beautiful, concerning which it is true that it is beautiful; and that alone deformed, which is truly deformed. Thus virtue, vice, sweet, bitter, beautiful, or deformed, originally denote 'conformity to reason,' antecedently to perceptions of any sense. The idea of virtue is particularly that concerning which it is truth, 'that it is virtue'; or virtue is virtue; a wonderful discovery!

So when some tell us, 'that truth is naturally pleasant, and more so than any sensible perception; this must therefore engage men more than any other motive, if they attend to it.' Let them observe that as much truth is known about vice as virtue. We may demonstrate the public miseries which would ensue upon perjury, murder, and robbery. These demonstrations would be attended with that pleasure which is peculiar to truth; as well as the demonstrations of the public happiness to ensue from faith, humanity, and justice. There is equal truth on both sides.

We may transiently observe what has occasioned the use of the word 'reasonable,' as an epithet of only virtuous actions. Though we have instincts determining us to desire ends, without supposing any previous reasoning; yet it is by use of our reason that we find out the means of obtaining our ends. When we do not use our reason, we often are disappointed of our end. We therefore call those actions which are effectual to their ends, 'reasonable,' in one sense of that word.

Again, in all men there is probably a moral sense, making publicly useful actions and kind affections grateful to the agent, and to every observer: most men who have thought of human actions, agree, that the publicly useful are in the whole also privately useful to the agent, either in this life or the next: we conclude, that all men have the same affections and senses: we are convinced by our reason, that it is by publicly useful actions alone that we can promote all our ends. Whoever then acts in a contrary manner, we presume mistaken, ignorant of, or inadvertent to these truths which he might know; and say he acts 'unreasonably.' Hence some have been led to imagine, some reasons either exciting or justifying previously to all affections or a moral sense.

Two arguments are brought in defence of this epithet, as antecedent to any sense, *viz.* 'that we judge even of our affections and senses themselves, whether they are morally good or evil.'

The second argument is, that 'if all moral ideas depend upon the constitution of our sense, then all constitutions would have been alike reasonable and good to the deity, which is absurd.'

As to the first argument, it is plain we judge of our own affections, or those of others, by our moral sense, by which we approve kind affections, and disapprove the contrary. But none can apply moral attributes to the very faculty of perceiving moral qualities; or call his moral sense morally good or evil, any more than he calls the power of tasting, sweet or bitter; or of seeing, straight or crooked, white or black.

Everyone judges the affections of others by his own sense; so that it seems not impossible that in these senses men might differ as they do in taste. A sense approving benevolence would disapprove that temper, which a sense approving malice would delight in. The former would judge of the latter by his own sense, so would the latter of the former. Each one would at first view think the sense of the other perverted. But then, is there no difference? Are both senses equally good? No certainly, any man who observed them would think the sense of the former more desirable than of the latter; but this is, because the moral sense of every man is constituted in the former manner. But were there any nature with no moral sense at all observing these two persons, would he not think the state of the former preferable to that of the latter? Yes, he might: but not from any perception of moral goodness in the one sense more than in the other. Any rational nature observing two men thus constituted, with opposite senses might by reasoning see, not moral goodness in one sense more than in the contrary, but a tendency to the happiness of the person himself, who had the former sense in the one constitution, and a contrary tendency in the opposite constitution: nay, the persons themselves might observe this; since the former sense would make these actions grateful to the agent which were useful to others; who, if they had a like sense, would love him, and return good offices; whereas the latter sense would make all such actions as are useful to others, and apt to engage their good offices, ungrateful to the agent; and would lead him into publicly hurtful actions, which would not only procure the hatred of others, if they had a contrary sense, but engage them out of their self-love to study his destruction, though their senses agreed. Thus any observer, or the agent himself with this latter sense, might perceive that the pains to be feared, as the consequence of the malicious actions, did overbalance the pleasures of this sense; so that it would be to the agent's interest to counteract it. Thus one constitution of the moral sense might appear to be more advantageous to those who had it, than the contrary; as we may call that sense of tasting 'healthful,' which made wholesome meat pleasant; and we would call a contrary taste 'pernicious.' And yet we should no more call the moral sense 'morally good' or 'evil,' than we call the sense of tasting, 'savoury' or 'unsavoury,' 'sweet' or 'bitter.'

But must we not own, that we judge of all our senses by our reason, and often correct their reports of the magnitude, figure, colour, taste of objects, and pronounce them right or wrong, as they agree or disagree with reason? This is true. But does it then follow, that extension, figure, colour, taste, are not sensible ideas, but only denote reasonableness, or agreement with reason? Or that these qualities are perceivable antecedently to any sense, by our power of finding out truth? Just so a compassionate temper may rashly imagine the correction of a child, or the execution of a criminal, to be cruel and inhuman: but by reasoning may discover the superior good arising from them in the whole; and then the same moral sense may determine the observer to approve them. But we must not hence conclude, that it is any reasoning antecedently to a moral sense, which determines us to approve the study of public good, any more than we can in the former case conclude, that we perceive extension, figure, colour, taste, antecedently to a sense. All these sensations are often corrected by reasoning, as well as our approbations of actions as good or evil [see T4.IV]: and yet nobody ever placed the original idea of extension, figure, colour, or taste, in conformity to reason.

'Tis manifest we have in our understanding, moral ideas, or they are perceptions of the soul: we reason about them, we compare, we judge; but then we do all the same acts about extension, figure, colour, taste, sound, which perceptions all men call 'sensations.' All our ideas, or the materials of our reasoning or judging, are received by some immediate powers of perception internal or external, which we may call 'senses'; by these too we have pleasure and pain. All perception is by the soul, not by the body, though some impressions on the bodily organs are the occasions of some of them; and in others the soul is determined to other sorts of feelings or sensations, where no bodily impression is the immediate occasion. A certain incorporeal form, if one may use that name, a temper observed, a character, an affection, a state of a sensitive being, known or understood, may raise liking, approbation, sympathy, as naturally from the very constitution of the soul, as any bodily impression raises external sensations. Reasoning or intellect seems to raise no new species of ideas, but to discover or discern the relations of those received. Reason shows what acts are conformable to a law, a will of a superior; or what acts tend to private good, or to public good: in like manner, reason discovers contrary tendencies of contrary actions. Both contraries are alike the object of the understanding, and may give that sort of pleasure which arises upon discovery of truth. A demonstration that certain actions are detrimental to society is attended with the peculiar pleasure of new knowledge, as much as a like demonstration of the benefit of virtue. But when we approve a kind beneficent action, let us consider whether this feeling, or action, or modification of the soul more resembles an act of contemplation, such as this, when straight lines intersect each other, the vertical angles are equal; or that liking we have to a beautiful form, a harmonious composition, a grateful sound.

Thus though no man can immediately either approve or disapprove as morally good or evil his own moral sense, by which he approves only affections and actions consequent upon them; yet he may see whether it be advantageous to him in other respects, to have it constituted one way rather than another. One constitution may make these actions grateful to this sense which tend to procure other pleasures also. A contrary constitution may be known to the very person himself to be disadvantageous, as making these actions immediately grateful, which shall occasion all other sorts of misery. His self-love may excite him, though with dissatisfaction, to counteract this sense, in order to avoid a greater evil. Mr. Hobbes seems to have had no better notions of the natural state of mankind. An observer, who was benevolent, would desire that all had the former sort of sense; a malicious observer, if he feared no evil to himself, from the actions of the persons observed, would desire the latter constitution. If this observer had a moral sense, he would think that constitution which was contrary to his own, strange and surprising, or unnatural. If the observer had no affections towards others, and were disjoined from mankind, so as to have neither hopes nor fears from their actions, he would be indifferent about their constitutions, and have no desire or preference of one above another; though he might see which were advantageous to them, and which pernicious.

As to the second argument, what means alike 'reasonable or good to the deity?' Does it mean, 'that the deity could have no reasons exciting him to make one constitution rather than another?' 'Tis plain, if the deity had nothing essential in his nature, resembling or analogous to our sweetest and most kind affections, we can scarce suppose he could have any reason exciting him to anything he has done: but grant such a disposition in the deity, and then the manifest tendency of the present constitution to the happiness of his creatures was an exciting reason for choosing it before the contrary... Each sort of constitution might have given men an equal immediate pleasure in present self-approbation for any sort of action; but the actions approved by the present sense, procure all pleasures of the other senses; and the actions which would have been approved by a contrary moral sense, would have been productive of all torments of the other senses.

If it be meant, that 'upon this supposition, that all our approbation presupposes in us a moral sense, the deity could not have approved one constitution more than another': where is the consequence? Why may not the deity have something of a superior kind, analogous to our moral sense, essential to him? How does any constitution of the senses of men hinder the deity to reflect and judge of his own actions? How does it affect the divine apprehension, which way soever moral ideas arise with men?

If it means 'that we cannot approve one constitution more than another, or approve the deity for making the present constitution': this consequence is also false. The present constitution of our moral sense determines us to approve all kind affections: this constitution the deity must have foreseen as tending to the happiness of his creatures; it does therefore evidence kind affection or benevolence in the deity, this therefore we must approve.

We have got some strange phrases, 'that some things are antecedently reasonable in the nature of the thing,' which some insist upon: 'that otherwise, say they, if before man was created, any nature without a moral sense had existed, this nature would not have approved as morally good in the deity, his constituting our sense as it is at present.' Very true;

and what next? If there had been no moral sense in that nature, there would have been no perception of morality. But 'could not such natures have seen something reasonable in one constitution more than in another?' They might no doubt have reasoned about the various constitutions, and foreseen that the present one would tend to the happiness of mankind, and would evidence benevolence in the deity; so also they might have reasoned about the contrary constitution, that it would make men miserable, and evidence malice in the deity. They would have reasoned about both, and found out truths: are both constitutions alike reasonable to these observers? No, say they, 'the benevolent one is reasonable, and the malicious unreasonable': and yet these observers reasoned and discovered truths about both: an action then is called by us 'reasonable' when it is benevolent, and 'unreasonable' when malicious. This is plainly making the word 'reasonable' denote whatever is approved by the moral sense, without relation to true propositions. We often use that word in such a confused manner: but these antecedent natures, supposed without a moral sense, would not have approved one constitution of the deity as morally better than another.

Had it been left to the choice of these antecedent minds, what manner of sense they would have desired for mankind, would they have seen no difference? Yes they would, according to their affections which are presupposed in all election. If they were benevolent, as we suppose the deity, the tendency of the present sense to the happiness of men would have excited their choice. Had they been malicious, as we suppose the devil, the contrary tendency of the contrary sense would have excited their election of it. But is there nothing preferable, or eligible antecedently to all affections too? No certainly, unless there can be desire without affections, or superior desire, *i.e.* election antecedently to all desire.

Some farther perplex this subject, by asserting, that 'the same reasons determining approbation, ought also to excite to election.' Here, 1. We often see justifying reasons where we can have no election; *viz.* when we observe that actions of others, which were even prior to our existence. 2. The quality moving us to election very often cannot excite approbation;

viz. private usefulness, not publically pernicious. This both does and ought to move election, and yet I believe few will say, 'they approve as virtuous the eating a bunch of grapes, taking a glass of wine, or sitting down when one is tired.' Approbation is not what we can voluntarily bring upon ourselves. When we are contemplating actions, we do not choose to approve, because approbation is pleasant; otherwise we would always approve, and never condemn any action; because this is some way uneasy. Approbation is plainly a perception arising without previous volition, or choice of it, because of any concomitant pleasure. The occasion of it is the perception of benevolent affections in ourselves, or the discovering the like in others, even when we are incapable of any action or election. The reasons determining approbation are such as show that an action evidenced kind affections, and that in others, as often as in ourselves. Whereas, the reasons moving to election are such as show the tendency of an action to gratify some affection in the agent.

The prospect of the pleasure of self-approbation, is indeed often a motive to choose one action rather than another; but this supposes the moral sense, or determination to approve, prior to the election. Were approbation voluntarily chosen, from the prospect of its concomitant pleasure, then there could be no condemnation of our own actions, for that is unpleasant.

As to that confused word 'ought' it is needless to apply to it again all that was said about obligation.

Sect. IV.
Showing the use of reason concerning virtue and vice, upon supposition that we receive these ideas by a moral sense

[I.] Had those who insist so much upon the antecedent reasonableness of virtue, told us distinctly what is reasonable or provable concerning it, many of our debates had been prevented. Let us consider what truths concerning actions men could desire to know, or prove by reason. I fancy they may be reduced to these heads.

1. 'To know whether there are not some actions or affections which obtain the approbation of any spectator

> or observer, and others move his dislike and condemnation?' This question, as every man can answer for himself, so universal experience and history show, that in all nations it is so; and consequently the moral sense is universal.
>
> 2. 'Whether there by any particular quality, which, wherever it is apprehended, gains approbation, and the contrary raises disapprobation?' We shall find this quality to be kind affection, or study of the good of others; and thus the moral senses of men are generally uniform. About these two questions there is little reasoning; we know how to answer them from reflecting on our own sentiments, or by consulting others.
>
> 3. 'What actions do really evidence kind affections, or do really tend to the greatest public good?' About this question is all the special reasoning of those who treat of particular laws of nature, or even of civil laws: this is the largest field, and the most useful subject of reasoning, which remains upon every scheme of morals, and here we may discover as certain, invariable, or eternal truths, as any in geometry.
>
> 4. 'What are the motives which, even from self-love, would excite each individual to do those actions which are publicly useful?' It is probable indeed, no man would approve as virtuous an action publically useful, to which the agent was excited only by self-love, without any kind affection: it is also probable that no view of interest can raise that kind affection, which we approve as virtuous; nor can any reasoning do it, except that which shows some moral goodness, or kind affections in the object; for this never fails, where it is observed or supposed in any person to raise the love of the observer.

Yet since all men have naturally self-love as well as kind affections, the former may often counteract the latter, or the latter the former; in each case the agent is uneasy, and in some degree unhappy. The first rash views of human affairs often represent private interest as opposite to the public: when this is apprehended, self-love may often engage men in publically hurtful actions, which their moral sense will condemn; and this is the ordinary cause of vice. To represent these motives of self-interest, to engage men to publicly useful actions, is certainly the most necessary point in morals. This has been so well done by the ancient moralists, by Dr. Cumberland, Pufendorf, Grotius, Shaftesbury; it is made so certain from the divine government of the world, the state of mankind, who cannot subsist without society, from universal experience and consent, from inward consciousness of the pleasure of kind affections, and self-approbation, and of the torments of malice, or hatred, or envy, or anger; that no man who considers these things, can ever imagine he can have any possible interest in opposing the public good; or in checking or restraining his kind affections; nay, if he had no kind affections, his very self-love and regard to his private good might excite him to publicly useful actions, and dissuade him from the contrary.

What further should be provable concerning virtue, whence it should be called 'reasonable' antecedently to all affections, or interest, or sense, or what it should be fit for, one cannot easily imagine.

Perhaps what has brought the epithet 'reasonable,' or 'flowing from reason,' in opposition to what flows from instinct, affection, or passion, so much into use, is this, 'That it is often observed, that the very best of particular affections or desires, when they are grown violent and passionate, through the confused sensations and propensities which attend them, make us incapable of considering calmly the whole tendency of our actions, and lead us often into what is absolutely pernicious, under some appearance of relative or particular good.' This indeed may give some ground for distinguishing between passionate actions, and those from calm desire or affection which employs our reason freely: but can never set rational actions in opposition to those from instinct, desire or affection. And it must be owned, that the most perfect virtue consists in the calm, unpassionate benevolence, rather than in particular affections...

Thus there seems no part of that reasoning which was ever used by moralists, to be superseded by supposing a moral sense. And yet without a moral sense there is no explication can be given of our ideas of morality; nor of that reasonableness supposed antecedent to all instincts, affections, or sense.

'But may there not be a right or wrong state of our moral sense, as there is in our other senses, according as they represent their objects to be as they really are, or represent them otherwise?' So may not our moral sense approve that which is vicious, and disapprove virtue, as a sickly palate may dislike grateful food, or vitiated sight misrepresent colours or dimensions? Must we not know therefore antecedently what is morally good or evil by our reason, before we can know that our moral sense is right?

To answer this, we must remember that of the sensible ideas, some are allowed to be only perceptions in our minds, and not images of any external quality, as colours, sounds, tastes, smells, pleasure, pain. Other ideas are images of something external, as duration, number, extension, motion, rest: these latter, for distinction, we may call 'concomitant' ideas of sensation, and the former 'purely sensible.' As to the purely sensible ideas, we know they are altered by any disorder in our organs, and made different from what arise in us from the same objects at other times. We do not denominate objects from our perceptions during the disorder, but according to our ordinary perceptions, or those of others in good health: yet no body imagines that therefore colours, sounds, tastes, are not sensible ideas. In like manner many circumstances diversify concomitant ideas: but we denominate objects from the appearances they make to us in a uniform medium, when our organs are in no disorder, and the object not very distant from them. But none therefore imagines that it is reason and not sense which discovers these concomitant ideas, or primary qualities.

Just so in our ideas of actions. These three things are to be distinguished,

1. The idea of external motion, known first by sense, and its tendency to the happiness or misery of some sensitive nature, often inferred by argument or reason, which on these subjects suggests as invariable, eternal or necessary truths as any whatsoever.

2. Apprehension or opinion of the affections in the agent, inferred by our reason: so far the idea of an action repre-

sents something external to the observer, really existing whether he had perceived it or not, and having a real tendency to certain ends.

3. The perception of approbation or disapprobation arising in the observer, according as the affections of the agent are apprehended kind in their just degree, or deficient, or malicious. This approbation cannot be supposed an image of anything external, more than the pleasures of harmony, of taste, of smell. But let none imagine, that calling the ideas of virtue and vice 'perceptions of a sense,' upon apprehending the actions and affections of another does diminish their reality, more than the like assertions concerning all pleasure and pain, happiness or misery. Our reason often corrects the report of our senses, about the natural tendency of the external action, and corrects rash conclusions about the affections of the agent. But whether our moral sense be subject to such a disorder, as to have different perceptions, from the same apprehended affections in an agent, at different times, as the eye may have of the colours of an unaltered object, it is not easy to determine: perhaps it will be hard to find any instances of such a change. What reason could correct, if it fell into such a disorder, I know not; except suggesting to its remembrance its former approbation, and representing the general sense of mankind. But this does not prove ideas of virtue and vice to be previous to a sense, more than a like correction of the ideas of colour in a person under the jaundice, proves that colours are perceived by reason, previously to a sense…

Sect. V.
Showing that virtue may have whatever is meant by merit… upon the supposition that it is perceived by a sense, and elected from affection or instinct

[I.] Some will not allow any merit in actions flowing from kind instincts: 'Merit, say they, attends actions to which we are excited by reason alone, or to which we freely determine ourselves. The operation of instincts or affections is necessary, and not voluntary; nor is there more merit in them than in the shining of the sun, the fruitfulness of a tree, or the overflowing of a stream, which are all publicly useful.'

But what does 'merit' mean? Or 'praiseworthiness'? Do these words denote the 'quality in actions, which gains approbation from the observer, according to the present constitution of the human mind?' Or, secondly, are these actions called meritorious, 'which, when any observer does approve, all other observers approve him for his approbation of it; and would condemn any observer who did not approve these actions?' These are the only meanings of 'meritorious,' which I can conceive as distinct from 'rewardable,' which is considered hereafter separately. Let those who are not satisfied with either of these explications of merit, endeavour to give a definition of it, reducing it to its simple ideas: and not, as a late author[3] has done, quarrelling these descriptions, tell us only that it is 'deserving or being worthy of approbation,' which is defining by giving a synonymous term.

Now we endeavoured already to show, that 'no reason can excite to action previously to some end, and that no end can be proposed without some instinct or affection.' What then can be meant by 'being excited by reason,' as distinct from all motion or instincts or affections? Some perhaps take the word 'instinct' solely for such motions of will, or bodily powers, as determine us without knowledge or intention of any end. Such instincts cannot be the spring of virtue. But the soul may be as naturally determined to approbation of certain tempers and affections, and to the desire of certain events when it has an idea of them, as brutes are, by their lower instincts, to their actions. If any quarrel the application of the word 'instinct' to anything higher than what we find in brutes, let them use another word. Though there is no harm in the sound of this word, more than in 'a determination to pursue fitness,'[4] which they must allow in the divine will, if they ascribe any will to him at all.

---

3 [Hutcheson does ont cite anyone specifically, but in his edition of the *Illustrations*, Aaron Garrett (p. 217) suggests that Hutcheson has in mind John Balguy (1686–1748), rationalist and author of *The Foundation of Moral Goodness*.]

4 [Most likely a reference to the theory of rationalist philosopher, Samuel Clarke (1675–1729), who is the main target of Section II of the *Illustrations*, not included here.]

Then 'determining ourselves freely,' does it mean 'acting without any motive or exciting reason'? If it did not mean this, it cannot be opposed to acting from instinct or affections, since all motives or reasons presuppose them. If it means this, that 'Merit is found only in actions done without motive or affection, by mere election, without prepollent desire of one action or end rather than its opposite, or without desire of that pleasure which [...see Archbishop King's *The Origin of Evil*] some suppose follows upon any election, by a natural connection': Then let any man consider[,] whether he ever acts in this manner by mere election, without any previous desire? And again, let him consult his own breast, whether such kind of action gains his approbation? Upon seeing a person not more disposed by affection, compassion, or love or desire, to make his country happy than miserable, yet choosing the one rather than the other, from no desire of public happiness, nor aversion to the torments of others, but by such an unaffectionate determination, as that by which one moves his first finger rather than his second, in giving an instance of a trifling action; let anyone ask if this action should be meritorious: and yet that there should be no merit in a tender compassionate heart, which shrinks at every pain of its fellow-creatures, and triumphs in their happiness; with kind affections and strong desire labouring for the public good. If this be the nature of meritorious actions, every honest heart would disclaim all merit in morals, as violently as the old Protestants rejected it in justification.

But let us see which of the two senses of merit or praiseworthiness is founded on this (I will not call it 'unreasonable' or 'casual,' but) unaffectionate choice. If 'merit' denotes the quality moving the spectator to approve, then there may be unaffectionate election of the greatest villainy, as well as of the most useful actions; but who will say that they are equally approved?—But perhaps it is not the mere freedom of choice which is approved, but the free choice of public good, without any affection. Then actions are approved for public usefulness, and not for freedom. Upon this supposition, the heat of the sun, the fruitfulness of a tree, would be meritorious qualities, motions, attractions, etc. And a casual invention may be meritorious.—Perhaps free election is a *conditio sine qua non*,[5] and public usefulness the immediate cause of approbation; neither separately, but both jointly are meritorious: free election alone is not merit; but both concurring. Then should any person by mere election, without any desire to serve the public, set about mines, or any useful manufacture; or should a person by mere election stab a man without knowing him to be a public robber; here both free election and public usefulness may concur: yet will anyone say there is merit or virtue in such actions? Where then shall we find merit, unless in kind affections, or desire and intention of the public good? This moves our approbation wherever we observe it: and the want of this is the true reason why a searcher for mines, a free killer of an unknown robber, the warming sun, or the fruitful tree, are not counted meritorious.

But it may be said, that to make an action meritorious, it is necessary not only that the action be publicly useful, but that it be known or imagined to be such, before the agent freely chooses it. But what does this add to the former scheme? Only a judgment or opinion in the understanding, concerning the natural tendency of an action to the public good: few it may be presumed, will place virtue in assent or dissent, or perceptions. And yet this is all that is superadded to the former case. The agent must not desire the public good, or have any kind affections. This would spoil the freedom of choice, according to their scheme, who insist on a freedom opposite to affections or instincts: but he must barely know the tendency to public good, and without any propensity to, or desire of the happiness of others, by an arbitrary election, acquire his merit. Let every man judge for himself, whether these are the qualities which he approves.

What has probably engaged many into this way of speaking, 'that virtue is the effect of rational choice, and not of instincts or affections,' is this; they find that 'some actions flowing from particular kind affections, are sometimes condemned as evil,' because of their bad influence upon the state of larger societies; and that the hurry and confused sen-

---

5 [Necessary condition.]

sation of any of our passions, may divert the mind from considering the whole effect of its actions: they require therefore to virtue a calm and undisturbed temper.

There is indeed some ground to recommend this temper as very necessary in many cases; and yet some of the most passionate actions may be perfectly good. But in the calmest temper there must remain affection or desire, some implanted instinct for which we can give no reason; otherwise there could be no action of any kind. As it was shown above in the first section.

If meritorious actions are these which whosoever does not approve, is himself condemned by others: the quality by which they are constituted meritorious in this sense, is the same which moves our approbation. We condemn any person who does not approve that which we ourselves approve: we presume the sense of others to be constituted like our own; and that any other person, would he attend to the actions which we approve, would also approve them, and love the agent; when we find that another does not approve what we approve, we are apt to conclude, that he has not had some kind affections toward the agent, or that some evil affections makes him overlook his virtues, and on this account condemn him...

Some strongly assert (which is often the only proof) that 'to make an action rewardable, the agent should have inclinations to evil as well as to good.' What means this? That a good governing mind is only inclined to make an agent happy, or to confer a reward on him when he has some evil affections, which yet are surmounted by the benevolent affections? But would not a benevolent superior incline to make any benevolent agent happy, whether he had any weaker evil inclinations or not? Evil inclinations in an agent would certainly rather have some tendency to diminish the love of the superior mind. Cannot a good mind love an agent, and desire his happiness, unless he observes some qualities, which, were they alone, would excite hatred or aversion? Must there be a mixture of hatred to make love strong and effectual, as there must be a mixture of shade to set off the lights in a picture? Is there any love, where there is no inclination to make happy? Or is strong love made up of love and hatred?...

Those who think 'no person punishable for any quality or action, if he had it not in his power to have had the opposite quality, or to have abstained from the action if he had willed it'; perhaps are not mistaken: but then let them not assert on the other hand, that it is unjust to reward or make happy those, who neither had any dispositions to evil, nor could possibly desire any such dispositions. Now if men's affections are naturally good, and if there be in their fellows no quality which would necessarily raise malice in the observer; but, on the contrary, all qualities requisite to excite at least benevolence or compassion: it may be justly said to be in the power of everyone, by due attention, to prevent any malicious affections, and to excite in himself kind affections toward all. So that the intricate debates about human liberty do not affect what is here alleged, concerning our moral sense of affections and actions, any more than any other schemes.

Some allege, that merit supposes, beside kind affection, that the agent has a moral sense, reflects upon his own virtue, delights in it, and chooses to adhere to it for the pleasure which attends it [see Shaftesbury, pp. 163–92 of the *Characteristics*]. We need not debate the use of the word 'merit': it is plain, we approve a generous kind action, though the agent had not made this reflection. This reflection shows to him a motive of self-love, the joint view to which does not increase our approbation: but then it must again be owned, that we cannot form a just conclusion of a character from one or two kind, generous actions, especially where there has been no very strong motives to the contrary. Some apparent motives of interest may afterwards overbalance the kind affections, and lead the agent into vicious actions. But the reflection on virtue, the being once charmed with the lovely form, will discover an interest on its side, which, if well attended to, no other motive will overbalance. This reflection is a great security to the character; and must be supposed in such creatures as men are, before we can well depend upon a constancy in virtue. The same may be said of many other motives to virtue from interest; which, though they do not immediately influence the kind affections of the agent, yet remove these obstacles to them, from false appearances of interest. Such are these from the sanctions of divine laws by future rewards and punishments, and even the manifest advantages of virtue in this life: without reflection on which, a steady course of virtue is scarce to be expected amidst the present confusion of human affairs.

Seven

Natural Law & Political Philosophy

From *A Short Introduction to Moral Philosophy*

Book II.
Elements of the Law of Nature.
Chapter I.
Of the Law of Nature

[I.] That we may show how all the several parts of life may be brought into a conformity to nature, and the better discern the several rights and duties of mankind, we shall premise the more general doctrine in morals, explaining some pretty complex notions and terms constantly occurring; and this is the subject of this and the two following chapters.

In the preceding book we showed, how from the very structure of our nature we derived our first notions of right and wrong, virtuous and vicious, in our affections and actions: and that it was then right and just that any person should act, possess, or demand from others, in a certain manner, 'when his doing so tended either directly to the common interest of all, or to the interest of some part or some individual, without occasioning any detriment to others.' And hence we say in such cases that a man has a right thus to act, possess or demand: and whoever would obstruct or hinder him thus to act or possess, or would not comply with such demand, is said to do an injury or wrong.

But resuming this matter a little higher; 'tis plain that this structure of our nature exhibits clear evidences of the will of God and nature about our conduct, requiring certain actions and prohibiting others. The notion of a law to which our actions may be compared, is, no doubt, artificial, formed upon observation: and yet it has in all ages been so obvious and familiar to men that it may also be called natural. For the notion of a just power, or right of governing others, is obviously intimated, from that power nature has invested the parent with, over his children, so manifestly tending to their good. And this too is known to all by constant experience, that the bulk of mankind don't by any nice reasonings or observation of their own discover what is advantageous or hurtful in life; nay that the greater part of the practical sagacity and wisdom of the generality depends upon the discoveries and instructions of a few, who have had greater penetration and sagacity: and since 'tis commonly known, and even the men of less sagacity acknowledge it, that there are great diversities of genius, and that some few have superior abilities to the common herd: that moral principle implanted in all must also recommend it as advantageous to all, that large societies of men united for their common interest, should commit the administration of their common concerns to a council of a few of the wiser sort, and compel any who may thereafter be refractory to submit to their orders, who have thus obtained a just right of governing. Hence the notion of just power, or of a right of governing, is among the most common and familiar with mankind, when from the very plan and model of power constituted, there's tolerable precaution taken that the rulers shall have either no inducements to abuse it to the detriment of the whole body, or no hopes of doing so with impunity. Hence the notion of law too is obvious to all, to wit, 'The will of those vested with just power of governing, declared to their subjects, requiring certain actions and forbidding others with denunciations of rewards or punishments.'

II. Now since 'tis generally agreed among men, that the deity is endued with the highest goodness, as well as with wisdom and power; it must obviously follow that a universal compliance with the will of God must tend both to the general good, and to that of each individual; to which compliance also we are most sacredly bound in gratitude, as we were created by him, and are constantly deriving good from his munificent hand: it must also in like manner follow, that all disobedience to the will of God must be opposite to the common felicity, and show a base ungrateful mind. Now these considerations plainly show that it is perfectly just and right in the deity to assume to himself the government of his rational creatures, and that his right is founded upon his own moral excellencies.

But since no man can give sufficient evidence to the satisfaction of all, that he is possessed even of superior wisdom, and much less of his stable inflexible goodness; since ambitious dissimulation would always make the greatest show of goodness, if this were a sure step to ascend to power; nor can men search into each other's hearts to detect such hypocrisy: and since no power generally suspected and dreaded can make a people, who are diffident of their most important interests, easy or happy; no man can justly assume to himself power over others upon any persuasion of his own superior wisdom or goodness, unless the body of the people are also persuaded of it, or consent to be subjected to such power, upon some reasonable security given them, that the power entrusted shall not be abused to their destruction.

III. And further since it was God our Creator who implanted this sense of right and wrong in our souls, and gave us these powers of reason, which observing our own constitution, and that of persons and other things around us, discovers what conduct tends either to the common prosperity of all, or that of individuals, and what has a contrary tendency; and shows also that all sorts of kind offices generally tend to the happiness of the person who discharges them, and the contrary offices to his detriment: all these precepts or practical dictates of right reason are plainly so many laws [see the Introduction to and first chapter of Cumberland's *A Treatise of the Laws of Nature*], enacted, ratified by penalties, and promulgated by God in the very constitution of nature. (As words or writing are not essential to the nature of a law, but only the most convenient way of notifying it.)

In every law there are two parts, the precept and the sanction. The precept shows what is required or forbidden; and the sanctions contain the rewards or punishments abiding the subjects, as they observe or violate the precept. In civil laws, beside the peculiar rewards or premiums proposed in some of them, there is this general reward understood in them all, that by obedience we obtain the defence and protection of the state, with the other common advantages of a civilized life, and the rights of citizens. The penalties of human laws are generally expressed. The sanctions of the law of nature are known and promulgated in like manner with the perceptive part. The rewards are all those internal joys and comfortable hopes which naturally attend a virtuous course; and all these external advantages whether immediately arising from good actions, or generally obtained by the good-will and approbation of others, or of the deity, whether in this life or in a future state. The penalties are all those evils internal or external, which naturally ensue upon vice; such as remorse, solicitude, and distressing fears and dangers: in fine, all these evils which right reason shows may probably be expected to ensue through the just resentment of the deity or of our fellow-creatures...

VII... From the doctrine of the former book it must appear, that all our duties, as they are conceived to be enjoined by some divine precept, are included in these two general laws, the one that 'God is to be worshipped with all love and veneration': and in consequence of it, that 'he is to be obeyed in all things.' The second is that 'we ought to promote as we have opportunity the common good of all, and that of particular societies or persons, while it no way obstructs the common good, or that of greater societies.'

Book II, Chapter II.
Of the Nature of Rights and their Several Divisions

[I.] Since it is manifestly necessary to the common interest of all that large numbers of men should be joined together in amicable societies, and as this is the sum of all our duties toward men that we promote their happiness as we have opportunity; it must follow that all actions by which anyone procures to himself or his friends any advantage, while he obstructs no advantage of others, must be lawful: since he who profits one part without hurting any other plainly profits the whole. Now since there are many enjoyments and advantages naturally desired by all, which one may procure to himself, his family or friends, without hurting others, and which 'tis plainly the interest of society that each one should be allowed to procure, without any obstruction from others (since otherwise no friendly, peaceable society could be maintained), we therefore deem that each man has a right to procure and obtain for himself or his friends such advantages and enjoyments; which right is plainly established and secured to him by the second general precept above mentioned, enjoining and confirming whatever tends to the general good of all, or to the good of any part without detriment to the rest. In all such cases therefore men are said to act according to their right. And then, as the several offices due to others are recommended to us by the sense of our own hearts; so others in a social life have a claim to them, and both desire, and naturally or justly expect them from us, as some way due to them: in consequence of this it must appear, that the several rules of duty, or special laws of nature, cannot be delivered in a more easy manner than by considering all the several claims or rights competent either to individuals, to societies, or to mankind in general as a great body or society; all which are the matter of some special laws.

The several rights of mankind are therefore first made known, by the natural feelings of their hearts, and their natural desires, pursuing such things as tend to the good of each individual or those dependent on him: and recommending to all certain virtuous offices. But all such inclinations or desires are to be regulated by right reason, with a view to the general good of all.

Thus we have the notion of rights as moral qualities, or faculties, granted by the law of nature to certain persons. We have already sufficiently explained how these notions of our rights arise from that moral sense of right and wrong, natural to us previous to any consideration of law or command. But when we have ascended to the notion of a divine natural law, requiring whatever tends to the general good, and containing all these practical dictates of right reason, our definitions of moral qualities may be abridged by referring them to a law; and yet they will be of the same import; if we still remember that the grand aim of the law of nature is the general good of all, and of every part as far as the general interest allows it.

A right therefore may be defined 'a faculty or claim established by law to act, or possess, or obtain something from others'; though the primary notion of right is prior to that of a law, nor does it always include a reference to the most extensive interest of the whole of mankind. For by our natural sense of right and wrong, and our sympathy with others, we immediately approve any persons procuring to himself or his friends any advantages which are not hurtful to others, without any thought either about a law or the general interest of all. For as the general happiness is the result of the happiness of individuals; and God has for the benefit of each individual, and of families, implanted in each one his private appetites and desires, with some tender natural affections in these narrower systems: actions flowing from them are therefore naturally approved, or at least deemed innocent, and that immediately for themselves, unless they should appear hurtful to others, or opposite to some nobler affection. Hence everyone is conceived to have a right to act or claim whatever does no hurt to others, and naturally tends to his own advantage, or to that of persons dear to him.

And yet this we must still maintain, that no private right can hold against the general interest of all. For a regard to the most extensive advantage of the whole system ought to control and limit all the rights of individuals or of particular societies.

II. Now since a friendly society with others, and a mutual intercourse of offices, and the joint aids of many, are absolutely necessary not only to the pleasure and convenience of human life, but even to the preservation of it; which is so obvious [see Book II, section 3–5, ff. of Cicero's *Offices*] that we need not reason upon it. Whatever appears necessary for preserving an amicable society among men must necessarily be enjoined by the law of nature. And in whatever circumstances the maintaining of peace in society requires, that certain actions, possessions, or claims should be left free and undisturbed to anyone, he is justly deemed to have a right so to act, possess, or claim from others. As some law answers to each right, so does an obligation. This word has two senses, 1) We are said to be obliged to act, or perform to others, 'when the inward sense and conscience of each one must approve such action or performance, and must condemn the contrary as vicious and base': in like manner we conceive an obligation to omit or abstain. This sort of obligation is conceived previous to any thought of the injunction of a law. 2) Obligation is sometimes taken for 'a motive of interest superior to all motives on the other side, proposed to induce us to certain actions or performances, or omissions of action.' Such motives indeed must arise from the laws of an omnipotent Being. This latter meaning seems chiefly intended in these metaphorical definitions of great authors, who would have all obligation to arise from the law of a superior,[1] 'a bond of right binding us by a necessity of acting or abstaining' or an 'absolute necessity imposed upon a man, to act in certain manner.'

III. Rights according as they are more or less necessary to the preservation of a social life are divided into perfect and imperfect. Perfect rights are of such necessity that a general allowing them to be violated must entirely destroy all society: and therefore such rights ought to be maintained to all even by violence: and the severest punishments inflicted upon the violation of them.

Imperfect rights or claims are sometimes indeed of the greatest consequence to the happiness and ornament of society, and our obligation to maintain them, and to perform to others what they thus claim, may be very sacred: yet they are of such a nature that greater evils would ensue in society from making them matters of compulsion, than from leaving them free to each one's honour and conscience to comply with them or not. 'Tis by a conscientious regard to these imperfect rights or claims of others, which are not matters of compulsion, that virtuous men have an occasion of displaying their virtues, and obtaining the esteem and love of others.

Yet the boundaries between perfect and imperfect rights are not always easily seen. There is a sort of scale or gradual ascent, through several almost insensible steps, from the lowest and weakest claims of humanity to those of higher and more sacred obligation, till we arrive at some imperfect

---

1 [Hutcheson ascribes these 'definitions' to Pufendorf and Jean Barbeyrac (1674–1744), philosopher of law and commentator on Pufendorf and Grotius.]

rights so strong that they can scarce be distinguished from the perfect, according to the variety of bonds among mankind, and the various degrees of merit, and claims upon each other. Any innocent person may have some claim upon us for certain offices of humanity. But our fellow-citizen or neighbour would have a stronger claim in the like case. A friend, a benefactor, a brother, or a parent would have still a stronger claim, even in these things which we reckon matters of imperfect obligation.

There's also a third kind of right, or rather an external show of it, which some call an external right: when some more remote considerations of distant utility require that men should not be restrained in certain actions, enjoyments; or demands upon others, which yet are not consistent with a good conscience, or good moral dispositions. These external shows of right, which will never satisfy a good man as a foundation of conduct, often arise from imprudent contracts rashly entered into by one of the parties, and often even from the wisest civil laws.

'Tis plain here, that there can be no opposition either between two perfect rights or two imperfect ones. But imperfect rights may be contrary to these called external. Since however the imperfect rights are not matters of just force or compulsion; wars, which are violent prosecutions or defences of some alleged rights, cannot be just on both sides…

From *An Inquiry Concerning Moral Good and Evil*

Sect. VII.
A deduction of some complex moral ideas, *viz.* of obligation, and right, perfect, imperfect, and external, alienable, and unalienable, from this moral sense.
[Perfect rights, imperfect rights, and external rights]

VI. …Instances of perfect rights are those to our lives; to the fruits of our labours; to demand performance of contracts upon valuable considerations, from men capable of performing them; to direct our own actions either for public, or innocent private good, before we have submitted them to the direction of others in any measure: and many others of like nature…

Instances of imperfect rights are those which the poor have to the charity of the wealthy; which all men have to offices of no trouble or expense to the performer; which benefactors have to returns of gratitude, and such-like...

Instances of external rights are these; that of a wealthy miser to recall his loan from the most industrious poor tradesman at any time; that of demanding the performance of a covenant too burdensome on one side; the right of a wealthy heir to refuse payment of any debts which were contracted by him under age, without fraud in the lender; the right of taking advantage of a positive law, contrary to what was equity antecedent to that law; as when a registered deed takes place of one not registered although prior to it, and known to be so before the second contract...

From *A Short Introduction to Moral Philosophy*

Book II, Chapter II.
Of the Nature of Rights
and their Several Divisions (cont.)

IV. Rights are also divided into the alienable, and such as cannot be alienated or transferred. These are alienable, where the transfer can actually be made, and where some interest of society may often require that they should be transferred from one to another. Unless both these qualities concur, the right is to be deemed unalienable. 'Tis plain therefore, for instance, that for defect of both these qualities, our opinions in matters of religion are unalienable; and so are our internal affections of devotion; and therefore neither of them can be matters of commerce, contract, or human laws. No man can avoid judging according to the evidence which appears to him; nor can any interest of society require one to profess hypocritically contrary to his inward sentiments; or to join in any external worship which he judges foolish or impious, and without the suitable affections.

From the general account given of the nature of right, these must be the two fundamental precepts of a social life; first, that 'no man hurt another' or occasion any loss or pain to another which is neither necessary nor subservient to any superior interest of society. The second is 'that each one on his part, as he has opportunity, should contribute toward the general interest of society'; at least by contributing toward the interest of his friends or family. And he who innocently profits a part, contributes also in fact to the good of the whole...

Book II, Chapter IV.
Concerning the Natural Rights of Individuals

I. We have already shown that the several duties of life may be naturally explained by explaining the several rights belonging to men, and the corresponding obligations, in all the several states and relations they stand in to each other. By a state we understand 'some permanent condition one is placed in, as it includes a series of rights and obligations.' Our state is either that of the freedom in which nature placed us; or an adventitious state, introduced by some human acts or institution.

The state of natural liberty, is 'that of those who are subjected to no human power': which plainly obtained at first in the world, among persons adult and exempt from the parental power. This state too must always subsist among some persons, at least among the sovereign princes of independent states, or among the states themselves, with respect to each other.

The character of any state is to be taken from the rights and laws which are in force in it, and not from what men may do injuriously contrary to the laws. 'Tis plain therefore from the preceding account of our nature and its laws, that the state of nature is that of peace and good-will, of innocence and beneficence, and not of violence, war, and rapine: as both the immediate sense of duty in our hearts, and the rational considerations of interest must suggest to us.[2]

For let us observe what's very obvious, that without society with a good many of our fellows, their mutual aids, and an intercourse of friendly offices, mankind could neither be brought to life or preserved in it; much less could they obtain any tolerably convenient or pleasant condition of life.

---

2 This suffices to overturn the fallacious reasonings of Hobbes upon the state of nature as a state of war of all against all.

'Tis plain too that no one has such strength that he could promise to himself to conquer all such as he may desire to wrong or spoil, and all such enemies as he may raise up against himself by an injurious course of life; since an honest indignation at wrongs will make many more enemies to him than those he immediately injures: and there are few who won't find considerable strength to avenge themselves or their neighbours, when they have conceived a just indignation. And then men have it generally in their power much more certainly and effectually to make others uneasy and miserable, than to make others easy and happy. External prosperity requires a perfectly right state of the body, and all its tender and delicate parts, many of which may be disturbed and destroyed by very small forces; it requires also a considerable variety of external things, which may be easily damaged, taken away, or destroyed. A just consideration of this infirm, uncertain condition of mankind, so that their prosperity may so easily be disturbed, must engage every wise man rather to cultivate peace and friendship with all, as far as possible, than to provoke any by unnecessary enmity or injury.

II. The rights of men according as they immediately and principally regard either the benefit of some individual, or that of some society or body of people, or of mankind in general as a great community, are divided into private, public, and common to all. The private rights of individuals are pointed out by their senses and natural appetites, recommending and pursuing such things as tend to their happiness: and our moral faculty or conscience, shows us, that each one should be allowed full liberty to procure what may be for his own innocent advantage or pleasure, nay that we should maintain and defend it to him.

To discover therefore these private rights we should first attend to the several natural principles or appetites in men [see Book II.III.i, not included here, and Grotius, *On the Law of War and Peace*, Book I, Chapter II, Section I], and then turn our views toward the general interests of society, and of all around them: that where we find no obstruction to the happiness of others, or to the common good, thence ensuing, we should deem it the right of each individual to do, possess, or demand and obtain from others, whatever may tend to his own innocent advantage or pleasure.

Private rights are either natural or adventitious. The former sort, nature itself has given to each one, without any human grant or institution. The adventitious depend upon some human deed or institution...

IV. In this respect all men are originally equal, that these natural rights equally belong to all, at least as soon as they come to the mature use of reason; and they are equally confirmed to all by the law of nature, which requires that we should consult the interest of each individual as far as the common utility will allow; and maintain to the feeble and weak their small acquisitions or advantages, as well as their greater acquisitions or advantages to the ingenious and active. For 'tis plainly for the common good, that no mortal endued with reason and forethought should without his own consent, or crime, be subjected to the will of his fellow, without regard to his own interest, except in some rare cases, that the interest of a society may make it necessary. None of mankind are so stupid and thoughtless about their own interests, as not to count it next to death to have themselves and all that's dear to them, subjected to another's pleasure or caprice, and thus exposed to the greatest contumelies. Nature makes none masters, none slaves: and yet the wiser and better sort of men have many imperfect rights superior to those of others, and superior offices and services of humanity are due to them...

V. To every imperfect right of individuals there answers a like obligation or duty which our conscience plainly enjoins, and in some cases most sacredly. These are the chief imperfect rights: each one may justly claim such offices as are profitable to him, and no burden or expense to the performer. Nay every innocent person has a right to such offices of others, as are of high advantage to him, and of small burden or expense to the performers. This is particularly the case of men under great calamities, needing the charitable aids of others. Men of eminent characters, though under no calamity, have a right to some higher offices from others, as particularly to their friendly suffrages for their advantage or promotion. Each one whose vices have not made him infamous has a right to be admitted on equitable terms into any societies civil or religious, which are instituted in his neighbourhood, for his more convenient subsistence, or his improvement in piety. And lastly each one, who has not forfeited by some crime, has a right to be treated on an equal footing of humanity with his equals, and with others in proportion to their merits.

VI. Concerning beneficence and liberality, these general maxims are evident [see Cicero, *Offices*, Book I, Sections 14–15, ff.] that the importance of any benefit to the receiver, is proportioned jointly to the quantity of the benefit and his indigence: and that benefits are less burdensome to the giver the smaller their value is and the greater his wealth. Hence liberality may be exceedingly advantageous in many cases to him that receives it, and yet of small or no burden to the giver.

Beneficence, which is peculiarly becoming a good man, and eminently displays the goodness of his heart, ought to be practised with these cautions; first, that it don't hurt the persons it is employed about or the community. Secondly, that it be proportioned to our fortunes, so as not to exhaust its own fountain. Thirdly, that it be proportioned to the merits or claims of others. Among these claims we regard, first, the moral characters of the objects, and next their kind affections towards us, and thirdly the social intercourses we have had with them, and lastly the good offices we formerly received from them. None of these considerations are to be neglected, and least of all the last one; since there's no obligation more sacred than that of gratitude, none more useful in life; nor is any vice more odious than ingratitude, or more hurtful in society. When therefore in certain cases we cannot exercise all the beneficence we desire, offices of gratitude should take place of other offices of liberality…

Book II, Chapter IX.
Of Contracts in General

I. Since a perpetual commerce and mutual aids are absolutely necessary for the subsistence of mankind, not to speak of the conveniences of life, God has imbued men not only with reason but the powers of speech; by which we can make known to others our sentiments, desires, affections, designs, and purposes. For the right use of this faculty we have also a sublime sense implanted, naturally strengthened by our keen desires of knowledge, by which we naturally approve veracity, sincerity, and fidelity; and hate falsehood, dissimulation, and deceit. Veracity and faith in our engagements, beside their own immediate beauty thus approved, recommend themselves to the approbation and choice of every wise and honest man by their manifest necessity for the common interest and safety; as lies and falsehood are also manifestly destructive in society.

In an intercourse of services, in commerce, and in joint labour, our sentiments, inclinations and designs must be mutually made known: and 'when we affirm to others that we will pay or perform anything, with that professed view, that another shall pay or perform something on his part' then we are said to promise or contract. A covenant or contract is the 'consent of two or more to certain terms, with a view to constitute or abolish some obligation.' Nor does the law of nature distinguish between... contracts and pactions.

Contracts are of absolute necessity in life, and so is the maintaining of faith in them. The most wealthy must need the goods and labours of the poor, nor ought they to expect them gratuitously. There must be conferences and bargains about them, that the parties may agree about their mutual performances. Suppose all men as just and good as one could desire, nay ready for all kind offices: yet without contracts no man can depend upon the assistance of others. For when I need the aid of a neighbour, he may be engaged in some more important services to a third person, or in some services to those who can give him a recompense more requisite in his affairs.

The sacred obligation of faith in contracts appears, not only from our immediate sense of its beauty, and of the deformity of the contrary, but from the mischiefs which must ensue upon violating it. 'Tis plainly more contrary to the social nature, and frequently a baser injury, to break our faith, than in other equal circumstances to have omitted or declined a duty we owe another way. By violating our faith we may quite defeat the designs of such as trusted to our integrity, and might have otherwise obtained the aid they wanted: and, from the necessity of commerce, it must appear, that the rights founded on contracts are of the perfect sort, to be pursued even by force. The perfidious for his part breaks of all social commerce among men…

Book III.
The Principles of Economic and Politics.
Chapter I.
Concerning Marriage

[I.] We have in the former book treated of the rights and obligations of that state of liberty constituted by nature. We proceed to the adventitious states, founded upon some human deed or institution.

These states are either domestic, regarding the utility of a few, so many only as can subsist in one family; or public, respecting the utility of a whole nation or state, or even of many states.

Economics treat of the rights and obligations in a family; the chief points of which are delivered in these first three chapters. There are many other adventitious states of persons united in some narrower communities or corporations included within some political body, and subject to it; of which there are innumerable multitudes, which are not under the cognizance of philosophy.

II. All kinds of terrestrial animals must have subsisted only for one age, if nature had not consulted their preservation by a difference of sex, a desire of offspring, and a tender care of it till it can subsist by itself. In the brute animals nature has done little more; as their young can be sufficiently preserved and reared by the care of their dams, since they need scarce any instruction for their simple ways of life. Nature finds all the clothing and armour they need; and the earth of itself sends up their food in abundance. But for improvement and even preservation of human life a multitude of arts and inventions are necessary; as their bodies are more delicate, needing nicer food, and clothing, and other care; and their minds capable of many delightful arts. Their offspring therefore, by the wise order of nature, continues far longer tender and infirm, needing the constant care of the adult; that thus they may be more easily governed and instructed in the various arts of life, before they acquire intractable strength.

Now as the mothers are quite insufficient alone for this necessary and laborious task, which nature also has plainly enjoined on both the parents by implanting in both that strong parental affection; both parents are bound to concur in it, with joint labour, and united cares for a great share of their lives: and this can never be tolerable to them unless they are previously united in love and stable friendship: as new children also must be coming into life, prolonging this joint charge. To engage mankind more cheerfully in this laborious service nature has implanted vehement affections between the sexes; excited not so much by views of brutal pleasure, as by some appearances of virtues, displayed in their behaviour, and even by their very form and countenances. These strong impulses plainly show it to be the intention of nature that human offspring should be propagated only by parents first united in stable friendship, and in a firm covenant about perpetual cohabitation and joint care of their common children. For all true friendship aims at perpetuity: there's no friendship in a bond only for a fixed term of years, or in one depending upon certain events which the utmost fidelity of the parties cannot ensure…

IV. We must not therefore through fear of a few inconveniences counteract what nature has so strongly recommended: but rather look upon all such deductions of reason, as show how a faithful friendship may be maintained in wedlock, for the proper education of offspring, as so many sacred laws of nature. Men ought to restrain not only all monstrous lusts; as outrages against God and nature, but also all dissolute procreation without any proper covenant about a friendly society for life. For if such indulgence were allowed to all, it must destroy both the bodies and minds of the youth, produce a race destitute of all paternal assistance, and expose the incautious mothers to infamy, poverty and a perpetual course of debauchery, without any hopes of ever attaining any reputable state in life. It were to be wished that an equal infamy attended the other sex, the common authors of or solicitors to such vices.

Such adult persons as have a sufficient stock both of wealth to support a family in their condition of life, and of prudence to govern it, seem obliged to marry, unless they are hindered by some important offices inconsistent with the cares of a family. It would be dishonourable for one without a weighty cause to decline his share of the cares and services requisite for the preservation of the human race.

V. The chief articles in this covenant are these,

1. 'That the woman be faithful to the man in cohabitating,' as it must be the greatest injury to impose upon him an adulterous offspring, for heirs to his fortune, and objects of that affection which is naturally due only to his own.

2. The second is, 'that the husband should be equally faithful to the wife.' For it is a natural iniquity that the wife's conjugal affection, and all her cares and fortune, should be devoted to one man and his offspring; while the affections of the husband are allowed to be intercepted by, or dispersed among several women and their children, and along with it his fortune.

Simultaneous polygamy is not to be allowed to men, not only on account of the inequality or iniquity now mentioned, but because it also destroys all friendship in marriage; must be the cause of perpetual contentions; must tempt women so injuriously treated into adulteries; must corrupt the minds of men with wandering lust, destroying their natural affection to their children; and must occasion to some an offspring too numerous, which therefore will be neglected, and be void of all sense of duty to such dissolute parents. And further since providence preserves the numbers of males at least equal to that of females, if 'tis allowed to men to have more wives at once, many must be excluded altogether from marriage or having offspring; and thus be free from these tender bonds which chiefly civilize and unite men in society: nor does polygamy contribute to make nations more populous, but has rather the contrary effect.

3. The third article is that persons married should by a perpetual union of interests and pursuits, consult the prosperity of their family, and chiefly the right education of their common children, and the improving their condition as they have opportunity.

That we may be the better fitted for observing these articles, from our infancy we should be inured to modesty and chastity; a high sense of which is deeply fixed by nature in the finest spirits. All obscenity and lasciviousness in discourse or behaviour is detestable as it relaxes these bonds of modesty by which the young, and women especially, are restrained from exposing themselves to all infamy and misery.

4. The fourth article is, 'that the bond be perpetual, to end only by death.' This is necessary to make marriage a state of friendship; as also generally for the right education of children, who are successively born to us for a considerable part of life; and this lasting duty or charge is imposed by nature equally on both parents. It would also be most inhuman to divorce or separate from a faithful and affectionate consort for any causes which include no moral turpitude; such as barrenness, or infirmity of body; or any mournful accident which no mortal could prevent, and which must be equally afflicting to the person abandoned, the death of all the common children.

As to any proper power, or right of commanding, vested in either of the parties, it seems opposite to that tender affection the spring of marriage; which rather points out an equal friendly society. Nor seems there any other reason for giving any superiority to the husband, expect this, that men are generally more fit for managing the more important business of the family, to which the less important within doors should give place.

The four articles above mentioned seem so necessary, that no covenants of the parties in opposition to them can be valid... Marriage therefore may be defined, 'a covenant between a man and woman about perpetual faithful cohabitation and joint care of their common offspring.'...

VII. The causes which break off a valid marriage are, any violation of the essential articles; such as adultery, obstinate desertion, capital enmity or hatred, and such gross outrages as take away all hopes of any friendly society for the future. When a marriage is dissolved for such causes, the guilty party and the associate in the crime deserve the highest punishments; as these injuries in marriage do greater mischief, and cause deeper distress than stealing or robbery, for which capital punishments are inflicted. The innocent party should be allowed to marry again: for it would be strangely inhuman because one has suffered injury, that the law should inflict another hardship, by depriving them of a new marriage and offspring. Nay if the guilty parties are allowed to live, they should not be hindered from marrying, except it be with the partners of their guilt. They should rather be obliged to marry persons equally infamous with themselves...

The duties of persons married consist chiefly in a faithful and constant affection, sweetness of manners, and prudent care of their families; and to this purpose 'tis necessary they improve their minds in all virtue; especially in meekness and calmness of temper; that they may restrain such passions as their family-affairs will be apt to excite. Without these virtues a continual society and community of all things can never be tolerable. As to the ways of improving their fortunes, this they must learn from other arts, and not from philosophy [see I Corinthians VII.15].

Book III, Chapter III.
The Rights of Masters and Servants

[I.] When mankind were considerably multiplied, there would be many who had no other fund of support than their labours; and others of greater opulence, who for their ease would need much of the labours and services of others. And hence the relation of master and servant would arise, founded on some contract. Nor is it of consequence whether such contracts at first were for life, or only for a certain term: since excepting the point of duration, the rights and obligations were the very same. The points following are of more consequence.

1. The labours of any person sound in body and mind, are of much more value than the bare simple food and clothing of a servant; as we plainly see that such can purchase all this by their labours, and something further for the support of a family, and even for some pleasure and ornament. If anyone therefore has incautiously insisted for no more in his contract; yet as the contract is plainly

onerous, he has a right to have this inequality redressed [see Book II.XII.iv, not included here].

2. Where the labours were not specified, the servant is deemed to have engaged only for such as men of humanity in such stations commonly exact from their servants; and to have submitted only to such coercion of his master as is necessary for the good order of a family, if he should neglect his work or misbehave. But he retains all other natural or acquired rights.

3. If indeed the custom is known to have obtained, that heads of families assume a sort of civil power over their domestics; the servant is justly deemed to have consented to this also, as far as it is managed consistently with humanity. The servant is bound to perform his work; but retains all the rights of subjects under civil government; particularly all such as are naturally unalienable: and may justly defend them, even by violence, against any invasions of them by his master.

4. Where the services have been specified in the contract, the servant is bound to no other. Nay though they were not, and the contract was perpetual or for life, yet the master cannot transfer him to another without his own consent; since 'tis of high importance to the servant what master he is subjected to, and in what family. And for the children of such servants they are all born free.

II. Hitherto we have treated of service founded on contract. But there is a far worse kind, to wit, of those who for some great damage done, which they can no other way repair; or on account of some great crime, are adjudged by way of punishment unto perpetual labours to others.

And yet even in these cases, they don't lose all the rights of mankind, but only such as are naturally fit to compensate the damage, or are necessary to give security to the public against like injuries for the future. If the lives even of the worst criminals are spared; after they have endured all such public punishments as the safety of society may require, 'tis unjust to treat them with any further cruelty; provided they are willing to perform the labours they are condemned to. And they have a right to defend themselves even by violence, against new injuries, or violations of any rights still remaining to them. But as slavery of this kind is constituted solely for the behoove of others; the master may transfer to another such a slave without his own consent. But no cause whatsoever can degrade a rational creature from the class of men into that of brutes or inanimate things, so as to become wholly the property of another, without any rights of his own.

Nations in other respects not barbarous, condemned all captives in war into this most miserable condition; establishing an inhuman law even against themselves, and strangely conspiring to subject themselves and their posterity, upon many very possible contingencies, to the most miserable and ignominious treatment. Upon which subject the following maxims seem just…

> 5. Under pretense of repairing damages, the conqueror can demand nothing from the innocent citizens, except upon the same grounds that one demands it for damage done by another's slaves or cattle, to wit this, 'that, whoever contrives or procures anything for his own utility, by which others without their fault receive hurt, is bound either to repair the damage or deliver up the goods, or contrivance whatever it was, to the person injured.' The conqueror may therefore justly demand from the conquered citizens, that they abandon their unjust governors the causes of the war; or that they oblige these governors to repair the damages; or that they repair them themselves; and these three should be left to their choice. This holds most evidently as to these first citizens who at first constituted the government; or those who have great power in the state, by whose council the war was undertaken; or who have it in their power to restrain their princes in their unjust designs. As to others who are of no weight in public affairs, their plea against compensating of damages is more favourable…
>
> 8. Whoever purchases a person for a slave, or detains him as such, is always bound to show that this person was deprived of his liberty upon some just ground. The original proprietor of the matter in question is always at hand: since nature made every man master of himself, or

of his own liberty. 'Tis plainly therefore incumbent upon the violent possessor to prove his title; and not upon the person deforced, and claiming his liberty, to prove a negative, that he did not lost, or forfeit his liberty. (Without a previous inquiry of this kind no man can in this case be a fair purchaser.)...

III. As it is the duty of servants who are justly subjected to others, to perform their work with diligence and fidelity; regarding God the common master of all, who is ever present with us: so 'tis the duty of masters to exact no more from servants than what they have a right to, and to abstain from all cruelty and insolence; as it becomes those who remember that all are of one blood, and naturally allied to each other, and that fortune is inconstant, that the souls and bodies of servants are of the same stuff with our own, and of a like constitution; and that all of us must give an account of our conduct to God the common parent and Lord of all.

Book III, Chapter IV. The Original of Civil Government

[I.] Having finished the account of domestic society, we proceed to show the origin and rights of civil society (in which 'tis universally understood, there is included a right vested in some person or council to decide all controversies arising amongst large numerous bodies, to direct the actions of all for the common interest, and to compel all by force to obey their orders). By the associations already explained, if all men were faithful in discharging their duties, human life must have sufficient affluence and pleasure. It must therefore have been some fear of mischiefs to arise either from the weakness or vices of men, which has moved them to subject themselves to civil power. But we must not therefore, call civil society unnatural or contrary to nature. For whatever that reason, nature has endued us with, shows to be necessary or very conducive to obtain those advantages we naturally desire, or avert the contrary evils, must plainly be deemed natural to a creature endued naturally with reason and forethought. Men therefore are justly called 'creatures fitted by nature for civil polity.'

Let us suppose all men so just that none would do to others anything he judged injurious, but that they are pretty liable to mistakes about their own and others rights, through their strong selfish desires, and the bias of impetuous passions: this would frequently occasion controversies among them. Let us further suppose that many honest men are yet too suspicious, so that they won't submit their disputes to the arbitration of others, each fearing perhaps the interest of his adversary with the arbiters, or his art in seducing them: if there be added to this, too much confidence on both sides in their own force, and obstinacy in opinion; their controversies in natural liberty can be decided no other way than by violence and all the mischiefs of war.

But there's something in our nature which more immediately recommends civil power to us. Some of our species are manifestly superior in wisdom to the vulgar, as the vulgar are often sensible. These of superior sagacity, as all must own, are capable of contriving and inventing many things of consequence to the common utility of multitudes, and of pointing out more effectual methods for each one to promote his own interest, if their directions are complied with. If to these abilities be added also eminent moral virtues, goodness, justice, fortitude; the appearance of such excellencies obtains the trust and confidence of all, and kindles their zeal to promote such persons to honour and power; as they conclude that under their direction all may obtain every sort of prosperity. 'Tis highly probable therefore that not only the dread of injuries, but eminent virtues, and our natural high approbation of them have engaged men at first to form civil societies.

II. But if we consider how much injustice, depravation of manners, avarice, ambition, and luxury prevail among men: it will be manifest, that without civil power, men cannot be preserved in safety, not to speak of any high advantages or pleasures to be enjoyed in society: and that it is by civil power alone an effectual remedy, and such a one as must strike the senses of the most inconsiderate, can be found for the evils to be dreaded from these vices of men. For though all the members of a large assembly were so unjust, that upon a fit opportunity each one for his own interest would do injuries to others; yet each one would abhor like injustice done by his fellow, when he had no share in the gain of it. An assembly therefore of such men, of whom each condemned that injustice in his neighbour which he would indulge in himself, will never make unjust decrees for their whole body. Each one will be ashamed to own his dishonesty, and will live in dread of receiving injuries from others, unless they are all restrained by equal laws enforced by proper punishments.

Nor is there any other way of preserving society in safety. For although men were not generally so depraved, and that even humanity and conscience restrained the generality from injuries, and inclined them to give aid to any who happened to be wronged: yet multitudes would omit this duty through fear and cowardice, if it exposed themselves to danger. Nay further; a sufficient number of honest brave men, if they were not directed by some head, and that united in their efforts, would run into the most different measures, according to their different sentiments; and when thus disjoined would become a prey even to a smaller number of less bravery, who were united in their counsels.

'Tis therefore very probable that some of the wiser and more sagacious, observing these inconveniences of a state of anarchy, fell upon this as the only remedy, that a large number of men should covenant with each other about entering into a firm society, to be regulated by the counsel of the wiser few, in all matters relating to the safety and advantage either of individuals or the whole body. And discerning the many conveniences to ensue upon such a project, have explained it to others, and persuaded them to put it in execution.

III. They who ascribe the first origin of all civil power to the violence of ambitious men, plainly presuppose that already existing, whose original they are searching for: as no one man could have force enough, without a large number of others already subjected to his direction and government, to compel a multitude sufficient to form a state, to submit themselves to his power. A civil power therefore was constituted previously to that conquest they suppose to have produced the first civil power.

Should one allege that a potent head of a family, with his numerous domestics, might have conquered and thus compelled his neighbours around to submit to him as their prince. This may have happened no doubt. But we are not to regard names, but things themselves. Heads of families no doubt sometimes had a proper regal power over their domestics. And further, we are not inquiring into the possible injurious methods of usurpation, but into the probable just causes of just power.

IV. That it must conduce much to the interest of a multitude to be governed by a council of the wise, no man can deny. And although under some foolish plans of government, power may often be entrusted to bad hands, and thence great mischiefs arise, as the corruptions of the best things may be most pernicious; yet this is no dishonour to civil government, as if it were in general of little use or pernicious. For God has given men sufficient powers of reason to choose some of the more prudent convenient forms out of the innumerable multitudes conceivable.

A state or civil society is, 'a society of free men united under one government for their common interest.' That the common interest of the whole body is the end of all civil polity, is owned by all. This all subjects insist upon; and all governors glory in it as their dignity; except some vain monsters, who forgetting their mortal state, arrogate to themselves the rights of almighty God, or even powers more extensive. The very notion of civil life, or polity, is opposite to despotism, or the power of masters over slaves. That civil power therefore alone is just which is naturally adapted to this end: other power though granted by the rash deed of an ignorant people, has no foundation of right. There was an essential defect in the deed granting it, as it was founded in an error about what is owned by all to be most essential in such contracts.

One can scarce avoid wondering how some ingenious authors [*i.e.* Hobbes and Pufendorf] seem to pique themselves upon aggravating and exaggerating all the burdens of civil subjection, as if they designed to deter men from entering into it; but then [lest] they should do so, they paint a state of liberty and anarchy as the most frightful monster of all. Whereas 'tis plain both states have both their advantages and disadvantages. There are no doubt many dangers in a state of liberty, but these not continual: generally they are greater and more frequent than in civil life; unless a people have been exceedingly incautious in the plan of power they constituted: as in civil life we have a much surer prospect of protection from injuries by the united force of all. Nor are there any evils peculiar to a civil life under regular government; the like or worse, men were also exposed to in liberty[3] (as it will appear by considering the several parts of civil power in the following chapter).

Book III, Chapter V.
The Internal Structure of States: and the Several Parts of Supreme Power

[I.] As no governors are the natural parents or progenitors of their people, nor if they were, could they transmit to any one heir the parental power over his adult brethren: as this power is founded solely upon the parental affection, and the weakness of immature years: the parental power can never be the foundation of the civil; though it be a natural sketch or emblem of it. Nor can any person have such power over a whole people as masters have over slaves; as appears from what was already said. Nor has God by any revelation nominated magistrates, showed the nature or extent of their powers, or given a plan of civil polity for mankind. Nor lastly can mere force without some foundation of right constitute any just power. It must therefore remain that some deed or contract of a people must be the sole natural origin of all just power.

In some extraordinary circumstances the case may be otherwise. For since the good of the whole body; as all allow, is the sole end of all civil power; if any person of eminent

---

3 Thus subjects are bound to pay taxes, for the common interest, for fortifying or defending the state. But each one in liberty must on his part be at greater charges, either for his own conveniency, for fortifying his house and arming his domestics, or for hiring assistance. Each subject may be obliged to hazard his life for the state. But so each one in anarchy may more frequently for his own defence. Subjects submit to a power of life and death over themselves in criminal jurisdictions. But so each one in anarchy is subjected to a worse power of any enraged person who alleges he is injured by him, and entitled to use force for redress. If by a power of life and death one means an arbitrary power in a governor, upon any caprice, without a crime alleged, to take men's lives away; no such power is in any wise polity; nor can any human deed constitute it.

wisdom and great power consults this end sufficiently, in prescribing a legal plan, which all upon trial shall soon heartily embrace, he may perhaps without any iniquity impose this plan upon a rude and unexperienced people, which upon experience they shall soon approve, though he could not obtain their previous consent to it. But as no people can be happy while they live in perpetual doubts and fears, as to the security of their highest interests from the invasions of men in power; we may pronounce in general that there can be no right to power except what is either founded upon, or speedily obtains, the hearty consent of the body of the people.

II. To constitute a state or civil polity in a regular manner these three deeds are necessary; first a contract of each one with all, that they shall unite into one society to be governed by one counsel. And next a decree or ordinance of the people, concerning the plan of government, and the nomination of the governors; and lastly another covenant or contract between these governors and the people, binding the rulers to a faithful administration of their trust, and the people to obedience. 'Tis true that in the first constitutions of power, 'tis scarce credible that a rude and incautious multitude, full of admiration of the shining virtues of some more eminent characters, took these three formal steps. But then in every just constitution of power,[4] something was originally done which plainly included the whole force of these three transactions; since the end known and professed by all sides in this constitution of power was the common good of the whole body.

As to the transmitting of these civil obligations to posterity, the following observations will explain it.

1. Each citizen in subjecting himself to civil power stipulated protection from the whole body, with all the other advantages of a civilized life, not only for himself but for

---

4 [Hutcheson cites Book 2, Chapter VI of *Supplements and Observations upon Samuel Pufendorf's On the Duty of Man and Citizen* by Gershom Carmichael (1672–1729), who was Hutcheson's predecessor and one-time teacher at the University of Glasgow.]

his posterity: and in this, though uncommissioned, did them a most important service. They are bound therefore [see Book II.XIV.ii, not included here], whether they consent or not, to perform to the body of the state, as far as their power goes, all that which could reasonably be demanded from persons adult for such important benefits received. Now 'tis highly reasonable that all such should on their parts contribute to the defence and support of that state, by which they have been so long protected in a civilized life, and not desert it unreasonably; but transmit that association with its beneficent influence to posterity.

2. As it must be extremely dangerous to any political body settled in any district, that any lands within the same should remain exempt from the civil power of the united body, to be a receptacle to fugitives or foreign enemies; 'tis justly presumed that when any body of men possessing such a district of land constitute a civil power, each one thus subjects his lands to it, that no person can hold the same without also subjecting himself to it, and uniting with the body politic.

3. And yet, in times of ease and peace, it would seem unjust and dishonourable to any state to hinder its citizens from selling their lands, removing to any other state they please, and freeing themselves from their former political relation. For the several subjects by the taxes or tributes they pay annually, compensate all the ordinary advantages they receive from the community: and it would be unjust to hinder them to consult better their own interest if they can elsewhere. Nor is there danger that any state will be deserted by many of its subjects, unless it be either miserably constituted or administered; and in such cases the citizens have a better right to quit it, and cannot be compelled to remain its subjects.

III. A state constituted in this manner becomes as one person in law, holding rights different from those of the several members; and under obligations, which bind no individual; and committing to certain persons or councils the management of its common interests. Among several states thus constituted, as they are all with respect to each other in natural liberty and independence, the like rights and laws obtain as among individuals in liberty. States have their perfect rights, and obligations to each other, and are bound to offices of humanity, in a like manner as individuals in natural liberty: and have like rights of self-defence. This is the case of all states which are independent, whether greater or smaller, whatever names and titles they bear, more humble or more ostentatious. By an easy substitution therefore of states for individuals, the natural law with respect to individuals in liberty, makes all that public law of states with respect to each other, which is of necessary obligation…

Book III, Chapter VI.
Of the Various Plans of Government

[I.] The simple forms of government are divided into three classes, according as the power is committed to one person or to one council. When it is committed to one person, it is called monarchy; when to a council of some few eminent citizens, it is an aristocracy; and when it is committed to a popular assembly either of all the free citizens, or of some more reputable persons deputed by them, 'tis democracy…

V. We have said enough to show that none of the simple forms of government are well adapted to preserve any state happy. Nor is it of any avail to plead antiquity here. If all the most ancient ways were best, we should return to caves and beast-skins for our shelter and dress. What flatterers of princes often tell us, that monarchy was the earliest form, is rather dishonourable to it; importing indeed that it at first pleased a rude and unexperienced populace, but could not continue to please upon experience and the increase of wisdom. And indeed in nothing could one less expect that the first essays would be perfect, than in the constitution of civil polity; a work requiring the greatest knowledge and prudence, to be acquired only by much thought and experience of human life. The several great inconveniences attending each of the simple forms show the necessity of having recourse to the mixed and complex; and the several great advantages peculiar to each of the simple, show that those mixed forms are best where all the three kinds are artfully compounded: and this was the opinion of the wisest men of antiquity.[5]

As a council of delegates or deputies duly elected by a general popular interest can never want fidelity or good intention, and seldom can be deficient in wisdom, it may seem advisable that a large share of the civil power should be lodged in such a body; such as that of enacting laws and even determining definitively the most weighty affairs in deliberation. And this part of a constitution should be secured by agrarian laws: not so strait however as to discourage industry, or exclude any innocent elegance or ornament of life.

If there be also a senate of a few who have approved their abilities and fidelity in discharging the great offices of the commonwealth; it may safely be entrusted with the sole right of deliberating, debating, and proposing business to the popular assembly. In both councils it may be proper to contrive a rotation, by new members gradually succeeding to the old, so that neither council may have above one third of unexperienced new men, nor yet any one man continue a member perpetually. Laws limiting the times that any general, minister of state, or magistrate can continue in office have also great advantages, to prevent any person's so rooting himself in power or popularity, as to be dangerous to the constitution; and to train up greater numbers in political wisdom, by experience in all the important offices; so that the state may never be obliged to have all its hopes depending upon one mortal life. Where such laws are sacredly established, the state will never want the benefit of the wisdom or experience of such as have served out their legal time. For it will be no matter of offence that at the expiration of it they must lay down their offices according to law.

And lastly, for sudden unexpected exigencies or dangers, and for the secret and speedy execution of what the public interest may require, some sort of regal or dictatorial power

---

5 [Here Hutcheson lists Plato, Aristotle, Zeno, and Cicero. Zeno (334–262 B.C.E) was the Greek philosopher who founded the Stoic school of thought.]

is requisite; but such a one as has no other foundation of its force but the laws themselves. And to this power may be committed the command in war, and the execution of the laws. This third branch may be as an arbitrator, holding the balance between the two other parts of the constitution, if there should arise any high contention between the senatorial order and the plebeian.

The power of promoting to all sorts of offices may be some way veiled in these three jointly, or divided among them; so that offices requiring great abilities and wisdom should be filled by the nomination of the senate; such officers as are to be employed in speedy execution, to be nominated by the prince: and such as are to protect the rights of the people, and administer justice among them, to be elected by the people.

A censorial power too would be of the highest use, to reform, or prevent the corruption of manners; by degrading persons of any dignity whatsoever, as soon as they run into a dissolute course of debauchery.

Book III, Chapter VII.
The Rights of Supreme Power: and the Ways of Acquiring It

[I.] The persons vested with the supreme power, have it with that extent which the constitution or fundamental laws have given them. The sum of civil power in all states is the same; the same quantity of it in every state resides somewhere or other, at least with the body of the people. But the powers vested in the king, or, in any councils, in one state, may be very different from what is vested in like persons or councils in others. For in some, certain rights of the people are expressly exempted from the power of any prince or political council; but in others, there's no such exemptions. But as the end of all civil power is acknowledged by all to be the safety and happiness of the whole body; any power not naturally conducive to this end is unjust; which the people, who rashly granted it under an error, may justly abolish again, when they find it necessary to their safety to do so. Nor can anything be conceived more insolent or perfidious, than that persons entrusted with power solely for the good of a people, should strive to retain it by force, for their own grandeur, when it is found destructive to the people.

It were to be wished that in these cases, such powers should be abolished in a peaceable manner, by mutual consent, rather than by force. Nor is it justifiable in a people to have recourse for any lighter causes to violence and civil wars against their rulers, while the public interests are tolerably secured and consulted. But when it is evident, that the public liberty and safety is not tolerably secured, and that more mischiefs, and these of a more lasting kind, are like to arise from the continuance of any plan of civil power than are to be feared from the violent efforts for an alteration of it, then it becomes lawful, nay honourable, to make such efforts, and change the plan of government.

What is alleged about some peculiarly divine right, and inviolable sanctity of governors, especially monarchs, is a mere dream of court-flatterers. In one sense every right is divine which is constituted by the law of God and nature. The rights of the people are thus divine, as well as those of princes: nay since the later were constituted for the defence and protection of the former; the former should be deemed the more divine and sacred. The rights of the governor, as they are more important than those of any one private man, may be deemed more sacred than his private rights; but can never be deemed more sacred than the rights of the whole body. A good subject ought to bear patiently many injuries done only to himself, rather than take arms against a prince in the main good and useful to the state; provided the danger only extends to himself. But when the common rights of the community are trampled upon; and what at first is attempted against one, is to be made a precedent against all the rest, then as the governor is plainly perfidious to his trust, he has forfeited all the power committed to him…

II. …As to that question, who shall be judge in this disputed point, whether the governors by their perfidy and maladministration have forfeited their right? If 'tis alleged, the people cannot judge as they are parties: for the same reason the governors cannot judge. The only recourse then should be to impartial arbiters, either within the state, or in some other nation, if this could be the case; but if not; surely the people have a better claim to judge in this point; since they at first entrusted their governors with such powers, and the powers were designed for the management of the people's interests, and were constituted for their behoove. 'Tis true there are great dangers of mistakes on this head: but the governors are not exempted from errors more than the people. Men have often erred both about public rights, and the private ones too of self-defence: but we must not for that reason deny that they have such rights.

In this most important matter, no doubt, persons concerned are bound to use the utmost caution, and weigh all things on both sides. Nor ought we to involve our fellow-citizens in civil-wars, the most miserable of all wars, for any such lighter injuries, or wrong conduct of our governors, as may be incident sometimes to persons in the main good and of upright intentions. But when there's no other way of preserving a people; and when their governors by their perfidious frauds have plainly forfeited their right; they may justly be divested of their power, and others put into their places, or a new plan of power established.

Nor does this doctrine of the right of resistance in defence of the rights of a people, naturally tend to excite seditions and civil wars. Nay they have been more frequently occasioned by the contrary tenets. In all ages there has been too much patience in the body of the people, and too stupid a veneration for their princes or rulers; which for each one free kingdom or state has produced many monstrous herds of miserable abject slaves or beasts of burden, rather than civil polities of rational creatures, under the most inhuman and worthless masters, trampling upon all things human and divine with the utmost effrontery…

V. As natural liberty is 'the right of acting as one inclines within the bounds of the law of nature' (nor could we hold any such liberty were there no laws to defend it from the force of the stronger); so we say a people enjoys liberty when 'each one is allowed to act as he inclines, within the bounds of civil law, and not subjected to the caprice of any other.' We should never look upon laws as eversive of liberty; but that 'tis sole enemy is the capricious humorous will or command of men in power. The Romans indeed in speaking of a free people, generally meant a democratical state; where men had their turns of commanding, as well as of obeying.

VI. It was already shown that civil power can scarce be constituted justly any other way than by the consent of the people: and that rulers have no other sacred rights or majesty, than what may arise from this: that of a large multitude of men, each one for himself subjected part of his rights to the administration of a certain person or council. And thus from a part of our natural liberty transferred to the ruler, and our property in a certain degree subjected to his disposal, arises the legislative power. In natural liberty also each one had a right to expose his life to the greatest dangers, in any honourable services in defence of his family or his neighbours, and when the common interest required it he could commit himself to the direction of others in such services; and hence the right of military command. Men had also this right of repelling injuries, and punishing by violence anyone who attempted or executed any injury, and even of putting him to death if this was necessary for the common safety: and hence arises all criminal jurisdiction, even to the inflicting of capital punishments. Nor need we have recourse to any extraordinary grants or commissions from God to explain any of these rights of civil sovereigns…

VII. …What we have said relates not only to monarchs but all sorts of governors, and to the power of a state itself over its colonies, or provinces. If any citizens, with permission of the government, leave their country, and at their own expense find new habitations; they may justly constitute themselves into an independent state, in amity with their mother-country. If any are sent off at the public charge as a colony, to make settlements subject to the state, for augmenting its commerce and power; such persons should hold all the rights of the other subjects, and whatever grants are made to them are to be faithfully observed. If the mother-country attempts anything oppressive toward a colony, and the colony be able to subsist as a sovereign state by itself; or if the mother-country lose its liberty, or have its plan of polity miserably changed to the worse: the colony is not bound to remain subject any longer: 'tis enough that it remain a friendly state. Nor are we to imagine that any early covenants founded upon errors about the most essential points in view, can still bind large societies of men fit to subsist as happy independent states, to continue in a submission eversive of all prosperity and safety. Nor has anything occasioned more misery in human life than a vain and insolent ambition, both in princes and popular states of extending their empires, and bringing every neighbouring state under subjection to them; without consulting the real felicity either of their own people or of their new acquisitions. And hence have arose there vast unwieldy empires; the plagues of all around them; which after some time are ruined by their own bulk, with vast destruction of mankind.

Book III, Chapter VIII.
Of Civil Laws and their Execution

[I.] The power of making and executing laws is the most important internal power. Every law should be intended for some real utility to the state; and as far as human power can go, laws should enjoin whatever is of consequence to the general prosperity. But if in the very constitution of the civil polity, the sovereign or chief magistrate is only entrusted with such power as is requisite for the preservation of the secular rights of men; then they cannot exert any sort of coercive power about the means of forming men's minds to religion or inward virtue. But when they are entrusted with certain revenues, to be employed for the public utility at their discretion; and where they are not expressly restricted to the care of the secular rights of men; since human happiness chiefly depends upon virtue, the civil governors must think it belonging to their office to instil into the minds of their subjects the true sentiments of religion and virtue, and to influence their hearts to relish them, by the best instruction and discipline from their infancy, that they may be furnished for all the honourable offices of life.

But at the same time they must maintain to all, their sacred right of judging for themselves; which would be plainly encroached upon by any penal laws about such opinions, whether secret or divulged, which don't lead to any practices destructive to society. Nay though such tenets should be divulged by men who imagine themselves bound in conscience to divulge them; it would generally be more advisable only to insist that such persons give proper security that they will give no disturbance to the state, and bear their share in all services required of them for the public; and to punish rigorously only the injuries done in consequence of such dangerous opinions; rather than to inflict any penalties on men for these opinions themselves. 'Tis often better to leave such tenets to be exploded by the juster reasonings of wise men, than to proceed to any severities on account of the tenets themselves.

But as the far greater part of every people will not use this right; but induced by specious appearances of sanctity, and ostentation of superior wisdom in some deigning men, will incautiously give up themselves to be led by them; it must plainly be the business of the magistrate to get this leading into his own hands; by appointing men of character and learning to teach the people the just sentiments of religion and virtue, and to confirm them by the most effectual reasonings; that they may not be perverted by the wicked arts of others. And if men in power have any tolerable wisdom, and hold any tolerable scheme of religion, they will always find the far greater part of the people very tractable to follow as they lead them, so that little need be apprehended from a few who may dissent from the public schemes.

The exacting by law, under any penalties, that people should conform in opinion and practice to any tenets or rites of worship, that are either false and absurd, or though true yet of little consequence, generally occasions great mischief to any state; since according to the different geniuses and tempers of men, they have and always will run into different opinions and practices in matters of religion: and thence some of the most useful hands will desert the country when they are harassed about such matters: the state will be plagued with sedition and discord: and the activity of men turned off from the services and occupations which are most useful to the community, and occupied upon trifles. No good subject should meet with any vexation, or be excluded from any civil right, on account of any opinions or modes of worship which don't hurt any of their neighbours.

II. The example of those in supreme power will have the highest influence in promoting the virtue of the people: especially if they advance to honours only such as are of approved integrity and purity of manners. The populace in their elections, if they are truly free, always follow some appearance of virtue; and will seldom promote any but such as are of distinguished integrity. Nor will honour or power alter the tempers of the persons advanced, if there are proper terms fixed by law for the holding of offices; so that upon expiration of the term, they must return into the common condition of the people. Where the power of promoting to offices is in the monarch, the men promoted will probably resemble their political creator…

VII. It is one great design of civil laws to strengthen by political sanctions the several laws of nature; and to appoint such forms of business, and of process in courts, as may prevent frauds and promote justice. The populace often needs also to be taught, and engaged by laws, into the best methods of managing their own affairs, and exercising their mechanic arts: and in general, civil laws should more precisely determine many points in which the law of nature leaves much latitude.

From the very best body of civil laws certain external rights must arise, which though no man can insist upon with a good conscience, yet if the persons to whom they are granted claim them, they must hold them with impunity: nor can anyone rightly have recourse to violence against such rights, or obtain redress at law. Many also of the most sacred duties can be no matters of compulsion, but must be left to the honour and conscience of those concerned. There are certain benefits granted by law, which no good man would claim, but when claimed they cannot be refused.[6] Any such covenants or testaments too as for want of the legal formalities are not confirmed by human laws, a good man would often think himself bound to hold as valid, if there's nothing appointed in them beyond the moral power of the parties or testator, nor contrary to equity. But if they are wrong in either of these respects, a good man may take the benefit of the law.

VIII. The sanctions of laws are rewards and punishment. There's this common reward annexed to obedience to civil

---

6 [See 'two good orations' that Barbeyrac 'annexed' to his translation of Pufendorf's *The Whole Duty of Man*.]

laws, that these who obey them continue to enjoy all the advantages of civil life. Some few civil laws have peculiar rewards, such as honours, and premiums in money. The natural honour is 'the good opinion others entertain of our moral excellencies.' Civil honours are 'these external indications of deference which are appointed by law.'

The simple estimation, or character of common honesty, is so much every man's right, that no governors can deprive one of it at pleasure, without a cause determined in judgment. The higher estimation, or intensive, as some call it, is not a matter of perfect right; as no man can at the command of others form high opinions of any person, without he is persuaded of his merit. But as to external marks of deference, and precedencies, the civil powers have a right to determine about them, as they do about other civil rights. If these are conferred only upon real merit, they will be of high account with wise men. But if they are often conferred injudiciously, they will grow mean and despicable to wise men, and matter of scorn and jest: as they are often seen where they are hereditary, and there's no censorial power to degrade the unworthy.

IX. The true end of all punishment is this, that all bad men by the terror of them may be restrained from doing anything injurious, and thus the community be preserved in safety. Chastisement as distinguished from punishment, has in view only the reformation of the sufferer: and reparation of damage, aims at the utility of the one who sustained the loss: to this men are often bound even without any preceding crime or fault.

Neither anger, nor hatred of the criminal, nor even that honest indignation at moral evil, which is natural to every good man, should be the sole springs of punishing: but rather a calm regard to the common interest, and the safety of the innocent. The true measure of punishment is not to be taken from the degrees of moral turpitude, but the exigency of society. A great deal of high moral turpitude must past unpunished: and yet on the other hand if the safety of the community require it, some actions which show smaller depravity of temper, must be punished severely. Thus no penalties are inflicted on ingratitude, and want of humanity; while any insurrection against the supreme power, though upon plausible pretenses of the right of some competitor, must be punished severely. But the crimes which deserve the highest punishments on both accounts, are the public ones of men in power, perverting what was entrusted to them for the safety of others, to the oppression of the citizens.

Though it may not be necessary to punish the first motions or hasty intentions of wickedness, nor is it often practicable; as such rash motions may upon sudden provocation arise in the breasts of good men, who will soon restrain them of themselves: yet such as have proceeded to any external actions which might have effectually accomplished the evil, but were prevented by accident, or force, or the timely aid of others, and which show furious malice and obstinate purposes of injury, these deserve as high punishments as if they had obtained their effect. Sometimes indeed the public interest may require the granting even rewards to some bad actions, and pardoning the greatest criminals.

The respect of persons which is highly culpable in judgment, is when any regard is had to such qualities of actions or circumstances of the guilty as neither affect the turpitude of the crime, nor the sense of the punishment, nor the common interest of society. But circumstances which affect any of these three must always be regarded. And therefore when other circumstances are equal, pecuniary fines are to be enlarged for equal crimes according to the fortunes of the criminals, and corporal punishments according to their strength of body; and ignominious ones are to be abated according to the dignity of the persons.

But we must not go on in increasing without bounds the severities of punishment upon the higher crimes. For frequent spectacles of tortures have a tendency to diminish our natural compassion and tenderness of heart, and to make the tempers of men more savage and cruel…

XII. These are the obligations of subjects toward their governors:

[1.] First, they are sacredly bound to obey all their just laws and commands…

[2.] If the thing commanded be a matter committed to the power of the governor; 'tis generally the duty of subjects to obey, even when they judge that the orders are imprudent. This holds most obviously in military operations. For to allow the inferior to judge of his orders, and only to obey when he thinks them prudent for the good of the state, would destroy all military discipline, and reduce an army into a tumultuous mob.

3. Hence it follows that in matters committed to the wisdom of governors, the subjects may act a just nay an honourable part in obeying such orders as were very criminal to their governor: the subject by obeying is preventing the greatest mischief; since from the relaxing of all order and government, far greater evils must generally ensue, than from the execution of very imprudent orders.

4. But if the thing commanded seems to the subject so entirely pernicious and ruining to the state, that it were better to break through and destroy the authority of such commanders, than to execute such destructive orders: the subject may refuse obedience. But in such matters they should use the utmost caution that they don't judge amiss.

5. Where we are commanded to do any act directly irreverent and impious toward God, or contrary to the perfect rights of others; or where the matter commanded was not committed to the power of the commander; we are under no obligation to obedience. Nay 'tis often highly honourable to endure rather any punishment, than submit to a precedent that may be ruinous to our country. We showed above [see Book III.VII.ii] in what cases it is lawful for subjects to resist their governors.

The common duties of all subjects must easily appear from the nature and origin of civil power and the political union. Their peculiar duties arise from their several stations, relations, and offices in the state.

Index of Names